INTERNATIONAL BACCALAUREATE

MATHEMATICAL STUDIES
STANDARD LEVEL

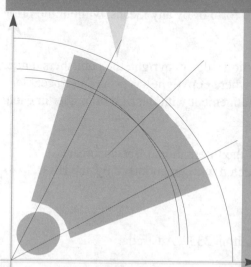

Series editor: Fabio Cirrito

Contributing author:

Vicki Strid,
The Kooralbyn International
School

Copyright ©IBID Press, Victoria.

First published in 1998 by IBID Press, Victoria,
2nd impression.

 Published by IBID Press, Victoria.
Library Catalogue:

Cirrito
1. Mathematics, 2. International Baccalaureate. Series Title: International
    Baccalaureate in Detail

ISBN: 0 9585686 2 6

Cover design by Adcore.

Published by IBID Press, 36 Quail Crescent, Melton, 3337, Australia.

Printed by Shannon Books Australia Pty. Ltd. using paper harvested from plantation
forests.

PREFACE

I am very pleased to finally see in complete form the third of the maths book in this series. Mathematical Studies (Standard Level) has been prepared so as to take into account the needs of students who are studying this subject. At times, the content or depth of the mathematics as gone slightly beyond that required for examination purposes. However, this has been done sparingly and always being conscious of the students' needs. Each (Core) chapter finishes with an *Examination Style Questions* section as well as a *Self Assessment Test*. These sections are meant to be used for consolidation purposes in the lead up to the final examinations. The questions in both these sections reflect the views of the authors and editor.

A number of people have been involved with the final production of this book. In particular, the contribution made by Vicki Strid has made this book all the better. I thank her for the work she has done in writing a large part of the book as well as her suggestions on how to improve other areas. Also, on behalf of Vicki, I would like to acknowledge the assistance provided by Jill Weitz and Bill Flynn.

This text has been produced independently as a resource to support the teaching of the Mathematical Studies Standard Level Course of the International Baccalaureate. The examples and questions do not necessarily reflect the views of the official senior examining team appointed by the International Baccalaureate Organisation.

The **notation** used is, as far as possible, that specified in the appropriate syllabus guidelines of the IB. The **units** of physical measurements are in S.I. The **language** and **spelling** are U.K. English. **Currency** quantities are specified in dollars, though these could be read as any currency that is decimalised, such as Swiss francs, Lire etc.

The graphic calculators covered directly in the text are the Texas TI/82 and 83. Supplementary material is available from the publisher for students using some other makes and models of calculators. As it is important that students learn to interpret graphic calculator output, the text and answers present a mixture of graphic calculator screens and conventional diagrams when discussing graphs.

The text has been presented in the order in which the topics appear in the syllabus. This does not mean that the topics have to be treated in this order, though it is generally the case that the more fundamental topics appear at the front of the book. Students are reminded that it is the IB Syllabus that specifies the contents of the course and not this text. One of the keys to success in this course is to be thoroughly familiar with the course contents and the styles of questions that have been used in past examinations.

As always, we welcome suggestions, critisms (constructive) or any other comment from teachers, students and those that use this book.
You can call or fax through on + 61 03 9 747 0840.

Fabio Cirrito, July 1998.

NOTATION

The list below represents some of the signs and symbols which are recommended by the International Organization for Standardization and other symbols that are used in the text.

Sets

$\mathbb{R}$ The set of real numbers

$\mathbb{R}*$ The set of real numbers excluding zero

Operations

$$\sum_{i=1}^{i=n} u_i = u_1 + u_2 + \ldots + u_n.$$

Functions and Calculus

$f : x \longmapsto f(x);$

$$f'(x) = \frac{df}{dx}; \quad \int f(x)dx$$

Circular functions

sin, cos, tan

Geometry, Vectors and Matrices

AB Length of $[AB]$

$\overrightarrow{AB}$ The vector displacement from A to B; $\vec{a}$ or $\boldsymbol{a}$ (vector).

$\vec{i}, \vec{j}$ Unit vectors in the direction Ox and Oy respectively (or simply $\boldsymbol{i}, \boldsymbol{j}$)

$|\overrightarrow{AB}|$ The magnitude of $\overrightarrow{AB}$; $|\vec{a}|$, the magnitude of $\vec{a}$ (or $|\boldsymbol{a}|$)

$\vec{a} \cdot \vec{b}$ The scalar product

$\hat{A}$ The angle at A; $C\hat{A}B$ the angle between (CA) and (AB)

$\triangle ABC$ The triangle whose vertices are A, B and C.

M^{-1} The matrix inverse to M; det M, the determinant of M

Probability and Statistics

$p(A)$; $p(A|B)$ Conditional probability.

μ, σ Population mean and standard deviation; m (or $\bar{x}$), s_n sample mean and standard deviation.

CONTENTS

1. THEORY OF KNOWLEDGE.

CORE

2. NUMBER & ALGEBRA 1: NUMBER SYSTEMS

3. NUMBER & ALGEBRA 2: SEQUENCES & SERIES

4. NUMBER & ALGEBRA 3: EQUATIONS & INEQUATIONS

5. NUMBER & ALGEBRA 4: QUADRATICS

6. SETS AND LOGIC:

7. GEOMETRY AND TRIGONOMETRY 1:
SOLUTION OF TRIANGLES

8. GEOMETRY AND TRIGONOMETRY 2:
COORDINATE GEOMETRY

9. GEOMETRY AND TRIGONOMETRY 3:
3–D TRIGONOMETRY

10.GEOMETRY AND TRIGONOMETRY 4:
VECTORS

11. STATISTICS AND PROBABILITY 1:   STATISTICS

12. STATISTICS AND PROBABILITY 2:   PROBABILITY

13. FUNCTIONS 1:   FUNCTIONS & RELATIONS

14. FUNCTIONS 2: TRIGONOMETRIC FUNCTIONS

15. FUNCTIONS 3: EXPONENTIAL FUNCTIONS

16. FINANCIAL MATHEMATICS 1: FINANCE

17. FINANCIAL MATHEMATICS 2: LINEAR PROGRAMMING

OPTIONS

18. MATRICES AND GRAPH THEORY 1: MATRICES & GRAPH THEORY

19. FURTHER STATISTICS AND PROBABILITY 1: THE NORMAL DISTRIBUTION

20. FURTHER STATISTICS AND PROBABILITY 2: BIVARIATE ANALYSIS

21. FURTHER STATISTICS AND PROBABILITY 2:
CONTINGENCY TABLES

22. INTRODUCTION TO DIFFERENTIAL CALCULUS 1:
RATES OF CHANGE

23. INTRODUCTION TO DIFFERENTIAL CALCULUS 2:
DIFFERENTIATION & APPL.

24. INTRODUCTION TO DIFFERENTIAL CALCULUS 3:
INTEGRATION

ANSWERS

THEORY OF
KNOWLEDGE

1

Chapter contents

1.1 PURE AND APPLIED MATHEMATICS

Mathematics has clearly played a significant part in the development of many past and present civilisations. There is good evidence that mathematical, and probably astronomical techniques, were used to build the many stone circles of Europe which are thought to be at least three thousand years old (Thom). It is likely that the Egyptian pyramids and constructions on Aztec and Mayan sites in South America were also built by mathematically sophisticated architects. Similarly, cultures in China, India and throughout the Middle East developed mathematics a very long time ago. It is also the case that there have been very successful cultures that have found little use for mathematics. Ancient Rome, handicapped, as it was, by a non-place value number system did not develop a mathematical tradition at anything like the same level as that of Ancient Greece. Also, the Australian Aborigines who have one of the most long lasting and successful cultures in human history did not find much need for mathematical methods. The same is true of the many aboriginal cultures of Africa, Asia and the Americas. This may well be because these aboriginal cultures did not value ownership in the way that western culture does and had no need to count their possessions. Instead, to aboriginal cultures, a responsible and sustainable relationship with the environment is more important than acquisition and exploitation. Maybe we should learn from this before it is too late!

Mathematics has developed two distinct branches. Pure mathematics, which is studied for its own sake, and applied mathematics which is studied for its usefulness. This is not to say that the two branches have not cross-fertilised each other, for there have been many examples in which they have.

The pure mathematician Pierre de Fermat (1601-1665) guessed that the equation $x^n + y^n = z^n$ has whole numbered solutions for $n = 2$ only. To the pure mathematician, this type of problem is interesting for its own sake. To study it is to look for an essential truth, the 'majestic clockwork' of the universe. Pure mathematicians see 'beauty' and 'elegance' in a neat proof. To pure mathematicians, their subject is an art.

Applied mathematics seeks to develop mathematical objects such as equations and computer algorithms that can be used to predict what will happen if we follow a particular course of action. This is a very valuable capability. We no longer build bridges without making careful calculations as to whether or not they will stand. Airline pilots are able to experience serious failures in commercial jets without either risking lives or the airline's valuable aeroplanes or, indeed, without even leaving the ground.

1.2 AXIOMS

Mathematics is based on axioms. These are 'facts' that are assumed to be true. An axiom is a statement that is accepted without proof. Early sets of axioms contained statements that appeared to be obviously true. Euclid postulated a number of these 'obvious' axioms. An example is: 'Things equal to the same thing are equal to each other'; if $y = a$ and $x = a$ then $y = x$. Euclid was mainly interested in geometry and we still call plane geometry 'Euclidean'. In Euclidean space, the shortest distance between two points is a straight line. We will see later that it is possible to develop a useful, consistent mathematics that does not accept this axiom.

Most axiom systems have been based on the notion of a 'set', meaning a collection of objects. An example of a set axiom is the 'axiom of specification'. In crude terms, this says that if we have a set of objects and are looking at placing some condition or specification on this set, then the set thus specified must exist.

Examples of this axiom are:
Assume that the set of citizens of China is defined. If we impose the condition that the members of this set must be female, then this new set (of Chinese females) is defined. As a more mathematical example, if we assume that the set of whole numbers exists, then the set of even numbers (multiples of 2) must also exist.

A second example of a set axiom is the 'axiom of powers'. For each set, there exists a collection of sets that contains amongst its elements all the subsets of the original set. If we look at the set of cats in Bogota, then there must be a set that contains all the female cats in Bogota, another that contains all the cats with green eyes in Bogota, another that contains all the Bogota cats with black tails, etc. A good, but theoretical, account of axiomatic set theory can be found in Halmos, 1960.

Mathematics has, in some sense, been a search for the smallest possible set of consistent axioms. In the section on paradox, we will look further at the notion of axioms and the search for a set of assumptions that does not lead to contradictions. There is a very strong sense in which mathematics is an unusual pursuit in this respect. Pure mathematics is concerned with absolute truth only in the sense of creating a self-consistent structure of thinking.

As an example of some axioms that may not seem to be sensible, consider a geometry in which the shortest path between two points is the arc of a circle and all parallel lines meet. These 'axioms' do not seem to make sense in 'normal' geometry. The first mathematicians to investigate non-Euclidean geometry were the Russian, Nicolai Lobachevsky (1793-1856) and the Hungarian, Janos Bolyai (1802-1860). Independently, they developed self consistent geometries that did not include the so called parallel postulate which states that for every line AB and point C outside AB there is only one line through C that does not meet AB.

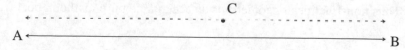

Since both lines extend to infinity in both directions, this seems to be 'obvious'. Non-Euclidean geometries do not include this postulate and assume either that there are no lines through C that do not meet AB or that there is more than one such line. It was the great achievement of Lobachevsky and Bolyai that they proved that these assumptions lead to geometries that are self consistent and thus acceptable as 'true' to pure mathematicians. In case you are thinking that this sort of activity is completely useless, one of the two non-Euclidean geometries discussed above has actually proved to be useful; the geometry of shapes drawn on a sphere. This is useful because it is the geometry used by the navigators of aeroplanes and ships.

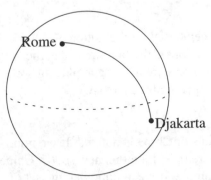

The first point about this geometry is that it is impossible to travel in straight lines. On the surface of a sphere, the shortest distance between two points is an arc of a circle centred at the centre of the sphere (a great circle). The shortest path from Rome to Djakarta is circular. If you want to see this path on a geographer's globe, take a length of sewing cotton and stretch it tightly between the two cities. The cotton will follow the approximate great circle route between the two cities.

If we now think of the arcs of great circles as our 'straight lines', what kind of geometry will we get? You can see some of these results without going into any complex calculations. For example, what would a triangle look like?

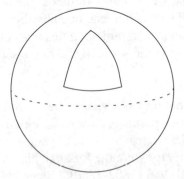

The first point is that the angles of this triangle add up to more than 180°. There are many other 'odd' features of this geometry. However, fortunately for the international airline trade, the geometry is self consistent and allows us to navigate safely around the surface of the globe. Thus non-Euclidean geometry is an acceptable pure mathematical structure.

While you are thinking about unusual geometries, what are the main features of the geometry of shapes drawn on the 'saddle surface'?

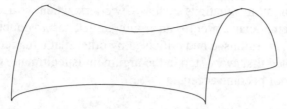

One final point on the subject of non-Euclidean geometries; it seems to be the case that our three dimensional universe is also curved. This was one of the great insights of Albert Einstein (1879-1955). We do not yet know if our universe is bent back on itself rather like a sphere or whether another model is appropriate. A short account of non-Euclidean Geometries can be found in Cameron (pp31-40).

By contrast, applied mathematics is judged more by its ability to predict the future, than by its self-consistency. Applied mathematics is also based on axioms, but these are judged more on their ability to lead to calculations that can predict eclipses, cyclones, whether or not a suspension bridge will be able to support traffic loads, etc. In some cases such mathematical models can be very complex and may not give very accurate predictions. Applied mathematics is about getting a prediction, evaluating it (seeing how well it predicts the future) and then improving the model.

In summary, both branches of mathematics are based on axioms. These may or may not be designed to be 'realistic'. What matters to the pure mathematician is that an axiom set should not lead to contradictions. The applied mathematician is looking for an axiom set and a mathematical structure built on these axioms that can be used to model the phenomena that we observe in nature. As we have seen, useful axiom sets need not start out being 'sensible'.

The system of deduction that we use to build the other truths of mathematics is known as **proof**.

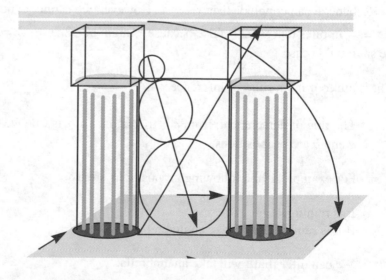

1.3 PROOF

Proof has a very special meaning in mathematics. We use the word generally to mean 'proof beyond reasonable doubt' in situations such as law courts when we accept some doubt in a verdict. For mathematicians, proof is an argument that has *no* doubt at all. When a new proof is published, it is scrutinised and criticised by other mathematicians and is accepted when it is established that every step in the argument is legitimate. Only when this has happened does a proof become accepted.

Technically, every step in a proof rests on the axioms of the mathematics that is being used. As we have seen, there is more than one set of axioms that could be chosen. The statements that we prove from the axioms are known as **theorems**. Once we have a theorem, it becomes a statement that we accept as true and which can be used in the proof of other theorems. In this way we build up a structure that constitutes a 'mathematics'. The axioms are the foundations and the theorems are the superstructure. In the previous section we made use of the idea of consistency. This means that it must not be possible to use our axiom set to prove two theorems that are contradictory.

There are a variety of methods of proof available. This section will look at three of these in detail. We will mention others.

RULES OF INFERENCE

All proofs depend on rules of inference. Fundamental to these rules is the idea of 'implication'. As an example, we can say that $2x = 4$ (which is known as a **proposition**) implies that $x = 2$ (provided that x is a normal real number and that we are talking about normal arithmetic). In mathematical shorthand we would write this statement as $2x = 4 \Rightarrow x = 2$. This implication works both ways because $x = 2$ implies that $2x = 4$ also. This is written as $x = 2 \Rightarrow 2x = 4$ or the fact that the implication is both ways can be written as $x = 2 \Leftrightarrow 2x = 4$. Not every implication works both ways in this manner. If $x = 2$ then we can conclude that $x^2 = 4$. However, we cannot conclude the reverse: $x^2 = 4$ implies that $x = 2$ is false because x might be –2. $x = 2 \Rightarrow x^2 = 4$ is all that can be said in this case.

There are four main rules of inference:

1. The rule of detachment: from a is true and $a \Rightarrow b$ is true we can infer that b is true. a and b are propositions.

   For example, if the following propositions are true:

   It is raining.
   If it is raining, I will take an umbrella.

   We can infer that I will take an umbrella.

2.   The rule of syllogism: from $a \Rightarrow b$ is true and $b \Rightarrow c$ is true, we can conclude that $a \Rightarrow c$ is true. a, b & c are propositions.

For example, if we accept as true that:
if x is an odd number then x is not divisible by 4 ($a \Rightarrow b$)and,
if x is not divisible by 4 then x is not divisible by 16 ($b \Rightarrow c$)

we can infer that the proposition; if x is an odd number then x is not divisible by 16 ($a \Rightarrow c$) is true.

3.   The rule of equivalence: at any stage in an argument we can replace any statement by an equivalent statement.

For example, if x is a whole number, the statement x is even could be replaced by the statement x is divisible by 2.

4.   The rule of substitution: If we have a true statement about all the elements of a set, then that statement is true about any individual member of the set.

For example, if we accept that all lions have sharp teeth then Benji, who is a lion, must have sharp teeth.

Now that we have our rules of inference, we can look at some of the most commonly used methods of proof

PROOF BY EXHAUSTION
This method can be, as its name implies, exhausting! It depends on testing every possible case of a theorem.

Example:

Consider the theorem: Every year must contain at least one 'Friday the thirteenth'.

There are a limited number of possibilities as the first day of every year must be a Monday or a Tuesday or a Wednesday.... or a Sunday (7 possibilities). Taking the fact that the year might or might not be a leap year (with 366 days) means that there are going to be fourteen possibilities.

Once we have established all the possibilities, we would look at the calendar associated with each and establish whether or not it has a 'Friday the thirteenth'. If, for example, we are looking at a non-leap year in which January 1st is a Saturday, there will be a 'Friday the thirteenth' in May. Take a look at all the possibilities (an electronic organiser helps!). Is the theorem true?

DIRECT PROOF

The following diagrams represent a proof of the theorem of Pythagoras described in 'The Ascent of Man' (Bronowski pp 158-161). The theorem states that the area of a square drawn on the hypotenuse of a right angled triangle is equal to the sum of the areas of the squares drawn on the two shorter sides. The method is direct in the sense that it makes no assumptions at the start. Can you follow the steps of this proof and draw the appropriate conclusion?

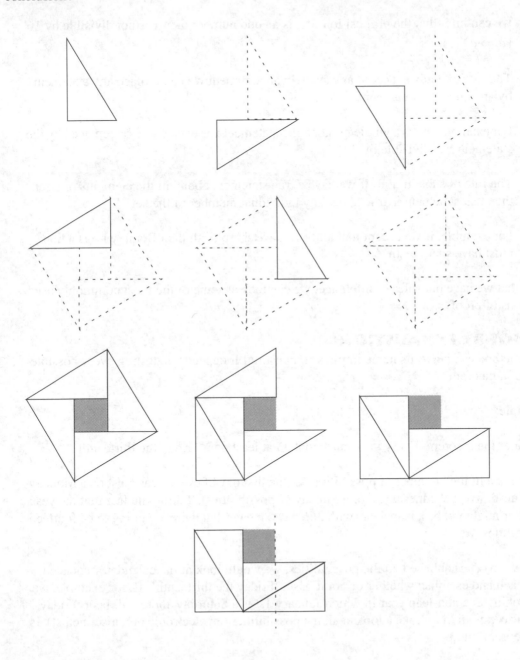

PROOF BY CONTRADICTION

This method works by assuming that the proposition is false and then proving that this assumption leads to a contradiction.

Example: The number $\sqrt{2}$ greatly interested classical Greek mathematicians who were unable to find a number that, when it was squared, gave exactly 2.
Modern students are often fooled into thinking that their calculators give an exact square root for 2 as when 2 is entered and the square root button is pressed, a result (depending on the model of calculator) of 1.414213562 is produced. When this is squared, exactly 2 results. This is not because we have an exact square root. It results from the way in which the calculator is designed to calculate with more figures than it actually displays.

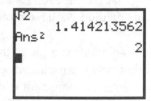

The first answer is stored to more figures than are shown, the result is rounded and then displayed. The same is true of the second result which only rounds to 2. Try squaring 1.414213562, the answer is not 2.

The theorem we shall prove is that there is *no* fraction that when squared gives 2. This also implies that there is no terminating or recurring decimal that, when squared, gives exactly 2, but this further theorem requires more argument.

The method begins by assuming that there *is* a fraction $\dfrac{p}{q}$ (p & q are integers) which has been cancelled to its lowest terms, such that $\dfrac{p}{q} = \sqrt{2}$. From the assumption, the argument proceeds:

$$\frac{p}{q} = \sqrt{2} \Rightarrow \frac{p^2}{q^2} = 2 \Rightarrow p^2 = 2q^2 \Rightarrow p^2 \text{ is even} \Rightarrow p \text{ is even}$$

As with most mathematical proofs, we have used simple axioms and theorems of arithmetic. The most complex theorem used is that if p^2 is even, then p is even. Can you prove this?
The main proof continues with the deduction that if p is even there must be another *integer, r,* that is half p.

$$p = 2r \Rightarrow p^2 = 4r^2 \Rightarrow 2q^2 = 4r^2 \Rightarrow q^2 = 2r^2 \Rightarrow q^2 \text{ is even} \Rightarrow q \text{ is even}$$

We now have our contradiction as we assumed that $\dfrac{p}{q}$ was in its lowest terms so p & q cannot both be even. This proves the result, because we have a contradiction.

This theorem is a very strong statement of *impossibility*. There are very few other areas of knowledge in which we can make similar statements. We might be virtually certain that we will never travel faster than the speed of light but it would be a brave physicist who would state with certainty that it is *impossible*. Other methods of proof include proof by induction which is mainly used to prove theorems involving sequences of statements.

Whilst on the subject of proof, it is worth noting that it is much easier to disprove a statement than to prove it. When we succeed in disproving a statement, we have succeeded in proving its negation or reverse. To disprove a statement, all we need is a single example of a case in which the theorem does not hold. Such a case is known as a **counter-example**.

Example: The theorem 'all prime numbers are odd' is false. This can be established by noting that 2 is an even prime and, therefore, is the only counter-example we need to give. By this method we have proved the theorem that 'not every prime number is odd'.

This is another example of the way in which pure mathematicians think in a slightly different way from other disciplines. Zoo-keepers (and indeed the rest of us) might be happy with the statement that 'all giraffes have long necks' and would not be very impressed with a pure mathematician who said that the statement was false because there was one giraffe (with a birth defect) who has a very short neck. This goes back to the slightly different standards of proof that are required in mathematics.

Counter-examples and proofs in mathematics may be difficult to find. Consider the theorem that every odd positive integer is the sum of a prime number and twice the square of an integer. Examples of this theorem that do work are:
$5 = 3 + 2 \times 1^2, 15 = 13 + 2 \times 1^2, 35 = 17 + 2 \times 3^2$. The theorem remains true for a very large number of cases and we do not arrive at a counter-example until 5777.

Another similar 'theorem' is known as the Goldbach Conjecture. Christian Goldbach (1690-1764) stated that every even number larger than 2 can be written as the sum of two primes. For example, $4 = 2 + 2, 10 = 3 + 7, 48 = 19 + 29$ etc. No-one has every found a counter-example to this 'simple' conjecture and yet no accepted proof has ever been produced, despite the fact that the conjecture is not exactly recent!

Finally, whilst considering proof, it would be a mistake to think that mathematics is a complete set of truths that has nothing which needs to be added. We have already seen that there are unproved theorems that we suspect to be true. It is also the case that new branches of mathematics are emerging with a fair degree of regularity. During this course you will study linear programming which was developed in the 1940s to help solve the problems associated with the distribution of limited resources. Recently, both pure and applied mathematics have been enriched by the development of 'Chaos Theory'. This has produced items of beauty such as the Mandelbrot set and insights into the workings of nature. It seems, for example, that the results of Chaos Theory indicate that accurate long term weather forecasts will never be possible (Mandelbrot).

1.4 PARADOX

Pure mathematics is a quest for a structure that does not contain internal contradictions. A satisfactory mathematics will contain no 'nonsense'. Consider the following proof:

Let $x = 1$

Then $x^2 - 1 = x - 1$ Try substituting $x = 1$ to check this line.

$(x + 1)(x - 1) = x - 1$ Factorising using the difference of two squares.

$x + 1 = 1$ Dividing both sides by $x - 1$.

$2 = 1$ Substituting $x = 1$.

There is obviously something wrong here as this is the sort of inconsistency that we have discussed earlier in this chapter, but what is wrong? To discover this, we must check each line of the argument for errors or faulty reasoning.

Line 1 must be acceptable as we are entitled to assign a numerical value to a pronumeral. Line 2 is true because the left hand and right hand sides are the same if we substitute the given value of the pronumeral.
Line 3 is a simple factorisation of the left hand side.
Line 4 is obtained from line 3 by dividing both sides of the equation by $x - 1$ and should be acceptable as we have 'done the same thing' to both sides of the equation.
Line 5 is obtained from line 4 by substituting $x = 1$ and so should give the correct answer.

Obviously we have an unacceptable conclusion from a seemingly watertight argument. There must be something there that needs to be removed as an acceptable operation in mathematics.

The unacceptable operation is dividing both sides by $x - 1$ and then using a value of 1 for x. What we have effectively done is divide by a quantity that is zero. It is this operation that has allowed us to prove that $2 = 1$, an unacceptable result. When a **paradox** of this sort arises, we need to look at the steps of the proof to see if there is a faulty step. If there is, then the faulty step must be removed. In this case, we must add this rule to the allowed operations of mathematics:

> Never divide by a quantity that is, or will become, zero.

This rule, often ignored by students, has important implications for Calculus.

Some paradoxes are arguments that seem to be sound but contain a hidden error and thus do not contain serious implications for the structure of mathematical logic. An amusing compilation of simple paradoxes can be found in Gardner (1982). An example is the 'elevator paradox'.

Why does it always seem that when we are waiting for an elevator near the bottom of a tall building and wanting to go up, the first elevator to arrive is always going down? Also, when we want to go back down, why is the first elevator to arrive always going up? Is this a real phenomenon or is it just a subjective result of our impatience for the elevator to arrive? Or is it another example of Murphy's Law; whatever can go wrong will go wrong?

This is quite a complex question, but a simple explanation might run as follows:

If we are waiting near the bottom of a tall building, there are a small number of floors below us from which elevators that are going up might come and then pass our floor.

By contrast, there are more floors above us from which elevators might come and then pass our floor going down.

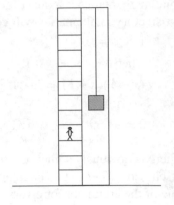

On the basis of this and assuming that the elevators are randomly distributed amongst the floors, it is more likely that the next elevator to pass will come from above and will, therefore, be going down.

By contrast, if we are waiting near the top of a tall building, there are a small number of floors above us from which elevators that are going down might come and then pass our floor.

Also, there are more floors below us from which elevators might come and then pass our floor going up.

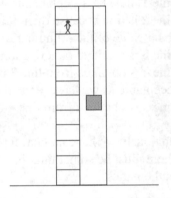

It is more likely that the next elevator to pass will come from below and will, therefore, be going up.

A fuller analysis of this paradox can be found in Gardner (pp96-97).

The elevator paradox does not contain serious implication for the structure of mathematics like our first example. We will conclude this section with a look at a modern paradox that did cause a re-evaluation of one of the basic ideas of mathematics, the set.

RUSSELL'S PARADOX

Bertrand Russell (1872-1970) looked in detail at the basic set axioms of mathematics. We do regard the existence of sets as axiomatic in all mathematical structures. Does this mean that we can make a set that contains 'everything'? There would seem to be no difficulty with this as we just move around the universe and sweep everything that we meet into our set, numbers, words, whales, motorcycles etc. and the result is the set that contains everything.

Russell posed the following question which we will relate in the context of library catalogues.

Every library has a catalogue. There are various forms that this catalogue might take; a book, a set of cards, a computer disc etc. Whatever form the catalogue in your local library takes, there is a sense in which this catalogue is a book (or publication) owned by the library and, as such, should appear as an entry in the catalogue:

CATALOGUE	NEWEL LIBRARY
Castle, The. F Kafka 231.72	Catherine the Great A Biography J Nelson 217.42
Catalogue At reception	
Catcher in the Rye JD Salinger 123.64	Catullus The complete works Edited by F Wills 312.42

Of course, many librarians will decide that it is silly to include the catalogue as an entry in the catalogue because people who are already looking at the catalogue know where to find it in the library! It follows that library catalogues can be divided into two distinct groups:

- Catalogues that do contain an entry describing themselves.
- Catalogues that do not contain an entry describing themselves.

Next, let us make a catalogue of *all* the catalogues of type two, those that do not contain themselves.

This gives us a problem. Should we include an entry describing our new catalogue? If we do, then our catalogue ceases to be a catalogue of all those catalogues that do not contain themselves. If we do not, then our catalogue is no longer a complete catalogue of all those catalogues that do not contain themselves.

The conclusion is that making such a catalogue is impossible. This does not mean that the library catalogues themselves cannot exist. We have, however, defined an impossible catalogue.

In set terms, Russell's paradox says that sets are of two types:

Type 1   Sets that do contain themselves.
Type 2   Sets that do not contain themselves.

The set of all sets of type 2 cannot be properly defined without reaching a contradiction.

The most commonly accepted result of Russell's paradox is the conclusion that we have to be very careful when we talk about sets of everything. The most usual way out is to work within a carefully defined universal set, chosen to be appropriate to the mathematics that we are undertaking. If we are doing normal arithmetic, the universal set is the set of real numbers.

1.5 MATHEMATICS AND OTHER DISCIPLINES

When writing Theory of Knowledge essays, students are required to develop their arguments in a cross disciplinary way. For more details on this, you are strongly advised to read the task specifications and the assessment criteria that accompany the essay title. You are reminded that it is these statements that define what is expected of a good essay, not the contents of this Chapter which have been provided as a background resource. A good essay will only result if you develop your own ideas and examples in a clear and connected manner. Part of this process may include comparing the 'mathematical method' described earlier with the methods that are appropriate to other systems of knowledge.

As we have seen, mathematics rests on sets of axioms. This is true of many other disciplines. There is a sense in which many ethical systems also have their axioms such as 'Thou shalt not kill'.

The Ancient Greeks believed that beauty and harmony are based, almost axiomatically, on mathematical proportions. The golden mean is found by dividing a line in the following ratio:

The ratio of the length AB to the length BC is the same as the ratio of the length BC to the whole length AC. The actual ratio is $1:\frac{1}{2}(1 + \sqrt{5})$ or about 1:1.618. The Greek idea was that if this line is converted into a rectangle, then the shape produced would be in perfect proportion:

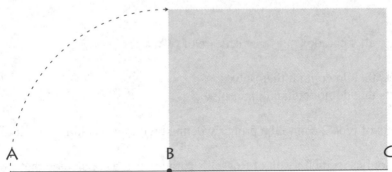

Likewise, the correct place to put the centre of interest in a picture is placed at the golden mean position between the sides and also at the golden mean between top and bottom. Take a look at the way in which television pictures are composed to see if we still use this idea:

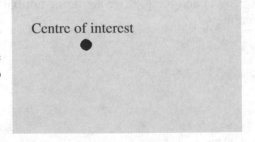

Centre of interest

14

In a similar way, the Ancient Greeks believed that ratio determined harmony in music. If two similar strings whose lengths bear a simple ratio such as 1:2 or 2:3 are plucked together the resulting sound will be pleasant (harmonious). If the ratio of string lengths is 'awkward', such as 17:19, then the notes will be discordant. The same principle of simple ratios is used in tuning musical instruments (in most cultures) today.

The most common connection between mathematics and other disciplines is the use of mathematics as a tool. Examples are: the use of statistics by insurance actuaries, probability by quality control officers and of almost all branches of mathematics by engineers. Every time mathematics is used in this way, there is an assumption that the calculations will be done using techniques that produce consistent and correct answers. It is here that pure mathematical techniques, applied mathematical modelling and other disciplines interface.

In some of these examples, we apply very precise criteria to our calculations and are prepared to accept only very low levels of error. Navigation satellite systems work by measuring the position of a point on or above the Earth relative to the positions of satellites orbiting the Earth.

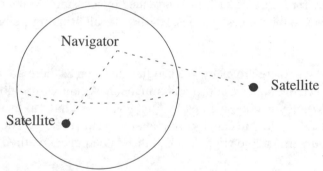

This system will only work if the positions of the satellites are known with very great precision.

By contrast, when calculations are made to forecast the weather, whilst they are done with as much precision as necessary, because the data is incomplete and the atmospheric models used are approximate, the results of the calculations are, at best, only an indication of what might happen. Fortunately, most of us expect this and are much more tolerant of errors in weather forecasting than we would be if airlines regularly failed to find their destinations!

There are, therefore a large number of ways in which mathematics complements other disciplines. In fact, because computers are essentially mathematical devices and we are increasingly dependent on them, it could be argued that mathematics and its methods underpin the modern world.

That is not to say that mathematics is 'everywhere'. Many very successful people have managed to avoid the subject altogether. Great art, music and poetry has been produced by people for whom mathematical ideas held little interest.

In using mathematical ideas in essays, remember that you should produce original examples, look at them in a mathematical context and then compare the ways in which the example might appear to a mathematician with the way in which the same example might appear to a thinker from another discipline.

As a very simple example, what should we think of gambling?

To the mathematician (Pascal was one of the first to look at this activity from the mathematical perspective), a gambling game is a probability event. The outcome of a single spin of a roulette wheel is unknown. If we place a single bet, we can only know the chances of winning, not whether or not we *will* win. Also, in the long run, we can expect to lose one thirtyseventh of any money that we bet every time we play. To the mathematician, (or at least to this mathematician) this rather removes the interest from the game!

Other people look at gambling from a different standpoint. To the politician, a casino is a source of revenue and possibly a focus of some social problems. To a social scientist, the major concern might be problem gamblers and the effect that gambling has on the fabric of society. A theologian might look at the ethical issues as being paramount. Is it ethical to take money for a service such as is provided by a casino? Many of these people might use mathematics in their investigations, but they are all bringing a slightly different view to the discussion.

As we can see, there are many sides to this question as there are many sides to most questions. Mathematics can often illuminate these, but will seldom provide all the answers. When you choose an essay title, you do not have to use mathematical ideas or a mathematical method to develop your analysis. However, we hope that if you do choose to do this, you will find the brief sketch of the mathematical method described in this Chapter helpful.

We will finish with one observation. Mathematics and mathematicians are sometimes viewed as dry and unimaginative. This may be true in some cases, but definitely not all. We conclude with some remarks by the mathematician Charles Dodgson (1832-1898), otherwise known as Lewis Carroll:

> 'The time has come', the Walrus said,
> 'To talk of many things:
> Of shoes and ships and sealing wax,
> Of cabbages and kings,
> Of why the sea is boiling hot
> And whether pigs have wings'.
>
> Through the Looking Glass

References:
Megalithic Sites in Britain. Thom, A. (1967). U.K. Oxford University Press.
Heritage Mathematics. Cameron, M. (1984).U.K. E.J. Arnold.
The Ascent of Man, Bronowski, J. (1973).U.K. BBC.
The Fractal Geometry of Nature, Mandelbrot, B (1977), U.S.A W.H. Freeman & Co. 1977.
Gotcha!, Gardner, M. (1977). U.S.A. W.H. Freeman & Co.

NUMBER & ALGEBRA 1

NUMBER SYSTEMS

2

Chapter contents

2.1 NUMBER SYSTEM

We will not be looking at the history of numbers as such but rather an awareness of the need to consider how and why the number system needed to expand and evolve over time.

Consider the set of numbers $\{1, 2, 3, 4, 5, \ldots\}$. If we select any two numbers from this set, say 4 and 6, when they are added we obtain another number in this set, i.e., $4 + 6 = 10$. Similarly, when we multiply these two numbers, namely $4 \times 6 = 24$, again we end up with a number that belongs to this set. Such a set is called a closed set under addition and multiplication. But what happens when we divide 6 by 4, does the result belong to this set? This basic question proved to be quite an issue in the early development of mathematics. We will briefly look at the evolution of the number system which enabled mathematics to develop the different number systems that we so readily use (and take for granted) today.

The set so far considered, i.e., $\{1, 2, 3, 4, \ldots\}$ is known as the set of natural numbers and is denoted by the letter $\mathbb{N}$, i.e., the set of **Natural numbers** is $\mathbb{N} = \{1, 2, 3, \ldots\}$ which is also referred to as the set of positive integers. Now, although this appears as if we were born with the ability to possess such 'trivial knowledge', it was only in the nineteenth century that the Italian mathematician Peano (1858–1932) and others like him, were successful in describing the set $\mathbb{N}$ in a way which brought about (in a mathematical way) the nature of the basic properties of $\mathbb{N}$. One of the properties that he formalised became the basis of the so called "Principle of Mathematical Induction"(see HL Mathematics).

What happens when two numbers are subtracted? If we choose 6 and 4, then $6 - 4 = 2$, which is still a natural number, but $4 - 6 = -2$. What about $4 - 4 \,(= 0)$, where did this fit in this particular number system? The question then naturally arose (as it did when we considered $6 \div 4$), where do these numbers belong?

Because of questions like these, it was necessary to expand the number system to sets that included negative numbers, zero and fractions.

The **set of integers** is defined as $\mathbb{Z} = \{\ldots, -3, -2, -1, 0, 1, 2, 3, \ldots\}$. This now enabled mathematicians to solve problems like, find x where $x + 6 = 4 \,(x = -2)$. This also meant that we now had two sets, one of which was wholly contained within the other. That is, we now had that $\mathbb{N} \subset \mathbb{Z}$

We still had to deal with fractions. To this end, the set $\mathbb{Z}$ was extended to the set of rational numbers, $\mathbb{Q}$, where $\mathbb{Q} = \left\{ \dfrac{m}{n} : m \in \mathbb{Z}, n \in \mathbb{Z}, n \neq 0 \right\}$. Notice that the restriction on this set is that division by zero is not allowed. For example, we could now solve equations of the form $3x + 1 = 5 \left(\Leftrightarrow x = \dfrac{4}{3} \right)$. We now had the relationship that $\mathbb{N} \subset \mathbb{Z} \subset \mathbb{Q}$.

At this stage all seems to be in order—until we try to solve a problem of the form $x^2 = 2$, or determine the area of a circle (given by πr^2). Numbers generated from such problems could not be found in any of the sets found so far. This is where the set of **irrational numbers** came into play. Irrational numbers became the set of numbers that did not belong to the set $\mathbb{Q}$ and it was denoted by $\overline{\mathbb{Q}}$. Numbers that belong to this set are π, e, $\sqrt{2}$ (i.e., surds) and all numbers that cannot be expressed as a fraction.

Sometimes we run into numbers like, 0.33333..., what type of number is this? It appears as if it is an irrational number, but in fact, it is a rational number. This can be shown as follows:

$\qquad$ Let $x = 0.33333\ldots \therefore 10x = 3.33333\ldots$

$\qquad$ That is, we have that $\quad 10x = 3 + 0.33333\ldots$

$\qquad$ But, $x = 0.33333\ldots$, so, $10x = 3 + x$

$\qquad$ Therefore, $\qquad\qquad 9x = 3 \Leftrightarrow x = \dfrac{3}{9}\left(= \dfrac{1}{3}\right)$

Therefore, we have that $0.33333\ldots = \dfrac{1}{3}$, which is a rational number.

The **union of** the **rational set** and the **irrational set** produce the **set of real numbers**.

That is, $\mathbb{Q} \cup \overline{\mathbb{Q}} = \mathbb{R}$. The set of real numbers contains every number that can be thought up (excluding some numbers that belong to a set known as **complex numbers** (see Higher Level course). Also, as the number system has developed over many hundreds of years, it might very well be the case that a new set of numbers, which contains new numbers that cannot be accounted for using our present system is yet to be developed! We now provide a diagram highlighting the relationship between the sets covered.

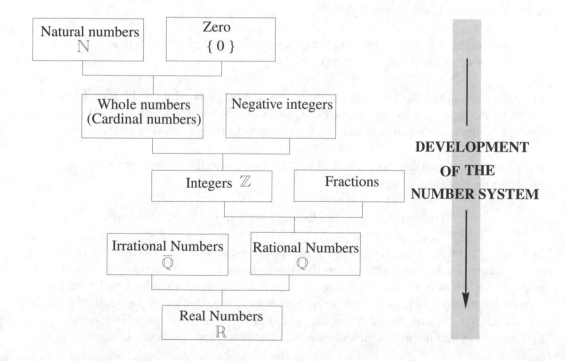

2.2 SIGNIFICANT FIGURES

Whenever a quantity is measured, there is some error in the measurement. The amount of error usually depends on the quality of the device used to make the measurement. Here are two attempts to measure the length of a rod:

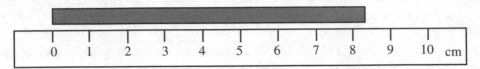

This ruler is only marked with centimetre graduations and suggests that the length of the rod is 8cm.

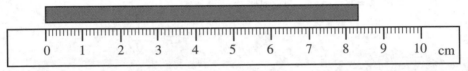

This ruler is marked with millimetre graduations and allows us to estimate the length of the rod as 8.3cm.

In the first case, the length is given as 8cm which means that the length of the rod is somewhere between 7.5 and 8.5cm. In the second case, when using the more accurate ruler, giving the length as 8.3cm means that the true length is between 8.25cm and 8.35cm. In summary:

A measurement of 8cm means that the true value is in the range 7.5cm to 8.5cm and is said to be accurate to **1 significant figure**.

A measurement of 8.3cm means that the true value is in the range 8.25cm to 8.35cm and is said to be accurate to **2 significant figures**.

In most cases, the number of significant figures in a measurement can be found by counting the figures: 6.743gms is 4 significant figures, 45216kg is 5 significant figures etc. Generally, the more significant figures, the more accurate the measurement.

Large and small measurements need to be considered carefully when deciding their level of accuracy. Consider this statement:

"The distance from the Earth to the Sun is 150 000 000km"

How many significant figures is this? There is a sense in which this is not obvious, but it seems likely that the statement means that the distance is 150 million kilometres as opposed to 140 million or 160 million kilometres. This means that the 1 and 5 are the significant figures and the zeros are only there to hold the position of the decimal point and tell us that the units of measurement are tens of millions of kilometres. The safest assumption is that the measurement is only accurate to two significant figures.

If you interpret the statement as meaning that the distance from the Earth to the Sun is 150000000 as opposed to 149999999 or 150000001km (which seems to be highly unlikely!), then the measurement is correct to 9 significant figures. This is seldom the case and you should interpret leading and trailing zeros as not being significant figures.

EXAMPLES

Find the number of significant figures in the following measurements:

(a)	4035km	(b)	56000kg	(c)	56004kg
(d)	0.001600mm	(e)	2.0016mm	(f)	300m

SOLUTIONS

The significant figures are shown **bold**. Note that leading and trailing zeros do not count as 'significant'.

(a)	**4035**km[4 S.F.]	(b)	**56**000kg [2 S.F.]	(c)	**56004**kg [5 S.F.]
(d)	0.00**1600**mm [4 S.F.]	(e)	**2.0016**mm [5 S.F.]	(f)	**3**00m [1 S.F.]

ROUNDING

It is often necessary to round answers to calculations. As a general principle, if you do calculations with numbers that are accurate to, say, 3 significant figures, the answers should be rounded to the same level of accuracy (3 significant figures).

EXAMPLES

1. A rectangular field is measured as 91 metres long and 75 metres wide. What is the area of the field?

2. Find the area of a circle of radius 2.33cm.

SOLUTIONS

1. The area is $91 \times 75 = 6825 \text{m}^2$. This is four significant figures. It is not appropriate to quote an answer to a much higher level of accuracy than the data used in the calculations. In this case, the data is accurate to 2 significant figures and so the answer should be rounded to this level of accuracy. Rounding the answer to 2 significant figures gives 6800 square metres.

In this case, we should note that the largest possible values of the length and width are 91.5 and 75.5 metres giving a largest possible value for the area of 6908.25m^2. Similarly, the smallest possible area is 90.5 by $74.5 = 6742.25 \text{m}^2$. From these figures, it is evident that we are not able to calculate the area to a greater level of accuracy than 2 significant figures.

2. Area $= \pi \times 2.33^2 \approx 17.05539 \text{cm}^2$. It is appropriate to perform all calculations to a high level of accuracy. In this case, for example, you should use the 'π' key and not any less accurate approximation such as 3.14. The data is accurate to 3 significant figures and so the answer should be rounded to a similar level of accuracy. In this case the fourth figure is a 5 and so the result must be rounded up to 17.1cm^2

EXERCISE 2.1

1. State the number of significant figures in these values:

(a)	34.52	(b)	5673.7	(c)	1200
(d)	4.001	(e)	0.00452	(f)	0.00340
(g)	784520	(h)	0.450	(i)	4503450
(j)	0.00452	(k)	67.4500	(l)	0.56204

2. Round the following values to the number of significant figures given:

(a)	2.526 [2 S.F]	(b)	24650 [3 S.F]	(c)	0.347 [2 S.F]
(d)	45627 [4 S.F]	(e)	0.4523 [2 S.F]	(f)	3.624 [1 S.F]
(g)	56720 [2 S.F]	(h)	0.04537 [3 S.F]	(i)	0.0045 [2 S.F]
(j)	345620 [3 S.F]	(k)	0.0453 [2 S.F]	(l)	89000 [1 S.F]

3. A square has an area of $67\,cm^2$. Find the length of one of the sides, giving the answer to an appropriate number of significant figures.

4. A rectangle has an area of $56\,cm^2$ and a length of 5.1cm. Find the width of the rectangle, giving the answer to an appropriate number of significant figures.

5. The angle of elevation of a building is $34°$ when measured from a distance of 65 metres. Find the height of the building giving the answer to an appropriate number of significant figures.

6. A painting is 782mm wide and 679mm high. What is the length of the diagonal (to an appropriate level of accuracy)?

7. Consider the series of fractions $\frac{1}{2} + \frac{1}{3} + \frac{1}{4} + \frac{1}{5} + \frac{1}{6}$.............. How many terms of this series will you need to add before the total is equal to 3, correct to three significant figures?

8. The fraction $\frac{22}{7}$ is often used as an approximation to π. To how many significant figures is this accurate?

9. The expression $\left(1 + \frac{1}{n}\right)^n$ is equal to the irrational number e (press $e^x \wedge 1$ on a calculator). What is the smallest value of n that will give e correct to 2 significant figures?

2.3 SCIENTIFIC NOTATION

Very large and very small numbers can be written in a convenient, abbreviated, form known as scientific notation. To convert a number into scientific notation, it is first split into two factors, one of which is a power of ten and the other a number in the range 1 to 10.

(i.e., 3 'jumps' to the right)

$4000 = 4 \times 1000 = 4 \times 10^3$ (i.e., 6 'jumps')

$5603000 = 5.603 \times 1000000 = 5.603 \times 10^6$

$372000 = 3.72 \times 100000 = 3.72 \times 10^5$

$62420000 = 6.242 \times 10000000 = 6.242 \times 10^7$

Small numbers can be converted to scientific notation in a similar way:

(i.e., 3 'jumps' to the left)

$0.004 = 4 \times \dfrac{1}{1000} = 4 \times 10^{-3}$

(i.e., 5 'jumps' to the left)

$0.0000402 = 4.02 \times \dfrac{1}{100000} = 4.02 \times 10^{-5}$

Notice that this time, as the jumps are to the left the power is negative!

$0.0002049 = 2.049 \times \dfrac{1}{10000} = 2.049 \times 10^{-4}$

$0.2501 = 2.501 \times \dfrac{1}{10} = 2.501 \times 10^{-1}$

It is often desirable to give very large or small answers in scientific notation as it is concise and makes the number of significant figures very obvious.

In the case of the number 3.604×10^{-7}, all the figures in the 3.604 part of the number are significant and we can say that the number is accurate to 4 significant figures.

Many scientific quantities are either very large or very small. Here are some commonly used physical constants in scientific notation:

The speed of light: $2.998 \times 10^8 ms^{-1}$ The mass of a neutron: $1.67 \times 10^{-24} gm$

The charge on an electron: $1.6021 \times 10^{-19} coulombs$

You should know how to enter quantities that are in scientific notation on your calculator. Many scientific calculators have an 'EXP' key that allows the direct entry of a power of 10. Thus the speed of light would be entered as 2.998 'EXP' 8. Failing this, the number can be entered as $2.998 \times 10 x^y 8$ using the powers key.

USING A GRAPHICS CALCULATOR

Graphic and other calculators can be set to display answers correct to a fixed number of decimal places.

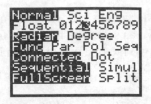

To display all answers correct to three decimal places, press the MODE key and select Float.... 3 from the screen. It is necessary to press ENTER to confirm this selection.

All subsequent calculations will now be rounded to three decimal places.

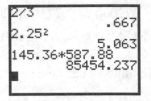

This screen shows some examples:

If it is desired to set the calculator to display answers correct to three significant figures, the calculator must be set to display answers in scientific notation and set the display to Float... **2** (ENTER).

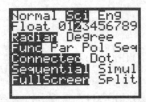

Calculations will now appear in scientific notation:

Numbers in scientific notation can be entered using the 2nd **EE** key. Note that the (-) and not the subtraction key must be used for negative indices

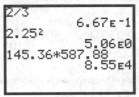

When calculating with numbers in scientific notation, the principle of giving answers to an appropriate level of accuracy discussed earlier, also applies.

EXAMPLE

If $a = 0.000982$ $b = 3.56 \times 10^{-4}$ $c = 4.56 \times 10^{6}$, evaluate:

    (i) $a(b + c)$ (ii) ab (iii) $\dfrac{b}{a + c}$

SOLUTION

(i) $a(b + c) = 0.000982(3.56 \times 10^{-4} + 4.56 \times 10^6) \approx 4.48 \times 10^3$ to 3 S.F.

(ii) $ab = 0.000982 \times 3.56 \times 10^{-4} \approx 3.50 \times 10^{-7}$ to 3 S.F.

(iii) $\dfrac{b}{a + c} = \dfrac{3.56 \times 10^{-4}}{0.000982 + 4.56 \times 10^6} \approx 7.81 \times 10^{-11}$ to 3 S.F.

 ## USING A GRAPHICS CALCULATOR

If using a graphic calculator, you should see these, or similar, screens if you first set the display to 'SCI' 'FLOAT' 2 format as described earlier. You must be able to interpret such screens and should give answers in correct scientific notation, not the calculator version depicted.

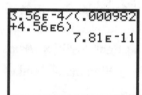

In example (iii) the use of brackets for the denominator is essential if your calculator is not to interpret the calculation as $\dfrac{b}{a} + c$ which gives 4.56×10^6, a substantially different and incorrect answer.

It is a good practice when using a calculator to estimate the answer before entering the calculation. This helps in the detection of errors in keying and is a technique that you are advised to practise.

EXERCISE 2.2

1. If $x = 3.8 \times 10^3$ $\quad y = 5.7 \times 10^{-3}$ $\quad z = 9.1 \times 10^5$, evaluate:

(i) xy (ii) $\dfrac{1+y}{z^2}$ (iii) $y(x+z)^2$

2. The radius of a planet has been estimated to be 4720000000 metres. Write this in standard form. Find the circumference and the volume of the planet correct to an appropriate level of accuracy.

3. A 2000 metre (to the nearest metre) length of optical fibre cable has a radius of 3.45×10^{-5} metres. Find the volume of the cable.

4. The world's oceans contain about 23 million cubic kilometres of water. If this water were made into a giant ice cube what would be the approximate length of a side? You may ignore the fact that water expands when it freezes.

5. Einstein's formula $E = mc^2$ gives the amount of energy, E, released when m kg of matter is destroyed in a process such as a nuclear reaction. The constant c is the velocity of light, $2.998 \times 10^8 ms^{-1}$. The unit of measurement of the energy released is kgm^2s^{-2}. Find the amount of energy released when 5.000×10^{-2} kg of matter is destroyed.

6. Lindy has an approximate heart rate of 83 beats per minute. How many beats will Lindy's heart make during her expected life-span of 78 years?

7. On average, people have children when they are 27 years old. Thus, a 'generation' lasts 27 years. Every human has two parents, four grand-parents and eight great grand-parents. Jesus Christ was born about 2000 years ago. If you traced your family back to the time when Jesus Christ was alive, how many generations would have passed and how many direct relations would you have?

8. A grain of salt is a cube of side length 0.2mm. Assuming that the grains fit together perfectly (i.e. no space is wasted), how many grains of salt will fit into a cubic box of side 10cm?

9. 2.0 grams of hydrogen contain 6.5×10^{23} molecules. What is the mass of one molecule of the gas?

10. Normal alternating current electricity is produced at 50 cycles per second. How many cycles are delivered in one day?

2.4 ROUNDING ERRORS

Earlier in this chapter we have seen that all measured quantities are subject to some level of error. It is also the case that calculated values are often subject to error. There are several sources of such error. The most common of these arises when we use a calculating device such as a hand held calculator or computer. These devices only calculate to a limited number of significant figures. This is usually quite sufficient for practical calculations. The TI-82 graphic calculator calculates and stores numbers of up to 14 digits with a 2 digit exponent. The display gives answers to a lower level of accuracy. The reason for this will be discussed later in this section. First we must consider the ways in which errors in calculations and measurement are defined:

ABSOLUTE ERROR

Absolute error = the absolute value of the difference between an approximation and the true value.

An 'absolute value' is merely the positive value of the error.

EXAMPLES

1. If the true value of a measurement of length is 23.735 metres, what are the absolute errors if three measurements of this length are 24.7 metres, 22.6 metres & 23.733 metres?

2. If the approximation 1.414 is used for $\sqrt{2}$, what is the absolute error.

3. The equatorial diameter of the Earth is 12756km. If the approximation 3.14 is used for π, what is the absolute error in calculating the equatorial circumference of the Earth? What is the error if $\dfrac{22}{7}$ is used as an approximation to π?

SOLUTIONS

1. The absolute errors are:

$|23.735 - 24.7| \quad = 0.965m$
$|23.735 - 22.6| \quad = 1.135m$
$|23.735 - 23.733| = 0.002m$

All the errors are positive whether or not the measurement is larger or smaller than the true value. This enables us to make direct comparisons of the three measurements and, for example, rank them in order of accuracy. In this case it is clear that the third measurement is the best and the second is the worst. Having all the errors positive also allows the averaging of a series of related errors. This would not give meaningful results if some errors were positive and some negative.

2. $\sqrt{2}$ cannot be written exactly as either a fraction or a decimal. This disturbing fact was first established by the Pythagorean school of Mathematics in Ancient Greece. Thus, all values of this quantity, including those produced by your calculator are approximate. In this case, we can only estimate the error as:

A graphic calculator display of the calculation and answer might appear as shown. You would need to interpret the answer as being about 0.00021.

```
abs (√2-1.414)
     2.135623731 E -4
```

3. The ratio π has a similar status to $\sqrt{2}$ in that there is no exact value available to use in calculations.

The π key on calculators is, however, a very good approximation. If using a calculator to evaluate these errors, the screen should appear somewhat like this example. Fewer key-strokes are used if the calculation

```
abs (π*12756-22/
7*12756)
        16.12982509
abs (π*12756-3.1
4*12756)
        20.31588919
```

is entered in factorised form: $\left| \pi - \dfrac{22}{7} \right| \times 12756$.

The answers are an error of 16km in the first case and about 20km in the case of the second approximation.

RELATIVE AND PERCENTAGE ERROR:

The second and third examples above illustrate one problem with absolute error as a measure. It appears that an error of 20km in the third case is much worse than the error of 0.00021 in the second. But there is a sense in which this is a false impression because the numbers are of such different size. The question is which is the larger:

An error of 0.00021 in a quantity of about 1.4142 OR:
An error of 20km in a quantity of about 40074km (the approximate equatorial circumference of the Earth.

To help decide this sort of question, we often use two additional error measures:

$$\text{Relative Error} = \frac{\text{Absolute Error}}{\text{True value}} \quad \text{AND: Percentage Error} = \frac{\text{Absolute Error}}{\text{True value}} \times \frac{100}{1}$$

With this definition, it should be noted that neither relative nor percentage error have units.

EXAMPLES

Find the relative and percentage errors in the previous set of examples. Which of these are the most accurate?

SOLUTIONS

1. The absolute errors are:

$$|23.735 - 24.7| = 0.965\text{m}$$
$$|23.735 - 22.6| = 1.135\text{m}$$
$$|23.735 - 23.733| = 0.002\text{m}$$

The relative errors are:

$$\frac{0.965}{23.735} \approx 0.0407$$

$$\frac{1.135}{23.735} \approx 0.0478$$

$$\frac{0.002}{23.735} \approx 0.0000843$$

The percentage errors are 100 times these figures: 4%, 5% & 0.008% (approx.).

2. Relative Error $= \dfrac{|1.414 - \sqrt{2}|}{\sqrt{2}} \approx 0.000151$ and percentage error is about 0.0151%

3. $\pi \approx \dfrac{22}{7}$ Relative Error $= \dfrac{\left(\pi - \dfrac{22}{7}\right)12756}{\pi \times 12756} = \dfrac{\pi - \dfrac{22}{7}}{\pi} \approx -0.000402$

As with absolute error, negative results such as the one above are usually given as the positive (absolute) value. So in this case, we would say that the relative error is approximately 0.000402 and the percentage error about 0.0402%.

$\pi \approx 3.14$ Relative Error $= \dfrac{(\pi - 3.14)12756}{\pi \times 12756} = \dfrac{\pi - 3.14}{\pi} \approx 0.000507$

The percentage error is about 0.0507% or a bit worse than the first approximation.

It is now possible to make much fairer comparison of the errors implied in these calculations. For example, if we wanted to compare the errors in the approximation of $\sqrt{2}$ (2.) with those in the approximation of π (3), we can see that the errors in example (3) are about five times larger than those in example (2).

In all cases, when you do calculations with numbers that are in error, your answers should show that you recognise that answers can only be quoted to a limited level of accuracy. You should also recognise that there are several ways of analysing error. Within one set of calculations in which all the results are of a similar size, absolute error is a good measure. When trying to compare the errors in measurements that differ largely in size, relative and percentage errors are probably the best measures to use.

EXERCISE 2.3

1. Find the absolute, relative and percentage errors if 0.33 is used as an approximation to $\frac{1}{3}$.

2. $\sqrt[3]{20} \approx 2.7$. Find the absolute, relative and percentage errors if 2.7 is used as an approximation to $\sqrt[3]{20}$.

3. A digital bathroom scale measures weights to the nearest 0.2kg. Find the absolute, relative and percentage errors involved in using these scales to weigh:

    (i)   Pericles the cat who weighs 7.4kg.
    (ii)   Texas the dog who weighs 19.6kg.
    (iii)   The luggage which weighs 22.4kg.
    (iv)   Leila who weighs 56.8kg.
    (v)   Uncle Bill who weighs 98.8kg.

4. It is possible to use a schoolroom ruler to measure lengths to the nearest millimetre. Find the absolute, relative and percentage errors in using such a ruler to measure lines of length:

    (i) 0.5cm   (ii) 1cm   (iii) 12cm   (iv) 25cm

5. Before the advent of the calculator, we used to find the trigonometric ratios, logarithms, square roots etc. from books of tables. Find the percentage errors involved in these approximations that come from an old book of tables:

    (i) $\tan 15° = 0.2679$ (ii) $\sin 2° = 0.0349$ (iii) $\cos 89° = 0.0175$ (iv) $\sqrt{5} = 2.236$

6. A stopwatch can measure time to the nearest tenth of a second. Find the percentage errors involved if this watch is used to measure the times taken for these events:

    (i)   A 100 metre sprint completed in 11.2sec.
    (ii)   A 400 metre race completed in 68.4sec.
    (iii)   A 1500 metre race completed in 4mins 6.7sec.
    (iv)   A 10000 metre race which took 38mins 7.9sec.

7. The Lockheed SR71 'Blackbird' surveillance aircraft was once quoted (in a television documentary) as having flown from New York to London in 2 hours, 7 minutes and 6.8sec. What is the percentage error implied by this statement? Is this a reasonable level of accuracy for this measurement?

2.5 COMPUTATION ERRORS

Whenever we calculate with one or more quantities that are in error, the results will also be in error. This section will look at the ways in which such errors propagate through such calculations.

EXAMPLE

A rectangular field has been measured as being 120metres long and 55metres wide. Both measurements are correct to two significant figures. What are the errors if these figures are used to calculate the perimeter and the area of the field?

SOLUTION

The length is 120metres to the nearest 10metres (2 significant figures). This means that the smallest possible length is 115metres and the largest is 125metres. In the same way, the width is correct to 2 significant figures and so is between 54.5 and 55.5metres.

Smallest perimeter = 2(smallest width + smallest length) = 2(115 + 54.5) = 339metres
Perimeter = 2(width + length) = 2(120 + 55) = 350metres
Largest perimeter = 2(largest width + largest length) = 2(125 + 55.5) = 361metres

The perimeter can now be given as: 350±11 metres.

This result is an example of a general principle. We have done a calculation with a length that has an error of 5metres and with a width that has an error of 0.5 metres. The calculation involved adding the length and the width and then doubling the total. The errors could have been calculated by adding and then doubling the errors to get:
Error = 2(5 + 0.5) = 11metres.

When calculating the areas, a similar process applies:

Smallest area = $115 \times 54.5 = 6267.5 \text{m}^2$

True area = $120 \times 55 = 6600 \text{m}^2$ (the data is in error, so this is not necessarily correct!)

Largest area = $125 \times 55.5 = 6937.5 \text{m}^2$

In this case, we can say that the true area is probably best given as being between 6267.5 and 6937.5 square metres. The situation is much more complicated than the case of the perimeter. The error range is not symmetrical: The difference between the 'true' area and the smallest area is 332.5m^2 and the difference between the largest area and the 'true' area is 337.5m^2.

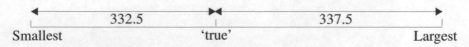

| 332.5 | | 337.5 |
| Smallest | 'true' | Largest |

In these calculations that are more complex than simple addition and subtraction, the only way to work out the effects of the errors is, as we have just done, work out the smallest and largest possible values that the calculation can produce, as well as the 'true' value.

EXAMPLES

If $a = 3.2 \pm 0.1$ $b = 6.9 \pm 0.1$ $c = 4.7 \pm 0.1$, find the errors that result from evaluating these expressions:

   (a) $2a + b$ (c) $a(b + c)$ (d) abc

SOLUTIONS

(a)   Smallest value   'True' value   Largest value
       $2 \times 3.1 + 6.8 = 13.0$ $2 \times 3.2 + 6.9 = 13.3$ $2 \times 3.3 + 7.0 = 13.6$

In this case, the answer can be given as 13.3 ± 0.3. This is a level of error that might be expected with a calculation in which the data is in error by 0.1

(b)   Smallest value   'True' value   Largest value
       $3.1(6.8 + 4.6) = 35.34$ $3.2(6.9 + 4.7) = 37.12$ $3.3(7.0 + 4.8) = 38.94$

Answer = 37.12, but we can only say that it is between 35.34 & 38.94. The error range is not symmetrical, but the average error is about 1.8.

(c)   Smallest value   'True' value   Largest value
       $3.1 \times 6.8 \times 4.6$ $3.2 \times 6.9 \times 4.7$ $3.3 \times 7.0 \times 4.8$
       $= 96.968$ $= 103.776$ $= 110.88$

The answer is best given as being in the range 96.968 & 110.88. A sensible answer could be 104 ± 7. In this case, it is a borderline decision as to whether or not we should quote three significant figures for the answer. There is a sense in which a better answer might be 100 ± 10. Once again, the data was given to an accuracy a bit better than two significant figures and the detailed error analysis indicates that a similar level of precision is appropriate in the answers.

In all these cases, the relative and percentage errors in the answers are of approximately the same size as those of the data (between about 2% & 7%).

In the following set of examples, you will see that in more complex calculations, it is necessary to be much more careful when calculating error bounds. It is also the case that there are some calculations in which the answer can be in error at a much higher level than the data. It is particularly necessary to be aware of this possibility when programming computers to perform calculations with data that contains errors.

EXAMPLES

If $x = 5.3 \pm 0.1$ $y = 12.2 \pm 0.1$ $z = 5.6 \pm 0.1$, find the errors that result from evaluating these expressions:

(a) $y - z$ (b) $\dfrac{y}{z-x}$ (c) $x^2 - y^2$

SOLUTIONS

(a) Smallest value   'True' value   Largest value

$12.1 - 5.7 = 6.4$ $12.2 - 5.6 = 6.6$ $12.3 - 5.5 = 6.8$

In this example the **smallest** possible result comes from subtracting the **largest** z from the **smallest** y. In the same way, the **largest** possible result comes from subtracting the **smallest** z from the **largest** y. It is often necessary to think carefully through the logic of these error analyses! The answer can be given as 6.6 ± 0.2. The absolute error is, in this case, equal to the sum of the absolute errors in the data. The percentage errors in the data are about 1%. However, the percentage error in the answer is about three times as much at 3%.

(b) Smallest value   'True' value   Largest value

$\dfrac{\text{Smallest } y}{\text{Largest } z - \text{Smallest } x}$ $\dfrac{\text{True } y}{\text{True } z - \text{True } x}$ $\dfrac{\text{Largest } y}{\text{Smallest } z - \text{Largest } x}$

$= \dfrac{12.1}{5.7 - 5.2}$ $= \dfrac{12.2}{5.6 - 5.3}$ $= \dfrac{12.3}{5.5 - 5.4}$

$= 24.2$ $= 40.667$ $= 123$

The results of these calculations show that the 'best' answer is about 40, however we can only say that the true answer is in the approximate interval [24,123], a more than 100% error. Considering that the original data contains errors in the 1% region, the errors in the answer are little short of disastrous! The size of this error results from the nature of the calculation and not from the size of the errors in the data. It is very important to look for calculations that produce this sort of error magnification when programming computers. It is possible for the very small errors that result from the storage of numbers in a computer to be significantly magnified during calculations.

(c) Smallest value   'True' value   Largest value

$5.2^2 - 12.3^2 = -124.25$ $5.3^2 - 12.2^2 = -120.75$ $5.4^2 - 12.1^2 = -117.25$

Note that -117.25 is larger than -124.25.

EXERCISE 2.4

1. If $a = 12.5 \pm 0.2$ $b = 3.4 \pm 0.1$ $c = 56.4 \pm 0.5$. Evaluate the following expressions and give error bounds for the answers:

(a) $\dfrac{a}{b+c}$ (b) $\dfrac{c^2}{a-b^2}$ (c) $\dfrac{a(b-c)}{b}$

2. An engine component consists of a cuboid whose dimensions are 334.7mm long by 126.8mm wide by 12.7mm high. These dimensions are known to the nearest tenth of a millimetre. The circular hole has a radius of 23.7mm also accurate to the nearest tenth of a millimetre. Find the volume of metal used in making this component and the errors that can be expected in this measurement.

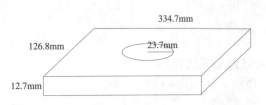

3. If we use a value of 3.14 for π to calculate the volume of a sphere of radius 34 ± 1 cm, what is the range of values we might expect to get and what is the percentage error?

$$\left[\text{Volume of a sphere} = \frac{4}{3}\pi r^3\right]$$

4. The period (time for a complete swing) of a pendulum, T seconds, is given by the formula $T = 2\pi\sqrt{\dfrac{l}{g}}$ where l is the length of the pendulum in metres and g is the acceleration due to gravity which is $9.81 \pm 0.01\,\text{ms}^{-2}$. Find the period of a pendulum of length 5.75 ± 0.01 metres. How many swings will the pendulum complete in one day and what are the approximate error bounds on this number?

5. The angle of elevation of a building is measured as being $31°$ to the nearest degree from a point 47 metres, to the nearest metre, from the base of the building. What is the height of the building and what level of accuracy can be claimed?

6. A rectangular park has a length of 95metres and a width of 46metres. Both measurements are correct to two significant figures. What is the length of the diagonal of the park and what errors are involved in the result?

7. If values of a & b are to be substituted into the formula $Z = \dfrac{a+b}{a-b}$, what values of a & b will lead to the largest errors?

8. The average weight of a group of netballers is to be calculated. The players have been weighed on digital scales that weigh to the nearest half kilogram. What will be the absolute error in the average weight?

9. An optical lens forms a focussed image when an object is placed in front of it.

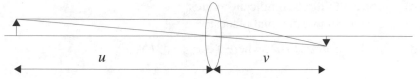

If the object is u metres in front of the lens, the image is v metres behind the lens (and is also upside down). The formula connecting these two values is:

$$\frac{1}{u} + \frac{1}{v} = \frac{1}{f}$$

where f is the focal length of the lens. A lens has a focal length of 7.5 ± 0.1 cm. If an object is placed 14.6 ± 0.1 cm in front of the lens, how far behind the lens will the image form and how accurate is this figure?

10. The resistance to motion of an object through a liquid, R, depends upon the velocity of the object, v and is given by the formula $R = 7v^3$. If an object is moving with a velocity of 12 (correct to two significant figures), what is the resistance to motion and what are the errors in this measurement?

11. The area of a cone is given by the formula: $A = \pi rs + \pi r^2$. A cone has a base radius (r) of 12cm and **vertical** height (h) of 45cm. Both measurements are correct to two significant figures. What is the surface area of the cone and what is the percentage error in this figure?

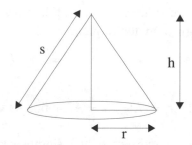

12. If a calculating device approximates all fractions by rounding them to five significant figures, what is the percentage error when calculating:

$$\frac{1}{2} + \frac{1}{3} + \frac{1}{4} + \frac{1}{5} + \frac{1}{6} ?$$

EXAMINATION STYLE QUESTIONS

1. If $a = 3.14$, $b = 0.98$ and $c = 1.04$, calculate $a(c - b)(c + b)$, giving the answer

    (a)   exactly;

    (b)   correct to three significant figures;

    (c)   correct to two decimal places;

    (d)   in the form $a \times 10^k$, where $1 \le a < 10$, $k \in \mathbb{Z}$.

2. If $a = 78.3$, $b = 0.32$ find the value of $4a^2 + ab$, giving the answer

    (a)   exactly;

    (b)   correct to three significant figures;

    (c)   correct to two decimal places;

    (d)   to the nearest whole number;

    (e)   in the form $a \times 10^k$, where $1 \le a < 10$, $k \in \mathbb{Z}$.

3. If $x = 12.9$, calculate the value of $\sqrt{\dfrac{5}{6}\pi x^3}$, giving the answer

    (a)   i. correct to three significant figures;

           ii. correct to two decimal places;

           iii. to the nearest whole number.

    (b)   Write your answer to (a) iii. in the form $a \times 10^k$, where $1 \le a < 10$, $k \in \mathbb{Z}$.

4. The volume, V cm^3, of the cone shown is given by the formula

$$V = \frac{1}{3}\pi r^2 h.$$

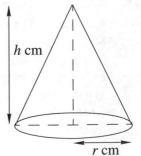

If $r = 7.8$, $h = 12.4$ find its volume, giving the answer

    (a)   correct to three significant figures;

    (b)   correct to two decimal places;

    (c)   to the nearest whole number;

SELF ASSESSMENT TEST (30 MINUTES)

1. If the fraction $\frac{1}{7}$ is approximated to 5 significant figures, find the percentage error in this measurement, correct to 2 significant figures.

[3 marks]

2. Express $\frac{\sqrt{12} - \sqrt{5}}{6}$ as a decimal, correct to 3 significant figures.

[2 marks]

3. State the number of significant figures in each of these measurements:

(a)　0.00315m　　　　(b)　40500gms　　　　(c)　0.020kg

[3 marks]

4. Evaluate each of these expressions, giving the answers in scientific form, correct to 3 significant figures.

(a)　5.27^{30}　　　　(b)　$\dfrac{2.6^3}{55.8^{10}}$　　　　(c)　$\sqrt{0.045}$

[3 marks]

5. Express the following numbers in normal decimal notation:

(a)　3.4×10^4　　　　(b)　7.05×10^{-4}

[2 marks]

6. If $a = 6.4 \pm 0.2$, $b = 7.1 \pm 0.4$, evaluate the following expressions, giving bounds on the errors.

(a)　$2a + b$　　　　(b)　$a \times b$　　　　(c)　$\dfrac{1}{b - a}$

[4 marks]

7. A method (due to Euler) that has been used to calculate approximations to π is:

$$\frac{\pi^2}{6} = \frac{1}{1^2} + \frac{1}{2^2} + \frac{1}{3^2} + \frac{1}{4^2} + \ldots\ldots\ldots\ldots$$

If the first 5 terms of the series are used to find π, what are the absolute and percentage errors produced by the method?

[3 marks]

NUMBER & ALGEBRA 2

SEQUENCES AND SERIES

3

Chapter contents

- Arithmetic sequences.
- Arithmetic series.
- Geometric sequences.
- Geometric series.

Key Formulae

- $u_n = a + (n-1)d$

- $S_n = \dfrac{n}{2}(2a + (n-1)d)$

- $u_n = ar^{n-1}$

- $S_n = \dfrac{a(r^n - 1)}{r - 1}$

3.1 ARITHMETIC SEQUENCES AND SERIES

A sequence is a set of quantities arranged in a definite order.

$$1, 2, 3, 4, 5, 6, ... \quad -1, 2, -4, 8, -16.... \quad\quad 1, 1, 2, 3, 5, 8, 13....$$

are all examples of sequences. When the terms of a sequence are added, we get a series. Sequences and series are used to solve a variety of practical problems in, for example, business,

There are two major types of sequence, arithmetic and geometric. This section will consider arithmetic sequences. The characteristic of such a sequence is that there is a common difference between successive terms:

1, 3, 5, 7, 9, 11,... (the odd numbers) has a first term of 1 and a common difference of 2. 18, 15, 12, 9, 6,... has a first term of 18 and a common difference of -3 (because the sequence is decreasing).

The terms of a sequence are generally labelled $u_1, u_2, u_3, u_4, ...u_n$. The '$n$th term' of a sequence is labelled u_n. In the case of an arithmetic sequence which starts with $a (= u_1)$ and has a common difference of d, the nth term can be found using the formula:

$$u_n = a + (n-1)d$$

EXAMPLE
(a)   Is the sequence 9, 12, 15, 18, . . . an arithmetic sequence?
(b)   Find the 8th term for the sequence described in part a.

SOLUTION
(a)   To decide if the sequence is arithmetic we need to show that consecutive terms increase by a fixed amount, i.e., that there is a common difference.
We have that $u_1 = 9, u_2 = 12, u_3 = 15, u_4 = 18, \ldots$, so that the difference between the first two terms is $u_2 - u_1 = 12 - 9 = 3$, the difference between the next two terms is $u_3 - u_2 = 15 - 12 = 3$, and so on. Therefore, we have a common difference, $d = 3$, and so we have an arithmetic sequence.

(b)   To find the 8th term we could keep adding 3 (another 4 times), to get the sequence 9, 12, 15, 18, 21, 24, 27, 30, . . . So that the 8th term, $u_8 = 30$.
We could also make use of the formula $u_n = a + (n-1)d$, with $a = 9(= u_1), d = 3$ and $n = 8$. So that $u_8 = 9 + (8-1) \times 3 = 9 + 7 \times 3$
$$= 9 + 21$$
$$= 30$$

EXAMPLE

An arithmetic sequence has 10 as its first term and a common difference of –4. Find its 12th term.

SOLUTION

We have that $u_1 = 10$ and $d = -4$, so that the general term, given by $u_n = a + (n-1)d$, becomes, $u_n = 10 + (n-1) \times -4$.

Therefore, the 12th term, u_{12}, is given by $u_{12} = 10 + (12-1) \times -4 = 10 + (-44) = -34$.

EXAMPLE

The 15th term of an arithmetic sequence is 45. If the first term is –11, find the common difference.

SOLUTION

We are given that $n = 15$, $u_{15} = 45$ and $a = -11$. Using the formula for the general term of an arithmetic sequence, $u_n = a + (n-1)d$, we have

$$45 = -11 + (15-1) \times d$$
$$\Leftrightarrow 45 = -11 + 14d$$
$$\Leftrightarrow 56 = 14d$$
$$\Leftrightarrow 4 = d$$

Therefore, the common difference is 4.

Notice that if the nth term of an arithmetic sequence is u_n and the common difference is d,

then the next term, $u_{n+1} = u_n + d$, or, $\boxed{d = u_{n+1} - u_n}$.

EXERCISE 3.1

1. (a) Show that the following sequences are arithmetic.
    (b) Find the common difference.
    (c) Define the rule that gives the nth term of the sequence.
        (i) $\{2, 6, 10, 14, \dots\}$ (ii) $\{20, 17, 14, 11, \dots\}$
        (iii) $\{1, -4, -9, \dots\}$ (iv) $\{0.5, 1.0, 1.5, 2.0, \dots\}$
        (v) $\{y+1, y+3, y+5, \dots\}$(vi) $\{x+2, x, x-2, \dots\}$

2. Find the 10th term of the sequence whose first four terms are 8, 4, 0, –4.

3. Find the value of x and y in the arithmetic sequence $\{5, x, 13, y, \dots\}$.

4. An arithmetic sequence has 12 as its first term and a common difference of –5. Find its 12th term.

5. An arithmetic sequence has –20 as its first term and a common difference of 3. Find its 10th term.

6. The 14th term of an arithmetic sequence is 100. If the first term is 9, find the common difference.

7. The 10th term of an arithmetic sequence is –40. If the first term is 5, find the common difference.

8. If $n + 5$, $2n + 1$ and $4n - 3$ are three consecutive terms of an arithmetic sequences, find n.

9. The first three terms of an arithmetic sequence are 1, 6, 11.
(a) Find the 9th term.
(b) Which term will equal 151?

10. Find x and y given that $4 - \sqrt{3}$, x, y and $2\sqrt{3} - 2$ are the first four terms of an arithmetic sequence.

EXAMPLES

1. For the sequence 7, 11, 15, 19,...., find the 20th term.
2. An arithmetic sequence has a first term of 120 and a 10th term of 57. Find the 15th term.
3. An arithmetic sequence has a 7th term of 16.5 and a 12th term of 24. Find the 24th term.
4. A car whose original value was $25600 decreases in value by $90 per month. How long will it take before the car's value falls below $15000?

SOLUTIONS

1. In this case $a = 7$ and $d = 4$ because the sequence starts with a 7 and each term is 4 bigger than the one before it. This means that the nth term is given by the formula:
$$u_n = a + (n - 1)d = 7 + (n - 1) \times 4$$
$$= 4n + 3 \qquad \text{from this it follows that the 20th term is:}$$
$$u_{20} = 4 \times 20 + 3$$
$$= 83$$

2. The data is: $a = 120$ and using $u_n = a + (n - 1)d$, we have:
$$u_{10} = 120 + (10 - 1)d = 57 \Rightarrow 120 + 9d = 57$$
So that $\qquad\qquad\qquad 9d = -63 \Leftrightarrow d = -7$
Therefore, $\quad \therefore u_n = 120 + (n - 1) \times (-7) = 127 - 7n$
Meaning that $u_{15} = 127 - 7 \times 15 = 22$

3. The data is:
$$u_7 = a + 6d = 16.5 \quad [1]$$
$$u_{12} = a + 11d = 24 \quad [2]$$

The result is a pair of simultaneous equations that can be solved by eliminating a, which can be done by subtracting [2] - [1] to get:

$$5d = 7.5$$
$$d = 1.5$$
$$a + 6d = 16.5$$
$$a + 6 \times 1.5 = 16.5$$
$$a = 7.5$$
$$u_n = a + (n-1)d$$
$$= 7.5 + (n-1) \times 1.5$$
$$= 1.5n + 6$$
$$\therefore u_{24} = 1.5 \times 24 + 6$$
$$= 42$$

4. The values can be seen as a sequence: \$25600, \$25510, \$25420 etc.
In this case $a = 25600$ and $d = -90$ so that:
$$u_n = 25600 + (n-1) \times (-90)$$
$$= 25690 - 90n \text{ it is necessary to solve}$$
$$15000 = 25690 - 90n$$
$$90n = 25690 - 15000$$
$$n = 118.777$$

The car will be worth less than \$15000 after 119 months

USING A GRAPHIC CALCULATOR

Most graphic calculators have an automatic memory facility (usually called Ans) that stores the result of the last calculation as well as an ability to remember the actual calculation. This can be very useful in listing a sequence.

EXAMPLE

List the arithmetic sequence 5, 12, 19, 26,......

SOLUTION

The sequence has a first term of 5. Enter this and press ENTER or EXE. The common difference of the sequence is 7 so enter + 7. The display will show Ans + 7 which means 'add 7 to the previous answer. From here, every time you press ENTER (or EXE), you will repeat the calculation, generating successive terms of the sequence.

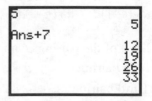

SERIES

If the terms of a sequence are added, the result is known as a series.

The sequence: 1, 2, 3, 4, 5, 6,....... gives the series: $1+2+3+4+5+6+$..........

and $-1, -2, -4, -8, -16$.... gives: $(-1)+(-2)+(-4)+(-8)+(-16)+$.... or $-1-2-4-8-16-$.....

The sum of the terms of a series is referred to as S_n, the sum of n terms of a series. For an arithmetic series,

$$S_n = a + (a + d) + (a + 2d) + \ldots\ldots\ldots + a + (n - 1)d$$

There is a second notation for a sum such as this:

$$S_n = \sum_{i=1}^{n} a + (i - 1)d$$

This second notation means: $\sum$ a Greek 's'- add up all the terms of the type $a + (i - 1)d$ for values of i from 1 to n. Thus:

$$\sum_{i=1}^{4} 2 + (i - 1)3 = \overset{i=1}{2} + \overset{i=2}{(2 + 3)} + \overset{i=3}{(2 + 6)} + \overset{i=4}{(2 + 9)}$$

$$= 2 + 5 + 8 + 11$$

$$= 26$$

There will be many cases in which we can add up the terms of a series in this way. If, however, there are a large number of terms to add, a formula is more appropriate. There is a story that, when the mathematician Gauss was a child, his teacher was having problems with him because he always finished all the work long before the other students. In an attempt to keep Gauss occupied for a period, the teacher asked him to add all the whole numbers from 1 to 100. '5050' Gauss replied immediately. It is probable that Gauss used a method similar to this:

1	2	3	4	5	6	....,,	96	97	98	99	100
100	99	98	97	96	95	....,,	5	4	3	2	1
101	101	101	101	101	101	....,,	101	101	101	101	101

Adding each of the pairings gives 100 totals of 101 each. This gives a total of 10100. This is the sum of two sets of the numbers $1+2+3+...+98+99+100$ and so the full answer is, as the young Gauss said, 5050.

If we apply this to the general arithmetic series the result is:

a	$a+d$	$a+2d$		$a+(n-3)d$	$a+(n-2)d$	$a+(n-1)d$
$a+(n-1)d$	$a+(n-2)d$	$a+(n-3)d$		$a+2d$	$a+d$	a

Each of the pairings comes to the same total. Here are some examples:

First pairing: $\quad a + a + (n - 1)d = 2a + (n - 1)d$

Third pairing: $\quad a + 2d + a + (n - 3)d = 2a + (n - 1)d$

There are n such pairings so the sum of n terms is: $S_n = \frac{n}{2}[2a + (n-1)d]$

This formula can now be used to sum large arithmetic series:

EXAMPLES

1. Find the sum of 20 terms of the series $-2 + 1 + 4 + 7 + 10 + \ldots$

2. Find the sum of 35 terms of the series $-\frac{3}{8} - \frac{1}{8} + \frac{1}{8} + \frac{3}{8} + \frac{5}{8} + \ldots$

3. An arithmetic series has a third term of 0. The sum of the first 15 terms is -300. What is the first term and the sum of the first ten terms?

4. A new business is selling home computers. They predict that they will sell 20 computers in their first month, 23 in the second month, 26 in the third and so on, in arithmetic sequence. How many months will pass before the company expects to sell their thousandth computer.

SOLUTIONS

1. $a = -2$ $d = 3$, therefore, using $S_n = \frac{n}{2}[2a + (n-1)d]$, we have;

$$S_{20} = \frac{20}{2}[2 \times (-2) + (20-1) \times 3]$$

$$= 10[-4 + 19 \times 3]$$

$$= 530$$

2. With $a = -\frac{3}{8}$ $d = \frac{1}{4}$ $n = 35$, we have $S_{35} = \frac{35}{2}\left[2 \times -\frac{3}{8} + (35-1)\frac{1}{4}\right]$

$$= 17.5\left[-\frac{3}{4} + 34 \times \frac{1}{4}\right]$$

$$= 135\frac{5}{8}$$

3. The data is: $u_3 = a + 2d = 0$ [1]

and: $S_{15} = \frac{15}{2}[2a + 14d] = -300$ [2]

The second equation becomes: $15a + 105d = -300$

$$a + 7d = -20$$

The pair of equations can now be solved as follows:

$a + 2d = 0$

$a + 7d = -20$

$5d = -20$ Subtracting the equations.

$d = -4$

$a + 2 \times -4 = 0$

$a = 8$

This establishes that the series is $8+4+0+(-4)+(-8)+\ldots$

45

So the first term is 8 and the sum of the first ten terms is:

$$S_{10} = \frac{10}{2}[16 + 9 \times -4] = -100$$

4. The series is: $20 + 23 + 26 + \ldots$

The question implies that the company is looking at the **total** number of computers sold, so we are looking at a series, not a sequence. The question asks how many terms (months) will need to be taken before the total sales reach more than 1000:

$$S_n = \frac{n}{2}[2 \times 20 + (n-1)3] \Rightarrow \frac{n}{2}[2 \times 20 + (n-1)3] = 1000$$

Therefore, $n[3n + 37] = 2000 \Rightarrow 3n^2 + 37n - 2000 = 0$.

To solve this equation, we can make use of the quadratic formula or the graphics calculator:

Method 1: Quadratic formula

Method 2: Graphics Calculator

$$n = \frac{-37 \pm \sqrt{37^2 - 4 \times 3 \times -2000}}{2 \times 3}$$

$$= 20.37 \text{ or } (-32.7)$$

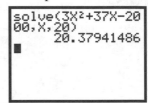

NB: To call up the **solve** function on the TI–83, we need to use press ⎡2nd⎤ ⎡0⎤ (to call up the **CATALOG**) then press ⎡ALPHA⎤ ⎡LN⎤ ⎡LN⎤ and then use the arrow key to move cursor down to **solve**. Type in equation, then the variable (X in this case) and then an initial guess (20 in this case). A third method (using the graphics calculator is shown below).

The answer is, therefore, that the company will sell its thousandth computer during the 20th month.

USING A GRAPHICS CALCULATOR:

The above problem leads to an unpleasant quadratic equation. Many graphic calculators can help in such a situation by tabulating formulas. In this case, we want to tabulate:

$$S_n = \frac{n}{2}[2 \times 20 + (n-1)3]$$

$$= \frac{n}{2}[3n + 37]$$

The following instructions are specific to the TI-82 calculator:

STEP 1   STEP 2   STEP 3
Enter the formula using Y=   Use 2nd TblSet   Use 2nd TABLE

The third display (which can be reached using the down arrow), indicates that the total sales after the 20th month are 970 and after the 21st month they are 1050, confirming the previous result. A similar technique can be used to list the terms in a sequence.

EXERCISE 3.2

1. Find the sum of the first ten terms in the arithmetic sequences
(a) $\{1, 4, 7, 10, \dots\}$ (b) $\{3, 9, 15, 21, \dots\}$ (c) $\{10, 4, -2, \dots\}$.

2. For the given arithmetic sequences, find the sum, S_n, to the requested number of terms.
(a) $\{4, 3, 2, \dots\}$ for $n = 12$
(b) $\{4, 10, 16, \dots\}$ for $n = 15$
(c) $\{2.9, 3.6, 4.3, \dots\}$ for $n = 11$.

3. Find the sum of the following sequences:
(a) $\{5, 4, 3, \dots, -15\}$
(b) $\{3, 9, 15, \dots, 75\}$
(c) $\{3, 5, 7, \dots, 29\}$

4. Find the twentieth term in the sequence 9, 15, 21, 27, 33,..............

5. Fill the gaps in this arithmetic sequence: -3, _, _, _, _, _, 12

6. An arithmetic sequence has a tenth term of 17 and a fourteenth term of 30, find the common difference.

7. If $u_{59} = \dfrac{1}{10}$ $u_{100} = -1\dfrac{19}{20}$ for an arithmetic sequence, find the first term and the common difference.

8. Find the sum of the first one hundred odd numbers.

9. An arithmetic series has twenty terms. The first term is -50 and the last term is 83, find the sum of the series.

10. Thirty numbers are in arithmetic sequence. The sum of the numbers is 270 and the last number is 38, what is the first number?

11. How many terms of the arithmetic sequence: 2, 2.3, 2.6, 2.9,......... must be taken before the terms exceed 100?

12. Brian and Melissa save $50 in the first week of a savings program, $55 in the second week, $60 in the third and so on, in arithmetic progression. How much will they save in ten weeks? How long will they have to continue saving if their target is to save $5000?

13. A printing firm offers to print business cards on the following terms:
$45 for design and typesetting and then $0.02 per card.
  (i)   What is the cost of 500 cards from this printer?
  (ii) How many cards can a customer with $100 afford to order?

14. A children's game consists of the players standing in a line with a gap of 2 metres between each. The child at the left hand end of the line has a ball which s/he throws to the next child in the line, a distance of 2 metres. The ball is then thrown back to the first child who then throws the ball to the third child in the line, a distance of 4 metres. The ball is then returned to the first child, and so on until all the children have touched the ball at least once.

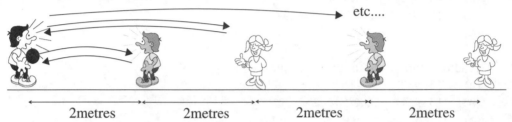

etc....

2metres   2metres   2metres   2metres

(a) If a total of five children play and they make the least number of throws so that only the leftmost child touches the ball more than once:
  (i)   What is the largest single throw?
  (ii) What is the total distance travelled by the ball?

(b) If seven children play, what is the total distance travelled by the ball?

(c) If n children play, derive a formula for the total distance travelled by the ball.

(d) Find the least number of children who need to play the game before the total distance travelled by the ball exceeds 100 metres.

(e) The children can all throw the ball 50 metres at most
  (i)   What is the largest number of children that can play the game?
  (ii) What is the total distance travelled by the ball?

15. If p, q, r and s are four consecutive terms of a arithmetic sequence, show that
$$(r-q)^2 = \frac{1}{2}(rq - ps).$$

16. If a, b, and c are consecutive terms of an arithmetic sequence, show that
$$2\left(\frac{b}{c} - \frac{c}{b}\right) = \frac{(a-c)(a+3c)}{c(a+c)}$$

3.2 GEOMETRIC SEQUENCES AND SERIES

Sequences such as 2, 6, 18, 54, 162,.... and 200, 20, 2, 0.2,...... in which each term is obtained by multiplying the previous one by a fixed quantity are known as geometric sequences.

In the case of these examples: 2, 6, 18, 54, 162,.... is formed by starting with 2 and then multiplying by 3 to get the second term, by 3 again to get the third term, and so on. For the sequence 200, 20, 2, 0.2,......, begin with 20 and multiply by 0.1 to get the second term, by 0.1 again to get the third term and so on.

The constant multiplier of such a sequence is known as the **common ratio**.

The common ratio of 2, 6, 18, 54, 162,.... is 3 and of 200, 20, 2, 0.2,...... it is 0.1.

If we have a geometric sequence, then the common ratio is obtained by dividing any one term by the previous term, that is,

$$r = \frac{u_2}{u_1} = \frac{u_3}{u_2} = \dots = \frac{u_n}{u_{n-1}}$$

The nth term of a geometric sequence is obtained from the first term by multiplying by $n-1$ common ratios. This leads to the formula for the nth term of a geometric sequence:

$$u_n = a \times r^{n-1}$$

where n is the term number, a the first term and r is the common ratio,

EXAMPLES

1. Find the tenth term in the sequence 2, 6, 18, 54, 162,....

2. Find the fifteenth term in the sequence 200, 20, 2, 0.2,......

3. Find the eleventh term in the sequence $1, -\frac{1}{2}, \frac{1}{4}, -\frac{1}{8}, \frac{1}{16}$ ......

SOLUTIONS

1. The first term $a = 2$. The common ratio $r = 3$ and n, the required term = 10. It can sometimes be difficult to find the common ratio, r. This can be done by dividing one term by the term that comes before it. If the sequence is geometric, it will not matter which pair of successive terms you take. In this case, some possibilities are:

$$\frac{6}{2} = 3 \qquad \frac{18}{6} = 3 \qquad \frac{54}{18} = 3 \text{ etc.}$$

Use the formula to solve the problem: $u_n = a \times r^{n-1}$

$$= 2 \times 3^{(10-1)}$$
$$= 2 \times 3^9$$
$$= 39366$$

2. In this case, $a = 200$ $\qquad r = \frac{1}{10} = 0.1$ $\qquad n = 15$

$$u_{15} = 200 \times 0.1^{(15-1)}$$

$$= 200 \times 0.1^{14}$$

$$= 2 \times 10^{-12} \qquad \text{Remember to interpret the calculator answer 2E–12.}$$

3. $1, -\dfrac{1}{2}, \dfrac{1}{4}, -\dfrac{1}{8}, \dfrac{1}{16}$ has a common ratio of $\dfrac{-\frac{1}{2}}{1} = -\dfrac{1}{2}$ $\qquad \dfrac{\frac{1}{4}}{-\frac{1}{2}} = -\dfrac{1}{2}$ etc.

Using the formula $u_{11} = 1 \times \left(-\dfrac{1}{2}\right)^{(11-1)}$

$$= \left(-\dfrac{1}{2}\right)^{10}$$

$$\approx 0.000977$$

Many questions will be more demanding in terms of the way in which you use this formula. You should also recognise that the formula can be applied to a range of practical problems.

Many of the practical problems involving growth and decay can be stated in terms of a geometric sequence, and can therefore be solved using methods relevant to geometric sequences (Especially as the general term $u_n = a \times r^{n-1}$ represents an exponential relation).

EXAMPLES

1. A geometric sequence has a fifth term of 3 and a seventh term of 0.75. Find the first term, the common ratio and the tenth term.

2. Find the number of terms in the geometric sequence: 0.25, 0.75, 2.25,.... 44286.75.

3. A car originally worth $34000 loses 15% of its value each year.
(i) Write a geometric sequence that gives the year by year values of the car.
(ii) Find the value of the car after 6 years.
(iii) After how many years will the value of the car fall below $10000?

4. The number of people in a small country town increases by 2% per year. If the population at the start of 1960 was 12500, what is the predicted population at the start of the year 2000?

SOLUTIONS

1. $u_5 = a \times r^4 = 3$ [1]

$u_7 = a \times r^6 = 0.75$ [2]

As with similar problems involving arithmetic sequences, the result is a pair of simultaneous equations. In this case these can best be solved by dividing [2] by [1] to get: $\dfrac{a \times r^6}{a \times r^4} = \dfrac{0.75}{3} \Leftrightarrow r^2 = 0.25 \Leftrightarrow r = \pm 0.5$

However, $ar^4 = 3 \Rightarrow a = \dfrac{3}{r^4} = \dfrac{3}{0.5^4} \quad \therefore a = 48$.

This means that $u_{10} = 48 \times (\pm 0.5)^9 = \pm \dfrac{3}{32}$

There are two solutions: 48, 24, 12,6,.... & 48, –24, 12,–6....

2. $0.25, 0.75, 2.25,.... 44286.75.$ has a first term $a = 0.25$ and a common ratio $r = 3$. In this problem it is n that is unknown. Substitution of the data into the formula gives:

$u_n = 0.25 \times 3^{(n-1)} = 44286.75$

The equation that results can be solved using logarithms or a graphics calculator:
Method 1 (Using logarithms, *this method is not required for exam purposes*).

$0.25 \times 3^{(n-1)} = 44286.75 \Rightarrow 3^{(n-1)} = \dfrac{44286.75}{0.25} = 177147$

$$\log_{10} 3^{(n-1)} = \log_{10} 177147$$

$$(n-1)\log_{10} 3 = \log_{10} 177147$$

$$n - 1 = \dfrac{\log_{10} 177147}{\log_{10} 3}$$

$$n - 1 = 11$$

$$n = 12$$

Method 2 (Using a graphics calculator):
Using the TI–83, we have (note this time we use a graphical approach rather than the solve function, where we would need to enter the following **solve(3^(X – 1) – 177147, X, 10)**.

A. Enter the equation (as Y_1 and the required value as Y_2).
B. Choose an appropriate **WINDOW**.
C. Sketch the graphs (Using the **GRAPH** function).
D. Use the **TRACE** function and the arrow key (or the use the **CALC** function and then select option **5:intersect**).

A.   B.   C.   D.

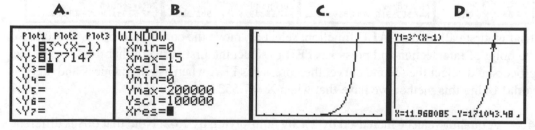

Using the trace function we see that when X = 11.968, Y = 171043, moving the cursor along once more we have that when X = 12.127, Y = 203818. Therefore, as n (and therefore X) is a whole number, we conclude that $n = 12$.

3. (i) If the car loses 15% of its value each year, its value will fall to 85% (100%-85%)

of its value in the previous year. This means that the common ratio is 0.85 (the fractional equivalent of 85%). Using the formula, the sequence is:

$u_n = 34000 \times 0.85^{(n-1)}$ i.e. $34000, $28900, $24565, $20880.25,......

(ii) The value after six years have passed is the **seventh** term of the sequence. This is because the first term of the sequence is the value after **no** years have passed.

$u_7 = 34000 \times 0.85^6 \approx 12823$ or $12823.

(iii) This requires solution of the equation $10000 = 34000 \times 0.85^n$:

Method 1 (Using logarithms, *this method is not required for exam purposes*)

$$10000 = 34000 \times 0.85^n \Rightarrow (0.85^n = 0.2941)$$

$$\log_{10}(0.85^n) = \log_{10}0.2941 \Leftrightarrow n\log_{10}0.85 = \log_{10}0.2941$$

$$n = \frac{\log_{10}0.2941}{\log_{10}0.85}$$

$$n \approx 7.53$$

This means that the car's value will fall to $10000 after about 7 years 6 months.

Method 2 (Using a graphics calculator)

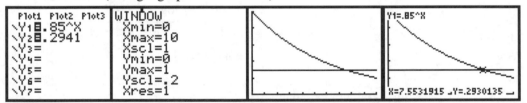

Using the trace function we have that when X = 7.4468, Y = 0.2981 and when X = 7.5532, Y = 0.2981.

Using the **CALC** and then selecting option **5:intersect**, we end up with:

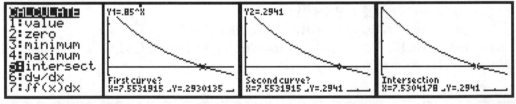

That is, first call up the **CALC** function, select **5:**, move the cursor as close as possible to the point of intersection and press **ENTER** to select the first curve (either one), repeat the process and select the second curve, then press **ENTER** when asked to Guess and then voila! Using this method we have that when X = 7.5531, Y = 0.2941.

4.   A quantity can be increased by 2% by multiplying by 1.02. Note that this is different from finding 2% of a quantity which is done by multiplying by 0.02. The sequence is: 12500, 12500×1.02, 12500×1.02^2 etc. with $a = 12500$, $r = 1.02$.

It is also necessary to be careful about which term is required. In this case, the population at the start of 1960 is the first term, the population at the start of 1961 the second term, and so on. The population at the start of 1970 is the **eleventh** term and at the start of 2000 we need the forty-first term:

$$u_{41} = 12500 \times 1.02^{40}$$

$$\approx 27600$$

In all such cases, you should round your answer to the level given in the question or, if no such direction is given, round the answer to a reasonable level of accuracy. In this question, the original population appears to have been given to the nearest 100 and so it is hardly reasonable to give a higher level of accuracy in the answer.

USING A GRAPHIC CALCULATOR:

As with arithmetic sequences, geometric sequences such as 50, 25, 12.5,........ can be listed using a graphic calculator. There are two ways of doing this:

Method 1: Using the 'Ans' facility: Enter the first term (50) and then multiply by the common ratio (0.5). The calculator should automatically produce the Ans entry. Every press of the ENTER (EXE) key will produce a new term in the sequence. These screens are specific to the TI-82.

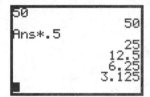
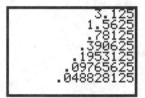

Method 2: Using the list facility. First enter the rule for the terms: $Y_1 = 50 \times 0.5^{\wedge}(X - 1)$ in the same way as you would enter a function to be graphed. Next, select the options for the way in which the table is to be set (2nd TblSet) and finally (2nd TABLE) displays the table. The TI-82 output is:

When using a graphic calculator to answer questions in tests and examinations, you should remember that there are often marks awarded for method.

SERIES

When the terms of a geometric sequence is added, the result is a geometric series. For example:

The sequence 3, 6, 12, 24, 48,..... gives rise to the series: 3 + 6 + 12 + 24 + 48 +.... and:

$24, -16, 10\frac{2}{3}, -7\frac{1}{9}$,.... leads to the series $24 - 16 + 10\frac{2}{3} - 7\frac{1}{9} +$....

Geometric series can be summed using the formula that is derived by first multiplying the series by r:

$$S_n = a + ar + ar^2 + ar^3 + \ldots\ldots\ldots + ar^{n-3} + ar^{n-2} + ar^{n-1}$$

$$r \times S_n = \quad ar + ar^2 + ar^3 + \ldots\ldots\ldots + ar^{n-3} + ar^{n-2} + ar^{n-1} + ar^n$$

$$S_n - r \times S_n = a - ar^n \quad \text{(subtracting the second equation from the first)}$$

$$S_n(1-r) = a(1-r^n)$$

$$S_n = \frac{a(1-r^n)}{1-r}$$

This formula can also be written as: $S_n = \dfrac{a(r^n - 1)}{r - 1}, r \neq 1$. It is usual to use the version of the formula that gives a positive value for the denominator. The following examples will illustrate this.

EXAMPLES

Sum the following series to the number of terms indicated.

(a) $2 + 4 + 8 + 16 + \ldots$ 9 terms.

(b) $5 - 15 + 45 - 135 + \ldots$ 7 terms.

(c) $24 + 18 + \dfrac{27}{2} + \dfrac{81}{8} + \ldots$ 12 terms.

(d) $20 - 30 + 45 - 67.5 + \ldots$ 10 terms.

SOLUTIONS

(a)   In this case $a = 2$, $r = 2$ and $n = 9$.
      Because $r = 2$ it is more convenient to use:

$$S_n = \frac{a(r^n - 1)}{r - 1}$$

$$S_9 = \frac{2(2^9 - 1)}{2 - 1}$$

$$= 1022$$

Using this version of the formula gives positive values for the numerator and denominator. The other version is correct but gives negative numerator and denominator and hence the same answer.

(b) $a = 5$, $r = -3$ and $n = 7$.

$$S_n = \frac{a(1-r^n)}{1-r} \qquad\qquad S_n = \frac{a(r^n - 1)}{r - 1}$$

$$S_7 = \frac{5(1-(-3)^7)}{1-(-3)} \quad \text{OR} \quad S_7 = \frac{5((-3)^7 - 1)}{(-3) - 1}$$

$$= 2735 \qquad\qquad\qquad\qquad = 2735$$

(c) $a = 24$, $r = 0.75$ and $n = 12$.

$$S_n = \frac{a(1 - r^n)}{1 - r}$$ This version gives the positive values.

$$S_{12} = \frac{24\left(1 - \left(\frac{3}{4}\right)^{12}\right)}{1 - \left(\frac{3}{4}\right)}$$

$$= 92.95907$$

(d) $a = 20$, $r = -1.5$ and $n = 10$.

$$S_n = \frac{a(1 - r^n)}{1 - r}$$

$$S_{10} = \frac{20(1 - (-1.5)^{10})}{1 - (-1.5)}$$

$$= -453.32031$$

When using a calculator to evaluate such expressions, it is advisable to use brackets to ensure that correct answers are obtained. For both the graphic and scientific calculator, the negative common ratio must be entered using the +/– or (–) key.

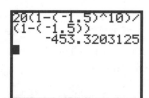

Other questions that may be asked in examinations could involve using both formulas. A second possibility is that you may be asked to apply sequence and series theory to some simple problems.

EXAMPLES

1. The 2nd term of a geometric series is –30 and the sum of the first two terms is –15. Find the first term and the common ratio.

2. A family decide to save some money in an account that pays 9% annual compound interest calculated at the end of each year. They put $2500 into the account at the beginning of each year. All interest is added to the account and no withdrawals are made. How much money will they have in the account on the day after they have made their tenth payment?

SOLUTIONS

1. The data is: $u_2 = ar = -30$

$$S_2 = \frac{a(r^2 - 1)}{r - 1} = -15$$

The result is a pair of simultaneous equations in the two unknowns. The best method of solution is substitution:

$$a = \frac{-30}{r}$$

$$\frac{\frac{-30}{r}(r^2 - 1)}{r - 1} = -15$$

$$\frac{(-30)(r^2 - 1)}{r(r - 1)} = -15$$

$$\frac{-30(r + 1)(r - 1)}{r(r - 1)} = -15$$

$$-30(r + 1) = -15r$$

$$-30r - 30 = -15r$$

$$r = -2$$

$$a = \frac{-30}{r}$$

$$= 15$$

The series is $15 - 30 + 60 - 120 + 240 - .....$ which meets the conditions set out in the question.

2. The problem is best looked at from the last payment of $2500 which has just been made and which has not earned any interest. The previous payment has earned one lot of 9% interest and so is now worth 2500×1.09. The previous payment has earned two years' worth of compound interest and is worth 2500×1.09^2. This process can be continued for all the other payments and the various amounts of interest that each has earned. They form a geometric series:

<table>
<tr><td>Last payment</td><td>First payment</td></tr>
</table>

$$2500 + 2500 \times 1.09 + 2500 \times 1.09^2 + ... + 2500 \times 1.09^9$$

The total amount saved can be calculated using the series formula:

$$S_n = \frac{a(r^n - 1)}{r - 1}$$

$$S_{10} = \frac{2500(1.09^{10} - 1)}{1.09 - 1}$$

$$= 37982.32$$

The family will save about $37982.

EXERCISE 3.3

1. Find the common ratios of these geometric sequences:

(a) 7, 21, 63, 189...   (b) $12, 4, \dfrac{4}{3}, \dfrac{4}{9}...$ (c) 1, –1, 1, –1, 1...

(d) $9, -3, 1, -\dfrac{1}{3}, \dfrac{1}{9}...$ (e) 64, 80, 100, 125,... (f) 27, –18, 12, –8 ,...

2. Find the term indicated for each of these geometric sequences:

(a) 11, 33, 99, 297,...   10th term.
(b) 1, 0.2, 0.04, 0.008,...   15th term.

(c) $9, -6, 4, -\dfrac{8}{3},...$ 9th term.

(d) $21, 9, \dfrac{27}{7}, \dfrac{81}{49},...$ 6th term.

(e) $-\dfrac{1}{3}, -\dfrac{1}{4}, -\dfrac{3}{16}, -\dfrac{9}{64}$ 6th term.

3. Find the number of terms in each of these geometric sequences and the sum of the numbers in each sequence:

(a) 4, 12, 36,....., 236196
(b) 11, –22, 44,........, 704
(c) 100, –10, 1,.........., -10^{-5}

(d) $48, 36, 27,.........., \dfrac{6561}{1024}$

(e) $\dfrac{1}{8}, -\dfrac{9}{32}, \dfrac{81}{128}, ..., \dfrac{6561}{2048}$

(f) 100, 10, 1,........, 10^{-10}

4. The third term of a geometric sequence is 36 and the tenth term is 78732. Find the first term in the sequence and the sum of these terms.

5. A bank account offers 9% interest compounded annually. If $750 is invested in this account, find the amount in the account at the end of the twelfth year.

6. When a ball is dropped onto a flat floor, it bounces to 65% of the height from which it was dropped. If the ball is dropped from 80 cm, find the height of the fifth bounce.

7. A computer loses 30% of its value each year.
(a) Write a formula for the value of the computer after n years.
(b) How many years will it be before the value of the computer falls below 10% of its original value?

8. A geometric sequence has a first term of 7 and a common ratio of 1.1. How many terms must be taken before the value of the term exceeds 1000?

9. A colony of algae increases in size by 15% per week. If 10grams of the algae are placed in a lake, find the weight of algae that will be present in the lake after 12 weeks. The lake will be considered 'seriously polluted' when there is in excess of 10000grams of algae in the lake. How long will it be before the lake becomes seriously polluted?

10. A geometric series has nine terms, a common ratio of 2 and a sum of 3577. Find the first term.

11. A geometric series has a third term of 12, a common ratio of $-\frac{1}{2}$ and a sum of $32\frac{1}{16}$. Find the number of terms in the series.

12. A geometric series has a first term of 1000, seven terms and a sum of $671\frac{7}{8}$. Find the common ratio.

13. A geometric series has a third term of 300, and a sixth term of 37500. Find the common ratio and the sum of the first fourteen terms (in scientific form correct to two significant figures).

14. A $10000 loan is offered on the following terms: 12% annual interest on the outstanding debt calculated monthly. The required monthly repayment is $270. How much will still be owing after nine months.

15. As a prize for inventing the game of chess, its originator is said to have asked for one grain of wheat to be placed on the first square of the board, 2 on the second, 4 on the third, 8 on the fourth and so on until each of the 64 squares had been covered. How much wheat would have been the prize?

There will be occasions on which questions will be asked that relate to both arithmetic and geometric sequences and series.

EXAMPLE

A geometric sequence has the same first term as an arithmetic sequence. The third term of the geometric sequence is the same as the tenth term of the arithmetic sequence with both being 48. The tenth term of the arithmetic sequence is four times the second term of the geometric sequence. Find the common difference of the arithmetic sequence and the common ratio of the geometric sequence.

SOLUTION

When solving these sorts of question, first write the data as equations:
Firstly, a is the same for both sequences.

$$ar^2 = a + 9d = 48 \qquad [1]$$

$$a + 9d = 4ar \qquad [2]$$

Equation [1] represents the information '

The third term of the geometric sequence is the same as the tenth term of the arithmetic sequence with both being 48'.

Equation [2] represents 'the information

The tenth term of the arithmetic sequence is four times the second term of the geometric sequence'.

There are three equations here and more than one way of solving them. One of the simplest is:

$$\text{From } [1], a + 9d = 48$$
$$\text{Substitute in}[2], 48 = 4ar$$
$$\text{Also from } [1] 48 = ar^2$$
$$\text{Dividing } \frac{48}{48} = \frac{4ar}{ar^2}$$
$$1 = \frac{4}{r}$$
$$r = 4$$
$$\text{Substitute in } [1], a \times 4^2 = 48$$
$$a = 3$$
$$\text{Substitute in } [1], a + 9d = 48$$
$$3 + 9d = 48$$
$$d = 5$$

The common ratio is 3 and the common difference is 5.

It is worth checking that the sequences are as specified:

Geometric sequence: 3, 12, 48
Arithmetic sequence: 3, 8, 13, 18, 23, 28, 33, 38, 43, 48

EXERCISE 3.4

1. Consider the following sequences:
Arithmetic: 100, 110, 120, 130,.....
Geometric: 1, 2, 4, 8, 16,......
Prove that:
The terms of the geometric sequence will exceed the terms of the arithmetic sequence after the 8th term.
The sum of the terms of the geometric sequence will exceed the sum of the terms of the arithmetic after the 10th term.

2. An arithmetic series has a first term of 2 and a fifth term of 30. A geometric series has a common ratio of –0.5. The sum of the first two terms of the geometric series is the same as the second term of the arithmetic series. What is the first term of the geometric series?

3. An arithmetic series has a first term of –4 and a common difference of 1. A geometric series has a first term of 8 and a common ratio of 0.5. After how many terms does the sum of the arithmetic series exceed the sum of the geometric series?

4. The second terms of an arithmetic and a geometric series are the same and are equal to 12. The sum of the first two terms of the arithmetic series is four times the first term of the geometric series. Find the first term of each series.

5. Bo-Youn and Ken are to begin a savings program. Bo-Youn saves $1 in the first week $2 in the second week, $4 in the third and so on, in geometric progression. Ken saves $10 in the first week, $15 in the second week, $20 in the third and so on, in arithmetic progression. After how many weeks will Bo-Youn have saved more than Ken?

6. Ari and Chai begin a training program. In the first week Chai will run 10km, in the second he will run 11km and in the third 12km, and so on, in arithmetic progression. Ari will run 5km in the first week and will increase his distance by 20% in each succeeding week.
   (a)   When does Ari's weekly distance first exceed Chai's?
   (b)   When does Ari's total distance first exceed Chai's?

7. The Fibonacci sequence: 1, 1, 2, 3, 5, 8, 13, 21,.... in which each term is the sum of the previous two terms is neither arithmetic nor geometric. However, after the eighth term (21) the sequence becomes approximately geometric. If we assume that the sequence is geometric:
   (a)   What is the common ratio of the sequence (to four significant figures)?
   (b)   Assuming that the Fibonacci sequence can be approximated by the geometric sequence after the eighth term, what is the approximate sum of the first 24 terms of the Fibonacci sequence?

EXAMINATION STYLE QUESTIONS

1. The terms of an arithmetic sequence are given by the formula $u_n = 5 + (n-1) \times 3$.
   - (a) State
     - (i) the first term and
     - (ii) the common difference
   - (b) Find the first 5 terms.
   - (c) Find the 20th term.
   - (d) Which term would 302 be?

2. The maximum that a part time worker can expect to earn in a year is £7200. The starting salary is £5100 and it is increased by £75 per year. How long will it take a part time worker to earn the maximum available amount?

3. The first term of an arithmetic sequence is 10 and the sixth term is 70.
   - (a) Show that the general term is given by $u_n = 12n - 2$.
   - (b) (i) Find the first four terms.
     - (ii) Find the 20th term.
   - (c) Find the sum of the first 10 terms.

4. The first four terms of a geometric sequence are $5, 15, 45, 135$.
   - (a) Find the common ratio.
   - (b) Find the 10th term.
   - (c) What is the sum of the first 10 terms?

5. A principal of $2500 is invested with a return rate of 12% per annum. Assume that no money was ever taken out of this account and that the interest is compounded annually
   - (a) What will the earnings (due to interest) be in the 7th year since the principal was deposited?
   - (b) How much will the investor have in the account after 7 years.

6. A small car costing $12 000 new depreciates at a rate of 15% per year, calculated on its value at the beginning of a year.
   - (a) What is the annual decay factor (i.e., the common ratio)?
   - (b) What will its value be in 4 years time?
   - (c) (i) If the value of the car n years after it was first purchased is u_n, find a formula for u_n.
     - (ii) How long will it be for the car to be worth just under $3000?

7. A ball rebounds to 0.85 of the height from which it was dropped. Given that the ball was allowed to fall 8 m before hitting the ground, find
   - (a) the height to which the ball rebounds after 2 bounces.
   - (b) how many bounces it takes before it first rebounds to a height of less than 1 m.
   - (c) the total distance the ball travels after 5 bounces.

SELF ASSESSMENT TEST (30 MINUTES)

1. Evaluate: $2 + 6 + 10 + 14, \ldots\ldots + 46$

[3 marks]

2. If: $3 - 6 + 12 - 24 + \ldots\ldots + x = -63$, then x is equal to:

[3 marks]

3. Find the number of terms in the sequence $27, -9, 3, -1, \ldots\ldots, \dfrac{1}{27}$.

[3 marks]

4. How many odd numbers (beginning with 1) must be added before the total reaches one million?

[3 marks]

5. An investment, originally worth $1250 grows at the rate of 12% per year, compounded annually. Find:
(a) The value of the investment after 5 years.
(b) The number of years that must pass before the investment is worth more than $10000.

[4 marks]

6. Two separate species of mice live in a national park.

The number of species A was 12000 at the start of 1990 and increased by 200 per month after that date. The number of species B was 8000 at the start of 1990 and increase by 5% per month after that date.

(a) If n is the number of months after the start of 1990 (when $n = 0$), write formulas for the populations of the two species A_n and B_n.
(b) After how many months will the population of species B exceed that of species A?

[4 marks]

NUMBER & ALGEBRA 3

LINEAR EQUATIONS & INEQUATIONS

4

Chapter contents

– The real number line.
– Linear equations.
– Linear inequations.

Key Formulae

- $ax + b = c \Leftrightarrow x = \dfrac{1}{a}(c - b)$

- $ax > b \Rightarrow \begin{cases} x > \dfrac{b}{a} & \text{if } a > 0 \\[2mm] x < \dfrac{b}{a} & \text{if } a < 0 \end{cases}$

4.1 THE REAL NUMBER LINE

In Chapter 2, we briefly looked at the different types of number sets that are available to us. One particular set that we are interested in is that of the real numbers, denoted by the letter $\mathbb{R}$. A geometric representation of the real numbers may be obtained by associating every real number with a unique point on a straight line. After establishing an origin on the straight line, which will be the number zero, we partition this straight line into three parts:

  1.   Negative real numbers, $\mathbb{R}^-$.

  2.   Zero, 0.

  3.   Positive real numbers, $\mathbb{R}^+$

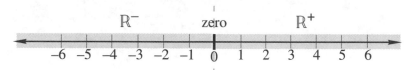

Next consider the task of listing all positive integers greater than 2 but less than 8. This is rather straight forward and is simply given by the set of numbers 3, 4, 5, 6 and 7. Or, using set notation, we can write it as {3, 4, 5, 6, 7}. The **braces** are used to denote *'the set of...'*. However, if we wanted to list all real numbers greater than 2 but less than 8, this could not be achieved. For example, what is the first real number greater than 2? Is it 2.1, 2.01, 2.001 etc. . . In this case, the only way that we can list this set is by writting it in **set builder notation**, i.e., if x represents any number satisfying the condition that it must be greater than 2 but less than 8, then we can write this as $2 < x < 8$. Using set builder notation, we write this as $\{x | 2 < x < 8\}$.

There other ways that this set can be written, for example, we can use **interval notation**, where in this case the set would be written as (2, 8) (NB: do not get this confused with the coordinates (2, 8) used with the Cartesian plane). Notice that as the numbers 2 and 8 are not included as part of the set, we use *'round brackets'*. However, if we were to include the number 2 but still exclude the number 8, then we would write $\{x | 2 \leq x < 8\}$ (in set builder notation) and [2, 8) (in interval notation), i.e., we use a square bracket to indicate that the number 2 is included.

We also want to be able to provided a visual representation of this set. To do this we use the real number line and the following rules:

If the number is not included in the set, you simply circle the point representing the number (that is, an **open circle**):

$$\{x | 2 < x < 8\} = (2, 8)$$

If the number is included in the set, you simply fill–in the circle at the point representing the number (that is, a **closed circle**):

$$\{x | 2 \leq x < 8\} = [2, 8)$$

SUMMARY OF NOTATION AND VISUAL REPRESENTATION ON THE REAL NUMBER LINE.

Set Notation	Interval Notation	Real number line	Example
$\{x \mid a \le x \le b\}$	$[a, b]$	●——● a b	$\{x \mid 2 \le x \le 5\} = [2, 5]$ ●——● 2 5
$\{x \mid a < x \le b\}$	$(a, b]$	○——● a b	$\{x \mid 2 < x \le 5\} = (2, 5]$ ○——● 2 5
$\{x \mid a \le x < b\}$	$[a, b)$	●——○ a b	$\{x \mid 2 \le x < 5\} = [2, 5)$ ●——○ 2 5
$\{x \mid a < x < b\}$	(a, b)	○——○ a b	$\{x \mid 2 < x < 5\} = (2, 5)$ ○——○ 2 5
$\{x \mid x \ge a\}$	$[a, \infty)$	●——→ a	$\{x \mid x \ge 2\} = [2, \infty)$ ●——→ 2
$\{x \mid x > a\}$	(a, ∞)	○——→ a	$\{x \mid x > 2\} = (2, \infty)$ ○——→ 2
$\{x \mid x \le a\}$	$(-\infty, a]$	←——● a	$\{x \mid x \le 2\} = (-\infty, 2]$ ←——● 2
$\{x \mid x < a\}$	$(-\infty, a)$	←——○ a	$\{x \mid x < 2\} = (-\infty, 2)$ ←——○ 2

Note then that if we wanted to represent the set of **integers** greater than 2 but less than 8 on the real number line, the diagram would be given by:

$$-3\ -2\ -1\ 0\ 1\ 2\ 3\ 4\ 5\ 6\ 7\ 8\ 9$$

EXERCISE 4.1

1. Represent each of the following sets on real number line

    (a) $\{x \mid 1 \le x \le 4\}$ (b) $\{x \mid 2 < x \le 6\}$ (c) $\{x \mid -3 \le x < 1\}$

    (d) $\{x \mid -4 < x < 4\}$ (e) $\{x \mid -5 \le x < -3\}$ (f) $\{x \mid -2 < x \le 2\}$

2. Represent each of the following sets on real number line

    (a) $\{x \mid x < 1\}$ (b) $\{x \mid x \le 6\}$ (c) $\{x \mid x > -1\}$

    (d) $\{x \mid -4 < x\}$ (e) $\{x \mid -5 \ge x\}$ (f) $\{x \mid x \ge 2\}$

4.2 LINEAR EQUATIONS (IN ONE VARIABLE)

All linear equations in one variable take on the form $ax + b = c$, where the variable (in this case) is x. Solving such equations simply requires the use of basic transposition techniques. These involve subtraction, addition, multiplication and division.

EXAMPLE

(a)   Solve for x, where $2x - 4 = 12$.

(b)   Solve for x, where $3 - \frac{1}{2}x = 1$.

SOLUTION

(a)   Given that $2x - 4 = 12 \Rightarrow 2x = 12 + 4$.   (Adding 4 to both sides)

Therefore, we have that $2x = 16$.

So that $x = \frac{16}{2} = 8$.   (Dividing both sides by 2)

(b)   Given that $3 - \frac{1}{2}x = 1$, then $-\frac{1}{2}x = 1 - 3$.   (Subtracting 3 from both sides).

Meaning that $-\frac{1}{2}x = -2$

Therefore, $x = -2 \times -2 = 4$. (Multiplying both sides by –2).

We can also use the **solve** function from the TI–83. To do this we

1.   first need to call up the **CATALOG** option by pressing $\boxed{2\text{ nd}}$ $\boxed{0}$.

Then **2.**   press $\boxed{\text{ALPHA}}$ $\boxed{\text{LN}}$ $\boxed{\text{ALPHA}}$ $\boxed{\text{LN}}$.
This will bring up the catalogue listing for those functions or operators that start with the letter 's'.

Then **3.**   use the down arrow key until the **solve(** function is located:

1.   **2.**   **3.**

```
CATALOG          CATALOG            CATALOG           solve(2X-4-12,X,
▶abs(            ▶2-SampFTest       Simul             0)
 and              2-SampTInt        sin(                           8
 angle(           2-SampTTest       sin⁻¹(            solve(3-.5X-1,X,
 ANOVA(           2-SampZInt(       sinh(             0)
 Ans              2-SampZTest(      sinh⁻¹(                        4
 augment(         Scatter           SinReg
 AxesOff          Sci              ▶solve(
```

Notice that when using the solve function, the information must be written in the form
solve(Equation = 0, variable, initial guess)
where the initial guess is a reasonable guess to the value which x might be.

This means that the original equations must be rewritten
(a)   from $2x - 4 = 12$ to $2x - 4 - 12 = 0$ (or $2x - 16 = 0$),

(b)   from $3 - \frac{1}{2}x = 1$ to $3 - \frac{1}{2}x - 1 = 0$ (or $2 - 0.5x = 0$).

This is shown in the fourth screen dump above.

EXAMPLE

(a)   Solve for x, where $5x + 4 = 20$.

(b)   Solve for x, where $\dfrac{1}{3}x + 1 = -7$.

SOLUTION

(a)   We have that $5x + 4 = 20 \Leftrightarrow 5x = 16$ ('-4')

$$\Leftrightarrow x = \frac{16}{5}$$ ('$\div 5$')

(b)   Given that $\dfrac{1}{3}x + 1 = -7$, then $\dfrac{1}{3}x = -8$ ('-1')

$$\Leftrightarrow x = 3 \times -8 = -24$$ ('$\times 3$')

Using the TI–83, we have:

```
solve(5X+4-20,X,
1)
              3.2
solve(X/3+1+7,X,
1)
              -24
■
```

EXAMPLE

Solve the equation $12x - 2 = 3x - 11$.

SOLUTION

This time we need to transpose all x terms to one side and all other terms to the other side.
That is, $12x - 2 = 3x - 11$

$$\Leftrightarrow 12x - 3x = -11 + 2 \qquad \text{('$-3x$' and '$+2$' to both sides)}$$

$$\Leftrightarrow 9x = -9 \qquad \text{Using the TI–83, we have:}$$

$$\Leftrightarrow x = -1$$

```
solve(12X-2-3X+1
1,X,1)
              -1
■
```

Note that we can also use the **Equation Solver** to solve the equations we have just dealt with. As we have already seen, the TI–83 still needs to have the equation in the form **Equation = 0**. To call up the **Equation Solver** follow these steps:

1.   MATH   0   This brings up the Equation Solver screen:

```
EQUATION SOLVER
eqn:0=■
```

2.   Enter the equation directly
(i.e., if solving $12X - 2 = 3X - 11$, enter $12X - 2 - 3X + 11$)

```
EQUATION SOLVER
eqn:0=12X-2-3X+1
1■
```

3.   Move the cursor to the variable for which you want to solve and then press   ALPHA   ENTER   (i.e., SOLVE)

```
EQUATION SOLVER
eqn:0=12■-2-3X+1
1
```

```
.12X-2-3X+11=0
 X=3.2
 bound={-1E99,1...
```

EXAMPLE

Solve the equation $\dfrac{3x-1}{2} = \dfrac{x+4}{3}$.

SOLUTION

We start by 'cross multiplying' by '3' (to transpose the 3 from the denominator on the right hand side) and '2' (to transpose the 2 from the denominator on the left hand side):

$$\frac{3x-1}{2} = \frac{x+4}{3} \Leftrightarrow 3 \times (3x-1) = 2 \times (x+4)$$

$$\Leftrightarrow 9x - 3 = 2x + 8$$

$$\Leftrightarrow 9x - 2x = 8 + 3$$

$$\Leftrightarrow 7x = 11$$

$$\Leftrightarrow x = \frac{11}{7}$$

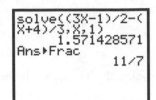

Note that we used the **Frac** function (from **MATH**) to convert the answer into a fraction.

EXAMPLE

Solve the equation $\dfrac{3}{2x-1} = 4$.

Given that $\dfrac{3}{2x-1} = 4$ we first transpose the expression in the denominator of the L.H.S by multiplying both sides of the equation by $(2x-1)$:

$$\frac{3}{2x-1} = 4 \Leftrightarrow 3 = (2x-1) \times 4$$

$$\Leftrightarrow 3 = 8x - 4$$

$$\Leftrightarrow 7 = 8x$$

$$\Leftrightarrow \frac{7}{8} = x$$

EXERCISE 4.2

1. Solve the following equations for the unknown

(a) $4x - 5 = 15$ (b) $3x + 8 = 23$

(c) $2 - 5x = 17$ (d) $7 + 4x = 91$

(e) $3a + 12 = 40$ (f) $4 - 6w = 42$

(g) $8 + 5w = 63$ (h) $4z - 8 = 36$

2. Check your answers to Question 1 using a graphics calculator.

3. Solve the following equations for the unknown

(a) $\dfrac{x}{3} + 1 = 4$ 　　(b) $\dfrac{x}{4} - 3 = 2$ 　　(c) $3 - \dfrac{x}{5} = 1$

(d) $\dfrac{3}{2}x + 2 = 4$ 　　(e) $3 - \dfrac{1}{3}x = 6$ 　　(f) $\dfrac{4}{5}w - 2 = 10$

4. Check your answers to Question 3 using a graphics calculator.

5. Solve the following equations for the unknown

(a) $4 - x = 2 - 3x$ 　　(b) $5y + 7 = 21 - 2y$

(c) $3x + 8 = 7x + 28$ 　　(d) $5 - 8x = 15 + 2x$

(e) $3(x - 1) + 4 = 6 - 2x$ 　　(f) $5(2 - 3x) - 4 = 1 - 2(3 + x)$

6. Check your answers to Question 5 using a graphics calculator.

7. Solve the following equations for the unknown

(a) $\dfrac{3x + 1}{2} = \dfrac{x - 5}{3}$ 　　(b) $\dfrac{3 - 2x}{4} = \dfrac{x + 5}{2}$

(c) $\dfrac{2x + 1}{5} = \dfrac{x + 5}{3}$ 　　(d) $\dfrac{4 - 5y}{7} = \dfrac{3y + 1}{2}$

(e) $\dfrac{x + 1}{2} + 1 = \dfrac{x - 5}{3}$ 　　(f) $\dfrac{w - 2}{4} - 3 = \dfrac{1 - 3w}{2}$

(g) $\dfrac{x - 3}{3} - 4 = x - 2$ 　　(h) $5 - \dfrac{2 - a}{3} = \dfrac{2a + 1}{4}$

8. Check your answers to Question 7 using a graphics calculator.

9. Solve the following equations for the unknown

(a) $\dfrac{2}{2x - 1} = 3$ 　　(b) $\dfrac{4}{2 + x} = 6$ 　　(c) $\dfrac{5}{1 - x} = 3$

(d) $\dfrac{3}{4 - 2x} = -2$ 　　(e) $\dfrac{5}{2x - 4} = -1$ 　　(f) $\dfrac{1}{y} - 3 = 1$

(g) $\dfrac{3}{2x - 1} = \dfrac{4}{1 - x}$ 　　(h) $\dfrac{2}{x - 4} = \dfrac{1}{1 - 2x}$ 　　(i) $\dfrac{1}{x - 1} + 1 = 4$

(j) $\dfrac{1}{a} + \dfrac{1}{2a} = 3$ 　　(k) $\dfrac{3}{a} - \dfrac{1}{2a} = 1$ 　　(l) $\dfrac{4}{3p} + \dfrac{1}{p} = 2$

10. Check your answers to Question 9 using a graphics calculator.

4.3 WORDED PROBLEMS

We now consider a few examples that involve setting up a linear equation in one variable.

EXAMPLE
The sum of two consecutive numbers is 27. What are the numbers?

SOLUTION
Let the first number be x. This means that the next number must be $(x + 1)$ (consecutive numbers come one after the other).

Therefore, we have that $\qquad x + (x + 1) = 27 \Leftrightarrow 2x = 26$

That is, we have that $x = 13$.

Therefore, the consecutive numbers are 13 ($= x$) and 14 ($= x + 1$).

EXAMPLE
My father is twice as old as I am. If the sum of our ages is 69, what is my age?

SOLUTION
Let my age be b years. This means that my father must be $2b$ years old (i.e., he is twice as old as I am). However, the sum of our ages is 69, meaning that $b + 2b = 69$.

That is, we have that $3b = 69 \Leftrightarrow b = 23$.

Therefore, I am 23 years old.

EXAMPLE
The two rectangles shown below have the same perimeter. Find the value of a.

SOLUTION
The perimeter of the first rectangle is $4a + 5 + 4a + 5 = 8a + 10$, whilst the perimeter of the second rectangle is $3a + 10 + 3a + 10 = 6a + 20$.

Seeing as they have the same perimeter, we then have that
$$8a + 10 = 6a + 20$$
$$2a = 10$$
$$\Leftrightarrow a = 5$$

EXERCISE 4.3

1. If y is subtracted from 12 the result is 5.
    (a) Set up a linear equation satisfying the above statement.
    (b) Solve for y.

2. Two more than four times a number is 30. If the number is x,
(a)   set up a linear equation satisfying the above statement.
(b)   solve for x.

3. Five less than twice a certain number is 19. Set up an equation and use it to find the number.

4. The sum of two consecutive numbers is 25. What are the numbers?

5. The sum of three consecutive numbers is 96. What are the numbers?

6. Three people, Fabio, Juan and Isabelle divide £84 amongst themselves. Isabelle receives twice as much as Juan and Fabio receives three times as much as Juan.
(a)   If Juan receives £x, set up an equation in x.
(b)   How much will each person get?

7. The sum of the perimeter of the two squares, one having side length x cm and the other 4 cm is 96 cm. Find x.

8. My mother is three times as old as I am. If the sum of our ages is 112, how old is my mother?

9. I have 4 times as many two–cent coins and I have five–cent coins. All up I have $6.50. How many two–cent coins do I have?

10. I invest in two types of shares, X and Y. X shares pay a dividend of 12% p.a. and Y shares pay a dividend of 10%. If I invest $4000 more in X than in Y and my total receipt from both investments is $1010, how much did I invest in Y shares?

4.4 LINEAR INEQUALITIES

The methods used in solving linear inequalities in one variable are identical to those used when solving linear equalities. The only difference is when we divide or multiply both sides of the equation by a negative number.
Basically,

when **dividing or multiplying** by a **negative number** the **direction of the inequality reverses**.

For example, if we have $-2x > 8$ then diving both sides by '–2' implies that $x < -4$. That is, the direction of the inequality has reversed.

EXAMPLE
(a)   Solve for x, where $2x - 4 \geq 12$.

(b)   Represent on the real number line, those values of x for which $3 - \frac{1}{2}x > 1$.

71

SOLUTION

(a) $2x - 4 \geq 12 \Leftrightarrow 2x \geq 16$. Meaning that $x \geq 8$.

(b)   Now, $3 - \dfrac{1}{2}x > 1 \Leftrightarrow -\dfrac{1}{2}x > -2$

$$\Leftrightarrow x < -2 \times -2 \; (= 4)$$

That is $x < 4$.

On the real number line we have:

EXAMPLE

Represent the following on the real number line $\dfrac{3x-1}{2} \leq \dfrac{x+4}{3}$.

SOLUTION

$$\dfrac{3x-1}{2} \leq \dfrac{x+4}{3} \Leftrightarrow 3 \times (3x - 1) \leq 2 \times (x + 4)$$

$$\Leftrightarrow 9x - 3 \leq 2x + 8$$

$$\Leftrightarrow 9x - 2x \leq 8 + 3$$

$$\Leftrightarrow 7x \leq 11$$

$$\Leftrightarrow x \leq \dfrac{11}{7}$$

On the real number line we have:

EXERCISE 4.4

1.   Find the value(s) of x for which

(a)	$x + 5 > 9$	(b)	$x - 2 \leq 7$	(c)	$5 - x > 1$
(d)	$x - 2 < -1$	(e)	$4 - x \geq -2$	(f)	$x + 9 \leq 8$
(g)	$4x - 5 \geq 15$	(h)	$3x + 8 < 23$	(i)	$2 - 5x \geq 17$
(j)	$7 + 4x > 91$	(k)	$3x + 12 \geq 40$	(l)	$4 - 6x < 42$
(m)	$8 + 5x \leq 63$	(n)	$4x - 8 < 36$	(o)	$4 + 2x < 1$

2.   Represent the solution to Question 1 on the real number line.

3.   Solve the following inequations for the unknown

(a)	$\dfrac{x}{3} + 1 < 4$	(b)	$\dfrac{x}{4} - 3 \geq 2$	(c)	$3 - \dfrac{x}{5} < 1$
(d)	$\dfrac{3}{2}x + 2 \leq 4$	(e)	$3 - \dfrac{1}{3}x < 6$	(f)	$\dfrac{4}{5}x - 2 \geq 10$

4. Represent the solution to Question 3 on the real number line.

5. Solve the following inequations for the given unknown

(a) $4 - x > 2 - 3x$ (b) $5y + 7 < 21 - 2y$

(c) $3x + 8 \geq 7x + 28$ (d) $5 - 8x \leq 15 + 2x$

(e) $3(x - 1) + 4 < 6 - 2x$ (f) $5(2 - 3x) - 4 > 1 - 2(3 + x)$

6. Represent the solution to Question 5 on the real number line.

7. Solve the following inequations for the given unknown

(a) $\dfrac{3x + 1}{2} < \dfrac{x - 5}{3}$ (b) $\dfrac{3 - 2x}{4} \geq \dfrac{x + 5}{2}$

(c) $\dfrac{2x + 1}{5} \geq \dfrac{x + 5}{3}$ (d) $\dfrac{4 - 5y}{7} \leq \dfrac{3y + 1}{2}$

(e) $\dfrac{x + 1}{2} + 1 \leq \dfrac{x - 5}{3}$ (f) $\dfrac{w - 2}{4} - 3 > \dfrac{1 - 3w}{2}$

8. Represent the solution to Question 7 on the real number line.

EXAMINATION STYLE QUESTIONS

1. Solve for x, where $3(2x - 1) = 12$.

2. Find the value(s) of x for which

(a) $7x + 5 = 3x - 10$.

(b) $\dfrac{4x - 3}{2} < 1$.

3. Represent the following on the real number line

(a) $\dfrac{3 - 2x}{4} \geq 3$

(b) $\dfrac{4 - x}{2} + \dfrac{3 - x}{4} > 2$

4. Solve for x, where

(a) $\dfrac{2}{3}(x - 1) - \dfrac{1}{3} = 8$

(b) $\dfrac{9}{5 - 2x} = 3$

5. Find the value(s) of x for which $2 + \dfrac{1 - x}{3} = 4$. Hence, represent the inequality

$2 + \dfrac{1 - x}{3} < 4$ on the real number line.

6. Solve the equations

(a) $\dfrac{x - 2}{3} - 1 = x$

(b) $\dfrac{x - 2}{3} - \dfrac{3 - x}{2} = 1$

7. What number when added to both the numerator and denominator of the fraction $\dfrac{1}{4}$ produces the fraction $\dfrac{8}{9}$?

8. Sally has kept her 2–cent and 5–cent coins from last week. In total she has $1.78. There are two more 5–cent coins than 2–cent coins. How many 5–cent coins does Sally have?

SELF ASSESSMENT TEST (30 MINUTES)

1. Solve the equations

    (a) $2a - 4 = 10$
    (b) $3y - 6 = 8y + 6$
    (c) $7(3x - 2) = 21$

        [2 + 2 + 2 marks]

2. Find the value(s) of x for which

    (a) $7(x - 3) = 3(2x - 5)$
    (c) $\dfrac{3 - 5x}{2} > 8$

        [3 + 3 marks]

3. Represent the following on the real number line

    (a) $2x - 1 \leq 4 - 3(1 - x)$
    (b) $\dfrac{y - 1}{5} - 3 > \dfrac{y - 2}{4}$.

        [4 + 5 marks]

4. Solve for x, where

    (a) $ax - a = ba, a \neq 0$
    (b) $\dfrac{x}{a} - b = \dfrac{x}{b} - a$

        [3 + 4 marks]

5. How much water must be added to 3 litres of 10% salt–water solution to produce a 5% salt–water solution?

        [5 marks]

NUMBER & ALGEBRA 4

QUADRATICS

5

Chapter contents

– Quadratic equations.
– The quadratic formula.
– Parabolic graphs.

Key Formulae

- $ax^2 + bx + c = 0$
- $x^2 + 2bx + b^2 = (x + b)^2$
- $x^2 - 2bx + b^2 = (x - b)^2$
- $x^2 - b^2 = (x - b)(x + b)$

5.1   FACTORISATION

Factorisation is a process which enables us to express a number as a product of its factors. For example, the number 12 can be expressed as the product of 2 and 6, i.e., $12 = 2 \times 6$. Or it can also be expressed as the product of 3 and 4, i.e., $12 = 3 \times 4$. However, when dealing with expressions that consist of more than one term we look for the highest common factor.

EXAMPLE

Factorise the following   (a) $5x^2 - 3x$ (b) $4x^3 + 9x^2$

SOLUTION

(a)   To factorise this expression we need to determine the factors of each term. The factors of

$$5x^2 \text{ are } 1, 5, x, 5x \text{ and } 5x^2$$
$$3x \text{ are } 1, 3, x \text{ and } 3x.$$

In this case we see that the highest common factor is x. This means that we can 'take out' the x term:

$$5x^2 - 3x = x \times 5x - x \times 3$$
$$= x(5x - 3)$$

(b)   The highest common factor of the expression $4x^3 + 9x^2$ is x^2, so that

$$4x^3 + 9x^2 = x^2 \times 4x + x^2 \times 9$$
$$= x^2(4x + 9)$$

FACTORISATION BY GROUPING

The general approach to factorisation by grouping follows the following pattern:

$$ax + ay + bx + by = a(x + y) + b(x + y)$$
$$= (x + y)(a + b)$$

That is, we first group the $ax + ay$ by 'taking out' the 'a', i.e., $a(x + y)$ and then do the same for $bx + by$, i.e., $b(x + y)$. This then means that we have the term $(x + y)$ as a common factor.

EXAMPLE

Factorise the following   (a) $3(x - y) + a(x - y)$ (b) $ab - cb + xa - xc$

SOLUTION

(a)   In the expresssion $3(x-y) + a(x-y)$ we see that the term $(x-y)$ is the highest common factor.

So, we have that $3(x-y) + a(x-y) = 3 \times (x-y) + a \times (x-y)$

$$= (3+a)(x-y)$$

(b)   This time we first need to set up the grouping. It seems reasonable to group the first two and then the second two terms.

Meaning that $ab - cb + xa - xc = b(a-c) + x(a-c)$.

Then, as in part (a), we have $= (b+x)(a-c)$.

EXERCISE 5.1

1.   Factorise the following

(a) $2ax + 4$ (b) $9y - ay$ (c) $4t + st$

(d) $x^2 + x^3$ (e) $3xy - xy^2$ (f) $r^3 s + rs^3$

(g) $2z^2 - 3zy$ (h) $ab^2 - a^4 b^3$ (i) $3x^2 y^2 - 8xy$

(j) $3xy^3 + 9y^2$ (k) $2wt + 8w^2 t$ (l) $3ps - 12(ps)^2$

2.   Factorise the following

(a) $2(x+y) + z(x+y)$ (b) $3(t-s) - r(t-s)$

(c) $x(x+2) - y(x+2)$ (d) $st(a-b) + 2(a-b)$

(e) $r^2(xy+1) + 4(xy+1)$ (f) $y^3(2+z) + 5(z+2)$

3.   Factorise the following

(a) $4(s+1) + xs + x$ (b) $a(2-c) + 2b - bc$

(c) $10x + 2y + t(5x+y)$ (d) $3x + 6 - 5k(x+2)$

(e) $ab^2 - b + 4(ab-1)$ (f) $y(a+b) - az - bz$

4.   Factorise the following

(a) $a^4 - a^3 + 4a - 4$ (b) $x + 1 - yxz - yz$

(c) $mn - m - n + 1$ (d) $y^3 - y^2 + 3y - 3$

5.2 FACTORISING QUADRATICS

A quadratic expression is one which takes on the form $ax^2 + bx + c$. Such expressions (where possible) can be factorised into the form $(Mx + N)(Px + Q)$. That is, we have that $ax^2 + bx + c = (Mx + N)(Px + Q)$. After expanding the brackets on the right–hand side, we end up with the following relationships:

$$MP = a, \qquad MQ + NP = b, \qquad \text{and} \quad NQ = c$$

Our task is to determine the numbers M, N, P and Q for which this can occur.

QUADRATICS OF THE FORM $x^2 + bx + c$ (i.e., $a = 1$)

When we have an expression of the form $x^2 + bx + c$ to factorise, we only need to consider the values of N and Q!

That is, $x^2 + bx + c = (x + N)(x + Q)$. (Because $M = 1$ and $P = 1$).
This therefore means that the numbers N and Q must satisfy the conditions

$$N + Q = b \quad \text{and} \quad NQ = c.$$

That is, we need to find two numbers such that their sum is 'b' and their product is 'c'.

For example, to factorise the quadratic $x^2 + 5x + 6$ we need to come up with two numbers so that their sum is 5 and their product is 6. We see that $2 + 3 = 5$ and $2 \times 3 = 6$, meaning that the two numbers we are looking for are '2' and '3'.

Therefore, we have that $x^2 + 5x + 6 = (x + 2)(x + 3)$.
NB: We could expand the right hand side to verify this result.

The only thing is, will it always be this straight forward? The answer is no. However, put simply, we a use trial and error method to determine the values that will satisfy these conditions. However, we can make use of some educated guess work:

First we note that the x^2 term can only be arrived at if both brackets start with 'x' i.e., we must have an expression of the form

$$(x\ldots\ )(x\ldots\ )$$

Next, we need to take into account the numbers and their signs, mena that we end up with expressions of the form

$$(x + \ldots)(x + \ldots) \text{ or } (x + \ldots)(x - \ldots) \text{ or } (x - \ldots)(x - \ldots)$$

EXAMPLE

Factorise the following (a) $x^2 + 7x + 10$ (b) $x^2 - x - 12$

SOLUTION

(a) We need to come up with two numbers so that they add up to 7 and when multiplied give 10. The only possible combinations is '5' and '2', i.e., $5 + 2 = 7$ & $5 \times 2 = 10$.

Therefore, we have $x^2 + 7x + 10 = (x + 2)(x + 5)$.

(b)   This time we need to find two numbers that add to '–1' and have a product of '–12'. The following pairs are available (using trial and error):

–12 and 1,   12 and –1,   3 and –4,   –3 and 4,   6 and –2,   –6 and 2

Numbers	Product	Sum
–12 and 1	–12	–11
12 and –1	–12	11
3 and –4	–12	–1
–3 and 4	–12	1
6 and –2	–12	4
–6 and 2	–12	–4

From the table we see that the only correct combination is 3 and –4.

Therefore, $x^2 - x - 12 = (x - 4)(x + 3)$.

QUADRATICS OF THE FORM $ax^2 + bx + c$

We deal with quadratics of the form $ax^2 + bx + c$ in exactly the same way as we deal with quadratics of the form $x^2 + bx + c$ — except this time we have an extra number to worry about. Nonetheless, we still make use of educated guesses and trial and error.

EXAMPLE

Factorise the following (a) $2x^2 + 7x + 3$

SOLUTION

Because of the '2' we must have an expression of the form $(2x...\ )(x...\ )$.

(That is, there is no other way that we can produce the $2x^2$ term). All that remains is to fill the rest of brackets. The last term in the quadratic is 3, this number can only be generated by multiplying 3 and 1.

That is, we have two options:

Option 1: $2x^2 + 7x + 3 = (2x + 3)(x + 1)$

Option 2: $2x^2 + 7x + 3 = (2x + 1)(x + 3)$

For option 1, the 'cross–product' term is $2x \times 1 + 3 \times 1x = 5x$ (not correct term).

For option 2, the 'cross–product' term is $2x \times 3 + 1 \times 1x = 7x$ (required term).

Therefore, we have that $2x^2 + 7x + 3 = (2x + 1)(x + 3)$

QUADRATICS OF THE FORM $x^2 + 2bx + b^2$

Quadratic that take on the form $x^2 + 2bx + b^2$ (e.g., $x^2 + 6x + 9$, $b = 3$) are known as **perfect squares**. The process for factorising these quadratics remains the same as before, the only difference being that the factors are repeated. That is,

$$x^2 + 2bx + b^2 = (x + b)(x + b) = (x + b)^2$$

EXAMPLE

Factorise the following (a) $x^2 + 8x + 16$ (b) $2x^2 + 8x + 8$

(a) For the quadratic $x^2 + 8x + 16$ we need to come up with a number such that when it is doubled it equals 8 (i.e., $2b = 8$) and when squared it equals 16 (i.e., $b^2 = 16$). In this case, we have that $b = 4$.

Therefore, we have that $x^2 + 8x + 16 = (x + 4)(x + 4) = (x + 4)^2$.

(b) The first thing that we notice about the quadratic $2x^2 + 8x + 8$ is that there is a common factor of '2', therefore we 'take out' the '2' and then proceed as before:

$$2x^2 + 8x + 8 = 2(x^2 + 4x + 4)$$
$$= 2(x + 2)(x + 2)$$
$$= 2(x + 2)^2$$

QUADRATICS OF THE FORM $x^2 - b^2$

Quadratic that take on the form $x^2 - b^2$ (e.g., $x^2 - 9$, $b = 3$) are known as **difference of perfect squares (i.e., D.O.P.S)**. The process for factorising these quadratics remains the same as before, the only difference being that there is no middle term. That is, we need to determine two numbers for which the sum is zero and their product is '$-b^2$'.

For the quadratic $x^2 - 9$, choosing the numbers '3' and '–3' gives a sum of '$3 + (-3) = 0$' and a product of '$3 \times -3 = -3^2 = -9$'. Therefore we have that $x^2 - 9 = (x - 3)(x + 3)$.

In general we have that

$$x^2 - b^2 = (x + b)(x - b)$$

EXAMPLE

Factorise the following (a) $x^2 - 16$ (b) $yx^3 - xy^3$

SOLUTION

(a) The only two numbers satisfying the conditions that their 'sum = 0' and that their 'product = -16' are '4' & '-4'.

Therefore, we have that $x^2 - 16 = (x+4)(x-4)$.

(b) First we observe that in the expression $yx^3 - xy^3$ there is a common factor of xy, meaning that $yx^3 - xy^3 = xy(x^2 - y^2)$.

Then the term $x^2 - y^2$ is in fact a D.O.P.S., so that $x^2 - y^2 = (x+y)(x-y)$.
Therefore, we have that

$$yx^3 - xy^3 = xy(x^2 - y^2)$$
$$= xy(x+y)(x-y)$$

FACTORISING BY COMPLETING THE SQUARE

Sometimes we have quadratic expressions for which 'obvious factors' are not immediately recognisable. For example, looking at the quadratic $x^2 + 6x - 1$, it is difficult (if not nearly impossible) to determine the two factors (as we have done so far). However, we can use an established method to help us. This method is known as **completing the square**.
The basis of this method lies in two steps:

STEP 1: Create a perfect square (by adding and subtracting an appropriate number).
STEP 2: Use the difference of two squares (i.e., D.O.P.S.) to factorise.

We illustrate this with the quadratic $x^2 + 6x - 1$.

Step 1: To create a perfect square, we set aside the '-1' term momentarily and concentrate on the $x^2 + 6x$ term.
To convert this term into a perfect square we would need to have a '$+9$' attached to it, i.e., $x^2 + 6x + 9$. However, this would actually alter the original expression, and so, we also need to subtract '9' (i.e., so that in fact we have not altered the $x^2 + 6x$ term).

That is we have $x^2 + 6x = x^2 + 6x + 9 - 9 = (x+3)^2 - 9$
Now, we mustn't forget that we still have that '-1' that we momentarily set aside. So, putting this back into the equation we have

$$(x+3)^2 - 9 - 1 = (x+3)^2 - 10.$$

Step 2: We now have a difference of two squares (note that $(\sqrt{10})^2 = 10$), so that

$$(x+3)^2 - 10 = (x+3)^2 - (\sqrt{10})^2$$
$$= (x+3+\sqrt{10})(x+3-\sqrt{10})$$

Now, this might look rather lengthy, however, we will see that in only takes a few lines.

EXAMPLE

Factorise the quadratics   (a) $x^2 + 8x + 10$ (b) $x^2 - 4x + 1$

SOLUTION

(a)   As there are no obvious factors, we use the completing the square method.

Placing aside the '+10' term momentarily, we see that to convert the $x^2 + 8x$ term into a perfect square we need to add 16.

Therefore, we have $x^2 + 8x = x^2 + 8x + 16 - 16 = (x^2 + 8x + 16) - 16 = (x + 4)^2 - 16$.
If we now re-introduce the '+10' term to get:

$$x^2 + 8x + 10 = (x + 4)^2 - 16 + 10$$
$$= (x + 4)^2 - 6$$
$$= (x + 4)^2 - (\sqrt{6})^2$$
$$= (x + 4 + \sqrt{6})(x + 4 - \sqrt{6})$$

(b) $x^2 - 4x + 1 = (x^2 - 4x + 4) - 4 + 1$ (i.e., add and subtract 4 to complete a square)

$$= (x - 2)^2 - 3 \qquad \text{(Factorise the quadratic and create a D.O.P.S.).}$$
$$= (x - 2 + \sqrt{3})(x - 2 - \sqrt{3})$$

EXERCISE 5.2

1.   Factorise the following

(a) $x^2 + 3x + 2$ (b) $x^2 + 7x + 6$ (c) $x^2 + 6x + 8$

(d) $x^2 + 9x + 20$ (e) $z^2 + 9z + 18$ (f) $x^2 + 7x + 10$

2.   Factorise the following

(a) $x^2 - 3x + 2$ (b) $x^2 - 7x + 6$ (c) $x^2 - 6x + 8$

(d) $x^2 - 9x + 20$ (e) $z^2 - 9z + 18$ (f) $x^2 - 7x + 10$

3.   Factorise the following

(a) $x^2 - 2x - 3$ (b) $y^2 + 3y - 10$ (c) $s^2 - 3s - 10$

(d) $x^2 - x - 12$ (e) $y^2 - 5y - 14$ (f) $r^2 - 4r - 45$

4. Facorise the following

(a) $2x^2 - 6x + 4$ (b) $3x^2 + 21x + 30$ (c) $4s^2 - 12s - 40$

(d) $3y^2 + 9y - 30$ (e) $5x^2 + 30x + 40$ (f) $6x^2 - 12x - 18$

5. Facorise the following

(a) $y^2 - 16xy + 15x^2$ (b) $z^2 + zw - 42w^2$ (c) $a^2 + 2ab - 35b^2$

(d) $2y^2 + 18xy + 36x^2$ (e) $3x^2 - 3yx - 36y^2$ (f) $5a^2 - 25ab + 30b^2$

6. Factorise the following

(a) $2x^2 + 5x + 2$ (b) $3x^2 + 5x + 2$ (c) $3x^2 + 7x + 2$

(d) $2x^2 - 5x + 2$ (e) $2x^2 + 3x - 2$ (f) $7s^2 + 2s - 5$

(g) $5x^2 + 2x - 3$ (h) $7x^2 - 36x + 5$ (i) $3y^2 - 5y - 2$

(j) $3z^2 - 10z + 8$ (k) $5w^2 - w - 4$ (l) $2x^2 - 7x - 15$

(m) $2y^2 + 7y + 6$ (n) $5x^2 + 9x + 4$ (o) $3z^2 + 8z + 4$

(p) $2 - 6x - 8x^2$ (q) $3 - 2x - 5x^2$ (r) $4 + x - 5x^2$

7. Factorise the following

(a) $x^2 + 8x + 16$ (b) $y^2 + 10y + 25$ (c) $z^2 + 6z + 9$

(d) $x^2 - 10x + 25$ (e) $b^2 - 12b + 36$ (f) $x^2 - 14x + 49$

(g) $y^2 - 25$ (h) $x^2 - 36$ (i) $z^2 - 16$

(j) $4x^3 - 36x$ (k) $3s^2 - 48$ (l) $4x^2 - 9y^2$

(m) $4x^2 + 4x + 1$ (n) $9z^2 + 12z + 4$ (o) $9z^2 + 6z + 1$

8. Factorise the following by completing the square

(a) $x^2 + 2x - 4$ (b) $x^2 - 2x - 2$ (c) $x^2 + 4x + 2$

(c) $x^2 + 4x - 3$ (d) $x^2 - 6x + 3$ (e) $x^2 + 6x + 2$

(f) $z^2 + 8z + 13$ (g) $y^2 - 8y + 14$ (h) $z^2 + 10z + 20$

(i) $x^2 - 10x + 20$ (j) $z^2 - 4z + 1$ (k) $a^2 + 14a + 30$

5.3 QUADRATIC EQUATIONS

Quadratic equations such as $2x^2 + 5x = 3$ can be solved by several methods. It is usually necessary to rearrange the equation so that it has a zero on one side and all non-zero terms on the other side. In the present case, the equation would need to be rearranged to give $2x^2 + 5x - 3 = 0$.

THE FACTORISATION METHOD

This method depends upon rearranging the equation so that one side is zero and then factorising the terms on the other side.

EXAMPLE

Solve the quadratic equations:

(a) $x^2 - 2x = 0$ (b) $3x^2 - 27 = 0$ (c) $2x^2 + 5x = 3$

SOLUTION

(a) $x^2 - 2x = 0 \Leftrightarrow x(x - 2) = 0$

The factorisation technique used is the 'single common factor' method.
Now that the equation is factorised (a product of terms) and equals zero, we can depend on the fact that the only way in which a multiplication ever gives zero as the result is if either of the two quantities being multiplied is zero. This is sometimes known as the 'Null Factor Law'.

$$x(x - 2) = 0 \Leftrightarrow x = 0 \text{ or } x - 2 = 0 \Rightarrow x = 2$$

There are two solutions to the equation, $x = 0$ or $x = 2$.

(b) $3x^2 - 27 = 0 \Leftrightarrow 3(x^2 - 9) = 0$

$$\Leftrightarrow 3(x + 3)(x - 3) = 0$$

There are two methods of factorisation used in solving this problem; first a common factor of 3 is removed and then the 'difference of two squares' completes the factorisation.
The Null Factor Law can now be used to solve the problem:
$3 = 0$, which is never true, or $x + 3 = 0 \Leftrightarrow x = -3$ or $x - 3 = 0 \Leftrightarrow x = 3$
Therefore, we have that x = -3 or 3.

(c) $2x^2 + 5x = 3 \Leftrightarrow 2x^2 + 5x - 3 = 0 \Leftrightarrow (2x - 1)(x + 3) = 0$

$$2x - 1 = 0 \Leftrightarrow x = \frac{1}{2} \text{ or } x + 3 = 0 \Leftrightarrow x = -3$$

Not every quadratic equation leads to an expression that will factorise and the method can generally only be applied to a minority of examples. There are also many quadratic equations that have no real solutions. The equation $x^2 + 1 = 0 \Rightarrow x^2 = -1$ has no real solution because the squares of all real numbers are zero or positive.

EXERCISE 5.3

1. Use the factorisation method to solve these quadratic equations.

(a) $x^2 - 7x = 0$ (b) $x^2 - 7 = 0$ (c) $x^2 + 3x = 0$

(d) $x^2 + 4 = 0$ (e) $x^2 + x - 12 = 0$ (f) $2x^2 = 4x$

(g) $x^2 + 2x - 8 = 0$ (h) $x^2 = 3x + 10$ (i) $10 + 3x - x^2 = 0$

(j) $30 = x + x^2$ (k) $6 - 5x - x^2 = 0$ (l) $x^2 - 3x - 28 = 0$

(m) $2x^2 + x - 28 = 0$ (n) $11x = 28 + x^2$ (o) $x^2 - 12x + 27 = 0$

(p) $x^2 = 6x + 27$ (q) $x^2 + 7x + 12 = 0$ (r) $3x^2 + 13x + 12 = 0$

(s) $2x^2 + 18x = -28$ (t) $4x^2 = 8 + 14x$ (u) $3x^2 - 11x - 4 = 0$

(v) $11x = 5 + 2x^2$ (w) $6x^2 - 13x + 5 = 0$ (x) $12x^2 - 23x + 5 = 0$

(y) $11x = 2 + 15x^2$ (z) $-2 + 9x - 4x^2 = 0$

2. If $x^2 - px - 2p^2 = 0$, express x in terms of p.

If the quadratic expression will not factorise, one method that can be used is 'completing the square'.

EXAMPLE

Solve the quadratic equations:

(a) $x^2 + 6x - 5 = 0$ (b) $x^2 - 5x = 3$

(c) $2x^2 + 4x - 12 = 0$ (d) $3x^2 + x + 7 = 0$

SOLUTION

(a) The method depends on writing the terms in x (or other letter) as a complete square. In this case, it is necessary to write a complete square expression: $(x + \ldots)^2$ that will expand to give $x^2 + 6x + \ldots$. The correct expression is $(x + 3)^2 = x^2 + 6x + 9$ This results in the following solution to the equation:

$$x^2 + 6x - 5 = 0 \Leftrightarrow [(x + 3)^2 - 9] - 5 = 0$$
$$\Leftrightarrow (x + 3)^2 - 14 = 0$$
$$[(x + 3) + \sqrt{14}][(x + 3) - \sqrt{14}] = 0 \qquad \text{(Using D.O.P.S.)}$$
$$\therefore x + 3 + \sqrt{14} = 0 \Leftrightarrow x = -3 - \sqrt{14} \text{ or } x + 3 - \sqrt{14} = 0 \Leftrightarrow x = -3 + \sqrt{14}$$

An alternative is to rearrange the equation and take square roots of both sides.

That is, $(x + 3)^2 - 14 = 0 \Leftrightarrow (x + 3)^2 = 14$

$$\Leftrightarrow x + 3 = \pm\sqrt{14}$$
$$\Leftrightarrow x = -3 \pm \sqrt{14}$$

These two examples illustrate the two notations for giving the solutions of quadratic equations. Either $x = -3 - \sqrt{14}, x = -3 + \sqrt{14}$ or $x = -3 \pm \sqrt{14}$.

(b) $x^2 - 5x = 3 \Leftrightarrow \left(x - \frac{5}{2}\right)^2 - \left(\frac{5}{2}\right)^2 = 3$

$$\Leftrightarrow \left(x - \frac{5}{2}\right)^2 = \frac{37}{4}$$

$$\Leftrightarrow x - \frac{5}{2} = \pm\sqrt{\frac{37}{4}}$$

$$\Leftrightarrow x = \frac{5}{2} \pm \sqrt{\frac{37}{4}}$$

(c) In this case, remove a common factor so that the coefficient of x^2 is 1. In the case of an equation, it is possible to simplify the problem by dividing both sides by this factor. $\quad 2x^2 + 4x - 12 = 0 \Leftrightarrow 2(x^2 + 2x - 6) = 0 \Leftrightarrow x^2 + 2x - 6 = 0$

$$\Leftrightarrow [(x + 1)^2 - 1] - 6 = 0$$

$$\Leftrightarrow (x + 1)^2 = 7$$

$$\Leftrightarrow x + 1 = \pm\sqrt{7}$$

$$\Leftrightarrow x = -1 \pm \sqrt{7}$$

(d) $\quad 3x^2 + x + 7 = 0 \Leftrightarrow x^2 + \frac{1}{3}x + \frac{7}{3} = 0$

$$\left(x + \frac{1}{6}\right)^2 - \left(\frac{1}{6}\right)^2 + \frac{7}{3} = 0$$

$$\left(x + \frac{1}{6}\right)^2 = -\frac{7}{3} + \frac{1}{36}$$

$$= -\frac{83}{36}$$

In this case, the solution cannot proceed since it is not possible as when the square root is taken, there is no real number equal to $\sqrt{-\frac{83}{36}}$. It is not uncommon for a quadratic equation to have no solutions. There will also be occasions on which there is exactly one solution to an equation.

EXERCISE 5.4

1. Use the method of completing the square to solve the following quadratic equations:

(a)	$x^2 + 5x + 2 = 0$	(b)	$x^2 + 4x - 3 = 0$
(c)	$x^2 - 2x - 5 = 0$	(d)	$x^2 - 2x + 3 = 0$
(e)	$x^2 + 5x = 7$	(f)	$x^2 + 7x - 9 = 0$
(g)	$x^2 + 11x = 9$	(h)	$x^2 + 3x - 12 = 0$

(i) $x^2 + 5x = 12$ (j) $-x^2 + 4x - 12 = 0$

(k) $-x^2 + 4x + 7 = 0$ (l) $x^2 = 6x + 11$

(m) $-x^2 - 4x + 20 = 0$ (n) $2x^2 + 20 = 4x$

(o) $2x^2 - 4x - 9 = 0$ (p) $2x^2 - 5x - 3 = 0$

(q) $2x^2 - 7x - 4 = 0$ (r) $2x^2 - 3x - 4 = 0$

(s) $3x(x - 1) = 4$ (t) $3x^2 - 5x - 4 = 0$

This next section is not on the course. However, we have included it for the sake of completeness.

THE FORMULA

The process of completing the square can be applied to solution of the general quadratic equation $ax^2 + bx + c = 0$. When this is carried out, we obtain a formula that will enable us to find all real solutions that correspond to any quadratic (as long as there are real solutions. In general, we then have that

$$ax^2 + bx + c = 0 \Leftrightarrow x = \frac{-b \pm \sqrt{b^2 - 4ac}}{2a}$$

The following examples illustrate the use of the formula:

EXAMPLE

Use the formula to solve the quadratic equations:

(a) $x^2 - x - 4 = 0$ (b) $2x^2 = 4 - x$ (c) $x^2 - 3x + 7 = 0$

SOLUTION

(a) $x^2 - x - 4 = 0$. In this case $a = 1, b = -1$ & $c = -4$. These values can now be substituted into the quadratic formula.

$$x = \frac{-b \pm \sqrt{b^2 - 4ac}}{2a} = \frac{1 \pm \sqrt{(-1)^2 - 4 \times 1 \times -4}}{2 \times 1} = \frac{1 \pm \sqrt{1 + 16}}{2} = \frac{1 \pm \sqrt{17}}{2}$$

(b) $2x^2 = 4 - x \Rightarrow 2x^2 + x - 4 = 0$

Therefore, using the quadratic formula we have that

$$x = \frac{-b \pm \sqrt{b^2 - 4ac}}{2a} = \frac{-1 \pm \sqrt{(-1)^2 - 4 \times 2 \times -4}}{2 \times 2} = \frac{-1 \pm \sqrt{33}}{4}$$

(c) $x^2 - 3x + 7 = 0 \therefore x = \dfrac{-b \pm \sqrt{b^2 - 4ac}}{2a} = \dfrac{3 \pm \sqrt{(-3)^2 - 4 \times 1 \times 7}}{2}$

$$= \frac{3 \pm \sqrt{-19}}{2}$$

The negative quantity in the square root, $\sqrt{-19}$ has no real value and so the equation has no real solutions.

EXERCISE 5.5

1. Use the quadratic formula to solve these equations:

(a) $x^2 - 3x - 7 = 0$ (b) $x^2 - 5x = 2$ (c) $x^2 - 3x - 6 = 0$

(d) $x^2 = 7x + 2$ (e) $x(x + 7) = 4$ (f) $x^2 + 2x - 8 = 0$

(g) $x^2 + 2x - 7 = 0$ (h) $x^2 + 5x - 7 = 0$ (i) $x^2 - 3x - 7 = 0$

(j) $x^2 - 3x + 9 = 0$ (k) $x^2 + 9 = 8x$ (l) $4x^2 - 8x + 9 = 0$

(m) $4x^2 = 8x + 9$ (n) $5x^2 - 6x - 7 = 0$ (o) $5x^2 - 12x + 1 = 0$

(p) $7x^2 - 12x + 1 = 0$

5.4 QUADRATIC GRAPHS

The techniques of solving quadratic equations can be helpful when sketching quadratic graphs. The simplest quadratic function is $y = x^2$. The table of values is:

x	-3	-2	-1	0	1	2	3
y	9	4	1	0	1	4	9

When plotted on a Cartesian graph, the result is a curve known as a parabola.

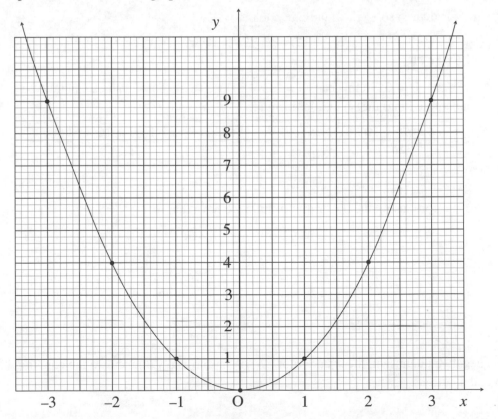

This diagram is a ''plot' of the graph. It is common to be asked to 'sketch' graphs of quadratics and other functions. A sketch must show the correct shape of the graph and other key features such as intercepts and turning points. There are two main techniques for sketching parabolas.

TURNING POINT FORM

This method depends on completing the square to obtain an expression of the type $y = a(x-h)^2 + k$. This can now be sketched using transformations. The graph is based on the standard parabola $y = x^2$. The graph is dilated (stretched) by a factor of a vertically. It is then translated h units to the **right** and k units **upwards**. This means that the vertex is translated from the origin to the point (h,k).

EXAMPLE

Use the method of completing the square to sketch the graphs of

    (a) $y = x^2 + 2x + 3$ (b) $y = x^2 - 3x - 4$

    (c) $y = 3x^2 - 6x + 4$

SOLUTION

(a)   Completing the square gives:

$$y = x^2 + 2x + 3$$
$$= (x + 1)^2 - 1 + 3$$
$$= (x + 1)^2 + 2$$

In this case $a = 1$, $h = -1$ and $k = 2$. There is no vertical dilation. The curve is translated one unit to the left and two units up so that the vertex is at the point $(-1,2)$. The y-intercept (found by substituting $x = 0$ into the equation) is $(0,3)$. A sketch should show these features.

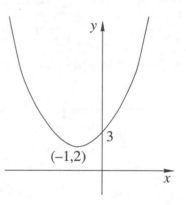

(b) $y = x^2 - 3x - 4$

$$= \left(x - \frac{3}{2}\right)^2 - \left(\frac{3}{2}\right)^2 - 4$$

$$= \left(x - \frac{3}{2}\right)^2 - \frac{25}{4}$$

In this example $a = 1$, $h = \frac{3}{2}$ and $k = -\frac{25}{4}$. There is no dilation and the vertex is translated to $\left(\frac{3}{2}, -\frac{25}{4}\right)$. The y-intercept is -4.

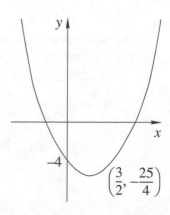

(c) $y = 3x^2 - 6x + 4$

$\quad = 3[x^2 - 2x]^2 + 4$

$\quad = 3[(x-1)^2 - 1] + 4$

$\quad = 3(x-1)^2 - 3 + 4$

$\quad = 3(x-1)^2 + 1$

There is a vertical dilation of 3 and the vertex is translated to (1,1). The y-intercept is 4.

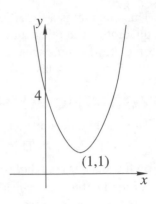

THE INTERCEPT METHOD

As an alternative (or in addition to) completing the square, many parabolas can be sketched by finding all their intercepts. The y-intercept was discussed in the previous section. To find the x-intercepts it is necessary to solve a quadratic equation.

EXAMPLE

Use the intercept method to sketch the graphs of:

(a) $y = x^2 - x - 2$ (b) $y = x^2 - 3x - 7$ (c) $y = -3x^2 - x + 5$

SOLUTION

(a) $y = x^2 - x - 2$

The y-intercept is –2.

The x-intercepts are found by solving:

$\quad x^2 - x - 2 = 0$

$(x - 2)(x + 1) = 0$

$\quad\quad\quad x = 2, -1$

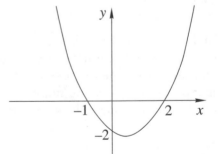

(b) $y = x^2 - 3x - 7$

The y-intercept is –7.

The x-intercepts are found by solving:

$x^2 - 3x - 7 = 0$

$\quad x = \dfrac{3 \pm \sqrt{(-3)^2 - 4 \times 1 \times (-7)}}{2}$

$\quad\ = \dfrac{3 \pm \sqrt{37}}{2}$

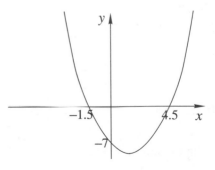

(b) $y = -3x^2 - x + 5$

The y-intercept is 5.

The x-intercepts are found by solving:

$$-3x^2 - x + 5 = 0$$

$$x = \frac{1 \pm \sqrt{(-1)^2 - 4 \times (-3) \times 5}}{2 \times (-3)}$$

$$= \frac{1 \pm \sqrt{61}}{-6}$$

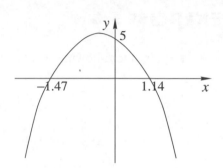

USING A GRAPHICS CALCULATOR

Graphics calculators can be used to check that parabola sketches are correct. The stages are similar to those needed to produce other graphs. To plot $y = x^2 + x - 5$

Step 1: **Set the equation using the Y= menu**

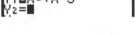

Step 2: **Set an appropriate viewing window.**

It can be a good idea to use the decimal window (**ZOOM4**) as this sets scales that are multiples of the numbers of screen pixels. In this case this window is not large enough to see all the graph.

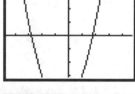

Step 3: **Adjust the viewing window.**

In this case the x scale is correct. If the y-scale is changed (using the **WINDOW** command) to exactly twice the range set by **ZOOM4**, there will still be an integral relationship between the scale and the number of pixels on the screen.

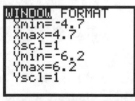

Step 4: **Display the graph.**

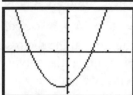

Step 5: If necessary, use **TRACE** to display the coordinates of points on the curve. The diagram shows the coordinates of the minimum point, $(-0.5, -5.25)$. Using **ZOOM4** tends to give better results from the **TRACE** facility. Other viewing windows will give long decimals for the coordinates.

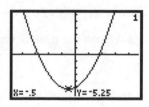

EXERCISE 5.6

1. Express the following functions in turning point form and hence sketch their graphs.

(a) $y = x^2 - 2x + 1$ (b) $y = x^2 + 4x + 2$ (c) $y = x^2 - 4x + 2$

(d) $y = x^2 + x - 1$ (e) $y = x^2 - x - 2$ (f) $y = x^2 + 3x + 1$

(g) $y = -x^2 + 2x + 1$ (h) $y = -x^2 - 2x + 2$ (i) $y = 2x^2 - 2x - 1$

(j) $y = \dfrac{-x^2}{2} + 3x - 2$ (k) $y = -\dfrac{x^2}{3} + x - 2$ (l) $y = 3x^2 - 2x + 1$

2. Find the axes intercepts of these quadratic functions (correct to 2 decimal places) and hence sketch their graphs.

(a) $y = x^2 + 3x + 2$ (b) $y = x^2 - x - 6$

(c) $y = 2x^2 - 5x - 3$ (d) $y = x^2 - 4$

(e) $y = x^2 + x - 5$ (f) $y = -x^2 + x + 6$

(g) $y = -x^2 + x + 1$ (h) $y = -2x^2 - 3x + 5$

(i) $y = 2x^2 + 5x - 3$ (j) $y = \dfrac{x^2}{3} - 2x + 3$

(k) $y = -\dfrac{x^2}{2} + x + 4$ (l) $y = 3x^2 - 2x - 4$

5.5 USING A GRAPHICS CALCULATOR TO FACTORISE QUADRATICS

Because of the relationship between a quadratic equation its roots and its factors, it is possible to factorise a quadratic given its graph. For example, given the graph of

$y = x^2 + 2x - 3$, we can see that its roots are $x = 1$ and $x = -3$. Meaning that the factors are $(x - 1)$ and $(x + 3)$.

By looking at the solving process for a quadratic equation in reverse, we can see why this is the case. Using an appropriate

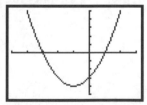

window, we consider the solution to $x^2 + 2x - 3 = 0$.

The first step is to factorise this expression: $x^2 + 2x - 3 = (x - 1)(x + 3)$.

Next we use the null factor theorem: $x^2 + 2x - 3 = 0 \Leftrightarrow (x - 1)(x + 3) = 0$

$$\Leftrightarrow x - 1 = 0 \text{ or } x + 3 = 0$$
$$x = 1 \text{ or } \qquad x = -3.$$

Reversing the process we start with $x = 1$ or $x = -3$, which leads the the previous step, i.e., $\Leftrightarrow x - 1 = 0$ or $x + 3 = 0$, which in turn leads to $(x - 1)(x + 3) = 0$ and finally to the original equation $x^2 + 2x - 3 = 0$.

EXAMPLE

Factorise the quadratic $x^2 - 2x - 8$

SOLUTION

We start by sketching the graph of $y = x^2 - 2x - 8$ using the graphics calculator.
Make sure that an appropriate **WINDOW** setting is selected as well as an appropriate
Xscl:
The Xscl setting here is one, therefore
we can clearly see that the graph cuts the
x–axis at $x = -2$ and $x = 4$.
Meaning that the factors are
$x + 2$ and $x - 4$.

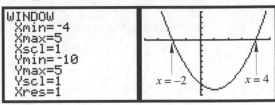

Therefore the quadratic $x^2 - 2x - 8 = (x + 2)(x - 4)$.

Although this process is great, sometimes we need to be very careful. For example, had the
equation been $2x^2 - 4x - 16$, using the same WINDOW as above, we would have ended
up with the graph shown below:

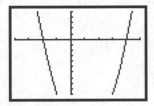

This graph still has intercepts at $x = -2$ and $x = 4$! It
would then be easy to think that the quadratic factorised
to $(x + 2)(x - 4)$. However, this is clearly not the case.
The first thing that should be done is factorise the '2' and
then proceed as in the above example, so that

$$2x^2 - 4x - 16 = 2(x^2 - 2x - 8) = 2(x + 2)(x - 4).$$

EXERCISE 5.7

1.   Use a graphics calculator to factorise the following

(a) $x^2 - 3x + 2$ (b) $x^2 - 7x + 6$ (c) $x^2 - 6x + 8$

(d) $x^2 - 9x + 20$ (e) $z^2 - 9z + 18$ (f) $x^2 - 7x + 10$

(g) $x^2 - 2x - 3$ (h) $y^2 + 3y - 10$ (i) $s^2 - 3s - 10$

(j) $x^2 - x - 12$ (k) $y^2 - 5y - 14$ (l) $r^2 - 4r - 45$

(m) $2x^2 - 6x + 4$ (n) $3x^2 + 21x + 30$ (o) $4s^2 - 12s - 40$

(p) $3y^2 + 9y - 30$ (q) $5x^2 + 30x + 40$ (r) $6x^2 - 12x - 18$

EXAMINATION STYLE QUESTIONS

1. (a) Factorise the expression $x^2 + 2x - 8$.

   (b) Determine the integer values for which $x^2 + 2x - 8$ is less than 0.

2. (a) Factorise the quadratics

   (i) $x^2 + 6x + 5$ (ii) $x^2 - 5x - 6$

   (b) Hence sketch the graphs of

   (i) $y = x^2 + 6x + 5$ (ii) $y = x^2 - 5x - 6$

3. Factorise each of the following

   (a) $x^2 - x - 12$

   (b) $6x^2 - 13x - 6$

   (c) $(x-1)^2 - y^2$

4. The area of a rectangle of width $(x - 4)$ cm and length x cm is 5 cm^2. Find x.

5. The graph of $y = x^2 - ax + b$ is shown.

   (a) Determine the values of a and b.

   (b) Hence, factorise the quadratic $x^2 - ax + b$

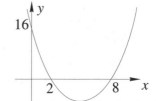

6. An arch follows a curve modelled by the equation $h = -x^2 + 10x - 13$ where x is the horizontal displacement from an origin placed at ground level.

   (i) Find the height of the arch at its highest point.

   (ii) Find the width of the arch at ground level, correct to 2 significant figures.

7. Sketch the graphs of   (a) $y = -x^2 + 9$ (b) $y = -x^2 + 6x - 9$

SELF ASSESSMENT TEST (45 MINUTES)

1. Write the quadratic $y = x^2 - 3x + 7$ in turning point form and hence find the coordinates of the vertex of the parabola.

[3 marks]

2. The graph shows a parabola with equation
$y = (x - a)^2 + b$.

Find the values of a and b.

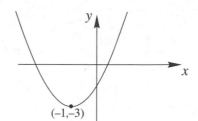

$(-1,-3)$

[2 marks]

3. Solve $x(2x + 5) = 3$

[2 marks]

4. Find the coordinates of the axis intercepts of the parabola with equation
$y = -x^2 + 2x + 7$

[3 marks]

5. Find the values of b for which the quadratic equation $x^2 + bx + 9 = 0$ has one real solution.

[3 marks]

6. The product of two consecutive multiples of 7 is 8918.

(i) Express this information as a quadratic equation.
(ii) Solve this equation and hence find the two numbers.

[3 marks]

7. The graph of $y = ax^2 + bx + c$ is shown.

(a) Determine the values of a and b and c.

(b) Hence, factorise the quadratic $ax^2 + bx + c$.

(c) (i) Find the range of integers for which $ax^2 + bx + c$ is less than 0.

(ii) Find the minimum value of $ax^2 + bx + c$

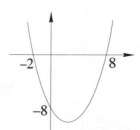

[7 marks]

SETS AND LOGIC

THEORY OF SETS & LOGIC

6

Chapter contents

6.1 SETS

A set is a collection of items, names, objects or numbers. Capital letters are usually used to denote a set. The items, names, objects or numbers are enclosed by {}.

Example 1   A = {Jack, Alison, Ismael, Baljeet, Yoshi}

Example 2   B = {Brisbane, Sydney, Melbourne, Canberra, Darwin, Adelaide, Perth}

Example 3   C = {Colombia, Peru, Ecuador, Brazil, Chile, Argentina}

Example 4   D = {Clinton, Reagan, Ford, Kennedy}

Example 5   E = {2, 3, 9, 14, 20}

Each item, name, object or number in the set is called an element of the set.

> $\in$ **denotes 'is an element of'**

Example 1   Jack $\in$ A   Jack is an element of set A

Example 2   Sydney $\in$ B   Sydney is an element of set B

Example 3   Colombia $\in$ C   Colombia is an element of set C

> $\notin$ **denotes 'is not an element of'**

Example 4   Thatcher $\notin$ D   Thatcher is not an element of set D

Example 5   5 $\notin$ E   5 is not an element of set E

EXERCISE 6.1

1.   Write the following in words.

    (a)   hammer $\in$ A   (b)   axe $\in$ C   (c)   Tuesday $\in$ B
    (d)   Tuesday $\notin$ A   (e)   January $\in$ B   (f)   Sunday $\notin$ C

2.   Write the following using set notation.

    (a)   32 is an element of set C   (b)   45 is an element of set N
    (c)   green is not an element of set K   (d)   Mary is not an element of set P
    (e)   Horse is not an element of set M   (f)   Banana is an element of set H

SETS OF NUMBERS

The set of Natural Numbers $\mathbb{N}$

The set of Natural numbers is the set of positive whole numbers and zero.

$$\mathbb{N} = \{0, 1, 2, 3, 4...\}$$

The set of Integers $\mathbb{Z}$

The set of Integers is the set of natural numbers with their negative opposites.

$$\mathbb{Z} = \{... -3, -2, -1, 0. 1, 2, 3...\}$$

The set of integers can be broken into 3 distinct parts.

- The set of positive integers $\mathbb{Z}^+ = \{1, 2, 3...\}$
- The set containing Zero $\{0\}$
- The set of negative integers $\mathbb{Z}^- = \{... -3, -2, -1\}$

The set of Rational numbers $\mathbb{Q}$

A rational number is a number that can be expressed as a ratio of two integers.

$$\text{A number } m \text{ is rational if } m = \frac{a}{b} \text{ where } a \text{ and } b \in \mathbb{Z} \text{ and } b \neq 0$$

Integers are rational numbers because they can be expressed as the ratio of two integers.

Example 1 $\quad 4 = \frac{4}{1} = \frac{8}{2}$

Example 2 $\quad -5 = \frac{5}{-1} = \frac{-10}{2}$

Terminating decimals are rational numbers because they can be expressed as the ratio of two integers.

Example 1 $\quad 0.2 = \frac{2}{10}$

Example 2 $\quad 0.345 = \frac{345}{1000} = \frac{69}{200}$

Example 3 $2.87 = \dfrac{287}{100}$

Recurring decimals are rational numbers because they can be expressed as the ratio of two integers.

(At this level it is not required that students know how to convert recurring decimals to fractions. However the process has been shown in the first example for interest's sake.)

Example 1 $0.235235... = \dfrac{235}{999}$

Proof: Let $x = 0.235235...$

There are three recurring digits, so multiply both sides by 1000

$1000x = 235.235235...$

Subtract $x = 0.235235235...$ from the equation above

$$1000x - x = 235.235235... - 0.235235...$$
$$999x = 235$$
$$x = \frac{235}{999}$$

Check this result on your calculator.

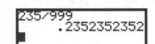

Example 2 $0.3434... = \dfrac{34}{99}$

Example 3 $0.33... = \dfrac{33}{99} = \dfrac{1}{3}$

THE SET OF IRRATIONAL NUMBERS

An irrational number is simply a number that cannot be expressed as the ratio of two integers.

Non terminating, non recurring decimals are irrational.

The square root of numbers that are not square numbers are irrational.

Example 1   2.3256487456239088...

Example 2 π

Example 3 $\sqrt{2}, \sqrt{3}, \sqrt{5}$

THE SET OF REAL NUMBERS $\mathbb{R}$

The set of real numbers encompasses all of the sets of numbers discussed so far. The set of real numbers can be thought of as all the numbers on the real number line.

EXERCISE 6.2

State whether the following are true or false.

(a) $-3 \in \mathbb{N}$

(b) $\frac{4}{5} \in \mathbb{Q}$

(c) $0.3333... \in \mathbb{Q}$

(d) $\sqrt{2} \in \mathbb{Q}$

(e) $-4.7 \in \mathbb{Z}$

(f) $2\frac{1}{4} \in \mathbb{R}$

(g) $\pi \in \mathbb{R}$

(h) $\pi \in \mathbb{Q}$

(i) $\sqrt{3} \in \mathbb{Q}$

(j) $0 \in \mathbb{Z}^+$

(k) $0.3456723... \in \mathbb{Q}$

THE NUMBER OF ELEMENTS IN A SET

$n(A)$ denotes the number of elements in set A

Example 1 $A = \{\text{apple, pear, orange, pineapple, banana}\}$
$n(A) = 5$

Example 2 $B = \{1, 2, 4, 6, 8, 10\}$
$n(B) = 6$

FINITE SETS

A finite set has a countable number of elements.

Example 1 $C = \{\text{The people in Austria}\}$
Example 2 $D = \{\text{The grains of sand on the beach}\}$
Example 3 $E = \{\text{The fish in the sea}\}$

INFINITE SETS

An infinite set has an infinite number of elements.

Example 1 $\mathbb{N} = \{\text{The natural numbers}\}$
Example 2 $\mathbb{Z} = \{\text{The integers}\}$
Example 3 $\mathbb{R} = \{\text{The real numbers between 1 and 2}\}$

It is possible for an infinite set to be countable. That is, it is possible to use the natural numbers to count the set of even numbers (an infinite set); 2 is the 1st even number, 4 is the 2nd, 6 the 3rd etc. The integers are also 'countable' in this sense, though the real numbers are not. The proofs of these statements are beyond the scope of this course.

EXERCISE 6.3

A = {hammer, axe, mower, nail}
B = {Months of the year}
C = {Days of the week}
D = {0, 1, 2, 3, 4, 5, 6, 7, 8, 9, 10}

1. State whether the following are true or false.

(a)	hammer $\in$ A	(b)	axe $\in$ C	(c)	Tuesday $\in$ B
(d)	Tuesday $\notin$ A	(e)	January $\in$ B	(f)	Sunday $\notin$ C
(g)	4.5 $\notin$ D	(h)	3 $\in$ D	(i)	10 $\in$ D

2. Evaluate

(a)	$n(A)$	(b)	$n(B)$	(c)	$n(C)$
(d)	$n(D)$				

3. State whether each of the following is a finite or infinite set.

(a)   A = {Letters of the English alphabet}
(b)   B = {Natural Numbers}
(c)   C = {Capital cities in Europe}
(d)   D = {Planets in our solar system}
(e)   E = {Fractions between 4 and 10}
(f)   F = {people in China}

DESCRIBING SETS

1.   Empty sets

Where **there are no elements in a set**, the set is referred to as the empty set or the null set.

> **The empty set is denoted by:{ } set brackets which enclose no elements.**
> **or $\varnothing$, a scandinavian letter.**

Example 1   A = {The days of the week that end in the letter "m" when spelt in English}

Since no day of the week ends in the letter "m" when spelt in English, A = { }

Example 2   B = {The natural numbers less than zero}

Since there are no natural numbers less than zero, B = { }

2.   Sets with a few elements

Where there are a small number of elements it is convenient to list each element individually. Each element is separated by a comma.

Example 1   C = {apple, pear, orange. pineapple}
Example 2   D = {Madrid, Barcelona, Seville}

3.   Sets with many elements

When a set has a large number of elements, listing individual elements is inconvenient. In this instance it is more appropriate to give a description of the elements of the set. When this form is used the curly brackets are left out.

Example 1   E = The names of the people living in India today
Example 2   F = Capital cities of the world
Example 3   G = Languages spoken in the world

SET BUILDER NOTATION

Set builder notation is another way of defining sets.

$$F = \{x \mid x \text{ is odd}\}$$

This form can be divided into three parts.

$$\{ \boxed{x} \mid \boxed{x \text{ is odd}} \}$$

In the first part a variable is identified, in this case the variable is x.

In the second part the symbol '|' which means 'such that' is used to introduce the conditions that applies to the variable.

The final part is the conditions that the variables follow. In this case there is only one condition, that x is odd. When more than one condition is used they are separated by commas.

Example 1 $G = \{x \mid x \in \mathbb{N}, 4 < x < 12\}$
The set G equals x such that x is an element of $\mathbb{N}$, and x is between 4 and 12. G is the set of natural numbers between 4 and 12. G = {5, 6, 7, 8, 9, 10, 11}

Example 2 $H = \{y \mid y \in \mathbb{Z}, y < 3\}$
The set H equals y such that, y is an element of $\mathbb{Z}$ and y is less than 3. Or simply H is the set of integers less than 3.

Example 3 $M = \{x \mid x \text{ is a capital city in Australia}\}$
In this instance, the set builder notation is used to describe a set containing names of places.

This set has an infinite number of elements

EXERCISE 6.4

1. List the elements in the following sets, if possible.

(a) A = {Letters that come before "a" in the English alphabet}.
(b) B = {Vowels in the word "zebra"}
(c) C = {Days of the week}
(d) D = $\{x \mid x \in \mathbb{N}, 4 \leq x \leq 5\}$
(e) E = $\{y \mid y \in \mathbb{N}, -4 \leq y \leq 5\}$
(f) F = $\{m \mid m \in \mathbb{Z}, -4 \leq m \leq 5\}$
(g) G = $\{x \mid x \in \mathbb{Q}, -4 \leq x \leq 5\}$
(h) H = $\{x \mid x \in \mathbb{R}, 4 \leq x \leq 5\}$

2. Evaluate the following

(a) $n(A)$ (b) $n(B)$ (c) $n(C)$
(d) $n(D)$ (e) $n(E)$ (f) $n(F)$
(g) $n(G)$ (h) $n(H)$

3. Which of the sets listed above are infinite?

4. Express the following using set builder notation.

(a) {The natural numbers between 3 and 18}
(b) {Real numbers less than 12}
(c) {Integers from –56 to 45}
(d) {Rational numbers greater than or equal to –5 but less than or equal to 5}

SUBSETS

A set B is a subset of set C if all the elements in set B are
in set C.

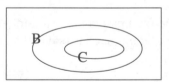

> ⊆ denotes is a subset of
> ⊄ denotes is not a subset of

Example 1   A = {apple, pear, orange}

The subsets of A are:

{}   [*The empty set as it is a subset of all sets*].
{apple}   {pear}   {orange}
{apple, pear}   {apple, orange}   {pear, orange}
{apple, pear, orange}   [*Every set is a subset of itself*].

PROPER SUBSETS

A set B is said to be a proper subset of a set C if all the elements of set B are in set C, but the two sets are not the same.

$\subset$ **denotes is a proper subset of**
$\not\subset$ **denotes is not a proper subset of**

From the previous example all the subsets listed are proper subsets except for

{apple, pear, orange}

Since this subset contains the same elements as set A it is not a proper subset.

If a set A has p elements $n(A) = p$, there are

2^p **subsets** and $2^p - 1$ **proper subsets**.

EXERCISE 6.5

1.   A = {Days of the week}   B = {Months of the year}

C = {Letters in the alphabet}   D = {Letters in the word "Standard"}

State which the following are true and which false.

(a)   {Saturday, Sunday} $\subseteq$ A   (b)   {January} $\subseteq$ A
(c)   February $\in$ B   (d)   {a, e, i, o, u} $\subseteq$ C
(e)   D $\subseteq$ C   (f)   C $\not\subset$ D
(g)   {Monday, Tuesday, Wednesday, Thursday, Friday, Saturday, Sunday} $\not\subset$ A
(h) $\varnothing \subseteq$ D   (i) $\varnothing \not\subset$ A

2.   State which the following are true and which false.

(a) $\mathbb{N} \subset \mathbb{R}$ (b) $\mathbb{R} \subseteq \mathbb{Q}$ (c) $\mathbb{Z} \subseteq \mathbb{Q}$
(d) $\mathbb{N} \subseteq \mathbb{Z}$ (e) $\mathbb{N} \subseteq \mathbb{Z} \subseteq \mathbb{R}$ (f) $\mathbb{Q} \supseteq \mathbb{N}$

(g) $\{\pi, \sqrt{2}\} \subseteq \mathbb{Q}$ (h) $\{\pi, \sqrt{2}\} \subseteq \mathbb{R}$ (i) $\left\{\dfrac{1}{2}, \dfrac{3}{4}\right\} \supseteq \mathbb{Q}$

3.   Write all the subsets of $\{\alpha, \beta, \mu, \sigma\}$

THE INTERSECTION OF SETS

The intersection of two sets is the elements that are common to both sets.

$\cap$ **denotes 'the intersection of'**

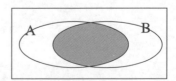

A $\cap$ B Reads 'A intersection B'

Example 1   A = {2, 4, 6, 8, 10, 12, 14, 16}B = {3, 6, 9, 12, 15}

$$A \cap B = \{6, 12\}$$

The intersection of the two sets is the set comprising 6 and 12 because these two elements are in both sets.

Example 2 $C = \{x \mid x \in \mathbb{Z}, x < 10\}D = \{x \mid x \in \mathbb{Z}, x > 5\}$

$$C \cap D = \{x \mid x \in \mathbb{Z}, 5 < x < 10\}$$

UNION OF SETS

The union of two sets is the set of all the elements in both sets listed once.

> $\cup$ **denotes the union of**

$A \cup B$ reads 'A union B'.

The number of elements in the union of two sets is not necessarily the sum of the numbers of elements in each set. Look at the people in a cinema audience and count the number of women and the number of people with fair hair. Is it true that the number of people who are women or who have fair hair is the sum of the two numbers? Not necessarily as this sum counts the fair haired women twice. This is the intersection of the set of women and the set of fair haired people.

> $n(A \cup B) = n(A) + n(B) - n(A \cap B)$

Example 1   M = {apple, pear, orange. pineapple}
N ={nut, carrot, pear, banana}
M $\cup$ N = {apple, pear, orange, pineapple, nut, carrot, banana}

Example 2 $P = \{t \mid t \in \mathbb{R}, -5 < t < 7\}$
$Q = \{t \mid t \in \mathbb{R}, -3 \leq t < 10\}$
$P \cup Q = \{t \mid t \in \mathbb{R}, -5 < t < 10\}$

EXERCISE 6.6

A = {3, 6, 9, 12, 15, 18}
B = {2, 4, 6, 8, 10, 12, 14, 16, 18}
C = {1, 4, 9, 16}

1. List the elements in

(a) $A \cap B$ (b) $B \cap C$ (c) $A \cap C$
(d) $A \cap B \cap C$ (e) $A \cup B$ (f) $A \cup C$
(g) $B \cup C$ (h) $A \cup B \cup C$ (i) $(A \cup B) \cap C$
(j) $(B \cap C) \cup A$ (k) $(A \cap C) \cup B$

2. Evaluate

(a) $n(A \cap B)$ (b) $n(B \cap C)$ (c) $n(A \cap C)$
(d) $n(A \cap B \cap C)$ (e) $n(A \cup B)$ (f) $n(A \cup C)$
(g) $n(B \cup C)$ (h) $n(A \cup B \cup C)$

$D = \{x \mid x \in \mathbb{Z}, -3 \leq x < 4\}$
$E = \{x \mid x \in \mathbb{Z}, -5 \leq x \leq -2\}$
$F = \{x \mid x \in \mathbb{Z}, -3 < x \leq 5\}$

3. List the elements in

(a) $D \cap E$ (b) $E \cap F$ (c) $D \cap F$
(d) $D \cap E \cap F$ (e) $D \cup E$ (f) $D \cup F$
(g) $E \cup F$ (h) $D \cup E \cup F$ (i) $(D \cup E) \cap F$
(j) $(E \cap F) \cup D$ (k) $(D \cap F) \cup E$

4. Evaluate

(a) $n(D \cap E)$ (b) $n(E \cap F)$ (c) $n(D \cap F)$
(d) $n(D \cap E \cap F)$ (e) $n(D \cup E)$ (f) $n(D \cup F)$
(g) $n(E \cup F)$ (h) $n(D \cup E \cup F)$

$G = \{x \mid x \in R, -3 \leq x < 4\}$
$H = \{x \mid x \in R, -5 \leq x \leq -2\}$
$J = \{x \mid x \in R, -3 < x \leq 5\}$

5. Write in set builder notation.

(a) $G \cap H$ (b) $H \cap J$ (c) $G \cap J$
(d) $G \cap H \cap J$ (e) $G \cup H$ (f) $G \cup J$
(g) $H \cup J$ (h) $G \cup H \cup J$ (i) $(G \cup H) \cap J$
(j) $(H \cap J) \cup G$ (k) $(G \cap J) \cup H$

THE UNIVERSAL SET

The universal set is the set from which the sets of a particular situation are drawn.

> **U denotes the universal set**

THE COMPLEMENT

The complement of a set B is all the elements that are not in the set B but are in the universal set.

> **B′ denotes the complement of set B**

$B \cup B' = U$ The union of a set and its complement is the universal set.

$B \cap B' = \varnothing$ The intersection of a set and its complement is the empty set.

$n(B) + n(B') = n(U)$ The sum of the elements in the set and its complement equals the total number of elements in the universal set.

Example 1 $U = \{x \mid x \in \mathbb{Z}, 0 < x < 10\}$
$A = \{2, 4, 6, 8\}$
$A' = \{1, 3, 5, 7, 9\}$

Example 2 $U = \{x \mid x \in \mathbb{Z}\}$
$B = \{x \mid x \in \mathbb{Z}, x \geq -6\}$
$B' = \{x \mid x \in \mathbb{Z}, x < -6\}$

Example 3 $U = \{$Students in year 11$\}$
$C = \{$Students with red hair$\}$
$C' = \{$Students without red hair$\}$

EXERCISE 6.7

$U = \{$Letters of the English alphabet$\}$
$A = \{$Letters in the word "mathematics"$\}$
$B = \{$The consonants in the alphabet$\}$
$C = \{a, b, d, m, n, o, p, l, j, z\}$

1. List the elements of

  (a) A' (b) B' (c) C'

  (d) $(A \cup B)'$ (e) $(A \cup B \cup C)'$ (f) $A' \cap B'$

  (g) $A' \cap B' \cap C'$ (h) $(B' \cap C') \cup A'$

$U = \{x \mid x \in \mathbb{Z}, -10 \leq x \leq 10\}$
$D = \{x \mid x \in \mathbb{Z}, -5 \leq x \leq 2\}$
$E = \{x \mid x \in \mathbb{Z}, -1 \leq x \leq 6\}$
$F = \{x \mid x \in \mathbb{Z}, 0 < x < 3\}$

2. List the elements of

(a) D' (b) E' (c) F'

(d) $(D \cup E)'$ (e) $(D \cup E \cup F)'$ (f) $D' \cap E'$

(g) $D' \cap E' \cap F'$ (h) $(E' \cap F') \cup D'$

3. Write the following using set builder notation.

(a) D' (b) E' (c) F'

(d) $(D \cup E)'$ (e) $(D \cup E \cup F)'$

$U = \{x \mid x \in \mathbb{R}, -10 \le x \le 10\}$
$G = \{x \mid x \in \mathbb{R}, -5 < x \le -3\}$
$H = \{x \mid x \in \mathbb{R}, 3 < x \le 10\}$
$J = \{x \mid x \in \mathbb{R}, -3 < x < 4\}$

4. Write the following using set builder notation.

(a) G' (b) H' (c) J'

(d) $(G \cup H)'$ (e) $(G \cup H \cup J)'$

5. $n(U) = 40, n(A) = 12\ n(B) = 21\ n(C) = 15$, find

(a) $n(A')$ (b) $n(B')$ (c) $n(C')$

6.2 VENN DIAGRAMS

Sets can be represented diagrammatically using Venn diagrams. Each individual set is represented by a circle and the universal set is represented by a rectangle which encloses all of the sets under investigation.

Disjoint sets

Sets are disjoint if they have no elements in common. This is shown in the Venn diagram below by two circles that do not overlap and are enclosed by a rectangle to represent the universal set.

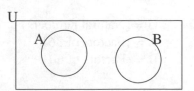

Example 1 $U = \{1, 2, 3, 4, 5, 6, 7, 8, 9, 10\}$
             $A = \{2, 4, 6, 8, 10\}$
             $B = \{1, 3, 5\}$

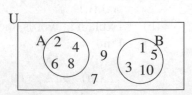

INTERSECTING SETS

When sets have elements in common the circles that represent the sets in a Venn diagram are drawn so that they overlap.

Example 1 $U = \{1, 2, 3, 4, 5, 6, 7, 8, 9, 10\}$
$C = \{2, 4, 6, 8, 10\}$
$D = \{1, 4, 9\}$
$C \cap D = \{4\}$

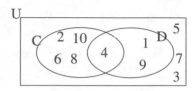

SUBSETS

A subset is shown using Venn diagrams by placing the circle representing the subset inside the circle representing the other set.

Example 1 $U = \{1, 2, 3, 4, 5, 6, 7, 8, 9, 10\}$
$D = \{2, 4, 6, 8, 10\}$
$F = \{2, 4, 8\}$

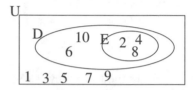

Note: When the Universal set is an infinite set the individual elements are not listed.

EXERCISE 6.8

1. $U = \{\text{Natural numbers}\}$
$A = \{\text{Multiples of 3 less than 40}\}$
$B = \{\text{Multiples of 4 less than 40}\}$

(a) Draw a Venn diagram to show this relationship, list all the elements of sets A and B.

(b) Explain in words, the significance of $A \cap B$.

(c) Find

      (i) $n(A)$ (ii) $n(B)$

      (iii) $n(A \cap B)$ (iv) $n(A \cup B)$

(d) Show that $n(A \cup B) = n(A) + n(B) - n(A \cap B)$

(e) Shade the region of the Venn diagram that represents A'.

2. $U = \{\text{Natural numbers}\}$
$A = \{\text{Factors of 36}\}$
$B = \{\text{Factors of 60}\}$

(a) Draw a Venn diagram to show this relationship, list all the elements of sets A and B.

(b) Explain in words, the significance of $A \cap B$.

(c) Find

      (i) $n(A)$ (ii) $n(B)$

      (iii) $n(A \cap B)$ (iv) $n(A \cup B)$

(d)   Show that $n(A \cup B) = n(A) + n(B) - n(A \cap B)$

(e)   Shade the region of the Venn diagram that represents B'.

Note: Prime numbers only have 1 and themselves as factors. 1 is neither prime nor composite.

3.   U = {Natural numbers}
A = {Prime numbers less than 30}
B = {Odd numbers less than 30}

(a)   Draw a Venn diagram to show this relationship, list all the elements of sets A and B.

(b)   Explain in words, the significance of $A \cap B$.

(c)   Find

      (i) $n(A)$ (ii) $n(B)$

      (iii) $n(A \cap B)$ (iv) $n(A \cup B)$

(d)   Show that $n(A \cup B) = n(A) + n(B) - n(A \cap B)$

(e)   Shade the region of the Venn diagram that represents $A \cap B$.

4.   U = {Fruits}
A = {Apple, pear, banana, pineapple, water melon}
B = {Banana, apple, pear}

(a)   Draw a Venn diagram to show this relationship, list all the elements of sets A and B.

(b)   Explain in words, the significance of $A \cap B$.

(c)   Find

(i) $n(A)$ (ii) $n(B)$ (iii) $n(A \cap B)$

(iv) $n(A \cup B)$

(d)   Show that $n(A \cup B) = n(A) + n(B) - n(A \cap B)$

(e)   Shade the region of the Venn diagram that represents $A \cup B$.

5.   U = {Capital cities of the world}
A = {Capital cities of Europe}
B = {Capital cities of South America}

(a)   Draw a Venn diagram to show this relationship.

(b)   Explain in words, the significance of $A \cap B$.

(c)   Find

(i) $n(A)$ (ii) $n(B)$ (iii) $n(A \cap B)$

(iv) $n(A \cup B)$

(d)   Show that $n(A \cup B) = n(A) + n(B) - n(A \cap B)$

(e)   Shade the region of the Venn diagram that represents $A' \cap B'$.

6. U = {Natural numbers}
A = {Factors of 36}
B = {Multiples of 6 less than 61}
C = {Even number less than 21}

(a) Draw a Venn diagram to show this relationship, list all the elements of sets A, B and C.

(b) Explain in words, the significance of A ∩ B ∩ C.

(c) Find

(i) n(A)   (ii) n(B)   (iii) n(C)

(iv) n(A ∩ B ∩ C.)   (iv) n(A ∪ B ∪ C)

(e) Shade the region of the Venn diagram that represents C′.

REGIONS OF VENN DIAGRAMS

Intersection
The elements in sets A **and** B.

Disjoint Sets	**Intersecting Sets**	**Subsets**
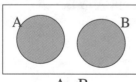	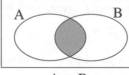	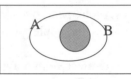
A ∩ B	A ∩ B	A ∩ B

Union
The elements that are in set A **or** set B **or** both.

Disjoint Sets	**Intersecting Sets**	**Subsets**
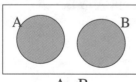	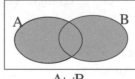	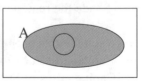
A∪B	A∪B	A∪B

The complement

Disjoint Sets	**Intersecting Sets**	**Subsets**
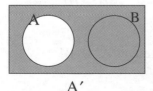	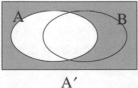	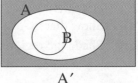
A′	A′	A′

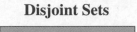

| Disjoint Sets | Intersecting Sets | Subsets |

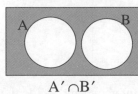 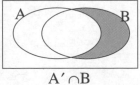 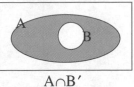

$A' \cap B'$ $A' \cap B$ $A \cap B'$

EXERCISE 6.9

1.

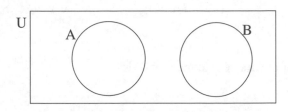

(a)   For each of the following copy the Venn diagram above and shade the region that represents:

(i)   A   (ii)   A′   (iii) A ∪ B

(iv)   A ∩ B   (v)   (A ∪ B)′   (vi)   A′ ∩ B

(vii) A′ ∩ B′

(b)   Explain each of the above regions in words.

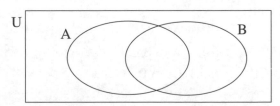

2.   (a)   For each of the following copy the Venn diagram above and shade the region that represents:

(i)   A   (ii)   A′   (iii) A ∪ B

(iv)   A ∩ B   (v)   (A ∪ B)′   (vi)   A′ ∩ B

(vii) A′ ∩ B′

(b) Explain each of the above regions in words.

3.

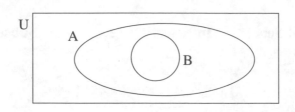

(a) For each of the following copy the Venn diagram above and shade the region that represents:

(i)   A

(ii)   A′

(iii)   A ∪ B

(iv)   A ∩ B

(v)   (A ∪ B)′

(vi)   A′ ∩ B

(vii)   A′ ∩ B′

(b) Explain each of the above regions in words.

4.

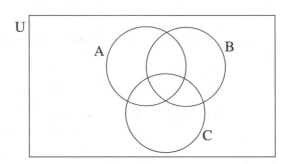

(a) For each of the following copy the Venn diagram above and shade the region that represents:

(i)   A

(ii)   A′

(iii)   B′

(iv)   C′

(v)   A ∪ B ∪ C

(vi)   A ∩ B ∩ C

(vii)   (A ∪ B ∪ C)′

(viii)   (A ∩ B ∩ C)′

(b) Explain each of the above regions in words.

6.3 APPLICATIONS OF SETS

THE NUMBER OF ELEMENTS IN EACH REGION
2 Sets

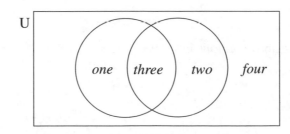

Region	Description of Region	Number of Elements
One	The elements that belong to **only** set A	$n(A) - n(A \cap B)$
Two	The elements that belong to **only** set B	$n(B) - n(A \cap B)$
Three	The elements that belong to A **and** B.	$n(A \cap B)$
Four	The elements that **do not** belong to set A or set B	$n(U) - n(A \cup B)$

EXAMPLE

Draw a Venn diagram to show the number of elements in each region if,
$$n(U) = 50, n(A) = 32, n(B) = 25, n(A \cap B) = 11$$

SOLUTION

The number of elements in A only = $n(A) - n(A \cap B) = 32 - 11 = 21$
The number of elements in B only = $n(B) - n(A \cap B) = 25 - 11 = 14$
The number of elements in U only = $n(U) - n(A \cup B) = 50 - (32 + 25 - 11) = 4$

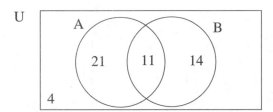

EXAMPLE

Out of a class of 30 IB students, 22 study Mathematical Studies (M), 15 study Biology (B) and 7 study both. Draw a Venn diagram to show the number of students in each region of the Venn diagram.

SOLUTION

The number of students who only study Maths = $n(M) - n(M \cap B) = 22 - 7 = 15$
The number of students who only study Biology = $n(B) - n(M \cap B) = 15 - 7 = 8$
The number of students who do study neither = $n(U) - n(M \cup B) = 30 - (22 + 15 - 7) = 0$

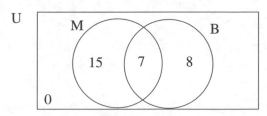

EXERCISE 6.10

1. Draw Venn diagrams to show the number of elements in each separate region for the following.

(a) $n(U) = 25$ $n(A) = 10$ $n(B) = 12$ $n(A \cap B) = 5$
(b) $n(U) = 55$ $n(A) = 34$ $n(B) = 27$ $n(A \cap B) = 16$
(c) $n(U) = 64$ $n(A) = 23$ $n(B) = 41$ $n(A \cap B) = 13$
(d) $n(U) = 30$ $n(A) = 19$ $n(B) = 17$ $n(A \cap B) = 8$
(e) $n(U) = 100$ $n(A) = 67$ $n(B) = 50$ $n(A \cap B) = 34$

2. In an athletics club with 20 members, 15 compete in the 100m, 12 compete in the 400m and 9 compete in both. Draw a Venn diagram to show this.

3. 50 people where surveyed as to whether they liked tea, coffee or both. Every person surveyed chose one of the three. If 38 people liked tea and 32 people liked coffee, how many people liked both. Draw a Venn diagram to show this information.

4. Out of 30 students, 19 play hockey and 15 play tennis. How many play both? Draw a Venn diagram to show this.

5. The number of elements in sets A and B are shown on the Venn diagram below.

If $n(A) = 2 \times n(B)$, find the value of p.

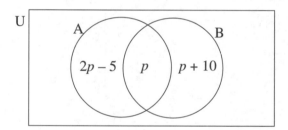

3 Sets

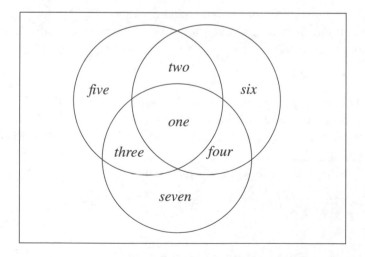

Region	Description of the region	Number of elements
One	The elements that belong to A **and** B **and** C	$n(A \cap B \cap C)$
Two	The elements that belong to A **and** B **but not** C	$n(A \cap B) - n(A \cap B \cap C)$
Three	The elements that belong to A **and** C **but not** B	$n(A \cap C) - n(A \cap B \cap C)$
Four	The elements that belong to C **and** B **but not** A	$n(C \cap B) - n(A \cap B \cap C)$
Five	The elements that belong to A **only**	$n(A) - [n(A \cap B) + n(A \cap C) - n(A \cap B \cap C)]$
Six	The elements that belong to B **only**	$n(A) - [n(A \cap B) + n(B \cap C) - n(A \cap B \cap C)]$
Seven	The elements that belong to C **only**	$n(A) - [n(A \cap C) + n(B \cap C) - n(A \cap B \cap C)]$

EXAMPLE

From a survey of 50 customers at a video store, the following was found.

        29 enjoyed Adventure videos

        22 enjoyed Comedies

        18 enjoyed horror videos

of these

        8 liked both adventure and comedy

        10 liked both comedies and horror

        5 liked both adventure and horror

and   4 liked all three types of videos

Draw a Venn diagram to show the number of people in each region of the Venn diagram.

SOLUTION

LetA = {people who liked adventure videos}

C = {people who liked comedy videos}

H = {people who liked horror videos}

Region	Method	Number of elements
One	4 liked all three types of videos	4
Two	8 liked both adventure and comedy but of these 4 liked all three	$8 - 4 = 4$
Three	5 liked both adventure and horror but of these 4 liked all three	$5 - 4 = 1$
Four	10 liked comedies and horror but of these 4 liked all three	$10 - 4 = 6$

Put this information in the Venn diagram. Then proceed with the second part of the table.

Five	29 enjoyed adventure but some of these already are accounted for on the Venn diagram	$29 - (4 + 4 + 1) = 20$
Six	22 enjoyed comedies but some of these already are accounted for on the Venn diagram.	$22 - (4 + 4 + 6) = 8$
Seven	18 enjoyed horror but some of these are already accounted for on the Venn diagram.	$18 - (4 + 1 + 6) = 7$

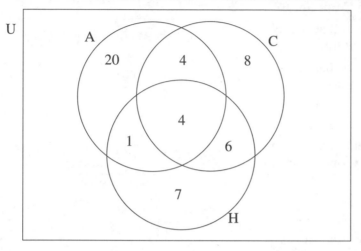

EXERCISE 6.11

1. 45 students were asked which of the following activities they enjoyed, roller blading, surfing or BMX racing. Each student listed at least one activity and the results are summarised below.

24 enjoy roller blading
24 enjoy surfing
15 enjoy BMX racing
11 enjoy both roller blading and surfing
6 enjoy both roller blading and BMX racing
4 enjoy both surfing and BMX racing
3 enjoy all three activities.
Draw a Venn diagram to show the number of students in each region.

2. 18 senior citizens all participate in at least one of the following activities, lawn bowls,

backgammon or cards.
11 participate in lawn bowls
4 participate in lawn bowls and backgammon
3 only participate in backgammon
2 participate only in cards
1 participates in all three activities
Draw a Venn diagram to show the number of senior citizens in each region.

3. In a class of 50 IB students, each student studies at least one of the following subjects,

computing, geography and/or biology.
19 study computing
23 study geography
31 study biology
8 study computing and geography
9 study geography and biology
11 study computing and biology
5 students study all three subjects
Draw a Venn diagram to show the number of students in each region.

6.4 LOGIC

Logic is the study of correct reasoning.

Propositions

> **A proposition is a statement that is either true or false.**

Examples

- Today is Saturday.
- All animals respire.
- Mary is 18 years old.
- $4 > 5$
- All mammals are warm blooded.
- Jose is sick.
- Frederick studies French.
- Jock plays football.
- The moon orbits the earth.
- All roses are red.
- $4 + 8 = 13$
- All swans are white.

Each of the above statements are either true or false and therefore can be defined as propositions.

- Go get the book.

    This is a command and it does not have either a true or a false response. However if it were worded Anne said "Go get the book" then this is a proposition as the truth or falsity is connected to whether or not Anne **said** "Go get the book".

- Have you seen my new shirt?

    This is a question and therefore not a proposition.

EXERCISE 6.12

Identify which of the following are propositions.

(a)	Juan studies French.	(b)	The cooker is on.
(c)	Is it raining?	(d)	All sheep are white.
(e)	Make the tea.	(f)	Emus can fly.
(g)	What is the date today?	(h)	$5 > 2$
(i)	The glass is full.	(j)	Have a good weekend.
(k)	All cows are herbivores.	(l)	The sun is shining.
(m)	Take out the rubbish.	(n)	Put your hat on.

Propositions are usually represented by the letters p, q and r. The truthfulness or falsity of a proposition is called its truth value.

Negation Not ¬p

The negation of a proposition can be formed by inserting in the proposition "not" or "do not" as appropriate.

> **The negation of a proposition p is not p and is denoted by ¬p**

EXAMPLES
Find the negations of the propositions:
- (i) Today is Saturday
- (ii) All mammals respire
- (iii) The glass is full

SOLUTIONS

(i) Proposition p: Today is Saturday
Negation   ¬p: Today is not Saturday

(ii) Proposition p: All mammals respire
Negation   ¬p: All mammals do not respire

(iii) Proposition p: The glass is full
Negation   ¬p: The glass is not full

(There is often a temptation here to write the negation as the glass is empty. However, if the glass is not completely empty it is still not full)

EXERCISE 6.13

Write the negation of the following propositions.

- (a) Brutus is sick.
- (b) The cup is empty.
- (c) Monday is a holiday.
- (d) There are twelve months in a year.
- (e) $4 < 6$
- (f) Ismael studies Geography.
- (g) Yoshi plays football.
- (h) All roses are red
- (i) March has 31 days.
- (j) All quadrilaterals are rectangles.
- (k) Carlos lives in Japan.

TRUTH VALUES

A proposition is a statement that can either be true or false. The truth values of a proposition is T (true) or F (false).

Truth Values of Negation

p	¬p	
T	F	If the original proposition is true then the negation of the proposition would be false
F	T	If the original proposition is false then the negation of the proposition is true.

Negation and Sets $\neg p$, P′

EXAMPLE

Find the negation of: p: x is a prime number

SOLUTION

$\neg p$: x is not a prime number

Let P be the truth set of the proposition p

Then P = {2, 3, 5, 7...}

Therefore P′ = {1, 4, 6, 8, 9...} which is the truth set for $\neg p$.

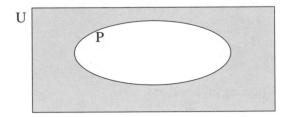

CONNECTIVES

Propositions can be combined to form compound statements. The truth or falsity of a compound statement is dependent on the truth or falsity of the individual propositions.

Conjunction 'and', ∧

A conjunction is formed when propositions are joined by the word 'and'

> **The conjunction of two propositions p and q is denoted by $p \wedge q$.**

EXAMPLES

Find the conjunctions of the propositions:

(i)	*p*:	John studies English.	*q*:	Juan studies Spanish
(ii)	*p*:	Rebecca has red hair.	*q*:	Carla has black hair
(iii)	*p*:	Liz is a teacher.	*q*:	Anne is a teacher.

SOLUTIONS

(i)   *p*:   John studies English.

         q: Juan studies Spanish

         $p \wedge q$:   John studies English **and** Juan studies Spanish.

(ii)   *p*:   Rebecca has red hair.

         q: Carla has black hair

         $p \wedge q$:   Rebecca has red hair **and** Carla has black hair.

(iii)   *p*:   Liz is a teacher.

         q: Anne is a teacher.

         $p \wedge q$:   Liz **and** Anne are both teachers.

EXERCISE 6.14

1.   Write the conjunctions of the following propositions

(a)   *p*:   All trees are green.

         q: All mammals are warm blooded.

(b)   *p*:   Josh studies French

         q: Anne studies French

(c)   *p*:   Abdul plays football

         q: Abdul plays squash

(d)   *p*:   The moon orbits the earth

         q: The earth orbits the sun

(e)   *p*:   It is raining

         q: Today is Saturday

2.   Write the two propositions that make up the following conjunctions

(a)   Jennifer studies both physics and chemistry

(b)   All mammals are warm blooded and all roses are red

(c)   Ruth is 16 years old and Janet is 17 years old

(d)   Today is Sunday and it is fine

(e)   Ronnie plays football and Renee plays tennis

TRUTH VALUES OF CONJUNCTION

p	q	$p \wedge q$
T	T	T
T	F	F
F	T	F
F	F	F

The truth value of a conjunction is only true when the truth value all of the individual conjunctions is true. Otherwise the truth value is false.

EXAMPLE

Find the truth values of the propositions:

  p: London is the capital of England
  q: Cardiff is the capital of Wales
  $p \wedge q$: London is the capital of England **and** Cardiff is the capital of Wales.

SOLUTION

  p: London is the capital of England   T
  q: Cardiff is the capital of Wales   T
  $p \wedge q$: London is the capital of England **and** Cardiff is the capital of Wales.   T

The "**and**" means that all parts of the conjunction must be true for the conjunction to be true.

EXAMPLE

Find the truth values of the propositions:

  p: London is the capital of England
  q: Cardiff is the capital of France
  $p \wedge q$: London is the capital of England **and** Cardiff is the capital of France.

SOLUTION

  p: London is the capital of England   T
  q: Cardiff is the capital of France   F
  $p \wedge q$: London is the capital of England **and** Cardiff is the capital of France.   F

The "**and**" means that all parts of the conjunction must be true for the conjunction to be true. It is false that Cardiff is the capital of France therefore the conjunction is false.

CONJUNCTION AND SETS ∧, ∩

EXAMPLE

Find the truth sets of p, q and $p \wedge q$.

   p: x is a multiple of 3 between 1 and 20

   q: x is a factor of 45

SOLUTION

   Let   P be the truth set of p

   and   Q be the truth set of q

   Therefore $P = \{3, 6, 9, 12, 15, 18\}$

   $Q = \{1, 3, 5, 9, 15, 45\}$

   $p \wedge q$: x is a multiple of 3 between 1 and 20 and is a factor of 45

Therefore the truth set of $p \wedge q$ is $\{3, 9, 15\}$ which is $P \cap Q$.

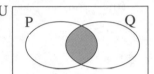

EXERCISE 6.15

   (i)   Write the truth sets P and Q for the propositions p and q.

   (ii)   Draw a Venn diagram and show all the elements.

   (iii)   Write the truth set for $p \wedge q$.

   (a) p: x is a multiple of 4 between 1 and 20

           q: x is a multiple of 6 between 1 and 20

   (b) p: x is a square number less than 100

           q: x is a number that ends in 6 less than 40

   (c) p: x is a prime number less than 20

           q: x is a multiple of 3 less than 20

DISJUNCTION 'OR' ∨

A disjunction is formed when propositions are joined by the word "or".

The disjunction of two propositions p and q is denoted by $p \vee q$.

EXAMPLES
Find the disjunctions of these propositions:

    (i) p: London is the capital of England
            q: Cardiff is the capital of Wales

    (ii) p: Enrique is a mathematician
            q: Bill is a pilot

    (iii) p: Paris is in France
            q: Paris is in England

SOLUTIONS

    (i) $p \vee q$:   London is the capital of England **or** Cardiff is the capital of Wales.

    (ii) $p \vee q$:   Enrique is a mathematician **or** Bill is a pilot

    (iii) $p \vee q$:   Paris is in either France **or** England

EXERCISE 6.16

1.   Write the disjunctions of the following pairs of propositions

    (a) p: All tree are green.
            q: All mammals are warm blooded.

    (b) p: Josh studies French
            q: Anne studies French

    (c) p: Abdul plays football
            q: Abdul plays squash

    (d) p: The moon orbits the earth
            q: The earth orbits the sun

    (e) p: It is raining
            q: Today is Saturday

2.   Write the two propositions that make up the following disjunctions.

    (a)   John will buy either a TV or a stereo
    (b)   Yoshi plays tennis or Mohammed plays squash
    (c)   The moon orbits the earth or the sun
    (d)   Emus are birds or goats are horses
    (e)   Ruth likes watching the theatre or watching sports

TRUTH VALUES OF DISJUNCTIONS

p	q	$p \lor q$
T	T	T
T	F	T
F	T	T
F	F	F

The truth value of a disjunction is true when at least one of the propositions is true.

EXAMPLES

Find the truth values of p, q and $p \lor q$:

      p: Bogota is the capital of Colombia

      q: Santiago is the capital of Wales

and

      p: Bogota is the capital of Sweden

      q: Santiago is the capital of Wales

SOLUTIONS

p:	Bogota is the capital of Colombia	T
q:	Santiago is the capital of Wales	F
$p \lor q$:	Bogota is the capital of Colombia **or** Santiago is the capital of Wales	T

The "**or**" in the statement means that only one of the propositions has to be true for the whole statement to be true.

The truth value of a disjunction is false when all of the individual propositions are false.

p:	Bogota is the capital of Sweden	F
q:	Santiago is the capital of Wales	F
$p \lor q$:	Bogota is the capital of Sweden **or** Santiago is the capital of Wales	F

Since no part of the disjunction is true the disjunction is false.

DISJUNCTION AND SETS $\lor, \cup$

EXAMPLE

Find the truth set of the disjunction of p and q.

      x is a multiple of 3 between 1 and 20

      q: x is a factor of 45

SOLUTION

Let   P be the truth set of p

and   Q be the truth set of q

Therefore   P = {3, 6, 9, 12, 15, 18}

             Q = {1, 3, 5, 9, 15, 45}

$p \lor q$: x is a multiple of 3 between 1 and 20 or is a factor of 45

Therefore the truth set of $p \lor q$ is {1, 3, 5, 6, 9, 12, 15, 45} which is P $\cup$ Q.

EXERCISE 6.17

(i)   Write the truth sets P and Q for the propositions p and q.

(ii)   Draw a Venn diagram and show all the elements.

(iii)   Write the truth set for $p \lor q$.

(a) p: x is a multiple of 4 between 1 and 20

        q: x is a multiple of 6 between 1 and 20

(b) p: x is a square number less than 100

        q: x is a number that ends in 6 less than 40

(c) p: x is a prime number less than 20

        q: x is a multiple of 3 less than 20

IMPLICATION IF _____ THEN _____ $\Rightarrow$

An implication is joined when propositions p and q are linked in the following ways.

- If p then q

- p only if q

- p is sufficient for q

- q is necessary for p

In the cases above the proposition p is called the antecedent and the proposition q is called the consequent.

The implication of two propositions p and q is denoted by p $\Rightarrow$ q.

EXAMPLES

Find $p \Rightarrow q$ in each of these cases:

    (i)   *p*:   John is not at work

            q: John is sick

    (ii)   *p*:   My watch is slow

            q: I will be late

    (iii)   *p*:   The radio works

            q: The power is on

SOLUTIONS

    (i) $p \Rightarrow q$:   **If** John is not at work **then** he is sick

    (ii) $p \Rightarrow q$:   **If** my watch is slow **then** I will be late

    (iii) $p \Rightarrow q$:   The radio works only if the power is on

EXERCISE 6.18

1. Write implication statements using the following pairs of propositions. Take p as the antecedent and q as the consequent.

    (a)   *p*: x is a multiple of 9

            q: x is divisible by 3

    (b)   *p*:   Yoshi is sick

            q: Yoshi is not at work

    (c)   *p*:   Paris is in France

            q: The sky is blue

    (d)   *p*:   This is the right time for an argument

            q: This is the right place for and argument

    (e)   *p*:   John works hard

            q: John earns money

2. Identify the antecedent and the consequent in the following implication statements.

    (a)   If a number is divisible by 10 then it ends in a zero

    (b)   I will earn more money only if I work hard

    (c)   The flowers will grow only if there is enough rain

    (d)   If a number is divisible by four then it is even

    (e)   If I think then I am

TRUTH VALUES FOR IMPLICATION

p	q	$p \Rightarrow q$
T	T	T
T	F	F
F	T	T
F	F	T

Consider the following propositions and the implication

p: You get an A on your maths test
q: Your mum buys you a pair of jeans
$p \Rightarrow q$: If you get an A on your maths test then your mum will buy you a pair of jeans.

p: You get an A on your maths test   T
q: Your mum buys you a pair of jeans   T
$p \Rightarrow q$: If you get an A on your maths test then your mum will buy you a pair of
            jeans.   T

The implication is true because you got the A and your mum kept her promise.

p: You get an A on your maths test   T
q: Your mum buys you a pair of jeans   F
$p \Rightarrow q$: If you get an A on your maths test then your mum will buy you a pair of
            jeans.   F
The implication is false because you got the A but your mum did not keep her promise.

p: You get an A on your maths test   F
q: Your mum buys you a pair of jeans   T
$p \Rightarrow q$: If you get an A on your maths test then your mum will buy you a pair of
            jeans.   T

The implication is true because even though you did not get an A there is no information given about what your mum will do if you didn't get an A. You may have only missed getting an A by a very small margin.

p: You get an A on your maths test   F
q: Your mum buys you a pair of jeans   F
$p \Rightarrow q$: If you get an A on your maths test then your mum will buy you a pair of
            jeans.   T

As mentioned previously there is no information given about what your mum will do if you do not get an A. In this example your mum has a choice of buying the jeans or not buying the jeans. In this case your mum decided not to buy the jeans but the important thing to remember is that in this case as in the previous case your mum has not lied.

IMPLICATION AND SETS ⇒ ⊂ (IS A SUBSET OF)

EXAMPLE

If

> x is a multiple of 4 greater than 1 but less than 20
>
> q: x is an even number greater than 1 but less than 20

Find $p \wedge q$ and $P \cap Q$

SOLUTION

Let   P be the truth set of p

and   Q be the truth set of q

Therefore   P = {4, 8, 12, 16}

Q = {2, 4, 6, 8, 10, 12, 14, 16, 18}

$p \Rightarrow q$:   If x is a multiple of 4 between 1 and 20 then it is an even number between 1 and 20

Therefore $p \wedge q$ is P ∩ Q.

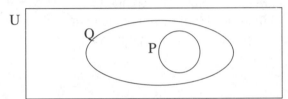

EXERCISE 6.19

(i)   Write the truth sets P and Q for the propositions p and q.

(ii)   Draw a Venn diagram showing the relationship between P and Q

(a) p: x is a square number between 10 and 50

      q: x is a number between 10 and 50 that ends in either 5,6 or 9

(b) p: Fuzzy is a bear

      q;   Fuzzy is a mammal

THE CONVERSE, INVERSE AND CONTRAPOSITIVE OF THE IMPLICATION P ⇒ Q

For the statements:

    p: A quadrilateral is a rectangle

    q: A quadrilateral is a parallelogram

The implication $p \Rightarrow q$ is:

If a quadrilateral is a rectangle then it is a parallelogram.

The converse p⟸q is:

If a quadrilateral is a parallelogram then it is a rectangle.
[Swap the antecedent and the consequent]

The inverse ¬p ⟹ ¬q is:

If a quadrilateral is not a rectangle then it is not a parallelogram.
[Negate both the antecedent and the consequent]

The contrapositive ¬p ⟸ ¬q is:

If a quadrilateral is not a parallelogram then it is not a rectangle.
[Swap the antecedent and the consequent and negate both]

[Note: If the implication is true then it does not mean that the converse, inverse or contrapositive will be true]

EXERCISE 6.20

Write the converse, inverse and contrapositive statements for the following implication statements.

  (a)   If a number is divisible by 10 then it ends in a zero
  (b)   I will earn more money only if I work hard
  (c)   The flowers will grow only if there is enough rain
  (d)   If a number is divisible by four then it is even
  (e)   If I think then I am

EQUIVALENCE 'IF AND ONLY IF', IFF, ⟺

If $p \Rightarrow q$ is true and its converse $p \Leftarrow q$ is true then $p \Leftrightarrow q$ is true

Equivalence is formed when the propositions are joined by the phrase 'if and only if' which has the abbreviation 'iff'.

The equivalence of two propositions p and q is denoted by $p \Leftrightarrow q$.

EXAMPLES

For p and q defined below, describe $p \Leftrightarrow q$.

  (i) p: We will play tennis
        q: It is fine
        $p \Leftrightarrow q$: We will play tennis **if and only if** it is fine

  (ii) p: Mary will pass maths
        q: The exam is easy
        $p \Leftrightarrow q$: Mary will pass maths **iff** the exam is easy

  (iii) p: Madrid is in Spain
        q: Spain is in Europe
        $p \Leftrightarrow q$: Madrid is in Spain **iff** Spain is in Europe

SOLUTIONS

(i) $p \Leftrightarrow q$: We will play tennis **if and only if** it is fine

(ii) $p \Leftrightarrow q$: Mary will pass maths **iff** the exam is easy

(iii) $p \Leftrightarrow q$: Madrid is in Spain **iff** Spain is in Europe

EXERCISE 6.21

Write equivalence statements for the following pairs of propositions.

(a) p: I will paint the house
       q: It is fine

(b) p: We will go to Disneyland
       q: There are exciting rides

(c) p: I will take my umbrella
       q: It is raining

(d) p: John will hit a home run
       q: The pitcher is useless

TRUTH VALUES FOR EQUIVALENCE

p	q	$p \Leftrightarrow q$
T	T	T
T	F	F
F	T	F
F	F	T

The truth value of equivalence is true only when all of the propositions have the same truth value.

Consider the following propositions and the implication.

p: I will buy you an ice-cream
q: You get an A on your maths exam
$p \Leftrightarrow q$: I will buy you an ice-cream if and only if you get an A on your maths exam

The implication statement is very clear that the only way you are going to get an ice-cream is if you get an A on your maths exam.

p:	I will buy you an ice-cream	F
q:	You get an A on your maths exam	T
$p \Leftrightarrow q$:	I will buy you an ice-cream if and only if you get an A on your maths exam	F

In this case you got an A but I didn't buy you an ice-cream so I lied therefore the equivalence statement is false.

p:	I will buy you an ice-cream	T
q:	You get an A on your maths exam	F
$p \Leftrightarrow q$:	I will buy you an ice-cream if and only if you get an A on your maths exam	F

In this case I bought you an ice-cream even though you didn't get an A which means I lied also so the equivalence statement is false.

EQUIVALENCE AND SETS $\Leftrightarrow$ = (EQUAL SETS)

EXAMPLE
If p: A polygon has 4 sides
q: A polygon is a quadrilateral
Show that P and Q are equal sets.

SOLUTION
$p \Rightarrow q$: If a polygon has 4 sides then it is a quadrilateral
$p \Leftarrow q$: If a polygon is a quadrilateral then it has 4 sides
$p \Leftrightarrow q$: A polygon has 4 sides iff it is a quadrilateral

The propositions p an q have the same truth sets. Therefore P and Q are equal sets.

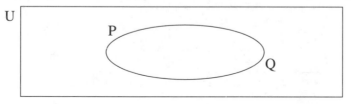

TRUTH TABLES
You have already seen tables being used to show the truth values of compound propositions formed by two propositions and a connective. This idea can be extended to find the truth values of compound propositions that are formed by a number of propositions and a number of connectives as well as negation.

EXAMPLE
Construct a truth table to show the truth values of the compound proposition:

$$\neg p \wedge q$$

SOLUTION

Step One: Identify the propositions and the connectives: p, q, $\neg p$, $\neg p \wedge q$

These become the headings of the truth table.

Step Two: Construct a table using the propositions above as headings and enter all combinations for the truth values of p and q.

p	q	$\neg p$	$\neg p \wedge q$
T	T		
T	F		
F	T		
F	F		

Step Three: Complete the truth table using the rules previously outlined.

p	q	$\neg p$	$\neg p \wedge q$
T	T	F	
T	F	F	
F	T	T	
F	F	T	

p	q	$\neg p$	$\neg p \wedge q$
T	T	F	F
T	F	F	F
F	T	T	T
F	F	T	F

Note the compound proposition is only true when the original proposition p is F and the proposition q is T.

EXERCISE 6.22

(i) Construct truth tables for each of the following compound propositions.

(ii) State the truth value of the original propositions when the truth value of the compound proposition is true.

(a) $\neg p \vee q$ (b) $\neg p \vee \neg q$ (c) $\neg p \wedge \neg q$

(d) $\neg p \Rightarrow q$ (e) $(p \vee \neg q) \Rightarrow q$ (f) $\neg p \Leftrightarrow q$

(g) $(p \vee \neg q) \Rightarrow (p \wedge \neg q)$ (h) $(\neg p \wedge q) \vee (q \wedge p)$ (i) $\neg(p \Rightarrow \neg q)$

(j) $(p \wedge q) \Rightarrow (p \vee q)$ (k) $\neg(p \wedge q) \vee \neg(q \Leftrightarrow p)$

TAUTOLOGIES AND CONTRADICTIONS

A tautology is a compound proposition that is always true regardless of the truth values of the individual propositions.

EXAMPLE

Show that the compound proposition p or not p is a tautology

SOLUTION

p	$\neg p$	$p \vee \neg p$
T	F	T
F	T	T

All the final entries are 'T' so the proposition is a tautology.

EXAMPLE

Show that the compound proposition 'If p, then p or q' is a tautology.

SOLUTION

p	q	$p \vee q$	$p \Rightarrow (p \vee q)$
T	T	T	T
T	F	T	T
F	T	T	T
F	F	F	T

All the final entries are 'T' so the proposition is a tautology.

A contradiction is a compound proposition which is always false regardless of the truth values of the individual propositions.

EXAMPLE

Show that the compound proposition 'p and not p' is a contradiction.

SOLUTION

p	$\neg p$	$p \wedge \neg p$
T	F	F
F	T	F

All the final entries are 'F' so the proposition is a contradiction.

TRUTH TABLES INVOLVING 3 PROPOSITIONS

Truth tables can be extended to deal with a number of propositions. 3 propositions is the limit required for this course.

The only difference in constructing truth tables for 3 propositions is that you must ensure that you have all the combinations of original truth values for *p*, *q* and *r*.

Your truth table for 3 propositions should start with the following three columns.

p	*q*	*r*
T	T	T
T	T	F
T	F	T
T	F	F
F	T	T
F	T	F
F	F	T
F	F	F

EXAMPLE

Construct a truth table to show all the truth values of the compound proposition:
$$(\neg p \vee q) \Rightarrow r$$

SOLUTION

p	*q*	*r*	$\neg p$	$\neg p \vee q$	$(\neg p \vee q) \Rightarrow r$
T	T	T	F	T	T
T	T	F	F	T	F
T	F	T	F	F	T
T	F	F	F	F	T
F	T	T	T	T	T
F	T	F	T	T	F
F	F	T	T	T	T
F	F	F	T	T	F

EXERCISE 6.22

(i) Construct truth tables for the following compound propositions.

(ii) State the truth value of the original propositions when the compound proposition is true.

(a) $(p \lor q) \Rightarrow r$

(b) $\neg p \lor \neg q \land r$

(c) $\neg p \land \neg q \land \neg r$

(d) $\neg p \Rightarrow (q \lor r)$

(e) $(p \lor \neg q) \Rightarrow r$

(f) $(\neg p \Leftrightarrow q) \lor r$

(g) $(p \lor \neg r) \Rightarrow (r \land \neg q)$

(h) $(\neg p \land q) \lor (q \land r)$

(i) $(p \land r) \Rightarrow (r \lor q)$

(k) $\neg (p \land q) \lor \neg (q \Leftrightarrow r)$

TESTING THE VALIDITY OF SIMPLE ARGUMENTS USING TRUTH TABLES

An argument is made up of one or more premises that lead to a conclusion. The premises and the conclusion are propositions. If the premises provide support for the conclusion then the argument is said to be valid. The conclusion of an argument can be identified as it is introduced by words such as therefore, hence, so, it follows.

EXAMPLE

Prove: If Fuzzy is a bear then Fuzzy is a mammal. Fuzzy is a bear. Therefore Fuzzy is a mammal.

SOLUTION

The premises are the propositions:

p: Fuzzy is a bear.

q: Fuzzy is a mammal.

The conclusion is the proposition: q: Fuzzy is a mammal.

The argument can be written in logical form in the following way.

- If Fuzzy is a bear then Fuzzy is a mammal. $p \Rightarrow q$

- Fuzzy is a bear p

- These two propositions combined $(p \Rightarrow q) \land p$

The premises logically imply the conclusion: $[(p \Rightarrow q) \land p] \Rightarrow q$

The argument is valid if the truth values of the logic statement form a tautology

p	q	$p \Rightarrow q$	$(p \Rightarrow q) \land p$	q	$[(p \Rightarrow q) \land p] \Rightarrow q$
T	T	T	T	T	T
T	F	F	F	F	T
F	T	T	F	T	T
F	F	T	F	F	T

Therefore the argument is valid because the compound proposition is a tautology.

EXAMPLE

Discuss the validity of the argument:

If Julia is sick she will not go to work. Julia is not sick. Therefore Julia will go to work.

SOLUTION

The premises are the propositions

p: Julia is sick

$\neg p$:   Julia will **not** go to work [Notice that $\neg$ is used because of 'not' in the proposition]

$\neg p$:   Julia is not sick

The conclusion is the proposition: q: Julia will go to work

The argument can be written in logical form in the following way.

- If Julia is sick then she will not go to work $p \Rightarrow \neg q$

- Julia is not sick $\neg p$

- These premises combined $(p \Rightarrow \neg q) \wedge \neg p$

The premises logically imply the conclusion: $[(p \Rightarrow \neg q) \wedge \neg p] \Rightarrow q$

p	q	$\neg q$	$p \Rightarrow \neg q$	$\neg p$	$(p \Rightarrow \neg q) \wedge \neg p$	q	$[(p \Rightarrow \neg q) \wedge \neg p] \Rightarrow q$
T	T	F	F	F	F	T	T
T	F	T	T	F	F	F	T
F	T	F	T	T	T	T	T
F	F	T	T	T	T	F	F

Since the compound proposition is not a tautology the argument in invalid.

EXERCISE 6.24

Express the following arguments symbolically and use truth tables to determine whether or not each argument is valid.

(a)   If it rains then the concert will be cancelled. If the concert is cancelled the money for the tickets will be refunded. It rains. Therefore the money for the tickets is refunded.

(b)   If Linda doesn't study then she will not pass her exam. Linda studies. Therefore Linda passes her exam.

(c)   If Hank is elected class captain then martin will be vice captain. If Julia is elected class captain then Hank will not be vice captain. Julia is not elected class captain. Therefore Hank is elected vice captain.

EXAMINATION STYLE QUESTIONS

1. Identify the individual propositions in each of the following statements and write the compound propositions in logical form.

    (a)   Today is not Tuesday.
    (b) x is either an even number or a prime number.
    (c)   Mary and John study French.
    (d)   If it is raining then the concert will be cancelled.
    (e)   Yoshi will go to the concert iff it is not raining.
    (f)   Birgit likes ice-cream and cake.
    (g)   Jessica will go to the concert if and only if Mary goes to the concert and it is not raining.
    (h)   If it is fine and the temperature is between 20°C and 30°C then Paul will play tennis.
    (i)   If I work hard then I will pass my exams
    (j)   If Bill wins this race then he will make the final.
    (k)   If Bill does not win this race then he will not make the final.

2. Given the propositions

    p: he eats too much
    q: he is healthy
    r: he is happy

    Write each of the following symbolic statements in verbal form.

    (a) $\neg p$ (b) $\neg p \wedge r$ (c) $q \vee r$
    (d) $p \Rightarrow \neg r$ (e) $(\neg p \wedge q) \Rightarrow r$ (f) $p \Leftrightarrow \neg r$
    (g) $p \vee q$ (h) $(\neg p \vee q) \Rightarrow r$ (i) $\neg p \Rightarrow (q \wedge r)$
    (j) $r \Leftrightarrow (\neg p \wedge q)$

3. Given the propositions

    p: x is a multiple of 3 between 0 and 40
    q: x is an even number between 0 and 40
    r: x is a factor of 36

    (a)   List the elements of the truth sets P, Q and R.

    (b)   For each of the following compound propositions
          (i)   Write in words
          (ii)   Construct a truth table to show the truth values
          (iii)   Draw a Venn diagram and shade the region that represents the truth set of the compound proposition
          (iv)   List the elements of the truth set of the compound propositions:
    (a) $\neg p$ (b) $p \wedge q$ (c) $p \wedge q \wedge r$
    (d) $p \vee q \vee r$ (e) $\neg p \wedge \neg q$ (f) $\neg p \wedge \neg q \wedge \neg r$
    (g) $\neg (p \wedge q \wedge r)$ (h) $\neg p \wedge (q \vee r)$

142

4. Construct truth tables for the following and state whether the compound proposition is a tautology, a contradiction or neither.

(a) $(p \wedge q) \vee (\neg p \wedge \neg q)$

(b) $\neg(p \vee q) \wedge p$

(c) $(p \vee q) \Rightarrow \neg(p \vee q)$

(d) $(p \Rightarrow q) \Leftrightarrow (p \wedge \neg q)$

(e) $\neg p \Rightarrow (p \Rightarrow q)$

(f) $[p \wedge (p \Rightarrow q)] \Rightarrow p$

(g) $(p \Rightarrow q) \Leftrightarrow (p \wedge \neg q)$

(h) $\neg(p \wedge q) \vee (p \vee q)$

5. Express the following arguments in logical form then use a truth table to determine whether or not the argument is valid.

(a) If I study then I will pass my exams. I study. Therefore I pass my exams.

(b) If I study then I will pass my exams. If I pass my exams I will go to university. I study. Therefore I go to university.

(c) If Fuzzy is a bear then Fuzzy is a mammal. Fuzzy is a mammal. Therefore Fuzzy is a bear.

(d) I study hard iff I go to university. I go to university. Therefore I study hard.

(e) All accountants are boring people. Mary is not an accountant. Therefore Mary is not boring.

SELF ASSESSMENT TEST (30 MINUTES)

1.   If A = {prime numbers} and B = {even numbers}, list A∩B.   [1 mark]

2.   State whether each of the following is a proposition.

    (a)   The moon is made of blue cheese
    (b)   Can you see the moon?
    (c)   Look at the moon
    (d)   What is the time?
    (e)   Yesterday was Tuesday.
    (f)   Margaret is 17   [6 marks]

3.   A group of 25 teenagers were asked what type of music they liked out of Rock, popular music and heavy metal.

17 liked Rock
13 liked heavy metal
2 liked popular music only
7 liked popular music and heavy metal
3 liked all three types of music
the same number of teenagers liked rock and popular music as liked rock and heavy metal.
Draw a Venn diagram to show the number of teenagers in each region.

[6 marks]

4.   Write the implication, the converse, the inverse and the contrapositive of the following pairs of propositions in both words and logical form.

    (a) p: Fuzzy is a bear
        q: Fuzzy is cute

    (b) p: Mary lives in Spain
        q: Mary loves fish

    (c) p: It is fine
        q: We will go to the concert

    (d) p: I work hard
        q: I pay taxes

    (e) p: John loves fishing
        q: John lives by the sea

[10 marks]

SOLUTION OF TRIANGLES

7

Key Formulae

- $\dfrac{a}{\sin A} = \dfrac{b}{\sin B} = \dfrac{c}{\sin C}$

- $a^2 = b^2 + c^2 - 2bc\cos A$

7.1 THE TRIGONOMETRIC RATIOS

Basic trigonometry depends on similar triangles. The following diagram shows two right angled triangles.

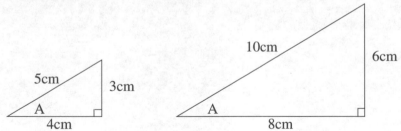

Because the triangles are similar (corresponding sides are in the ratio 1:2) the two triangles will have the same angles. In the case of the '3,4,5' triangle shown, the angle A is about 37°. One of the consequences of the similarity of these two triangles (and all other right angled triangles that contain 37°) is that the ratios of pairs of sides within the same triangle will all be the same. If, for example, we look at the ratio of the vertical side (the side opposite angle A) to the hypotenuse of the triangle, the result is 3:5 or $\frac{3}{5} = 0.6$ for the smaller triangle and 6:10 or $\frac{6}{10} = 0.6$ for the larger. The same result will be obtained for all right angled triangles that contain angle A and this ratio is known as the **sine** of angle A and can be found using a calculator. The ratios between the lengths of the sides of a right angled triangle are known as the **trigonometric ratios**.

The most commonly used method of remembering the trigonometric ratios is to label the sides of the triangle in the following way.

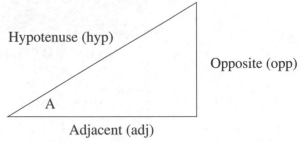

The **hypotenuse** is the side opposite the right angle. In all basic trigonometric problems one of the other angles will be important (either it is known or needs to be found). The side opposite this angle is known as the **opposite** side. The third side that is next to this angle is known as the **adjacent** side. The main trigonometric functions are now defined as follows:

$$\sin\theta = \frac{\text{opp}}{\text{hyp}} \qquad \cos\theta = \frac{\text{adj}}{\text{hyp}} \qquad \tan\theta = \frac{\text{opp}}{\text{adj}}$$

These definitions are the basis for solving right angled triangles and have a number of applications including navigation and surveying.

EXAMPLES

Find the values of *x* and *y* in these triangles (correct to three significant figures):

(i)

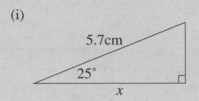

5.7cm

25°

x

(ii)

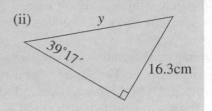

y

39°17'

16.3cm

SOLUTIONS

(i)   The sides are labelled:

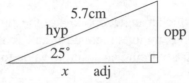

5.7cm

hyp

opp

25°

x   adj

The sides involved in this calculation are the adjacent and hypotenuse because we know the hypotenuse and want to find the adjacent side. This means that the

appropriate ratio is $\cos\theta = \dfrac{\text{adj}}{\text{hyp}}$. The solution steps are to substitute the

appropriate values and then solve for *x*.

$$\cos\theta = \frac{\text{adj}}{\text{hyp}}$$

$$\cos 25° = \frac{x}{5.7}$$

$$x = 5.7 \times \cos 25°$$

$$= 5.17 \text{ cm to 3S.F.}$$

(ii)   This time the important sides are the opposite and hypotenuse. The solution is:

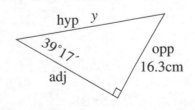

hyp *y*

39°17'

adj

opp

16.3cm

$$\sin\theta = \frac{\text{opp}}{\text{hyp}}$$

$$\sin 39°17' = \frac{16.3}{y}$$

$$y \times \sin 39°17' = 16.3$$

$$y = \frac{16.3}{\sin 39°17'}$$

$$= 25.7 \text{ cm to 3S.F.}$$

USING A CALCULATOR

Most models of scientific calculator can accept angles in degrees, minutes and seconds. The keying sequence to solve the second problem would probably be 16.3÷39[°′″]17[sin]= or 16.3÷[sin]39[°′″]17= if using a direct algebraic logic or DAL calculator. Remember to make sure that the calculator is in degree mode.

Graphic calculators can also handle the degree, minute, second angle format. The TI82/83 calculators accept angle inputs using the 2nd ANGLE menu. Option 1 allows entry of angles in degrees irrespective of the MODE setting of the calculator. Option 2 allows the entry of degrees, minute, seconds.

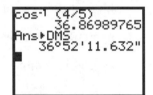

The problem would be solved using the keying sequence 16.3÷[sin]39 2nd ANGLE 2 17 2nd ANGLE 2 ENTER.

When using a calculator to find an angle, option 4 of the 2nd ANGLE menu will allow you to display an answer in degree, minute, second format. To return to the problem with which this section started, we will find an accurate value for the smallest angle in the '3,4,5' right angled triangle.

Any of the three trigonometric ratios will do, but when finding angles, it is generally best to use the cosine ratio. The reason for this should become apparent as this chapter progresses.

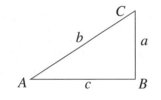

$\cos\theta = \dfrac{4}{5} \Rightarrow \theta \approx 36°52'12''$ rounded to the nearest second.

EXERCISE 7.1

1. The parts of this question refer to the triangle shown. Complete the blank spaces in this table, giving lengths correct to three significant figures and angles correct to the nearest degree.

	a cm	b cm	c cm	A	B	C
1			1.6		90°	23°
2		98.3			90°	34°
3			33.9		90°	46°
4		30.7			90°	87°
5	2.3				90°	33°
6		77			90°	51°
7	44.4		68.4		90°	57°
8			12.7	13°	90°	
9		94.4		52°	90°	

148

	a cm	b cm	c cm	A	B	C
10	71.8		64.6	48°	90°	
11		34.1		43°	90°	
12			2.3	87°	90°	
13	71.5			63°	90°	
14	33.5		6.5		90°	
15	6.1	7.2			90°	
16		30	7.3		90°	
17	29.0		2.0		90°	
18	34.5	88.2			90°	
19	24.0	29.7			90°	
20		46.2			90°	27°
21	59.6		41.8		90°	35°
22		6.8			90°	37°
23			14.9	41°	90°	49°
24			16.1	41°	90°	49°
25			33.3	68°	90°	22°

2. A hiker walks for 5km on a bearing of 053° true (north 53° east). She then turns and walks for another 3km on a bearing of 107° true (east 17° south).

(i) Find the distance that the hiker travels north/south and the distance that she travels east/west on the first part of her hike.

(ii) Find the distance that the hiker travels north/south and the distance that she travels east/west on the second part of her hike.

(iii) Hence find the total distance that the hiker travels north/south and the distance that she travels east/west on her hike.

(iv) If the hiker intends to return directly to the point at which she started her hike, on what bearing should she walk and how far will she have to walk?

3. A surveying team are trying to find the height of a hill. They take a 'sight' on the top of the hill and find that the angle of elevation is 23°27′. They move a distance of 250 metres on level ground directly away from the hill and take a second 'sight'. From this point, the angle of elevation is 19°46′.

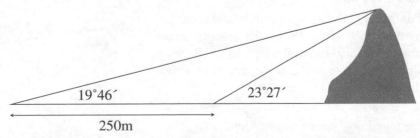

Find the height of the hill, correct to the nearest metre.

7.2 THE SINE RULE

The previous section dealt only with the trigonometry of right angled triangles. The trigonometric ratios can be used to solve non-right angled triangles. There are two main methods for solving non-right angled triangles, the sine rule and the cosine rule. Both are usually stated using a standard labelling of the triangle. This uses capital letters to label the vertices and the corresponding small letters to label the sides opposite these vertices.

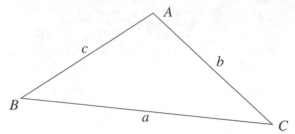

Using this labelling of a triangle, the sine rule can be stated as:

$$\frac{a}{\sin A} = \frac{b}{\sin B} = \frac{c}{\sin C} \qquad \text{or} \qquad \frac{\sin A}{a} = \frac{\sin B}{b} = \frac{\sin C}{c}$$

For a proof of the sine rule, refer to the end of the chapter.
Note that the sine rule can only be used in a triangle in which an angle and the side **opposite** that angle are known.

EXAMPLES

Solve the following triangles giving the lengths of the sides in centimetres, correct to one decimal place and angles correct to the nearest degree.

(i)

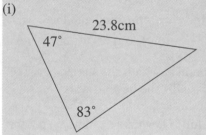

(ii)

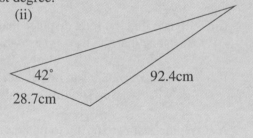

SOLUTIONS

(i) Firstly, label the triangle using the standard method of lettering. 'Solve the triangle' means find all the angles and the lengths of all the sides. Since two of the angles are known, the third is:

$C = 180° - 47° - 83° = 50°$. The lengths of the remaining sides must be found using the known pairing of side and angle, b and B.

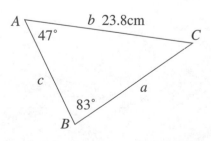

$$\frac{a}{\sin A} = \frac{b}{\sin B}$$

$$\frac{a}{\sin 47°} = \frac{23.8}{\sin 83°}$$

$$a = \frac{23.8 \times \sin 47°}{\sin 83°}$$

$$= 17.5 \text{ cm (correct to 1 dec. pl.)}$$

Similarly, the remaining side can be calculated:

$$\frac{c}{\sin C} = \frac{b}{\sin B}$$

$$\frac{c}{\sin 50°} = \frac{23.8}{\sin 83°}$$

$$a = \frac{23.8 \times \sin 50°}{\sin 83°}$$

$$= 18.4 \text{ cm (correct to 1 dec. pl.)}$$

(ii) This triangle is different from the previous example in that only one angle is known. It remains the case that a pair of angle and opposite side are known and that the sine rule can be used. The angle A must be found first.

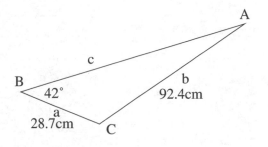

$$\frac{\sin A}{a} = \frac{\sin B}{b}$$

$$\frac{\sin A}{28.7} = \frac{\sin 42°}{92.4}$$

$$\sin A = \frac{28.7 \times \sin 42°}{92.4}$$

$$= 0.207836$$

$$A = \sin^{-1} 0.207836$$

$$= 11.9956°$$

$$= 11°59'44''$$

The answer to the first part of the question is 12° correct to the nearest degree. It is important, however, to carry a much more accurate version of this angle through to subsequent parts of the calculation. This is best done using the calculator memory.

The third angle can be found because the sum of the three angles is 180°.
$$C = 180° - 12° - 42° = 126°$$

An accurate version of this angle must also be carried to the next part of the calculation. Graphic calculators have multiple memories labelled A, B, C etc. and students are advised to use these in such calculations.

The remaining side is:

$$\frac{c}{\sin 126°} = \frac{28.7}{\sin 12°}$$

$$c = \frac{28.7 \sin 126°}{\sin 12°}$$

$$= 111.7 \text{ cm to 1 dec. pl.}$$

EXERCISE 7.2

Use the sine rule to complete the following table, which refers to the standard labelling of a triangle.

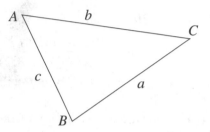

	a cm	b cm	c cm	A	B	C
1			48.2		29°	141°
2		1.2		74°	25°	
3			11.3	60°		117°
4			51.7	38°		93°
5	18.5	11.4		68°		
6	14.6	15.0			84°	
7		7.3			16°	85°
8			28.5	39°		124°
9	0.8		0.8	82°		
10			33.3	36°		135°
11	16.4			52°	84°	
12			64.3		24°	145°
13	30.9	27.7		75°		
14			59.1	29°		102°
15		9.8	7.9		67°	
16			54.2	16°		136°
17	14.8		27.2			67°
18			10.9		3°	125°
19			17.0		15°	140°
20			40.1	30°		129°

THE AMBIGUOUS CASE

The sine rule can result in non-unique (i.e. more than one) solutions for a given set of data.

EXAMPLE

Draw diagrams showing the triangles in which AC = 17cm, BC = 9cm and A = 29° and solve these triangles.

SOLUTION

Applying the sine rule to the triangle gives:

$$\frac{\sin B}{17} = \frac{\sin 29°}{9}$$

$$\sin B = \frac{17 \times \sin 29°}{9}$$

$$= 0.91575$$

$$B = 66°$$

$$C = 180° - 29° - 66° = 85°$$

$$\frac{c}{\sin 85°} = \frac{9}{\sin 29°}$$

$$c = 18.5cm$$

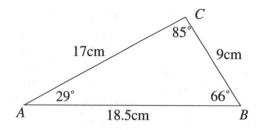

There is, however, a second solution that results from drawing an isosceles triangle BCE. This creates the triangle AEC which also fits the data. The third angle of this triangle is 37° and the third side is:

$$\frac{AE}{\sin 37°} = \frac{9}{\sin 29°}$$

$$AE = 11.2cm$$

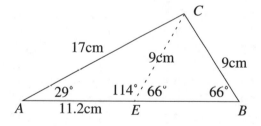

The original data is ambiguous in the sense that there are two triangles that are consistent with it.

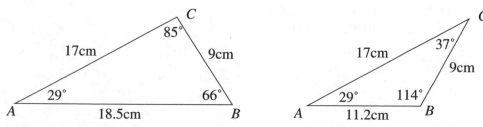

You should also notice that the two angles in the solution are 66° and 114° and that sin66° = sin114°. This point will be developed later in this chapter.

EXERCISE 7.3

Find the two solutions to these triangles which are defined using the standard labelling:

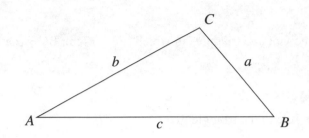

	a cm	b cm	A
1.	7.4	18.1	20°
2.	13.3	19.5	14°
3.	13.5	17	28°
4.	10.2	17	15°
5.	7.4	15.2	20°
6.	10.7	14.1	26°
7.	11.5	12.6	17°
8.	8.3	13.7	24°
9.	13.7	17.8	14°
10.	13.4	17.8	28°
11.	12.1	16.8	23°
12.	12	14.5	21°
13.	12.1	19.2	16°
14.	7.2	13.1	15°
15.	12.2	17.7	30°
16.	9.2	20.9	14°
17.	10.5	13.3	20°
18.	9.2	19.2	15°
19.	7.2	13.3	19°
20.	13.5	20.4	31°
21.	10.8	20.8	26°
22.	13	12.2	19°
23.	13.6	20.4	36°
24.	11.4	12.5	16°
25.	8	16.8	10°

7. 3 THE COSINE RULE

The cosine rule is usually applied to triangles in which we do not know a pairing of an angle and the opposite side. It is generally harder to use and should not be used if simple trigonometry or the sine rule can be used instead.

The cosine rule, with the standard labelling of the triangle has three versions:

$$a^2 = b^2 + c^2 - 2bc\cos A$$

$$b^2 = a^2 + c^2 - 2ac\cos B$$

$$c^2 = a^2 + b^2 - 2ab\cos C$$

The cosine rule can be remembered as a version of Pythagoras's Theorem with a correction factor.

EXAMPLES

Solve the following triangles giving the lengths of the sides in centimetres, correct to one decimal place and angles correct to the nearest degree:

(i)   (ii)

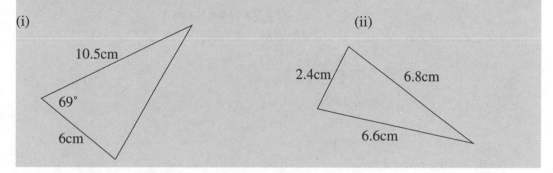

SOLUTIONS

(i)   The data does not include an angle and the opposite side so the sine rule cannot be used. The first step, as with the sine rule, is to label the sides of the triangle. Once the triangle has been labelled, the correct version of the cosine rule must be chosen. In this case, the solution is:

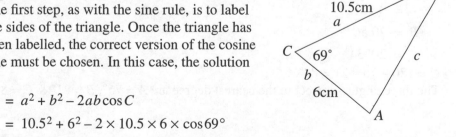

$$c^2 = a^2 + b^2 - 2ab\cos C$$

$$c^2 = 10.5^2 + 6^2 - 2 \times 10.5 \times 6 \times \cos 69°$$

$$= 101.0956$$

$$a = 10.1\text{cm}$$

The remaining angles can be calculated using the sine rule. Again, it is important to carry a high accuracy for the value of c to the remaining problem:

$$\frac{\sin B}{b} = \frac{\sin C}{c}$$

$$\sin B = \frac{6 \times \sin 69°}{10.0546}$$

$$= 0.5571$$

$$B = 34°$$

Finally, $A = 180° - 34° - 69° = 77°$

(ii)   In this case, there are no angles given. The cosine rule can be used to solve this problem as follows:

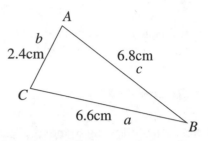

$$a^2 = b^2 + c^2 - 2bc\cos A$$

$$6.6^2 = 2.4^2 + 6.8^2 - 2 \times 2.4 \times 6.8 \times \cos A$$

$$2 \times 2.4 \times 6.8 \times \cos A = 2.4^2 + 6.8^2 - 6.6^2$$

$$\cos A = \frac{2.4^2 + 6.8^2 - 6.6^2}{2 \times 2.4 \times 6.8}$$

$$= 0.25858$$

$$A = 75.014°$$

$$= 75°1'$$

Next, use the sine rule:

$$\frac{\sin B}{b} = \frac{\sin A}{a}$$

$$\sin B = \frac{2.4 \times \sin 75}{6.6}$$

$$= 0.35127$$

$$B = 20.56°$$

$$= 20°34'$$

$C = 180 - 75 - 21 = 84°$

The three angles, correct to the nearest degree are $A = 75°$, $B = 21°$ & $C = 84°$.

EXERCISE 7.4

	a cm	b cm	c cm	A	B	C
1	13.5		16.7		36°	
2	8.9	10.8				101°
3	22.8		12.8		87°	
4	21.1	4.4				83°
5		10.6	15.1	74°		
6		13.6	20.3	20°		
7	9.2		13.2		46°	
8	23.4	62.5				69°
9		9.6	15.7	41°		
10	21.7	36.0	36.2			
11	7.6	3.4	9.4			
12	7.2	15.2	14.3			
13	9.1		15.8		52°	
14	14.9	11.2	16.2	63°	42°	75°
15	2.0	0.7	2.5			
16	7.6	3.7	9.0			
17	18.5	9.8	24.1			
18	20.7	16.3	13.6			
19		22.4	29.9	28°		
20	7.0		9.9		42°	
21	21.8	20.8	23.8			
22	1.1		1.3		89°	
23		1.2	0.4	85°		
24	23.7	27.2				71°
25	3.4	4.6	5.2			

7.4 APPLICATIONS

Trigonometry can be applied to a variety of practical problems.

EXAMPLES

1. The diagram shows a building frame used to support a house roof. The dimension shown is in metres.
Find the lengths of the other two sides, correct to three significant figures.

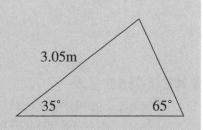

2. A yacht starts from a harbour and sails for a distance of 11km in a straight line. The yacht then makes a turn to port (left) of 38° and sails for 7km in a straight line in this new direction until it arrives at a small island. Draw a diagram that shows the path taken by the yacht and calculate the distance from the harbour to the island.

SOLUTIONS

1. As with skills problems, the first step is to label the sides.

$A = 180° - 35° - 65° = 80°$

$$\frac{b}{\sin 35°} = \frac{3.05}{\sin 65°}$$

$$b = \frac{3.05 \times \sin 35°}{\sin 65°}$$

$$= 1.93\,\text{m}$$

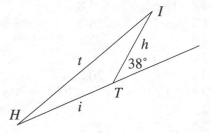

$$\frac{a}{\sin 80°} = \frac{3.05}{\sin 65°}$$

$$b = \frac{3.05 \times \sin 80°}{\sin 65°}$$

$$= 3.31\,\text{m}$$

2. The question does not give the bearing of the first leg of the trip so the diagram can show this in any direction. H is the harbour, I the island and T the point where the yacht makes its turn.

The angle in the triangle at T is $180° - 38° = 142°$. The problem does not contain an angle and the opposite side and so must be solved using the cosine rule.

$$t^2 = h^2 + i^2 - 2hi\cos T$$

$$= 7^2 + 11^2 - 2 \times 7 \times 11 \times \cos 142°$$

$$= 291.354$$

$$t = 17.1\,\text{km}$$

EXERCISE 7.5

1. The diagram shows a triangular building plot. The distances are given in metres. Find the length of the two remaining sides of the plot giving your answers correct to the nearest hundredth of a metre.

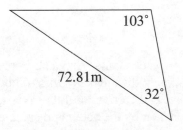

2. Xiang is standing on level ground. Directly in front of him and 32 metres away is a flagpole. If Xiang turns 61° to his right, he sees a post box 26.8 metres in front of him. Find the distance between the flagpole and the post box.

3. A triangular metal brace is part of the structure of a bridge. The lengths of the three parts are shown in metres. Find the angles of the brace.

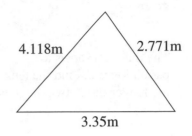

4.118m   2.771m

3.35m

4. Find the smallest angle in the triangle whose sides have length 35.6cm, 58.43cm and 52.23cm.

5. Ayton is directly north of Byford. A third town, Canfield, is 9.93km from Ayton on a bearing of 128° true. The distance from Byford to Canfield is 16.49km. Find the bearing of Canfield from Byford.

6. A parallelogram has sides of length 21.90cm and 95.18cm. The angle between these sides is 121°. Find the length of the long diagonal of the parallelogram.

7. A town clock has 'hands' that are of length 62cm and 85cm.

(i) Find the angle between the hands at half past ten.

(ii) Find the distance between the tips of the hands at half past ten.

8. A shop sign is to be made in the shape of a triangle. The lengths of the edges (in metres) are shown. Find the angles at the vertices of the sign.

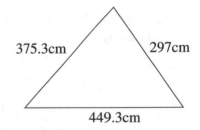

375.3cm   297cm

449.3cm

9. An aircraft takes off from an airstrip and then flies for 16.2 km on a bearing of 066° true. The pilot then makes a left turn of 88° and flies for a further 39.51km on this course before deciding to return to the airstrip.

(i) Through what angle must the pilot turn to return to the airstrip?

(ii) How far will the pilot have to fly to return to the airstrip?

10. A golfer hits two shots from the tee to the green.

How far is the tee from the green?

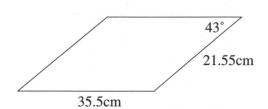

11. The diagram shows a parallelogram. Find the length of the longer of the two diagonals.

43°

21.55cm

35.5cm

12. A triangle has angles 64°, 15° and 101°. The shortest side is 49 metres long. What is the length of the longest side?

13. The diagram shows a part of the support structure for a tower. The main parts are two identical triangles, ABC and ADE. AC = DE = 27.4cm and BC = AE = 23.91cm The angles ACB and AED are 58°.

Find the distance BD.

14. The diagram shows a design for the frame for a piece of jewellery. The frame is made of wire.

Find the length of wire needed to make the frame.

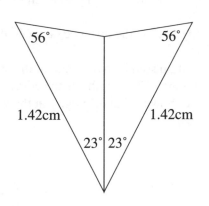

15. A triangular cross-country running track begins with the runners running north for 2050 metres. The runners then turn right and run for 5341 metres on a bearing of 083° true. Finally, the runners make a turn to the right and run directly back to the starting point.
 (i) Find the length of the final leg of the run.
 (ii) Find the total distance of the run.
 (iii) What is the angle through which the runners must turn to start the final leg of the race?
 (iv) Find the bearing that the runner must take on the final leg of the race.

EXAMINATION STYLE QUESTIONS

1. The angle of elevation of the top of a cliff from the deck of a ship at sea level is 2°. The ship is 2.5 km out to sea,
   (a) (i) Illustrate this information on the diagram.
   (ii) Find the height of the cliff.

   A lighthouse stands at the edge of the cliff top.
   (b) Find the angle of depression from the light house to the ship if the lighthouse is 40 m tall.

2. A plane is flying at 300 m above ground level. At 12 noon the angle of elevation from a point X was 10°. At 12:05 pm, its angle of elevation was 1°. Assuming that the plane remains at a constant level.
   (a) Draw a diagram illustrating this information.
   (b) How far (horizontally) is the plane from point X at noon?
   (c) How far has it travelled when its angle of elevation is 1°?
   (d) How fast is the plane flying at?

3. (a) A man standing 6 metres away from a lamp post casts a shadow of 10 metres on a horizontal ground. The angle of elevation from the tip of the shadow to the lamp light is 12°. How high is the lamp light?
   (b) If the shadow is cast onto a road sloping at 30° upwards, how long would the shadow be if the man is standing at the foot of the sloping road and 6m from the lamp post?

4. At noon the angle of elevation of the sun is 72° and is such that a three metre wall AC, facing the sun, is just in the shadow due to the overhang AB.
   The angle that the overhang makes with the vertical wall is 50°
   (a) Illustrate this information on the diagram shown.
   (b) Find the length of the overhang.
   At 4 pm the angle of elevation of the sun is 40° and the shadow due to the overhang just reaches the base of the window.
   (c) How far from the ground is the window?s

   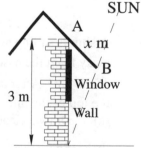

5. In a triangle ABC, $a = 75$, $b = 80$ and angle BAC is 60°.
   (a) Draw two triangles that satisfy these conditions.
   (b) Find the two possible magnitudes of angle ABC.
   (c) Find the two possible values of c.

SELF ASSESSMENT TEST (45 MINUTES)

1. Find the value of x, correct to three significant figures.

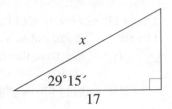

[2 marks]

2. Find the two possible values of a, correct to four significant figures.

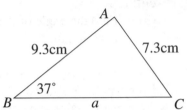

[5 marks]

3. Find the three angles of a triangle with sides of length 23.06cms, 20.25cm & 27.63cm.

[4 marks]

4. Find the area of the unit regular hexagon shown.

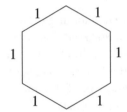

[3 marks]

5. A ship is sailing away from a cliff. When the ship first starts its engines it is x km away from the base of the cliff and makes an angle of elevation of $\alpha°$ with the top of the cliff. After travelling a distance of d km, the ship makes an angle of $\beta°$ with the top of the hill.

(a) Draw a clear diagram showing this situation.

(b) Show that $x = \dfrac{d\tan\beta}{\tan\alpha - \tan\beta}$.

[7 marks]

6. A tree is growing at the foot of a hill which is sloping at an angle of 10° to the horizontal. From a point 30 m up the hill the tree subtends an angle of 40°. Find the height of the tree.

[5 marks]

COORDINATE GEOMETRY

8

Key Formulae

- $d = \sqrt{(x_2 - x_1)^2 + (y_2 - y_1)^2}$
- $\left(\dfrac{x_1 + x_2}{2}, \dfrac{y_1 + y_2}{2} \right)$
- $y = mx + c, \; ax + by + c = 0$
- $m_1 \times m_2 = -1$

8.1 COORDINATE GEOMETRY

TWO DIMENSIONAL COORDINATE GEOMETRY

We will discuss geometry in two dimensions, by making reference to the Cartesian plane, i.e., the X–Y plane. In doing so, much of what follows will be based on two arbitrary points (x_1, y_1) and (x_2, y_2) that lie somewhere on this plane. We now describe this plane.

A Cartesian plane is made up of a two dimensional (flat) surface that is divided into four quadrants. These quadrant are the result of the plane being divided by two straight lines intersecting at right angles and meeting at a point called the origin, O. The horizontal axis is labelled as the x–axis and the vertical axis as the y–axis (although other labels can also be used).

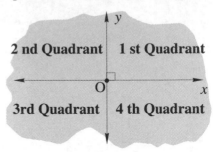

DISTANCE BETWEEN TWO POINTS

The distance between two points on a plane is given by

$$d = \sqrt{(x_2 - x_1)^2 + (y_2 - y_1)^2}$$

This formula can easily be derived by using Pythagoras' Theorem:

Let the two points be $P(x_1, y_1)$ and $Q(x_2, y_2)$.
Constructing a right–angled triangle (as shown) we can apply Pythagoras' formula ($a^2 = b^2 + c^2$) and obtain

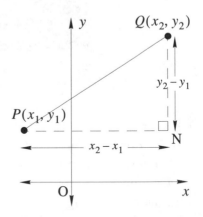

$$PQ^2 = PN^2 + QN^2$$
$$= (x_2 - x_1)^2 + (y_2 - y_1)^2$$
$$\therefore PQ = \sqrt{(x_2 - x_1)^2 + (y_2 - y_1)^2}$$

EXAMPLE

Find the distances between these pairs of points   (a) (2, 4) & (5, 8)
(b) (–2, 5) & (–4, –6)

SOLUTION

We solve these problems by first making use of Pythagoras' Theorem and then using the distance between two points formula:

(a) First we sketch a diagram to illustrate this information:

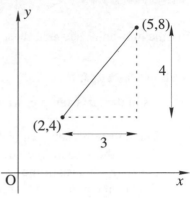

The **vertical distance** between the points is
$$8 - 4 = 4 \text{ units}$$
and the **horizontal distance** is
$$5 - 2 = 3 \text{ units.}$$
The distance between the points is now found using the theorem of Pythagoras:
$$d = \sqrt{3^2 + 4^2} = \sqrt{25} = 5.$$

The distance is measured in terms of the scales used by the axes.

Using the formula $d = \sqrt{(x_1 - x_2)^2 + (y_1 - y_2)^2}$ with $x_1 = 2$, $x_2 = 5$ and

$y_1 = 4$, $y_2 = 8$, ,we have that $d = \sqrt{(5-2)^2 + (8-4)^2} = \sqrt{3^2 + 4^2} = \sqrt{25} = 5$

(b) The **vertical distance** between the points is
$$5 - (-6) = 11 \text{ units}$$
and the **horizontal distance** is
$$(-2) - (-4) = 2 \text{ units.}$$

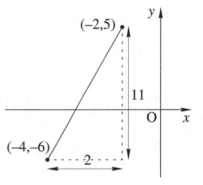

Using Pythagoras' Theorem, the distance between the points is:
$$d = \sqrt{2^2 + 11^2} = \sqrt{125} \approx 11.18.$$

Using the formula $d = \sqrt{(x_1 - x_2)^2 + (y_1 - y_2)^2}$ with $x_1 = -4$, $x_2 = -2$ and

$y_1 = -6$, $y_2 = 5$, ,we have that $d = \sqrt{((-2)-(-4))^2 + (5-(-6))^2} = \sqrt{2^2 + 11^2}$
$$= \sqrt{125}$$
$$\approx 11.18$$

MID–POINT BETWEEN TWO POINTS

The mid–point between two points has coordinates that are mid–way between the coordinates of the two points. That is, the coordinates of the mid–point, (x, y) of the line segment $\overline{AB}$, joining the two points $A(x_1, y_1)$ and $B(x_2, y_2)$ are given by

$$x = \frac{x_1 + x_2}{2}, y = \frac{y_1 + y_2}{2}$$

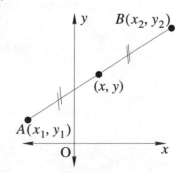

EXAMPLES

Find the mid-point between these pairs of points: (a)   (3,4) & (7,10)
                                                    (b)   (−3,7) & (5,−2)

SOLUTIONS

(a)   As in the last example, we illustrate the information on the Cartesian plane:

The mid-point between (3,4) & (7,10) is found by
finding the x-coordinate that is mid-way between
the x-coordinates of the two points.
That is, the point that is mid-way between 3 & 7.

This is given by $\dfrac{3+7}{2} = 5$.

The y-coordinate of the mid-point is mid-way

between 4 & 10. Which is given by $\dfrac{4+10}{2} = 7$.

Therefore, the mid-point is (5,7)

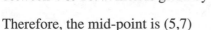

Using the mid–point formula: $\left(\dfrac{x_1+x_2}{2}, \dfrac{y_1+y_2}{2}\right)$ with $x_1 = 3$, $x_2 = 7$ and

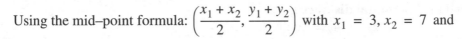

$y_1 = 4$, $y_2 = 10$, we have that the mid–point, is given by $\left(\dfrac{3+7}{2}, \dfrac{4+10}{2}\right) = (5, 7)$.

(b)

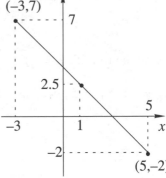

The x-coordinate of the mid-point is mid-way between (−3,7)

$-3\ \&\ 5\ \dfrac{-3+5}{2} = 1$.

The y-coordinate of the mid-point is mid-way between

$7\ \&\ -2\ \dfrac{7+(-2)}{2} = 2.5$.

Therefore, the mid-point is (1,2.5)

Using the mid–point formula: $\left(\dfrac{x_1+x_2}{2}, \dfrac{y_1+y_2}{2}\right)$ with $x_1 = -3$, $x_2 = 5$ and

$y_1 = 7$, $y_2 = -2$, we have that the mid–point, is given by $\left(\dfrac{-3+5}{2}, \dfrac{7+(-2)}{2}\right)$

$= (1, 2.5)$.

EXERCISE 8.1

1. Find the distances between these pairs of points, giving exact answers:

(i)	(2,4) & (6,9)	(ii)	(–8,–3) & (–2,3)	(iii)	(–7,6) & (8,6)
(iv)	(3,8) & (–2,–7)	(v)	(1,–1) & (8,5)	(vi)	(–5,0) & (8,2)
(vii)	(–4,6) & (0,1)	(viii)	(8,–6) & (0,–1)	(ix)	(–9,6) & (6,5)
(x)	(4,–1) & (–5,4)	(xi)	(–7,0) & (7,–3)	(xii)	(–9,6) & (–3,–6)
(xiii)	(–9,–7) & (7,5)	(xiv)	(6,7) & (–6,6)	(xv)	(–7,0) & (–3,0)

2. Find the mid-point of the line segments joining these pairs of points:

(i)	(–7,0) & (–3,0)	(ii)	(6,7) & (–6,6)	(iii)	(–9,–7) & (7,5)
(iv)	(–7,–7) & (2,–4)	(v)	(–7,6) & (–4,–5)	(vi)	(1,–1) & (4,3)
(vii)	(–9,2) & (4,–9)	(viii)	(3,5) & (5,0)	(ix)	(–6,8) & (3,0)
(x)	(–2,6) & (6,3)	(xi)	(9,1) & (8,9)	(xii)	(–6,3) & (4,4)
(xiii)	(4,–1) & (–5,4)	(xiv)	(–9,6) & (–3,–6)	(xv)	(3,8) & (–2,–7)

8.2 LINEAR EQUATIONS & GRAPHS

Any equation that relates two variables can be represented on a cartesian graph. It is often the case that the variables are x and y, though this is a matter of tradition rather than necessity. Other letters are often used, particularly when using computers. If the equation is simple and contains only multiples of the variables, the relation is said to be linear.

Equations such as: $y = 2x + 1, 2x - 5y = 7, 4s - t = 6t$ are all examples of linear relations of this type. By contrast, equations such as $y = \dfrac{2}{x} + 4, y = 4x^3 - 1, s = \cos t$ are all examples of non-linear relations which will be considered in later chapters.

The term 'linear' refers to the form that these relations take when they are shown on a casrtesian graph.

EXAMPLE

Make tables for the following relations and hence show each as a cartesian graph.

(i) $y = 2x + 1$ (ii) $x + y = 2$ (iii) $\dfrac{2t}{3} - s = 4$

SOLUTION

(i) An equation of this type in which one of the variables is the subject can be tabulated by choosing values of x and using the rule to calculate the corresponding values of y. Such a relation is sometimes called 'explicit'. On this occasion, there are no instructions as to what values of x are allowed, so any values can be chosen:

If $x = 5$ then $y = 2 \times 5 + 1 = 11$ and if $x = -4, y = 2 \times -4 + 1 = -8 + 1 = -7$.

A table of values for this relation could be:

x	−1	−0.5	0	0.5	1	1.5
y	−1	0	1	2	3	4

These table entries can be converted to number pairs: $(-1,-1)$, $(0,1)$, $(1,3)$, $(2,5)$ etc. Next, these number pairs can be plotted onto a cartesian graph:

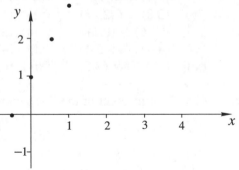

The points of the graph lie on a straight line, hence the description, 'linear'. It should also be noted that only a sample of the points has been plotted on the graph. If all the points are added, they will form a continuous straight line:

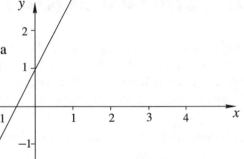

This line passes through the y-axis at 1 and has a slope of 2 (the line rises by 2 units for each unit moved to the right).

(ii) $x + y = 2$ is known as an implicit relation. It is possible to make y the subject of the relation (to get $y = 2 - x$), but this is not necessary. All that is required is to find pairs of numbers that add up to 2. Some examples are:

x	−1	0	1	2	3	4
y	3	2	1	0	−1	−2

As before, the entries in this table are only examples. If the complete set of such points is plotted on a cartesian graph, the result is:

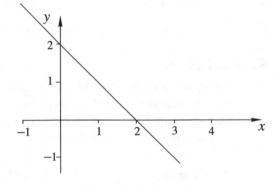

(iii) The previous examples used the variables x and y. In these cases it is conventional to plot x values on the horizontal axis and y values on the vertical axis. When other variables are used, if the relation is explicit (one of the variables is on its own on one side of the equation), this variable is plotted on the vertical axis. In this case, it is not clear which variable should be plotted on each axis. Also, it is probably easiest to make one of the variables the subject of the equation:

$$\frac{2t}{3} - s = 4 \Rightarrow \frac{2t}{3} = s + 4 \Rightarrow s = \frac{2t}{3} - 4$$

This can now be used as in part (i) to calculate values of s after choosing values of t. The table could be:

t	-3	0	3	6	9	12
s	-6	-4	-2	0	2	4

and the graph is:

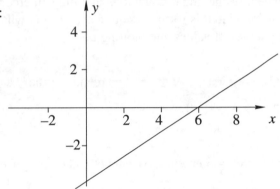

EXERCISE 8.2

1. For each of the following equations, make a table of values and hence plot their graphs.

(i) $y = x + 1$

(ii) $y = x - 2$

(iii) $y = 2x - 3$

(iv) $y = 2 - 3x$

(v) $y = \dfrac{x + 1}{2}$

(vi) $y = 3 + 4x$

(vii) $x + y = 3$

(viii) $x + 2y = 4$

(ix) $x - 3y = 6$

(x) $\dfrac{x}{2} + \dfrac{y}{5} = 1$

(xi) $x - \dfrac{y}{3} = 1$

(xii) $\dfrac{2t}{5} - 3p = 2$

(xiii) $x + \dfrac{5y}{4} = -1$

(xiv) $\dfrac{4 + t}{2} = q$

(xv) $x + 4y = 2 - x$

2. It costs \$4 to set the type to print business cards. Each card costs \$0.02 to print. Write an equation that could be used to calculate the cost (\$$C$) of printing n business cards.

3. It costs 35 cents per kilometre to run a car on petrol. If the car is converted to liquefied petroleum gas, the cost becomes 27 cents per kilometre. Write equations that give the cost of running the car on petrol (P) and gas (G) for k kilometres. If it costs \$1000 to convert a car from petrol to gas, how far would the owner have to drive before recovering the conversion costs?

8.3 STANDARD FORMS OF LINEAR EQUATIONS

1. $y = mx + c$

There are several forms that linear relations can take. Probably the most useful is known as the gradient intercept form:

$$y = mx + c .$$

In this case, the gradient of the line is equal to m and the y intercept is equal to c. This means that if the relation is in this form, it is quite easy to say what the graph looks like without constructing tables of values and plotting points.

EXAMPLE

State the gradient and y-intercepts of the graphs related to these equations:

(i) $y = 2x - 3$ (ii) $y = \dfrac{x-1}{3}$ (iii) $y = 2 - \dfrac{3x}{4}$

SOLUTION

(i) The gradient (2) and y-intercept (–3) can be read directly from the equation.

(ii) The equation can be written in the standard form: $y = \dfrac{x-1}{3} \Rightarrow y = \dfrac{1}{3}x - \dfrac{1}{3}$. The gradient is $\dfrac{1}{3}$ and the y-intercept is $-\dfrac{1}{3}$.

(iii) Similarly: $y = 2 - \dfrac{3x}{4} \Rightarrow y = \left(-\dfrac{3}{4}\right)x + 2$. The gradient is $-\dfrac{3}{4}$ and the y-intercept is 2.

2. $ax + by + c = 0$

Another common form for a linear equation is:

$$ax + by + c = 0$$

This form of the linear equation does not give the gradient and y-intercept of the line. When sketching or plotting linear equations in this form it is probably best to calculate the intercepts on both axes.
This is done as follows:

For x–intercept, let $y = 0$, so that $ax + c = 0 \Rightarrow x = -\dfrac{c}{a}$

For y–intercept, let $x = 0$, so that $by + c = 0 \Rightarrow y = -\dfrac{c}{b}$

EXAMPLE

Find the axes intercepts of these linear equations:

    (i) $2x - 3y = 12$ (ii) $\dfrac{2}{3}x - \dfrac{y}{4} = 4$ (iii) $2x + 3y - 4 = 0$

SOLUTION

    (i) $2x - 3y = 12,\ x = 0,\ -3y = 12 \Rightarrow y = -4,\ y = 0 \Rightarrow x = 6$

    (ii) $\dfrac{2}{3}x - \dfrac{y}{4} = 4,\ x = 0,\ -\dfrac{y}{4} = 4 \Rightarrow y = -16,\ y = 0,\ \dfrac{2}{3}x = 4 \Rightarrow x = 6$

    (iii) $2x + 3y - 4 = 0,\ x = 0,\ 3y - 4 = 0 \Rightarrow y = \dfrac{4}{3},\ y = 0,\ 2x - 4 = 0 \Rightarrow x = 2$

PROPERTIES OF STRAIGHT LINES

1.   Gradient of a line

The gradient, m, of the line through two points (x_1, y_1) and (x_2, y_2) is given by

$$m = \frac{y_2 - y_1}{x_2 - x_1}$$

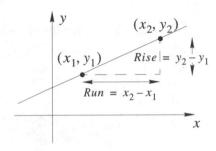

Which is also given by $m = \dfrac{\text{Rise}}{\text{Run}}$

From this we can obtain the point–gradient form of a line. That is, if (x, y) is any point on a straight line having a gradient m, and (x_1, y_1) is another fixed point on that line then the equation of that line is given by

$$y - y_1 = m(x - x_1)$$

2.   Parallel lines

Two straight lines are
     parallel if they have the same gradient
and two straight lines
     with the same gradient are parallel.

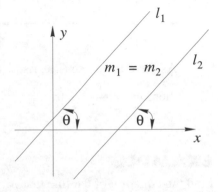

That is, the straight line l_1 with gradient m_1 is parallel to the straight line l_2 with gradient m_2 only if $m_1 = m_2$.

That is, $l_1 \ // \ l_2 \ \text{iff} \ m_1 = m_2$

Notice that if the two lines are parallel, they also make equal angles with the x–axis.

3. **Angle between a straight line and the x–axis**

If a straight line with gradient m, makes an angle
of magnitude θ with the positive x–axis, then
the relationship between the angle and the gradient
is given by

$$\tan\theta = m$$

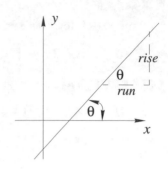

That is, $\tan\theta = \dfrac{Opp}{Adj} = \dfrac{rise}{run} = \dfrac{y_2 - y_1}{x_2 - x_1} = m$

4. **Perpendicular lines**

If two lines are **perpendicular**, then
the product of their gradients is –1.

That is, the straight line l_1 with gradient m_1 is

perpendicular to the straight line l_2 with gradient m_2

if and only if $m_1 \times m_2 = -1$.

That is,

$$l_1 \perp l_2 \text{ iff } m_1 \times m_2 = -1 \text{ or } m_1 = -\frac{1}{m_2}.$$

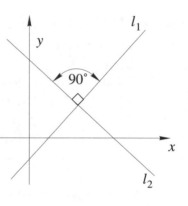

5. **Two special cases**

Case 1 $y = c$ (i.e., $m = 0$)

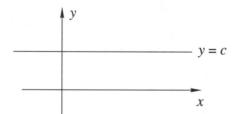

As there is no rise (i.e., rise = 0),

then, $m = \dfrac{0}{run} = 0$.

Case 2 $x = k$ (i.e., m is undefined)

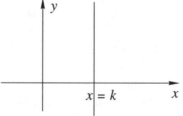

As there is no run (i.e., run = 0),

then, $m = \dfrac{rise}{0}$ which is undefined.

(Division by zero is not possible).

EXAMPLE

Find the equation of the line that passes through the point $(-1,3)$ and is parallel to the line
with equation $2x - y + 7 = 0$.

SOLUTION

The gradient of the line $2x - y + 7 = 0$ is found by rearranging to the form $y = mx + c$ to get: $y = 2x + 7$. The gradient is 2 and so all the lines parallel to this will also have gradient 2. The equation of the required line is $y = 2x + c$. The value of the constant c can be found by using the fact that the line passes through the point $(-1, 3)$.

$$y = 2x + c$$
$$3 = 2 \times -1 + c$$
$$c = 5$$
$$\therefore y = 2x + 5$$

EXAMPLE

Find the equation of the line which passes through the point $(-1, 4)$ and which is perpendicular to the line with equation $2x + 5y + 2 = 0$

SOLUTION

The gradient form of $2x + 5y + 2 = 0$ is $5y = -2x - 2 \Rightarrow y = -\frac{2}{5}x - \frac{2}{5}$ so the gradient

is $-\frac{2}{5}$. The gradient of all lines that are perpendicular to this is found by using the fact that

the product of the gradients is -1: $\left(-\frac{2}{5}\right)m = -1 \Rightarrow m = \frac{5}{2} = 2.5$.

The equation of the required line is $y = \frac{5}{2}x + c$. The constant c is found in the same way

as the previous example:

$$y = \frac{5}{2}x + c$$

$$4 = \frac{5}{2} \times -1 + c$$

$$c = 6.5$$

$$y = \frac{5}{2}x + 6\frac{1}{2}$$

EXERCISE 8.3

1. Find the gradient of the line joining the points

   (i)   (3, 2) and (5, 6)   (ii)   (4, 5) and (6, 11)
   (iii) (-1, 3) and (2, 8)   (iv)   (-5, -7) and (-3, 9)
   (v)   (3, 5) and (9, 5)   (vi)   (6, 3) and (4, -1)
   (vii) (2, 4) and (5, -2)   (viii) (4, 6) and (4, 12)

2. Find the angle that a straight line makes with the positive x–axis, if its gradient is

(i)   1   (ii)   2   (iii)   4   (iv) $\dfrac{1}{2}$

(v)   −1   (vi) $-\dfrac{3}{4}$ (vii)   −3   (viii) $\dfrac{3}{5}$

3. Use the gradient–point form equation to find the equation of the straight line if

    (a)   it passes through the point (1, 1) and has a gradient of 2.
    (b)   it passes through the point (–2, 3) and has a gradient of 3.
    (c)   it passes through the point (3, –4) and has a gradient of –1.

4. Find the gradient of the straight line that is perpendicular to the straight line with gradient equal to

    (a)   2.   (b)   − 3.   (c) $-\dfrac{2}{3}$.   (d) $\dfrac{5}{4}$

5. Find the equation of the straight line that passes through the origin and the point (2,4).

6. Find the equation of the straight line that passes through the points (–1,2) and (0,1).

7. A straight line passes through the point (4,3) and is perpendicular to the line joining the points (–1,3) and (1,–1). Find the equation of this line, giving the answer in the form $ax + by + c = 0$.

8. A triangle is made from the coordinate axes and the line $3x + 4y + p = 0$. The area of the triangle is 6 square units. What is the value of p?

9. The lines $px + 4y – 2 = 0$ and $2x – y + p = 0$ are perpendicular. Find the value of p.

10. The lines $x + 2y + 12 = 0, x – 2y + 3 = 0, 2y + x – 8 = 0 \,\&\, x – 2y – 2 = 0$ form a quadrilateral. What is the best description for this quadrilateral?

11. Find equations for each of the following lines.
Give answers in the gradient/intercept form:

(a)
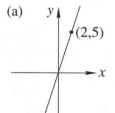

(b)
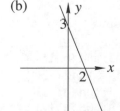

(c)
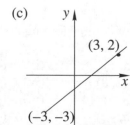

(d)
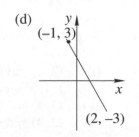

8.4 SIMULTANEOUS EQUATIONS

Pairs of simultaneous equations in two unknowns may be solved in several ways:

ELIMINATION

The elimination method depends on multiplying one or both equations by numbers chosen so that there are the same number of one of the variables in each equation. The equations can then be added or subtracted, eliminating one of the variables.

EXAMPLE

Use the elimination method to solve
$$x - 2y = -7$$
$$2x + 3y = 0$$

SOLUTION

In this case, if both sides of the first equation are doubled, then both equations will contain $2x$ which can then be removed by subtracting one equation from the other. y can then be found by substitution in either equation.

$$x - 2y = -7, [1]$$
$$2x + 3y = 0, [2]$$
$$2x - 4y = -14, [2 \times [1]]$$
$$7y = 14, [[2] - 2 \times [1]]$$
$$y = 2$$
$$\therefore 2x + 3 \times 2 = 0 \text{ from equation } [2]$$
$$2x = -6$$
$$x = -3 \qquad \text{So the solution is } x = -3, y = 2.$$

SUBSTITUTION

The substitution method relies on making one of the variables the subject of one of the equations. This can then be used to remove this variable from the other equation leaving an equation that can then be solved for the other variable. The final step is to substitute this result into either equation and solve for the remaining variable.

EXAMPLE

Use the substitution method to solve:
$$x - 2y = -7$$
$$2x + 3y = 0$$

SOLUTION

$$x - 2y = -7, [1]$$
$$2x + 3y = 0, [2]$$

From [1] $x = 2y - 7$

Substitute into [2] $2(2y - 7) + 3y = 0$

$$4y - 14 + 3y = 0$$
$$7y = 14$$
$$y = 2$$

Substituting $x = 2y - 7$
$$= 2 \times 2 - 7$$
$$= -3 \qquad \text{So the solution is } x = -3, y = 2.$$

THE GRAPHICAL METHOD

Finally, the graphical method can be used. This has the disadvantage that it can only give approximate answers. The graphs of the two equations are plotted on the same axes. The lines represent the full set of solutions of each equation. The point at which the lines intersect is the solution of both the equations.

Applying this method to the same set of equations gives:

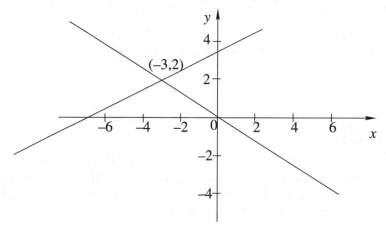

Again the solution is $x = -3$, $y = 2$.

The approximate value may not matter as in many applications an approximation is all that is required.

USING A GRAPHICS CALCULATOR

To solve a pair of two variable simultaneous equations using a graphic calculator, first transform each equation so that one of the variables is the subject of each. In the case of the example used above, this will result in:

$$x - 2y = -7 \Rightarrow 2y = x + 7 \Rightarrow y = \frac{x + 7}{2}$$

$$2x + 3y = 0 \Rightarrow 3y = -2x \Rightarrow y = -\frac{2x}{3}$$

These two equations can now be entered under the Y= instruction. You must use the negative key (–) and not the subtraction key to enter the second function. Failure to do this will result in an error message.

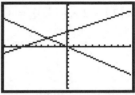

It is probably a good idea to use the standard viewing window. This uses [–10,10] on each axis. Press ZOOM 6 to do this.

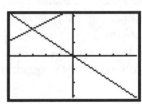

If you suspect that the equations have integer or whole numbered solutions, it can be a good idea to use a window that is an exact multiple of the number of screen pixels. The window [–4.7,4.7] for x and [–3.1,3.1] for y can be set by selecting ZOOM 4.

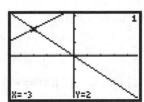

A first solution can be found using TRACE followed by the arrow keys to select the point of intersection of the two lines.

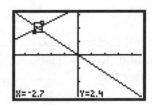

The solution to the equations is displayed at the bottom of the screen. If necessary, more accurate solutions can be found using the ZOOM facility. Try using ZOOM 1 (Box) and ZOOM 2 (Zoom In) as ways of finding more accurate solutions.

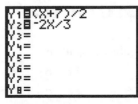

Not all simultaneous equations have solutions. Also, some pairs of equations have infinite solution sets. If equations are of these types, you will need to be able to recognise the 'problem' both in the processes of algebraic and graphical solution.

The following examples illustrate these possibilities:

EXAMPLES

Solve:

(i) $2x + 6y = 8$ (ii) $2x + 6y = 8$

$3x + 9y = 12$ $3x + 9y = 15$

SOLUTIONS

(i)

Algebraic solution: Graphical Solution

$2x + 6y = 8, [1]$

$3x + 9y = 12, [2]$

$3 \times [1] - 2 \times [2], 0 = 0$

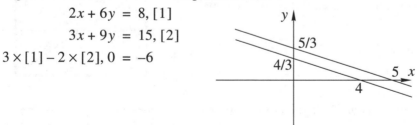

The algebraic method produces an equation that is always true. This means that any pair of numbers that satisfy either equation will satisfy both and are, therefore, solutions to the problem. Examples of solutions are: $x = 4, y = 0, x = 1, y = 1$ & $x = 7, y = -1$. Graphically, the two equations produce the same line. The coordinates of any point on this line will be solutions of both equations.

(ii)

Algebraic solution: Graphical Solution

$2x + 6y = 8, [1]$

$3x + 9y = 15, [2]$

$3 \times [1] - 2 \times [2], 0 = -6$

The algebraic method produces an equation that is never true. This means that there are no solutions to the equations. Graphically, the two lines are parallel and produce no points of intersection.

There is a matrix method for solving systems of simultaneous equations that will be discussed in Chapter 16. This method is particularly useful when using graphic calculators which can perform the matrix arithmetic necessary to solve simultaneous equations. A small number of models (e.g. the TI-85) have a direct menu driven simultaneous equation solver.

EXERCISE 8.4

1. Solve these simultaneous equations, giving exact answers:
   (i) $3x - 2y = -1$ (ii) $3x + 5y = 34$ (iii) $2x + 4y = 6$
        $5x + 2y = 9$ $3x + 7y = 44$ $4x - 3y = -10$

   (iv) $3x + 2y = 2$ (v) $5x + 4y = -22$ (vi) $5x - 9y = -34$
         $2x - 6y = -6$ $3x - y = -3$ $2x + 3y = -7$

2. Solve these simultaneous equations, giving fractional answers where appropriate:
   (i) $3x - y = 2$ (ii) $4x + 2y = 3$ (iii) $-3x + y = 0$
        $5x + 2y = 9$ $x - 3y = 0$ $2x - 4y = 0$

   (iv) $\dfrac{x}{2} - 3y = 4$ (v) $5x + \dfrac{2y}{3} = -4$ (vi) $\dfrac{3x}{5} - 4y = \dfrac{1}{2}$

   $4x + \dfrac{3y}{2} = -1$ $4x + y = 2$ $x - 2y = \dfrac{1}{3}$

3. Find the values of m such that these equations have no solutions:
   (i) $3x - my = 4$ (ii) $5x + y = 12$ (iii) $4x - 2y = 12$
        $x + y = 12$ $mx - y = -2$ $3x + my = 2$

4. Find the values of m and a such that these equations have infinite solution sets:
   (i) $4x + my = a$ (ii) $5x + 2y = 12$ (iii) $3x + my = a$
        $2x + y = 4$ $mx + 4y = a$ $2x - 4y = 6$

5. Two consecutive integers add up to 315. Find the numbers.

6. Three compact discs and two tapes cost $114 and two compact discs and five tapes cost $142. Find the cost of one compact disc.

7. The cost of entry for a football match is $87 for 3 adults and 4 children. For a family of two adults and two children, the entry charge is $52. What are the costs of entry for adults and for children?

8. Consider the equations: $3x + 2y = 4$
                             $9x + 6.1y = 5$
   (i) If all the coefficients are known exactly, what is the solution of these equations?
   (ii) If the coefficient of y in the second equation has been incorrectly measured and should be 6.05, what is the new solution of the equations?
   (iii) Explain why the solutions to these equations, whose coefficients are so similar, are so different.

8.5 APPLICATIONS OF COORDINATES GEOMETRY IN 2-D

EXAMPLE

A triangle is formed by the lines with equations: $3x + y - 12 = 0$
$$x - 3y + 6 = 0$$
$$x + 7y - 44 = 0$$

(a) Prove that the triangle is right angled.

(b) Find the coordinates of the vertices of the triangle.

(c) Find the area of the triangle thus formed.

(d) Prove that the triangle formed by joining the mid-points of the sides is also right angled.

SOLUTION

(a) The gradients of the three sides are:

$$3x + y - 12 = 0 \Rightarrow y = -3x + 12 \Rightarrow \text{Gradient} = -3, [A]$$

$$x - 3y + 6 = 0 \Rightarrow y = \frac{1}{3}x + 2 \Rightarrow \text{Gradient} = \frac{1}{3}, [B]$$

$$x + 7y - 44 = 0 \Rightarrow y = -\frac{1}{7}x + 6\frac{2}{7} \Rightarrow \text{Gradient} = -\frac{1}{7}, [C]$$

Since the product of the gradients of [A] and [B] is $-3 \times \frac{1}{3} = -1$, the lines [A] and [B] are perpendicular and the triangle must be right angled.

(b) The coordinates of the vertices are found by solving the equations of the lines simultaneously. If the gradient/intercept forms of these lines are used, then y can be eliminated immediately:

[A] and [B]	[A] and [C]	[B] and [C]

$$[A] \text{ and } [B]$$
$$-3x + 12 = \frac{1}{3}x + 2$$
$$\frac{10}{3}x = 10$$
$$x = 3$$
$$y = -3 \times 3 + 12$$
$$= 3$$

$$[A] \text{ and } [C]$$
$$-3x + 12 = -\frac{1}{7}x + \frac{44}{7}$$
$$-21x + 84 = -x + 44$$
$$20x = 40$$
$$x = 2$$
$$y = -3 \times 2 + 12$$
$$= 6$$

$$[B] \text{ and } [C]$$
$$-\frac{1}{7}x + \frac{44}{7} = \frac{1}{3}x + 2$$
$$-3x + 132 = 7x + 42$$
$$10x = 90$$
$$x = 9$$
$$y = \frac{1}{3} \times 9 + 2$$
$$= 5$$

(c)   The coordinates of the vertices of the triangle are (3,3), (2,6) and (9, perpendicular sides of the triangle are those joining (3,3) to (2,6) and (These can be used as the base and height of the triangle. Their lengths are

(3,3) to (2,6): $h = \sqrt{(3-2)^2 + (3-6)^2} = \sqrt{1+9} = \sqrt{10}$

(3,3) to (9,5): $b = \sqrt{(9-3)^2 + (5-3)^2} = \sqrt{36+4} = \sqrt{40}$

The area of the triangle is: $\frac{1}{2} \times b \times h = \frac{1}{2} \times \sqrt{40} \times \sqrt{10} = \frac{1}{2} \times \sqrt{40 \times 10} = 10u^2$.

(d)   The midpoints of the three sides have coordinates:

(3,3) to (2,6) mid-point is $\left(\dfrac{3+2}{2}, \dfrac{3+6}{2}\right) = \left(\dfrac{5}{2}, \dfrac{9}{2}\right) [P]$

(3,3) to (9,5) mid-point is $\left(\dfrac{3+9}{2}, \dfrac{3+5}{2}\right) = (6, 4) [Q]$

(9,5) to (2,6) mid-point is $\left(\dfrac{9+2}{2}, \dfrac{5+6}{2}\right) = \left(\dfrac{11}{2}, \dfrac{11}{2}\right) [R]$

The gradients of the lines joining these points are:

$[P]$ to $[Q]$ Gradient $= \dfrac{\frac{9}{2} - 4}{\frac{5}{2} - 6} = -\dfrac{1}{7}$, $[P]$ to $[R]$ Gradient $= \dfrac{\frac{9}{2} - \frac{11}{2}}{\frac{5}{2} - \frac{11}{2}} = \dfrac{1}{3}$

$[Q]$ to $[R]$ Gradient $= \dfrac{4 - \frac{11}{2}}{6 - \frac{11}{2}} = -3$

The product of the gradients of the lines $[P]$ to $[R]$ and $[Q]$ to $[R]$ is $\dfrac{1}{3} \times -3 = -1$ so the new triangle is also right angled.

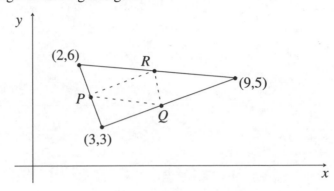

EXERCISE 8.5

1. A quadrilateral is formed by joining the points $(-1,-2)$ to $(1,4)$ to $(5,6)$ to $(3,0)$ and finally back to $(-1,-2)$.

   (a) Prove that the quadrilateral is a parallelogram.
   (b) Find the mid-points of the sides of the parallelogram and prove that these can be joined to form a second parallelogram.

2. The lines with equations $x + 2y - 12 = 0$, $x - 3y + 3 = 0$, $2x - y + 1 = 0$ form a triangle.

   (a) Find the coordinates of the vertices of this triangle.
   (b) The mid-points of the sides of this triangle are joined to make a second triangle. Prove that this second triangle is similar to the first.

3. A straight line has equation $x + 3y = 6$.

   (a) Find the equations of the set of lines that are perpendicular to this line.
   (b) Find the equation of the line that is perpendicular to $x + 3y = 6$ and which also passes through the point $(5,7)$.
   (c) Find the coordinates of the point of intersection of the line found in (b) with $x + 3y = 6$.
   (d) Hence find the shortest distance between the point $(5,7)$ and the line with equation $x + 3y = 6$.

4. Two lines have equations $y = 2.5x - 4$ and $y = 2.3x + 7$. The gradients of the two lines are known to 2 significant figures and the intercepts are known exactly. Find the range of possible points of intersection of these lines.

8.6 COORDINATE GEOMETRY IN 3-D

Many of the properties used when dealing with coordinate geometry in 2–D can be extended to coordinate geometry in 3–D. In three–dimensional space, the position of a point is determined by its directed distances from each of the three mutually perpendicular planes. These planes intersect at a point O (the origin) and they intersect in three mutually perpendicular lines as shown in the figure below:

That is, any point in space has its position determined by its directed perpendicular distances x, y and z from the yz–plane, xz–plane and xy plane respectively.

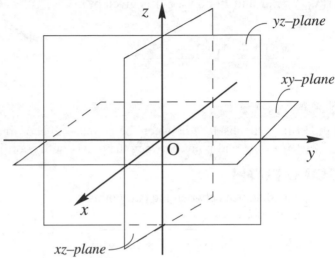

FINDING POINTS IN SPACE

Points in 3–D space are located by a set of ordered triplets (as opposed to an ordered pair in the 2–D plane). The order is (x–value, y–value, z–value), i.e., (x, y, z).

So that the point with coordinates (2, 3, –4) would be found by moving 2 units along the positive x–axis, 3 units along the positive y–axis and then 4 units along the negative z–axis.

Notice that the coordinates end up as being one vertex of a rectangular box.

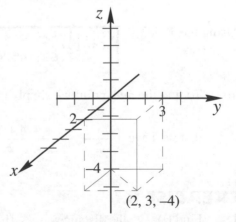

The nice thing about moving from a 2–D plane to a 3–D space is that many of the results from 2–D coordinate geometry can be carried through to 3–D (with some modifications). Further work on 3–D geometry will be dealt with when you look at vectors.

We next state two results relating to the distance between two points and their midpoint:

Coordinate Geometry

The **distance**, $d = AB$, between the points $A(x_1, y_1, z_1)$ and $B(x_2, y_2, z_2)$ is given by

$$d = \sqrt{(x_2 - x_1)^2 + (y_2 - y_1)^2 + (z_2 - z_1)^2}$$

The **mid-point**, M, between the two points $A(x_1, y_1, z_1)$ and $B(x_2, y_2, z_2)$ is given by

$$\left(\frac{x_1 + x_2}{2}, \frac{y_1 + y_2}{2}, \frac{z_1 + z_2}{2} \right)$$

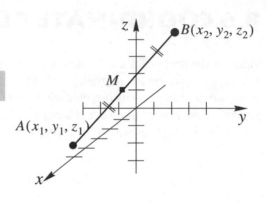

EXAMPLE

Find (a)   the distance between the points with coordinates $(2, -3, 4)$ and $(1, 4, 1)$.

        (b)   the mid-point between the points with coordinates $(2, -3, 4)$ and $(1, 4, 1)$.

SOLUTION

(a)   The distance between the two points is given by

$$d = \sqrt{(x_2 - x_1)^2 + (y_2 - y_1)^2 + (z_2 - z_1)^2}$$

$$= \sqrt{(2 - 1)^2 + (-3 - 4)^2 + (4 - 1)^2}$$

$$= \sqrt{1 + 49 + 9}$$

$$= \sqrt{59} \,(\approx 7.68)$$

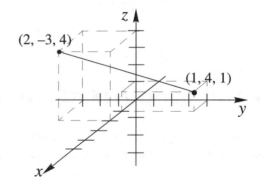

Using the TI–83, we have:

```
√((2-1)²+(-3-4)²
+(4-1)²)
          7.681145748
```

(b)   To find the mid–point we simply use the formula $\left(\frac{x_1 + x_2}{2}, \frac{y_1 + y_2}{2}, \frac{z_1 + z_2}{2} \right)$, so

that we have, $\left(\frac{2 + 1}{2}, \frac{-3 + 4}{2}, \frac{4 + 1}{2} \right)$ giving the mid–point as $\left(\frac{3}{2}, \frac{1}{2}, \frac{5}{2} \right)$.

EXERCISE 8.6

1.   Find (i)   the distance   (ii)   the mid–point between the points with coordinates

    (a) $(1, 2, 3)$ & $(3, 2, 1)$ (b) $(2, -3, -1)$ & $(-1, 0, 2)$

    (c) $(-3, 5, 6)$ & $(0, 1, 0)$ (d) $(2, 4, 6)$ & $(-1, -2, -3)$

    (e) $(0, 1, 8)$ & $(-1, 1, 2)$ (f) $(3, 4, 5)$ & $(2, 3, -4)$

    (g) $(-1, 0, -1)$ & $(0, -1, 0)$ (h) $(2, -2, 1)$ & $(-2, 2, -1)$

EXAMINATION STYLE QUESTIONS

1. The equation of the line l is $y + 3x = 6$.
- (a) Find the gradient (slope) of l.
- (b) Find the x–intercept and y–intercept of l.
- (c) Find the gradient of a line perpendicular to l.
- (d) Find the equation of the line in (c) if it passes through the point $(-3, 0)$.

2. (a) On the rectangular coordinate axes Ox, Oy and Oz, drawn alongside, plot the points $P(4, 1, 0)$, $Q(0, 4, 3)$ and $R(6, 0, 0)$.

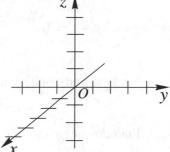

- (b) Draw the triangle PQR.

- (c) Find the length of the side PQ.

- (d) Find the mid–point of $\overline{PR}$.

3. A straight line passes through the points $(4, 0)$ and $(0, 8)$.
- (a) Find the gradient of this line.
- (b) Find the equation of this line.
- (c) The line passes through the points $(2, a)$ and $(b, 2)$. Find a and b.

4. Find the equation of the straight line, l, passing through the points $(-4, -2)$ and $(3, 4)$.
Hence, find the equation of the straight line perpendicular to l and passing through the point $(0, 4)$

5. Find the equation of each of the following straight lines, given that it passes through the point $(2, -1)$
- (a) and has a gradient of 4.
- (b) and passes through the point $(-1, 2)$.
- (c) and has a y–intercept of $(0, -2)$.
- (d) and is perpendicular to the line with equation $y + 2x = 5$.

6. Find the equation of the line passing through $(3, -1)$ and:
- (a) perpendicular to   (b) parallel to
the line with equation $x - 2y + 1 = 0$

7. Find the point of intersection of the lines with equations $2x - 4y + 1 = 0$ and $x + y - 2 = 0$.

8. The lines $ax - y + 1 = 0$ and $x + 2y + 2 = 0$ intersect at $(1, b)$. Find a and b.

SELF ASSESSMENT TEST (45 MINS.)

1. Find the equation of the straight line through the point $(-1,2)$ that is parallel to the line with equation $2y - 4x + 3 = 0$ giving your answer in the form $y = mx + c$.

[3 marks]

2. Find the equation of the straight line perpendicular to the line with equation $y = -\frac{2}{3}x + \frac{3}{7}$ which passes through the point $(2,4)$, giving your answer in the form $ax + by + c = 0$.

[3 marks]

3. Find the mid-point of the line segment joining the points $(-3,7)$ and $(5,1)$

[1 mark]

4. Find the length of the line segment joining the points $(-3,5)$ to $(2,-3)$:
   (i) exactly
   (ii) correct to 3 significant figures.

[3 marks]

5. Find the equation of the perpendicular bisector of the line segment joining the points $(1,2)$ and $(3,1)$, giving the answer in the form $y = mx + c$.

[4 marks]

6. Solve: $2x + y = 6$
   $3x - y = 14$

[3 marks]

7. (a) On the rectangular coordinate axes Ox, Oy and Oz, drawn alongside, plot the points $P(0, 2, 0)$, $Q(1, 3, 0)$ and $R(0, 0, 4)$.

   (b) Draw the triangle PQR.

   (c) Find the length of the side PQ.

   (d) Find the mid–point of $\overline{PR}$.

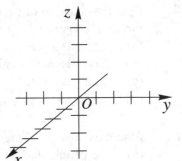

[7 marks]

GEOMETRY & TRIGONOMETRY 3

3–DIMENSIONAL TRIGONOMETRY

9

Chapter contents

– Applications of trigonometry in 3–D

9.1 3- D TRIGONOMETRY

When dealing with problems in three dimensions, we draw the figures in perspective, so that a model can be more accurately visualised. This does not mean that you must be an artist, simply that you take a little time (and a lot of practise) when drawing such diagrams. The key to many 3–D problems is locating the relevant right–angled triangles within the diagram. Once this is done, all of the trigonometric work that was covered in Chapter 7 can be applied here. So, we will not be learning new material, but rather developing new drawing and modelling skills. Some typical examples of solids that may be encountered are:

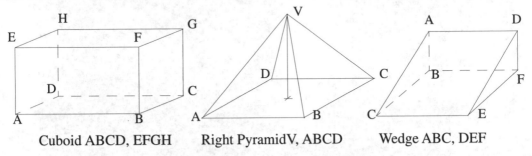

Cuboid ABCD, EFGH   Right Pyramid V, ABCD   Wedge ABC, DEF

We look at some of the basic concepts and drawing techniques to help us find the correct angles and lengths:

1. A line and a plane:

A line will always cut a plane at some point (unless the line is parallel to the plane). To find the angle between a line and a plane construct a perpendicular from the line to the plane and complete a right–angled triangle. In our diagram, we have that the segment $\overline{AB}$ is projected onto

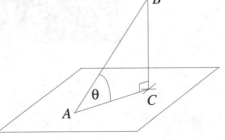

the plane, a perpendicular, $\overline{BC}$ is drawn, so that a right–angled triangle, ABC is completed. The angle that the line then makes with the plane is given by θ (which can be determiend by using the trig–ratios).

2. A plane and a plane:

To find the angle between two planes ABCD and ABEF (assuming that they intersect), take any point P on the intersecting segment $\overline{AB}$ and draw $\overline{PQ}$ and $\overline{PR}$ on each plane in such a way so that they are perpendicular to $\overline{AB}$. Then, the angle between $\overline{PQ}$ and $\overline{PR}$ (θ) is the angle between the two planes.

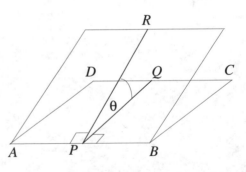

EXAMPLE

A cube ABCD, EFGH has a side length measuring 6 cm.

(a)   Find the length of the segment $\overline{AC}$.

(b)   The length of the diagonal $\overline{AG}$.

(c)   The angle that the diagonal $\overline{AG}$ makes with the base.

SOLUTION

First we need to draw a cube:

(a)   Now the base of the cube is a square,
so that $\angle ABC = 90°$, i.e., we have a
right–angled triangle, so we can use
Pythagoras' Theorem:

$$AC^2 = AB^2 + BC^2$$
$$= 6^2 + 6^2$$
$$= 72$$
$$\therefore AC = \sqrt{72} \approx 8.49$$

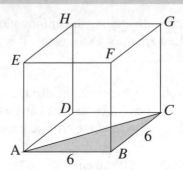

(b)   This time we have that $\angle ACG = 90°$,
therefore,

$$AG^2 = AC^2 + CG^2$$
$$= (\sqrt{72})^2 + 6^2$$
$$= 108$$
$$\therefore AC = \sqrt{108} \approx 10.39$$

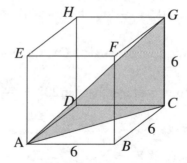

(c)   Using triangle ACG, we have that

$$\tan\theta = \frac{CG}{AC} \therefore \tan\theta = \frac{6}{\sqrt{72}}$$

$$\theta = \tan^{-1}\left(\frac{6}{\sqrt{72}}\right)$$

$$= 35.26°$$
$$= 35°16'$$

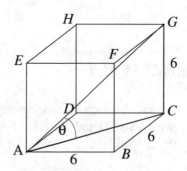

EXAMPLE

From a point X, 200m due south of a cliff, the angle of elevation of the top of the cliff is
30°. From a point Y, due east of the cliff, the angle of elevation of the top of the cliff is 20°.
How far apart are the points X and Y?

SOLUTION

We start by illustrating this information on a 3–D diagram (Note that North–South and
West–East are drawn on a plane. It is necessary to do this otherwise the diagram will not
make sense).

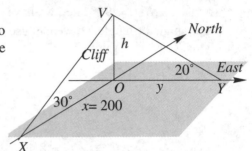

Let the cliff be h metres, the distance from X to
the base of the cliff be x metres and the distance
from Y to the base of the cliff be y metres.

As $\angle XOY = 90°$, then
$$XY^2 = x^2 + y^2 = 200^2 + y^2$$

But, $\tan 20° = \dfrac{h}{y}$, of which we know neither h or y.

However, using triangle XOV, we have that $\tan 30° = \dfrac{h}{200} \Rightarrow h = 200 \times \tan 30°$.

Therefore, we have that $\tan 20° = \dfrac{200 \times \tan 30°}{y} \Leftrightarrow y = \dfrac{200 \times \tan 30°}{\tan 20°}$

That is, $y = 317.25$

Therefore, $XY^2 = x^2 + y^2 = 200^2 + \left(\dfrac{200 \times \tan 30°}{\tan 20°} \right)^2$.

So that $XY \approx 375$.

EXERCISE 9.1

1. For the diagram shown, determine the angle of inclination between the plane
   (a) ABCD and the base, EABH (Figure 1).
   (b) ABC and the base EBFA (Figure 2).

Figure 1.

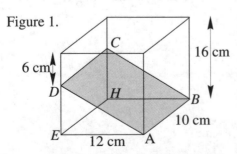

Figure 2.

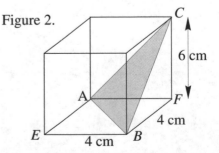

2. A right pyramid with a rectangular base and a vertical height of 60 cm is shown in the diagram alongside. The points *X* and *Y* are the mid–points of the sides *AB* and *BC* respectively

Find

(a)   the length of the *AP*.

(b)   the length of the edge *AV*.

(c)   the angle that the edge *AV* makes with the base ABCD.

(d)   the length of the $\overline{YV}$.

(e)   The angle that the plane *BCV* makes with the base.

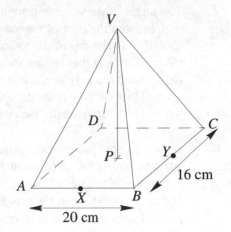

3. The diagram alongside shows a rectangular box with side lengths AB = 8 cm, BC = 6 cm and CG = 4 cm.

Find the angle between

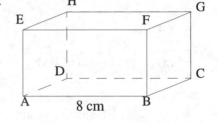

(a)   the line *BH* and the plane *ABCD*.

(b)   the lines *BH* and *BA*.

(c)   the planes *ADGF* and *ABCD*.

4. For the wedge shown alongside, given that the angle between the lines EA and ED is 50° find

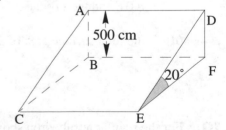

(a)   the length of AE.

(b)   the ∠*AEB*.

5. From a point *A*, 100m due south of a tower, the angle of elevation of the top of the tower is 40°. From a point *B*, due east of the tower, the angle of elevation of the top of the tower is 20°. How far apart are the points *A* and *B*?

6. For the triangular prism shown alongside find

(a)   the value of *h*

(b)   the value of α

(c)   the angle that the plane *ABV* makes with the base *ABD*.

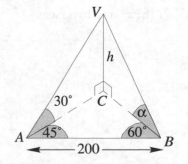

7. The angle of depression from the top of a tower to a point X on the ground and 120 metres from the foot of the tower is 24°. From point Y due west of X the an angle of elevation to the top of the tower is 19°.
   (a) Illustrate this information on a diagram.
   (b) Find the height of the tower.
   (c) How far is Y from the foot of the tower?
   (d) How far apart are the points X and Y?

8. A mast is held in a vertical position by four ropes of length 60 metres. All four ropes are attached at the same point at the top of the mast. So that their other end form the vertices of a square when pegged into the (level) ground. Each piece of rope makes and angle of 54° with the ground.
   (a) Illustrate this information on a diagram.
   (b) How tall is the mast?

9. A symmetrical sloping roof has dimensions as shown in the diagram below.

Find

   (a) the length of FM.

   (b) the angle between the plane BCEF and the ground.

   (c) the angle between the plane ABF and the ground

   (d) the total surface area of the roof.

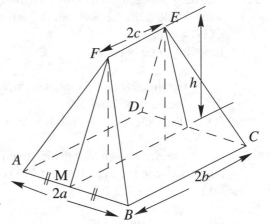

10. For the regular tetrahedron shown, find the angle between

   (a) any edge and an opposite face.

   (b) any two faces.

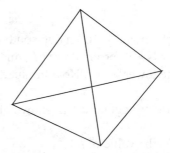

EXAMINATION STYLE QUESTION

1. A cube of edge length 20 cm is shown in the diagram. Find:

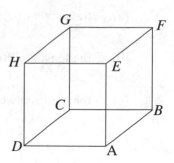

(a) the length of the segment $\overline{AC}$.

(b) the length of the segment $\overline{AG}$.

(c) the angle that the segment $\overline{AG}$ makes with the plane *ABCD*.

(d) the angle that the plane *AFGD* makes with the plane *ABCD*.

2. The figure shows a right pyramid with a rectangular base. Find

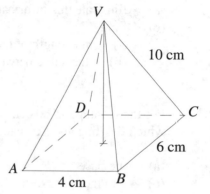

(a) the height of the pyramid.

(b) the angle that the plane *BCV* makes with the plane *ABCD*.

(c) the angle that the edge $\overline{BV}$ makes with the base *ABCD*.

3. From a point *A*, 150m due south of a tower, the angle of elevation of the top of the tower is 30°. From a point *B*, due east of the tower, the angle of elevation of the top of the tower is 40°.

(a) Illustrate this information on a diagram.

(b) How far apart are the points *A* and *B*?

SELF ASSESSMENT TEST (40 MINUTES)

1. In the figure shown, find

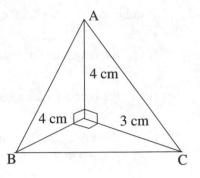

    (a)   the length of $\overline{AC}$.

    (b)   the length of $\overline{BC}$.

    (c)   the angle between the edges $\overline{AC}$ and $\overline{BC}$

[8 marks]

2. A right square pyramid has a height of 16 cm and an edge length of 20 cm.
    (a)   Illustrate this information on a diagram.
    (b)   Find
        (i)   the length of the sides of the base.
        (ii)   the angle between the sloping face and the base.

[6 marks]

3. For the rectangular box shown find the angle
which the diagonal *AG* makes with

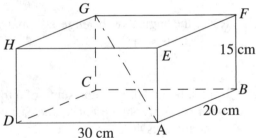

    (a)   the base.
    (b)   a longer edge of the box.

[5 marks]

4. An aeroplane is flying due east at a constant altitude of 10, 000 metres. At noon, an observer (facing north) notices that the plane flying directly in front of him at an angle of elevation of 25°. Some time later, the plane is at an angle of elevation of 20° with the observer.

    (a)   Illustrate this information on a diagram.

    (b)   How far away (along the ground) was the observer from the plane at noon?

    (c)   How far has the plane travelled between the observer's two sightings?

[8 marks]

VECTORS

1 0

Chapter contents

Key Formulae

- $\left| a\vec{i} + b\vec{j} \right| = \sqrt{a^2 + b^2}$

- $a\boldsymbol{i} + b\boldsymbol{j} = \begin{pmatrix} a \\ b \end{pmatrix}$

10.1 SCALAR AND VECTOR QUANTITIES

Numerical measurement scales are in widespread use. It is important to be able to distinguish between two distinct types of measurement scales, **scalars** and **vectors**.

SCALAR QUANTITIES

A scalar is a quantity that has **magnitude** (size) but no **direction**. For example, we measure the mass of objects using a variety of scales such as 'kilograms' and 'pounds'. These measures have **magnitude** in that more massive objects (such as the sun) have a larger numerical mass than small objects (such as this book). Giving the mass of this book does not, however, imply that this mass has a direction. This does not mean that scalar quantities must be positive. **Signed** scalar quantities, such as temperature as measured by the Celsius and Fahrenheit scales are also commonly used.

VECTOR QUANTITIES

Some measurements have both **magnitude** and **direction**. When we pull on a door handle, we exert what is known as a **force**. The force that we exert has both magnitude (we either pull hard or we pull gently) and direction (we open or close the door - or do something silly like pulling upwards!). Both the size of the pull and its direction are important in determining its effect. Such quantities are said to be **vectors**. Other examples of vectors are velocity, acceleration and translation. The mathematics that will be developed in this section can be applied to problems involving any type of vector quantity.

EXERCISE 10.1

The following situations need to be described using an appropriate measure. Classify the measure as a scalar (s) or a vector (v).

1. A classroom chair is moved from the front of the room to the back.

2. The balance in a bank account.

3. The electric current passing through an electric light tube.

4. A dog, out for a walk, is being restrained by a lead.

5. An aircraft starts its takeoff run.

6. The wind conditions before a yacht race.

7. The amount of liquid in a jug.

8. The length of a car.

9. The time that it takes to boil an egg.

10. The number of goals scored in a soccer match.

REPRESENTING VECTORS

Since vectors have magnitude and direction, one way of depicting them is to use arrows.

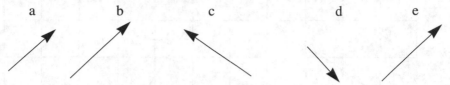

Examples a and b are in the same direction but are not of the same magnitude (length) and so are not considered to be the same vectors. Examples b and c have the same magnitude but different directions and are also different vectors. Example d has both a different length and direction fom the other vectors. Examples b and e have the same length and direction and so are equal vectors. It is not necessary for two vectors to be in the same place to be equal. All that is necessary is for the vectors to be of the same length and direction.

There are two commonly used notations for vectors:

This vector runs from A to B and is depicted as $\overrightarrow{AB}$ with the arrow giving the direction of the vector.

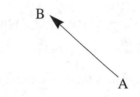

In the case where a vector starts at the origin (O), the vector running from O to another point C is said to be

the position vector of C, $\overrightarrow{OC}$

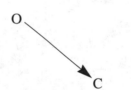

The other notation does not depend on labelled diagrams and is more a case of 'naming' a vector. If we want to give a vector a single name, such as 'a', we emphasise the fact that it is a vector by calling it $\vec{a}$., i.e., an 'a' with an arrow above it, or you may also use bold type ($\boldsymbol{a}$) or tilde ($\underset{\sim}{a}$). In this course we will make use of the $\vec{a}$ and $\boldsymbol{a}$ notation.

Finally, when describing vectors it is usual to do so by expressing them in terms of what is known as a **basis**. If we confine ourselves to vectors that exist in the plane of this page, the most commonly used basis is:

$$\begin{array}{c} \vec{j} \\ (\textbf{or } j) \end{array} \quad \vec{i} \; (\textbf{ or } i)$$

These two vectors can be used to define any vector lying in the plane of the page. The plane of the page is said to be **two-dimensional** as it requires two basis vectors.

Other vectors can now be expressed in terms of these basis vectors.

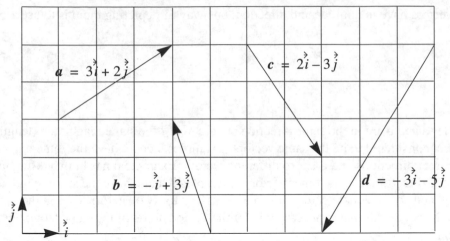

The vector a is 'three steps to the right and two steps up' and can be written in terms of the standard basis as $a = 3\vec{i} + 2\vec{j}$. The vector b is 'one step to the left and three steps up'. 'One step to the left' is in the opposite diection of the basis element $\vec{i}$ and is written $-\vec{i}$, giving the definition of the vector $b = -\vec{i} + 3\vec{j}$. The other definitions follow in a similar way. The vectors $-\vec{i}$ and $3\vec{j}$ are known as **components** of the vector b.

Finally on the subject of notation, a vector such as $a = 3\vec{i} + 2\vec{j}$ can be written as $\begin{pmatrix} 3 \\ 2 \end{pmatrix}$

and the vector $d = -3\vec{i} - 5\vec{j}$ can be written as $\begin{pmatrix} -3 \\ -5 \end{pmatrix}$ which is known as a **column**

vector.

When vectors are represented in three dimensional space, a third vector must be added to the basis:

The third basis vector, $\vec{k}$, points out of the page at right angles to the other two basis vectors. It is now possible to represent any vector in three dimensional space in terms of $\vec{i}, \vec{j}, \vec{k}$.

In addition, extra basis vectors can be added to generate higher dimensional vector spaces. These may not seem relevant to us, inhabiting as we do, a three dimensional space. However, it remains the case that it is possible to do calculations in higher dimensional spaces and these have produced many valuable results for applied mathematicians.

10.2 VECTOR ARITHMETIC

Vectors in the $\vec{i}, \vec{j}, \vec{k}$ notation can be added, subtracted and combined as follows:

EXAMPLE

If $\vec{a} = 2\vec{i} - \vec{j}$ and $\vec{b} = -\vec{i} + 3\vec{j}$, find:

   (i) $\vec{a} + \vec{b}$ (ii) $\vec{b} - \vec{a}$ (ii) $3\vec{b} - 2\vec{a}$

SOLUTION

Vectors are added 'nose to tail':

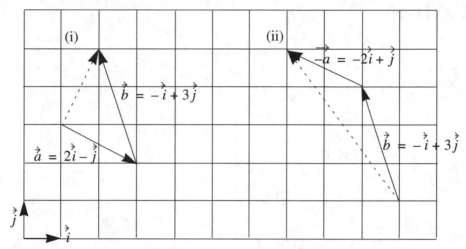

(i)   Vectors are added in much the same way as are algebraic terms. Only like terms can be added or subtracted.

$$\vec{a} + \vec{b} = 2\vec{i} - \vec{j} + (-\vec{i} + 3\vec{j})$$
$$= \vec{i} + 2\vec{j}$$

(ii)   This problem can be seen in two ways:

$$\vec{b} - \vec{a} = -\vec{i} + 3\vec{j} - (2\vec{i} - \vec{j}) \quad \text{OR} \quad \vec{b} - \vec{a} = \vec{b} + (-\vec{a})$$
$$= -3\vec{i} + 4\vec{j} \qquad\qquad\qquad\quad = -\vec{i} + 3\vec{j} + (-2\vec{i} + \vec{j})$$
$$\qquad\qquad\qquad\qquad\qquad\qquad\quad = -3\vec{i} + 4\vec{j}$$

The negative of a vector is the same length as the original vector but points in the opposite direction.

(iii) $3\vec{b} - 2\vec{a} = 3(-\vec{i} + 3\vec{j}) - 2(2\vec{i} - \vec{j})$

$$= -3\vec{i} + 9\vec{j} + -4\vec{i} + 2\vec{j}$$
$$= -7\vec{i} + 11\vec{j}$$

Similar calculations can be performed using the bracketed notation.

EXAMPLE

If $p = \begin{pmatrix} 3 \\ -1 \\ 4 \end{pmatrix}$ and $q = \begin{pmatrix} -2 \\ 0 \\ 3 \end{pmatrix}$, find:

(i) $\quad p + q$ (ii) $\quad p - \dfrac{q}{2}$ (iii) $\quad \dfrac{3q}{2} - p$

SOLUTION

(i) $\quad p + q = \begin{pmatrix} 3 \\ -1 \\ 4 \end{pmatrix} + \begin{pmatrix} -2 \\ 0 \\ 3 \end{pmatrix} = \begin{pmatrix} 1 \\ -1 \\ 7 \end{pmatrix}$

(ii) $\quad p - \dfrac{q}{2} = \begin{pmatrix} 3 \\ -1 \\ 4 \end{pmatrix} - \dfrac{1}{2}\begin{pmatrix} -2 \\ 0 \\ 3 \end{pmatrix} = \begin{pmatrix} 4 \\ -1 \\ 2.5 \end{pmatrix}$

(iii) $\quad \dfrac{3q}{2} - p = 1.5\begin{pmatrix} -2 \\ 0 \\ 3 \end{pmatrix} - \begin{pmatrix} 3 \\ -1 \\ 4 \end{pmatrix} = \begin{pmatrix} -6 \\ 1 \\ 0.5 \end{pmatrix}$

APPLICATIONS

Vector methods can produce simple solutions to a variety of practical problems.

EXAMPLE

A surveyor is standing at the top of a hill. Call this point 'the origin' (O). A lighthouse (L) is visible 4km to the west and 3km to the north. A town (T) is visible 5km to the south and 2km to the east. Using a vector basis in which $\vec{i}$ is a 1km vector running east and $\vec{j}$ is a 1km vector running north. Find the position vectors of the lighthouse, $\overrightarrow{OL}$ and the town $\overrightarrow{OT}$. Hence find the vector $\overrightarrow{LT}$ and the position of the town relative to the lighthouse.

SOLUTION

The position vectors are: lighthouse $\overrightarrow{OL} = -4\vec{i} + 3\vec{j}$ and town $\overrightarrow{OT} = 2\vec{i} - 5\vec{j}$.

$$\overrightarrow{LT} = \overrightarrow{LO} + \overrightarrow{OT}$$
$$= -\overrightarrow{OL} + \overrightarrow{OT}$$
$$= -(-4\vec{i} + 3\vec{j}) + (2\vec{i} - 5\vec{j})$$
$$= 4\vec{i} - 3\vec{j} + 2\vec{i} - 5\vec{j}$$
$$= 6\vec{i} - 8\vec{j}$$

This means that the town is 6km east of the lighthouse and 8km south.

EXERCISE 10.2

1. If $a = \vec{i} + 7\vec{j} - \vec{k}$ and $b = 4\vec{i} + 7\vec{j} + 5\vec{k}$ find:

(i) $4a$ (ii) $3b$

(iii) $2a - b$ (iv) $2(a - b)$

2. The position vectors of A and B are $\overrightarrow{OA} = -3\vec{i} + 4\vec{j} - 2\vec{k}$ and $\overrightarrow{OB} = \vec{i} - 4\vec{j} - 3\vec{k}$. Find:

(i) $\overrightarrow{AO}$ (ii) $\overrightarrow{OA} - 5\overrightarrow{OB}$

(iii) $-5\overrightarrow{OA} + 3\overrightarrow{OB}$ (iv) $3\overrightarrow{OA} + 6\overrightarrow{BO}$

3. The vectors $\vec{p}$ and $\vec{q}$ are defined by $\vec{p} = \begin{pmatrix} -1 \\ -2 \\ 4 \end{pmatrix}$ and $\vec{q} = \begin{pmatrix} 6 \\ 1 \\ 2 \end{pmatrix}$. Find:

(i) $\vec{p} + 2\vec{q}$ (ii) $-3\vec{p} - 5\vec{q}$

(iii) $3\vec{p}$ (iv) $2\vec{p} + 3\vec{q}$

4. Find the position vectors that join the origin to the points with coordinates A (2,-1) and B (-3,2). Express your answers as column vectors. Hence find $\overrightarrow{AB}$

5. A point on the cartesian plane starts at the origin. The point then moves 4 units to the right, 5 units up, 6 units to the left and, finally 2 units down. Express these translations as a sum of four column vectors and hence find the coordinates of the final position of the point.

6. Two vectors are defined $\vec{a} = \vec{i} + \vec{j} + 4\vec{k}$ and $\vec{b} = -7\vec{i} - \vec{j} + 2\vec{k}$.
Find:

(i) $-6\vec{a} - 2\vec{b}$ (ii) $-5\vec{a} + 2\vec{b}$

(iii) $4\vec{a} + 3\vec{b}$ (iv) $-2(\vec{a} + 3\vec{b})$

7. If $x = \begin{pmatrix} 4 \\ -4 \\ 2 \end{pmatrix}$ and $y = \begin{pmatrix} 4 \\ 3 \\ 7 \end{pmatrix}$, express the following as column vectors.

(i) $2x + 3y$ (ii) $x + 2y$

(iii) $5x - 6y$ (iv) $x - 6y$

8. Find the values of A and B if $A(7\vec{i} + 7\vec{j} + 4\vec{k}) - 3(3\vec{i} - \vec{j} + B\vec{k}) = -37\vec{i} - 25\vec{j} + 5\vec{k}$

9. Two vectors are defined as $a = \begin{pmatrix} -3 \\ 1 \\ 4 \end{pmatrix}$ and $b = \begin{pmatrix} 6 \\ -6 \\ -5 \end{pmatrix}$.

Find values of the scalars X and Y if $Xa + Yb$ is equal to:

(i) $\begin{pmatrix} -36 \\ 32 \\ 33 \end{pmatrix}$ (ii) $\begin{pmatrix} 30 \\ -22 \\ -31 \end{pmatrix}$ (iii) $\begin{pmatrix} -12 \\ 24 \\ 1 \end{pmatrix}$

10. A submarine (which is considered the origin of the vector system) is 60 metres below the surface of the sea when it detects two surface ships. A destroyer (D) is 600 metres to the east and 800 metres to the south of the submarine. An aircraft carrier (A) is 1200 metres to the west and 300 metres to the south.

(i) Define a suitable vector basis for this problem.

(ii) Using the submarine as the origin, state the position vectors of the destroyer and the aircraft carrier.

(iii) A helicopter pilot, based on the aircraft carrier wants to make a supplies delivery to the destroyer, find, in vector terms, the course along which the pilot should fly.

10.3 UNIT VECTORS

If a vector is expressed in terms of the unit length basis of vectors, $\vec{i}, \vec{j}, \vec{k}$, the **length** of the vector can be found using the Theorem of Pythagoras.

The length of a vector is sometimes known as its **magnutude** or **absolute value**. The length of a vector $\vec{a}$ (or a) is often represented by $|\vec{a}|$ (or $|a|$)If the vector represents some physical quantity such as a force, the length of the vector is the size of the force, without its direction. The length of a vector is a scalar quantity.

EXAMPLES

Find the lengths of the vectors:

(i) $3\vec{i} - 4j$ (ii) $-\vec{i} + 2\vec{j} - 5\vec{k}$ (iii) $\begin{pmatrix} 3 \\ -1 \\ 2 \end{pmatrix}$

SOLUTIONS

(i) $3\vec{i} - 4j$ is represented by the diagram:

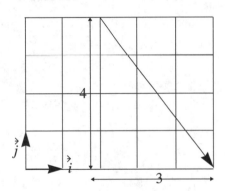

$$\left| 3\vec{i} - 4\vec{j} \right| = \sqrt{3^2 + (-4)^2}$$
$$= \sqrt{9 + 16}$$
$$= \sqrt{25}$$
$$= 5$$

(ii) $\left| -\vec{i} + 2\vec{j} - 5\vec{k} \right| = \sqrt{(-1)^2 + 2^2 + (-5)^2}$ This is the extended version of Pythagoras.
$$= \sqrt{1 + 4 + 25}$$
$$= \sqrt{30}$$

(iii) $\left\| \begin{pmatrix} 3 \\ -1 \\ 2 \end{pmatrix} \right\| = \sqrt{3^2 + (-1)^2 + 2^2}$

$$= \sqrt{9 + 1 + 4}$$
$$= \sqrt{14}$$

UNIT VECTORS

Now that we can find the length of a vector we are in a position to calculate **unit vectors**. If we are given a vector $\vec{a}$, the unit vector, sometimes called $\hat{a}$, is a vector of length one unit in the same direction as $\vec{a}$.

EXAMPLE

Find unit vectors in the same directions as the vectors:

(i) $\quad 5\vec{i} - 2\vec{j}$ 　　　 (ii) $\begin{pmatrix} -3 \\ 6 \\ 4 \end{pmatrix}$ 　　　 (iii) $\begin{pmatrix} 4 \\ 2 \\ -1 \\ 2 \end{pmatrix}$

SOLUTIONS

(i) $\left| 5\vec{i} - 2\vec{j} \right| = \sqrt{5^2 + (-2)^2} = \sqrt{29}$. This is the length of the vector. In order to produce a vector of unit length, we can keep the original components of the vector, scaling them down to produce the required unit vector: $\dfrac{1}{\sqrt{29}}(5\vec{i} - 2\vec{j})$

(ii) $\left| \begin{pmatrix} -3 \\ 6 \\ 4 \end{pmatrix} \right| = \sqrt{(-3)^2 + 6^2 + 4^2} = \sqrt{61}$ The required unit vector is: $\dfrac{1}{\sqrt{61}} \begin{pmatrix} -3 \\ 6 \\ 4 \end{pmatrix}$

(iii) $\left| \begin{pmatrix} 4 \\ 2 \\ -1 \\ 2 \end{pmatrix} \right| = \sqrt{4^2 + 2^2 + (-1)^2 + 2^2} = \sqrt{25} = 5$ The unit vector $= \begin{pmatrix} 0.8 \\ 0.4 \\ -0.2 \\ 0.4 \end{pmatrix}$

In the same way as there is a zero number, there is a **zero vector**. Consider the sum of these three vectors, $\vec{a} = 2\vec{i} - \vec{j}$, $\vec{b} = -3\vec{i} + 2\vec{j}$ and $\vec{c} = \vec{i} - \vec{j}$. The sum of these three vectors is: $\vec{a} + \vec{b} + \vec{c} = 2\vec{i} - \vec{j} + -3\vec{i} + 2\vec{j} + \vec{i} - \vec{j} = 0\vec{i} + 0\vec{j} = \vec{0}$, the **zero vector**.

The zero vector is a vector quantity, but cannot really be said to have a direction.

EXERCISE 10.3

1. Find the lengths of these vectors, expressing your answers as surds. It is not necessary to simplify these surds.

   (i) $\vec{i} + 3\vec{j}$

   (ii) $5(\vec{i} + \vec{j})$

   (iii) $5\vec{i} - 2\vec{j} + \vec{k}$

   (iv) $-(2\vec{i} + \vec{j} + 2\vec{k})$

   (v) $4\vec{i} + 6\vec{j} - \vec{k}$

   (vi) $2\vec{i} + 6\vec{j} + \vec{k}$

   (vii) $\begin{pmatrix} 2 \\ 3 \\ 1 \end{pmatrix}$

   (viii) $\begin{pmatrix} 2 \\ -3 \\ -2 \end{pmatrix}$

   (ix) $\begin{pmatrix} 2 \\ 4 \\ 2 \\ 5 \end{pmatrix}$

   (x) $\begin{pmatrix} 0 \\ 3 \\ 6 \\ 5 \end{pmatrix}$

   (xi) $\begin{pmatrix} 4 \\ 4 \\ -3 \\ 3 \end{pmatrix}$

   (xii) $\begin{pmatrix} 3 \\ -3 \\ -3 \\ 6 \end{pmatrix}$

2. Find unit vectors in the same directions as these vectors:

   (i) $4\vec{i} + 4\vec{j}$

   (ii) $4\vec{i} + 5\vec{j}$

   (iii) $-\vec{i} - 2\vec{j}$

   (iv) $\vec{i} + 6\vec{j} - 3\vec{k}$

   (v) $2\vec{j} + 4\vec{k}$

   (vi) $2\vec{i} - 2\vec{j} - 3\vec{k}$

   (vii) $\begin{pmatrix} 6 \\ -1 \\ -2 \\ 1 \end{pmatrix}$

   (viii) $\begin{pmatrix} 2 \\ 1 \\ 2 \end{pmatrix}$

   (ix) $\begin{pmatrix} -1 \\ 5 \\ 1 \end{pmatrix}$

   (x) $\begin{pmatrix} 6 \\ 4 \\ 6 \\ -1 \end{pmatrix}$

   (xi) $\begin{pmatrix} 6 \\ -1 \\ 3 \\ 2 \end{pmatrix}$

   (xii) $\begin{pmatrix} -1 \\ 1 \\ -3 \\ 2 \end{pmatrix}$

3. A mass sitting on the ground is being pulled by a force of 4 Newtons in a northerly direction, 3 Newtons in a westerly direction and 1 Newton upwards.

   (i)   Express the forces acting on the mass in terms of an appropriate vector basis.

   (ii) Find the total magnitude of the force acting on the mass

EXAMINATION STYLE QUESTIONS

1.   (a)   In the figure shown, draw directed line segments to represent the vectors

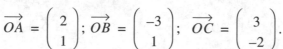

$$\overrightarrow{OA} = \begin{pmatrix} 2 \\ 1 \end{pmatrix}; \quad \overrightarrow{OB} = \begin{pmatrix} -3 \\ 1 \end{pmatrix}; \quad \overrightarrow{OC} = \begin{pmatrix} 3 \\ -2 \end{pmatrix}.$$

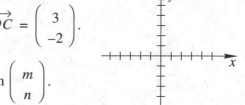

   (b)   Express the vector $\overrightarrow{AB}$ in the form $\begin{pmatrix} m \\ n \end{pmatrix}$.

2.   Using the grid shown

   (a)   write the vector $\overrightarrow{AB}$ in the form $\begin{pmatrix} p \\ q \end{pmatrix}$.

   (b)   write the vector $\overrightarrow{BC}$ in the form $\begin{pmatrix} p \\ q \end{pmatrix}$.

   Hence, find

   (c)   (i) $\overrightarrow{CA}$ (ii) $\left|\overrightarrow{CA}\right|$.

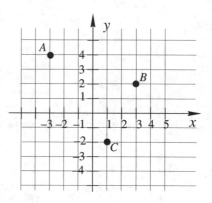

3.   For the position vector $a = \overrightarrow{OA}$ shown in the diagram

   (a)   draw the position vector $-2a = \overrightarrow{OB}$.

   (b)   write down the coodinates of the point B.

   (c)   find $\left|\overrightarrow{OB}\right|$.

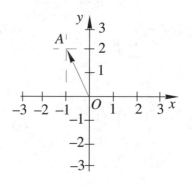

4.   Given the vectors $a = \begin{pmatrix} 1 \\ 0 \end{pmatrix}$ and $b = \begin{pmatrix} 0 \\ 1 \end{pmatrix}$,

   (a)   express (i) $\begin{pmatrix} 5 \\ 3 \end{pmatrix}$ (ii) $\begin{pmatrix} 2 \\ -4 \end{pmatrix}$ in terms of a and b.

   (b)   Show that any vector of the form $\begin{pmatrix} p \\ q \end{pmatrix}$ can be expressed in the form $ka + lb$.

   Where p, q, k and l are all real numbers.

SELF ASSESSMENT TEST (30 MINS.)

1. If $\vec{a} = 3\vec{i} - 2\vec{j}$ and $\vec{b} = -\vec{i} + 2\vec{j}$, express the following vectors in their simplest form:

(i) $2\vec{a}$ (ii) $2\vec{a} + \vec{b}$ (iii) $\frac{1}{2}\vec{a} - 3\vec{b}$

[3 marks]

2. Find the lengths of these vectors:

(i) $\vec{i} + 2\vec{j}$ (ii) $\vec{i} - 2\vec{j} - 3\vec{k}$

[2 marks]

3. Find a unit vector in the same direction as $-3\vec{i} + 4\vec{j} + 3\vec{k}$

[2 marks]

4. If $5\vec{i} - 2\vec{j} + \vec{k} + \vec{a} = \vec{0}$, then find the vector $\vec{a}$.

[1 mark]

6. Express the column vector $\begin{bmatrix} 3 \\ -2 \\ 5 \end{bmatrix}$ in the $\vec{i}, \vec{j}, \vec{k}$ notation.

[1 mark]

STATISTICS

11

Chapter contents

Key Formulae

- Sample mean $\bar{x} = \dfrac{\sum\limits_{i=1}^{n} x_i}{n}$

- Sample st.dev $s_n = \sqrt{\dfrac{\sum\limits_{i=1}^{n} f_i(x_i - \bar{x})^2}{n}}$

- Population st.dev $\sigma = \sqrt{\dfrac{\sum\limits_{i=1}^{n} f_i(x_i - \mu)^2}{n}}$

11.1 FREQUENCY DIAGRAMS

Statistics is the science of getting 'facts from figures'. Many investigations involve the collection of data which, on their own, tend to mean little.

The following figures are the heights (in centimetres) of a group of students:

156	172	168	153	170	160	170	156	160	160	172	174
150	160	163	152	157	158	162	154	159	163	157	160
153	154	152	155	150	150	152	152	154	151	151	154

These figures alone do not give us much information about the heights of this group of people. One of the first things that is usually done in undertaking an analysis is to make a frequency table. In this case as there are a large number of different heights, it is a good idea to group the height data into the categories (or classes) 148-150, 151-153, 154-156, etc. before making a tally.

Heights	Tally	Frequency
148-150	√√√	3
151-153	√√√√√√√√	8
154-156	√√√√√√√	7
157-159	√√√√	4
160-162	√√√√√√	6
163-165	√√	2
166-168	√	1
169-171	√√	2
172-174	√√√	3

Each height is recorded in the appropriate row of the tally column. Finally, the frequency is the number of tally marks in each row. As a check, the total of the frequency column should equal the count of the number of data items. In this case there are 36 heights.

The choice of class interval in making such a frequency table is generally made so that there are about ten classes. This is not inevitably the case and it is true to say that this choice is an art rather than a science. The objective is to show the distribution of the data as clearly as possible. This can best be seen when the data is shown graphically. There are a number of ways in which this can be done. In the present example, we are dealing with heights. Since heights vary continuously, we would most usually use a histogram to display the distribution.

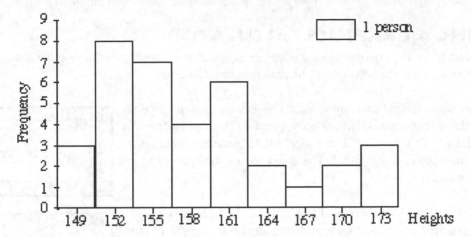

There are two details connected with the construction of histograms that you should not ignore. Firstly, as far as the horizontal scales are concerned, we are representing the continuous variable 'height'. The first class interval represents all the people with heights in the range 148 to 150cm. Since these have been rounded to the nearest whole centimetre, anyone with a height from 147.5 to 150.5cm, or [147.5,150.5), will have been placed in this class. Similarly, anyone with a height in the range [150.5,153.5) will be categorised in the class 151-153cm. If you want to label the divisions between the blocks on the histogram, technically these should be 147.5, 150.5 etc. Secondly, in a histogram it is the area of the bars and not their height that represent the number of data items in each class. To be completely correct, we should give the area as a measure of the vertical scale. This definition allows us to draw histograms with class intervals of varying widths. This is sometimes done to smooth out the variations at the extremes of a distribution where the data is sparse. This aspect will not be considered in this chapter.

Once we have drawn a histogram, it should be possible to see any patterns that exist in the data. In this case, there is a big group of students with heights from about 150 to 160cm. There are also quite a few students with heights significantly larger than this and very few with heights below the main group. The distribution has a much larger 'tail' at the positive end than at the negative end and is said to be positively skewed. Such patterns can also be seen using other graphical devices. The following shows the same data using a line graph:

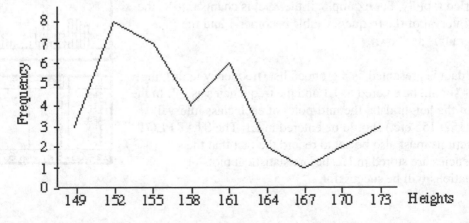

The same patterns are evident from this diagram as were seen from the histogram.

USING A GRAPHICS CALCULATOR

Data can be entered on the calculator either as separate figures from the original data or as a frequency table. In both cases, the data is entered as a list.

To enter the original data, press the STAT key and choose EDIT from the screen menus. If necessary, press 4 followed by the keys L1 (2nd 1), L2 (2nd 2) etc. ENTER to clear any previous lists. Next select STAT EDIT. The data can now be entered as a column under L1.

The data can now be displayed as a statistical graph. As with other types of graph, the appropriate window must be set. In the present case, the x data range should be set at 145 to 175. The Xscl setting determines the width of class interval that will be used.

Next, any cartesian graphs must be cleared. Press Y= and clear any rule that you see. The statistical plotting facility must now be activated. Press 2nd STAT PLOT. Choose plot 1 and turn it on by using the arrows to the word On and then press ENTER. Also select the histogram symbol from the list of available plot types. We entered the data as L1 so we must select this as the source of the data. Finally, because each height was entered separately, the frequency must be defined as 1.
Pressing GRAPH should now display the histogram. This should be similar to that produced earlier.

One advantage of using a calculator to produce such plots is that, once the data has been stored, the conditions of the plot can be varied rapidly. For example, if the Xscl is changed to 1, the class interval of the frequency table becomes 1 and the histogram is as shown.

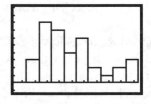

If the data is presented as a grouped list (frequency table), the x values should be entered as L1 and the frequencies as L2. In the case of the height data, the mid-point of each class interval (149, 152, 155 etc.) should be entered in L1. The STAT PLOT instructions must also be set to record the fact that the frequencies are stored in L2. before statistical plots or calculations will be successful.

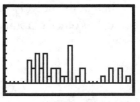

11.2 STATISTICAL MEASURES

After using a graphical presentation of some sort to look at the general pattern of the data, we would usually calculate some representative 'statistics'. The aim of producing these is to reduce the amount of data to a small number of figures that represent the data as well as possible. In the case of the height data we have been studying, we have already observed that the heights group around the range 150-160cm. This is sometimes known as a 'central tendency' and we have several ways in which we measure this:

MODE

This is the most frequent class of data. In the present case there were more students in the 151-153cm class than any other so we would give this class as the mode. It is possible for some data to have more than one mode. We describe this as being bimodal, trimodal etc. The mode tends only to be used when there is no alternative such as when we are collecting data on the television stations that people like best.

MEAN

This is the measure commonly (and incorrectly) called average. Numeric data is added and the result is divided by the number of items of data that we have.

Notation: The notation used for the mean depends on whether or not we are claiming to have the mean of all (the **population**) or part (a **sample**) of the possible data set. In the case of the students, we appear to have a small group of 36 selected from all the possible students in this age group and so we are looking at a sample. It is generally quite clear whether any set of data refers to a population (such as a **census**) or a sample (such as a **poll**).

The population mean is denoted by μ and a sample mean by $\bar{x}$.

For a data set x, with n items both means are calculated in the same way:

$$\text{Mean} = \frac{\sum x}{n}$$

The symbol Σ means 'add all the following'.

If the data is presented in the form of a frequency table in which each item of data x_i is present with a frequency of f_i, then the formula becomes:

$$\text{Mean} = \frac{\sum f_i x_i}{\sum f_i}$$

For the height data, we have two ways of approaching this calculation. One way is to return to the original data and add it all up. The total is 5694. There are 36 measurements

so: $$\text{Mean} = \frac{5694}{36} = 158.16667$$

Alternatively we can use the grouped data formula. There is a convenient way of doing this if we add an extra column to the orginal frequency table:

Heights	Mid-height	Frequency	$f \times h$
148-150	149	3	447
151-153	152	8	1216
154-156	155	7	1085
157-159	158	4	632
160-162	161	6	966
163-165	164	2	328
166-168	167	1	167
169-171	170	2	340
172-174	173	3	519
Totals:		36	5700

From the table: $\sum f_i = 36$ and $\sum f_i \times h_i = 5700$ so

$$\text{Mean} = \frac{\sum f_i \times h_i}{\sum f_i} = \frac{5700}{36} = 158.33333$$

This method of calculating the mean will not necessarily give exactly the same answer as the mean calculated from the original data as we have made the assumption that all the students with heights in the range 148-150cm had a height of 149cm. This will not generally be a seriously inaccurate assumption as the students with heights below this figure (148cm) will be balanced by those with heights above this (150cm). In this case, the difference is quite small.

MEDIAN

The median is found by arranging all the data in order of size and selecting the middle item. For the heights data, there is an even number of figures and so there is not a middle number. In this situation, we take the mean of the middle two data items.

Order	1	2	3	4	5	6	7	8	9
Ht:	150	150	150	151	151	152	152	152	152
	10	11	12	13	14	15	16	17	18
	153	153	154	154	154	154	155	156	156
	19	20	21	22	23	24	25	26	27
	157	157	158	159	160	160	160	160	160
	28	29	30	31	32	33	34	35	36
	162	163	163	168	170	170	172	172	174

The middle heights are the 18th and 19th (156 and 157cm) so the median is 156.5cm.

EXERCISE 11.1

1. The following figures are the weights (in grams) of a group of fish sampled from a reservoir:

226	233	233	244	224	235	238	244
222	239	233	243	221	230	237	240
225	230	236	242	222	235	237	240
220	235	238	243	222	232	232	242
229	231	234	241	228	237	237	245
229	231	237	244	225	236	235	240

(i) Construct a frequency table using the class intervals 218-220, 221-223, 224-226 etc. grams.

(ii) Draw a histogram showing this distribution.

(iii) Find the mode, mean and median weights.

2. In a study of the weights of a sample of semi-precious gem-stones, the following results were obtained (grams):

1.33	1.59	1.82	1.92	1.46	1.57	1.82	2.06
1.59	1.70	1.81	2.02	1.24	1.53	1.69	2.01
1.57	1.62	1.61	1.93	1.11	1.90	1.79	1.91
1.19	1.53	1.90	1.90	1.17	1.97	1.92	2.06
1.41	1.64	1.83	1.90	1.11	1.81	1.83	1.90
1.15	1.68	1.82	1.98	1.39	1.54	1.92	2.04

(i) Construct a frequency table using the class intervals [1.1,1.2), [1.2,1.3), [1.3,1.4) etc. grams.

(ii) Draw a histogram showing this distribution.

(iii) Find the mode, mean and median weights.

3. For the following sets of data, make frequency tables and calculate the mode, mean and median of each data set:

Set A:

21.1	28	26.9	31.9	23.7	28.8	27.9	31.3
21.5	26.8	27.4	31.2	21.4	29.9	29.4	31.5
20.4	25.1	25.8	33.6	23.7	25.6	29.1	30.3
21.5	28.2	28.2	31.3	22.4	25.7	25.1	30.3
21.9	29.1	28.7	30.1	21.8	27.8	29.1	34.3
22.5	25.2	25.5	32.9	22.3	29	27.2	33.3

Set B

7	6	5	70	9	9	25	72
7	7	4	72	8	9	28	73
9	9	9	72	6	7	27	71
7	7	9	70	6	8	27	73
8	5	26	73	5	6	26	70
9	9	28	73	5	8	26	71

Compare the two data sets.

4. The following numbers represent the annual salaries of the emplyoyees of a small company.

$20910	$20110	$20390	$20170	$20060	$20350
$21410	$21130	$21340	$21360	$21360	$21410
$20350	$20990	$20690	$20760	$20880	$20960
$21240	$21060	$21190	$21400	$76000	$125000

(i)   Find the mean salary.
(ii)   Find the median salary.
(iii) Which of the two figures is the better representative measure of salary?

5. The selling prices for the properties in a suburb over June 1996 were:

$191000	$152000	$152000	$181000
$180000	$163000	$169000	$189000
$184000	$169000	$167000	$172000
$190000	$169000	$159000	$172000
$202000	$162000	$160000	$154000
$181000	$166000	$163000	$196000
$201000	$154000	$166000	$154000
$178000	$164000	$157000	$185000
$177000	$169000	$157000	$172000
$195000	$150000	$163000	$1150000
$186000	$166000	$151000	$1155000
$185000	$151000	$168000	$1200000

(i)   Find the mean selling price.
(ii)   Find the median selling price.
(iii) Which of the two figures is the better representative measure of selling price?

6. For the figures given below, calculate the mean from the original data.

5	16	15	17	9	16	19	15
6	17	10	16	8	13	13	19
7	16	18	18	8	18	19	18
6	17	19	16	7	13	17	19
9	14	17	19	9	16	17	19
8	18	16	15	8	18	16	15

(i)   Use the frequency table method with class intervals 4-6, 7-9 etc. to calculate the mean of the data.

(ii)   Use the frequency table method with class intervals 1-5, 5-10 etc. to calculate the mean of the data.

11.3 MEASURES OF SPREAD

So far we have only looked at ways of measuring the central tendency of a set of data. This is not necessarily the only feature of a data set that may be important. The following sets of data are test results obtained by a group of students in two tests in which the maximum mark was 20.

Test 1.

4	12	11	10	5	10	12	12
6	8	19	13	3	7	11	13
4	9	12	10	6	13	19	11
3	12	14	11	6	13	16	11
5	10	12	13	7	8	13	14
6	10	12	10	7	10	12	10

Test 2.

9	8	10	10	8	9	10	11
8	8	11	10	9	8	11	10
9	8	10	11	8	9	11	10
9	8	11	11	9	9	11	10
8	9	11	10	8	9	11	11
8	8	11	10	8	9	10	10

The means of the two data sets are fairly close to one another (Test 1, 10.1, Test 2, 9.5). However, there is a substantial difference between the two sets which can be seen from the frequency tables.

Test 1

Mark	3	4	5	6	7	8	9	10	11	12	13	14	15	16	17	18	19
Freq.	2	2	2	4	3	2	1	8	5	8	6	2	0	1	0	0	2

Test 2

Mark	3	4	5	6	7	8	9	10	11	12	13	14	15	16	17	18	19
Freq.	0	0	0	0	0	13	11	12	12	0	0	0	0	0	0	0	0

The marks for Test 1 are quite well spread out across the available scores whereas those for Test 2 are concentrated around 9, 10 & 11. This may be important as the usual reason for setting tests is to rank the students in order of their performance. Test 2 is less effective at this than Test 1 because the marks have a very small spread. In fact, when teachers and examiners set a test, they are more interested in getting a good spread of marks than they are in getting a particular value for the mean. By contrast, manufacturers of precision engineering products want a small spread on the dimensions of the articles that they make. Either way, it is necessary to have a way of calculating a numerical measure of the spread of data. The most commonly used measures are variance, standard deviation and interquartile range.

VARIANCE AND STANDARD DEVIATION

To calculate the variance of a set of data, the frequency table can be extended as follows:
Test 1

Mark (M)	Frequency	$M - \mu$	$f(M - \mu)^2$
3	2	−7.10	100.82
4	2	−6.10	74.42
5	2	−5.10	52.02
6	4	−4.10	67.24
7	3	−3.10	28.83
8	2	−2.10	8.82
9	1	−1.10	1.21
10	8	−0.10	0.08
11	5	0.90	4.05
12	8	1.90	28.88
13	6	2.90	50.46
14	2	3.90	30.42
15	0	4.90	0.00
16	1	5.90	34.81
17	0	6.90	0.00
18	0	7.90	0.00
19	2	8.90	158.42
		Total:	640.48

The third column in this table measures the amount that each mark deviates from the mean mark of 10.10. Because some of these marks are larger than the mean and some are smaller, some of these deviations are positive and some are negative. If we try to calculate an average deviation using these results, the negative deviations will cancel out the positive deviations. To correct this problem, one method is to square the deviation. Finally, this result is multiplied by the frequency to produce the results in the fourth column. In detail, the last row is calculated: $2 \times (3 - 10.10)^2 = 2 \times 50.41 = 100.82$. The total of the fourth column is divided by the number of data items (48) to obtain the variance of the marks

$$\text{Variance} = \frac{640.48}{48} = 13.34$$

The measure most commonly used is the square root of the variance (remember that we squared the deviations). A measure that is known as the standard deviation of the marks. In the previous case:

$$\text{Standard deviation} = \sqrt{13.34} = 3.65$$

Repeating this calculation for the second set of marks:

Mark (M)	Frequency	$M - m$	$f(M - m)^2$
8	13	−1.48	28.475
9	11	−0.48	2.534
10	12	0.52	3.245
11	12	1.52	27.725
		Total:	61.979

$$\text{Variance} = \frac{61.979}{48} = 1.291$$

$$\text{Standard deviation} = \sqrt{1.291} = 1.136$$

This figure is about one third of the figure calculated for Test 1. This reflects the fact that Test 2 has not spread the students very well. In summary, the variance and population standard deviation are calculated using the formulas:

$$\text{Variance} = \frac{\sum f_i(x_i - \mu)^2}{\sum f_i} \qquad \text{Population Standard Deviation} = \sqrt{\frac{\sum f_i(x_i - \mu)^2}{\sum f_i}}$$

USING A GRAPHICS CALCULATOR

Standard deviation can be calculated directly by first entering the data as a list. For Test 2, this is best done with the marks as list 1 and the frequencies as list 2.

Next, use STAT CALC to access the 1-VarStats menu. Next, you must nominate the two lists that contain the data. List 1 is 2nd 1 and list 2 is 2nd 2. The two list names must be separated by a comma.

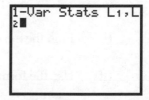

Finally, press ENTER. This screen gives the mean, ($\bar{x}$), the sum of the data, Σx, and the sum of the squares of the data, Σx^2. Sx is known as the sample standard deviation. This is the same as the standard deviation discussed above but with one less than the number of data items in the denominator (47 in this case). σx is the population standard deviation discussed above.

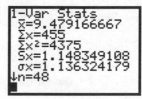

Statistics

It is important to realise that although the true sample variance is given by the formula

$$S_x = \sqrt{\dfrac{\sum\limits_{i=1}^{n} f_i(x_i - \bar{x})^2}{n-1}}$$, in this course (and for examination purposes) the sample standard

deviation should be calculated using the formula $s_n = \sqrt{\dfrac{\sum\limits_{i=1}^{n} f_i(x_i - \bar{x})^2}{n}}$. Therefore, it is

important that you are familiar with the notation that your calculator uses for sample
standard deviation and population standard deviation. In this course, regardless of whether
we are looking at a sample or a population, always use the output that represents the
population standard deviation (this will usually be the σ, σ_n or σ_X output on a
calculator).

EXERCISE 11.2

1. The weights (kg) of two samples of bagged sugar taken from a production line
Sample from machine A

1.95	1.94	2.02	1.94	2.07	1.95	2.02	2.06
2.09	2.09	1.94	2.01	2.07	2.05	2.04	1.91
1.91	2.02	1.92	1.99	1.98	2.09	2.05	2.05
1.99	1.97	1.97	1.95	1.93	2.03	2.02	1.90
1.93	1.91	2.00	2.03	1.94	2.00	2.02	2.02
2.03	1.96	2.04	1.92	1.95	1.97	1.97	2.07

Sample from machine B

1.77	2.07	1.97	2.22	1.60	1.96	1.95	2.23
1.79	1.98	2.07	2.32	1.66	1.96	2.05	2.32
1.80	1.96	2.06	1.80	1.93	1.91	1.93	2.25
1.63	1.97	2.08	2.32	1.94	1.93	1.94	2.22
1.76	2.06	1.91	2.39	1.98	2.06	2.02	2.23
1.75	1.95	1.96	1.80	1.95	2.09	2.08	2.29

(i) Find the mean weights of the bags in each sample.

(ii) Use the formula $S_x = \sqrt{\dfrac{\sum f_i(x_i - m)^2}{\sum f_i - 1}}$ to calculate the sample standard
deviations of each sample.

(iii) Use the formula $\sigma_x = \sqrt{\dfrac{\sum f_i(x_i - \mu)^2}{\sum f_i}}$ to calculate the population standard
deviations of each sample.

2. The following frequency table gives the numbers of passengers using a bus service over a week long period.

Passengers	0-4	5-9	10-14	15-19	20-24	25-29
Frequency	3	5	11	15	10	7

    (i)   Find the mean number of passengers carried per trip.
    (ii)   Find the population standard deviation of the number of passengers carried per trip.

3. The number of matches per box in a sample of boxes taken from a packing machine was:

Matches	47	48	49	50	51	52
Frequency	3	6	11	19	12	9

Find the mean and sample standard deviation of the number of matches per box.

QUARTILES

We have already seen that there is more than one way of measuring central tendency and the same is true of measures of spread. We have already seen that the median is, in some circumstances, a good measure of central tendency. Following on from this definition, we can define quartiles, the data items that are one quarter and three quarters of the way through a list.

The following numbers represent the number of employees absent from work over a nine day period: 2, 6, 5, 4, 7, 1, 0, 5, 2. Firstly, we order the data to get 0, 1, 2, 2, 4, 5, 5, 6, 7. The median is the middle figure:

$$0 \quad 1 \quad 2 \quad 2 \quad 4 \quad 5 \quad 5 \quad 6 \quad 7$$

Lower quartile (Q1)   Median   Upper quartile (Q3)

The median divides the distribution into an upper and lower group. The lower quartile is the middle figure of the lower group and the upper quartile is the middle figure of the upper group. As with finding the median, it may be necessary when dealing with a group with an even number of data items to take the mid point between two numbers. This is the case with the current data set. The lower quartile is 1.5 and the upper quartile is 5.5.

When dealing with large data sets or grouped data, there is an alternative method of finding the median and quartiles based on **cumulative frequency**.
This is calculated as follows:

These figures represent the numbers of customers in a small cinema:

Customers	Frequency	Cumulative Frequency
0-9	1	1
10-19	4	5
20-29	9	14
30-39	11	25
40-49	32	57
50-59	23	80
60-69	10	90
70-79	9	99
80-89	1	100

The cumulative frequency is calculated by 'accumulating' the frequencies as we move down the table. Thus the figure 25 in the shaded box means that on 25 occasions there were fewer than 40 customers.

Cumulative frequencies can now be used to produce a **cumulative frequency curve**:

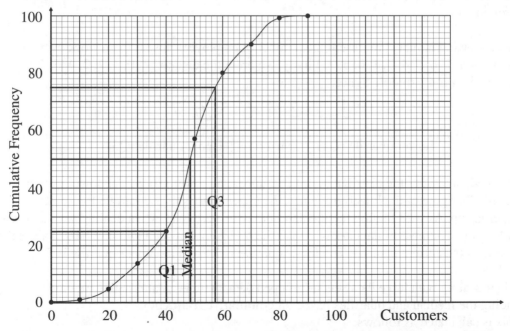

The cumulative frequency curve or **ogive** has effectively placed the data in order. This now enables us to read off estimates of the median and quartiles. The median is half way along the list of data. Since there are 100 figures, the median point is at 50. Technically this should be figure number 51, however, this method only produces an approximate figure and we seldom worry about this distinction. Reading across from 50 and down to the 'customers' scale gives a figure of about 48 customers as the median. Similarly, the lower quartile can be found at a cumulative frequency of 25. Reading across from this figure to the graph and then to the horizontal axis gives a lower quartile of approximately 40 customers. Similarly, the upper quartile is about 57 customers.

The difference between the two quartiles is known as the **inter-quartile range**. In this case, the inter-quartile range is $57 - 40 = 17$ customers. This is, like the standard deviation, a measure of the spread of the data. For these cinema attendance figures, the standard deviation is about 16 customers. It is not necessarily the case that these two measures of spread give similar answers. When comparing two data sets, choose which measure of spread you wish to use and use that measure throughout the analysis. Do not try to compare the inter-quartile range of one data set with the standard deviation of another.

In choosing which measure of spread to use, we generally use the quartiles and the median for a data set that contains a very few numbers that are very unusual. Such data are known as **outliers**. The data sets in Exercise 18.1 Questions 4 & 5 are examples of this type of data containing outliers. The standard deviation and mean are much more sensitive to outliers than are the median and inter-quartile range. Of course, you will need to look at a data set that has outliers and decide whether or not you want to minimise their effect on the representative statistics that you calculate.

USING A GRAPHICS CALCULATOR

The median and inter-quartile range of a data set can be found directly using a graphic calculator. The data can either be entered as a list or as a frequency table using two lists.

The data set: 5.7, 4.2, 7.9, 3.1, 9.4, 4.2, 7.7 & 8.0 can be entered as a single list.

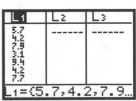

The statistics of this set can be calculated in the same way as the mean and standard deviation were calculated previously. The appropriate figures are found on the second screen (use the down arrow). This screen gives the **five figure summary** of the data: Minimum = 3.1, lower quartile = 4.2, median = 6.7, upper quartile = 7.95 and maximum = 9.4.

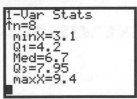

The five figure summary can be displayed using a graph known as a box-plot. This can be displayed on the TI-82/3 by choosing 2nd STATPLOT, turning on plot 1 and selecting the box-plot icon. An appropriate viewing window will also need to be set. The TRACE function can also be used to identify the five figure summary. The diagram shows the median.

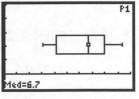

To construct a box-plot (not mentioned directly by the IB syllabus), draw an appropriate horizontal scale. For this data set, a horizontal scale of 1 to 10 with marks every unit is appropriate. The box plot can now be drawn:

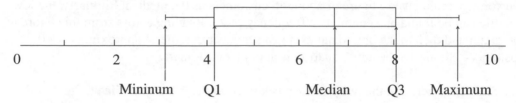

In the same way, the five figure summary for grouped data can be found by entering the data as list 1 and the frequencies as list 2. This frequency table gives the numbers of goals scored in 20 soccer matches:

Goals	0	1	2	3	4	5
Frequency	3	5	5	4	2	1

Enter the goals as L1 and the frequencies as L2.

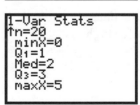

Next use the STAT CALC menu and identify the two lists that contain the data.

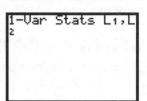

Press enter and use the down arrow to access the median part of the display.

EXERCISE 11.3

1. Find the median, quartiles and inter-quartile range of these data sets:

(i) 5, 6, 2, 8, 9, 2, 7, 0, 5, 3

(ii) 2.8, 4.9, 2.8, 0.9, 3.3, 5.8, 2.9, 3.7, 6.9, 3.3, 5.1

(iii) 142, 167, 143, 126, 182, 199, 172, 164, 144, 163, 192, 101, 183, 153

(iv) 0.02, 0.25, 1.72, 0.93, 0.99, 1.62, 0.67, 1.42, 1.75, 0.04, 1.12, 1.93

(v) 1200, 2046, 5035, 4512, 7242, 6252, 5252, 8352, 6242, 1232

2. Find the median, quartiles and inter-quartile range of these grouped data sets:

(i)

x	0	1	2	3	4	5
Frequency	1	3	6	6	7	1

(ii)

x	10	11	12	13	14	15
Frequency	12	45	56	78	42	16

(iii)

x	1.0	1.5	2.0	2.5	3.0	3.5
Frequency	2	4	9	9	2	1

(iv)

x	10	20	30	40	50	60
Frequency	4	8	15	19	20	5

(v)

x	0	5	10	15	20	25
Frequency	0	3	0	6	7	5

3. The weekly expenses paid to a group of employees of a small company were

$25	$0	$10	$10
$55	$0	$12	$375
$75	$445	$7	$2

(i) Find the mean weekly expense.

(ii) Find the population standard deviation of the expenses.

(iii) Find the median weekly expense.

(iv) Find the quartiles and the inter-quartile range of the expenses.

(v) Which of these statistics are the best representatives of the expenses data?

4. The table shows the numbers of cars per week sold by a dealership over a year.

Cars sold	0	1	2	3	4	5
Number of weeks	2	13	15	12	7	3

      (i)   Find the mean weekly sales.

      (ii)   Find the population standard deviation of the sales.

      (iii)   Find the median weekly sales.

      (iv)   Find the quartiles and the inter-quartile range of the sales.

5.   The table shows the weekly turnover of a small shop over a period during Spring and Summer.

Sales ($)	$0-$99	$100-$199	$200-$299	$300-$399
Number of weeks	2	9	15	7

      (i)   Find the mean weekly sales.

      (ii)   Find the population standard deviation of the sales.

      (iii)   Construct a cumulative frequency table and draw the cumulative frequency curve.

      (iv)   Find the median weekly sales from your graph.

      (v)   Find the quartiles and the inter-quartile range of the sales from your graph.

6.   Plot the cumulative frequency curves for these data and hence estimate the median, quartiles and inter-quartile range of the data.

x	0-4	5-9	10-14	15-19	20-24	25-29
Frequency	2	5	11	9	7	2

EXAMINATION STYLE QUESTIONS

1. The table below shows the frequency of the number of glazed cherries on top of ice–cream scoops on display at a buffet.

Number of cherries	0	1	2	3	4	5
Frequency	2	5	9	6	4	2

    (a)   How many cherries (on ice–cream scoops) where there on the buffet table?

    (b)   Find the mean number of cherries found on ice–cream scoops.

    (c)   What is the modal number of cherries found on ice–cream scoops.

2. The owner of a bistro wants to know how long customers stayed whilst enjoying the service. To do so a survey is conducted in which 50 people are randomly asked how long they had stayed. The results of this survey is shown below:

Time customer stayed in bistro	Frequency	Cumulative Frequency
1-10	11	
11-20	8	
21-30	9	
31-40	7	
41-50	13	
51-60	2	

    (a)   Complete the table shown by filling in the last column.

    (b)   Find the mean time spent in the bistro.

    (c)   Find the standard deviation of the time spent in the bistro.

    (d)   What is the modal class for this data?

SELF ASSESSMENT TEST (20 MINUTES)

1. The following table gives the numbers of pigs per litter born on a farm over a period of one year.

Pigs per litter	4	5	6	7	8	9
Frequency	3	7	11	12	6	3

    (i)   Find the mean number of pigs per litter.
    (ii)   Find the population standard deviation of the number of pigs per litter.

                    [4 marks]

2. Find the median and inter-quartile range of these data:
                6, 4, 2, 8, 5, 7, 3, 8, 2, 6, 0, 5, 3

                    [4 marks]

3. The diagram shows a cumulative frequency curve for some data. Find the median and inter-quartile range of these data.

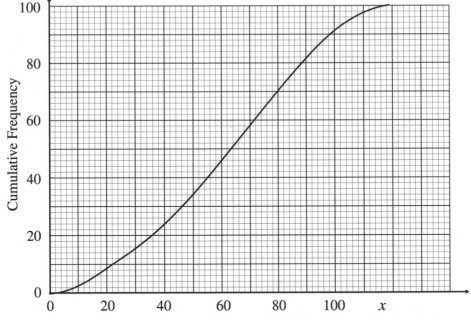

                    [3 marks]

PROBABILITY

12

Chapter contents

Key Formulae

- $\lim\limits_{N \to \infty} \dfrac{n(A)}{N} = p(A)$

- $p(A) = \dfrac{n(A)}{n(U)}$

- $p(A') = 1 - p(A)$

- $p(A \cup B) = p(A) + p(B) - p(A \cap B)$

- $p(A \cap B) = p(A) \times p(B)$

- $p(A|B) = \dfrac{p(A \cap B)}{p(B)}$

12.1 PROBABILITY

We are often faced with statements that reflect an element of likelihood, For example, "It is likely to rain later in the day" or "What are the chances that I roll a six?". Such statements relate to a level of uncertainty (or indeed, a level of certainty). It is this element of likelihood in which we are interested, in particular, we are interested in providing a measure of this likelihood — finding the associated probability of particular events.

PROBABILITY AS A LONG–TERM RELATIVE FREQUENCY

An experiment is repeated in such a way that a series of independent and identical trials are produced, so that a particular event A is observed to either occur or not occur. We let N be the total number of trials carried out and $n(A)$ be the number of times that the event A was observed. We then call the ratio $\dfrac{n(A)}{N}$ the **relative frequency** of the event A. This value provides some indication of the likelihood of the event A occuring. In particular, for large values of N we find that the ratio $\dfrac{n(A)}{N}$ tends to a number called the **probability** of the event A, which we denote by $p(A)$. As $0 \le n(A) \le N$, this number, $p(A)$, must lie between 0 and 1 (inclusive), i.e., $0 \le p(A) \le 1$.

A more formal definition is as follows:

If a random experiment is repeated N times, in such a way that each of the trials are identical and independent, then:

As $N \to \infty, \dfrac{n(A)}{N} \to p(A)$, where $n(A)$ is the number of times event A has occured after N trials.

It is possible to provide a graph of such a situation, which shows that as N increases, the ratio $\dfrac{n(A)}{N}$ tends towards some value p, where in fact, $p = p(A)$. Such a graph is called a relative frequency graph:

THEORETICAL PROBABILITY

When the circumstances of an experiment are always identical we can arrive at a value for the probability of a particular event by using mathematical reasoning, often based on an argument reflecting some form of symmetry (i.e., without the need to repeatedly perform the experiment). This type of probability is called **theoretical probability**.

For example, when we roll a die, every possible outcome, known as the **sample space**, can be listed as $U = \{1, 2, 3, 4, 5, 6\}$. The probability of obtaining a "four" (based on considerations of **symmetry of equal likelihood**) is given by $\frac{1}{6}$. Such a probability seems

obvious, as we would argue that;
"Given there are six possible outcomes and each of the numbers is equally likely to occur

(assuming a fair die), then the chances that a "four" occurs must be one in six, i.e., $\frac{1}{6}$."

LAWS OF PROBABILITY

We will restrict our arguments to **finite sample spaces**. Recall, that a **sample space** is the set of every possible outcome of an experiment, and that an **event** is any subset of the sample space. This relationship is often represented with Venn diagrams:

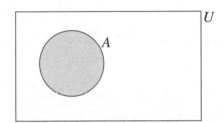

The Venn diagram shows the sample space U, with the event A, as a subset.

DEFINITION OF PROBABILITY

If an experiment has equally likely outcomes and of these the event A is defined, then the **theoretical probability of event A** occuring is given by

$$p(A) = \frac{n(A)}{n(U)} = \frac{\text{Number of outcomes in which A occurs}}{\text{Total number of outcomes in the sample space}}$$

Where $n(U)$ is the total number of possible outcomes in the sample space, U, (that is, $n(U) = N$).

As a consequence of this definition we have what are known as the **axioms of probability**:

1. $0 \le p(A) \le 1$
2. $p(\varnothing) = 0$ and $p(U) = 1$
   That is, if $A = \varnothing$, then the event A can never occur.
   $A = U$ implies that the event A is a certainty.
3. If A and B are both subsets of U and are mutually exclusive, then
   $p(A \cup B) = p(A) + p(B)$.

Note: Two events A and B are said to be **mutually exclusive** (or disjoint) if they have no elements in common, i.e., $A \cap B = \varnothing$.

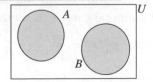

EXAMPLE

A fair die is thrown. List the sample space of the experiment and hence find the
probability of observing: i.   a multiple of 3
                             ii.   an odd number.
Are these events mutually exclusive?

SOLUTION

The sample space is $U = \{1, 2, 3, 4, 5, 6\}$.

i.   Let A be the event 'obtaining a multiple of 3'. We then have that $A = \{3, 6\}$.

Therefore, $p(A) = \dfrac{n(A)}{n(U)} = \dfrac{2}{6} = \dfrac{1}{3}$.

ii.   Let B be the event 'obtaining an odd number'. Here $B = \{1, 3, 5\}$ and so

$p(B) = \dfrac{n(B)}{n(U)} = \dfrac{3}{6} = \dfrac{1}{2}$.

In this case, $A = \{3, 6\}$ and $B = \{1, 3, 5\}$, so that $A \cap B = \{3\}$. Therefore, as $A \cap B \neq \varnothing$
A and B are not mutually exclusive.

EXAMPLE

Two coins are tossed. Find the probability that: i.   two tails are showing
                                                    ii.   a tail is showing.

SOLUTION

Let H denote the event a head is showing and T the event a tail is showing. This means that
the sample space (with two coins) is given by $\varepsilon = \{HH, HT, TH, TT\}$.

i.   The event that two tails are showing is given by the event $\{TT\}$, therefore, we have

that $p(\{TT\}) = \dfrac{n(\{TT\})}{n(U)} = \dfrac{1}{4}$.

ii.   The event that a tail is showing is given by $\{HT, TH\}$, therefore, we have that

$p(\{HT, TH\}) = \dfrac{n(\{HT, TH\})}{n(U)} = \dfrac{2}{4} = \dfrac{1}{3}$.

EXAMPLE

A card is drawn from a standard deck of 52 playing cards. What is the probability that a
diamond card is showing?

SOLUTION

Let D denote the event "a diamond card is selected". This means that $n(D) = 13$ as there
are 13 diamond cards in a standard deck of cards.

Therefore, $p(D) = \dfrac{n(D)}{n(U)} = \dfrac{13}{52} = \dfrac{1}{4}$.

PROBLEM SOLVING STRATEGIES IN PROBABILITY

Often when dealing with probability problems it is useful to use some form of diagram to help 'visualize' the situation at hand. Diagrams can be in the form of

1.   Venn diagrams.
2.   Tree diagrams.
3.   Lattice diagrams.
4.   Karnaugh maps (probability tables).
5.   As a last resort, any form of diagram that clearly displays the process under discussion.

It is fair to say that some types of diagrams lend themselves well to particular types of problems. These will be considered in due course.

EXAMPLE

Find the probability of getting a sum of 7 on two throws of a die.

SOLUTION

In this instance, we make use of a lattice diagram to display all possible outcomes. From the diagram, it then becomes relatively straight forward to list the required event (and hence find the required probability):

Let S denote the event "A sum of seven is observed". From the lattice diagram, we see that there are 6 possibilities where a sum of seven occurs.

In this case we have $S = \{(1, 6), (2, 5), (3, 4), (4, 3), (5, 2), (6, 1)\}$.

Therefore, we have that

$$p(S) = \frac{n(S)}{n(U)} = \frac{6}{36} = \frac{1}{6}$$

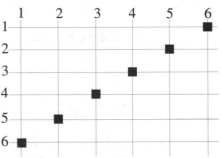

EXERCISE 12.1

1.   From a bag containing 6 white and 4 red balls, a ball is drawn at random. What is the probability that the ball selected is
(a)   red   (b)   white   (c)   not white

2.   From an urn containing 14 marbles of which 4 are blue and 10 are red, a marble is selected at random. What is the probability that
(a)   the marble is blue   (b)   the marble is red

3.   A letter is chosen at random from the letters of the alphabet. What is the probability that
(a)   the letter is a vowel   (b)   the letter is a consonant

4. A coin is tossed twice. List the sample space and find the probability of observing
   (a)   two heads,
   (b)   at least one head

5. A coin is tossed three times. List the sample space and find the probability that
   (a)   two heads, show uppermost
   (b)   at least two heads show uppermost
   (c)   three heads or three tails are showing.

6. A letter is chosen at random from the word FERTILITY. Find the probability that the letter chosen is
   (a)   a T   (b)   an I   (c)   a consonant   (d)   a vowel.

7. A bag has 20 coins numbered from 1 to 20. A coin is drawn at random and its number is noted.What is the probability that the coin drawn
   (a)   has an even number on it
   (b)   has a number that is divisible by 3
   (c)   has a number that is divisible by 3 or 5?

8. A die is rolled twice. Use a lattice diagram to illustrate the sample space. What is the probability of observing
   (a)   at least one five   (b)   a four and a three
   (c)   a pair   (d)   a sum of eight

9. A family has three children. List the sample space and hence find the probability that
   (a)   there are 3 boys
   (b)   there are 2 boys and 1 girl
   (c)   there are at least two girls

10. A card is selected from a pack of 52 cards. Find the probability that the card is
   (a)   red   (b)   a heart   (c)   red and a heart

11. From an urn containing 16 cubes of which 6 are red, 4 are white and 6 are black, a cube is drawn at random. Find the probability that the cube is
   (a)   red   (b)   white   (c)   black   (e)   red or black

12. A coin and a die are tossed simultaneously. Draw a lattice diagram to depict this situation.
   (a)   Using your lattice diagram, list the sample space.
   (b)   What is the probability of observing a tail and an even number?

13. A die is thrown three times. Find the probability of observing
   (a)   three sixes
   (b)   three even numbers
   (c)   two odd numbers
   Hint: You might need to draw a three dimensional lattice diagram.

12.2 PROBABILITY AND VENN DIAGRAMS

From the axioms of probability we can develop further rules to help solve problems that involve chance. We illustrate these rules with the aid of Venn diagrams.

Event	Set language	Venn diagram	Probability result
The **complement** of A is denoted by A'.	A' is the complement to the set A, i.e., the set of elements that do not belong to the set A		$p(A') = 1 - p(A)$ $p(A')$ is the probability that event A does not occur.
The **intersection** of A **and** $B : A \cap B$	$A \cap B$ is the intersection of the sets A and B, i.e., the set of elements that belong to **both** the set A **and** the set B.		$p(A \cap B)$ is the probability that both A and B occur.
The **union** of events A and $B : A \cup B$	$A \cup B$ is the union of the sets A and B, i.e., the set of elements that belong to A **or** B or both A **and** B.		$p(A \cup B)$ is the probability that either event A or event B (or both) occur. From this we have what is known as the **'Addition rule'** for probability: $$p(A \cup B) = p(A) + p(B) - p(A \cap B)$$
If $A \cap B = \varnothing$ the events A and B are said to be **disjoint**. That is, they have no elements in common.	If $A \cap B = \varnothing$ the sets A and B are **mutually exclusive**.		If A and B are mutually exclusive events then event A and event B cannot occur simultaneously, i.e., $n(A \cap B) = 0$ $\Rightarrow p(A \cap B) = 0$ From the addition rule, we now have $$p(A \cup B) = p(A) + p(B)$$

Although we now have a number of 'formulas' to help us solve problems that involve probability, using other forms of diagrams to clarify situations and procedures should not be overlooked.

EXAMPLE

A card is randomly selected from an ordinary pack of 52 playing cards.
Find the probability that it is either a 'black card' or a 'King'.

SOLUTION

Let B be the event 'A black card is selected.' and K the event ' A King is selected.'.
We first note that event B has as its elements the Jack of spades(J♠), the Jack of clubs (J♣),
the Queen of spades(Q♠), the Queen of clubs(Q♣) and so on.
This means that

B ={K♠,K♣,Q♠,Q♣,J♠,J♣,10♠,10♣,9♠,9♣,8♠,8♣,7♠,7♣,6♠,6♣,5♠,5♣,4♠,4♣,3♠,
   3♣,2♠,2♣,A♠,A♣} and

K = {K♠, K♣, K♦, K♥}, so that $B \cap K$ = {K♠, K♣}.

Using the addition rule, $p(B \cup K) = p(B) + p(K) - p(B \cap K)$

we have $$p(B \cup K) = \frac{26}{52} + \frac{4}{52} - \frac{2}{52} = \frac{7}{13}.$$

Notice the importance of subtracting $\frac{2}{52}$ as this represents the fact that we have included

the event {K♠, K♣} twice when finding B and K.

We now consider one of the problems from Exercise 17.1, but this time we make use of the
addition rule.

EXAMPLE

A bag has 20 coins numbered from 1 to 20. A coin is drawn at random and its number is
noted. What is the probability that the coin drawn has a number that is divisible by 3 or by
5?

SOLUTION

Let T denote the event "The number is divisible by 3" and S, the event "The number is
divisible by 5".

Using the addition rule we have; $\qquad p(T \cup S) = p(T) + p(S) - p(T \cap S)$

Now, T = {3, 6, 9, 12, 15, 18} and S = {5, 10, 15, 20} so that $T \cap S$ = {15}.

Therefore, we have $p(T) = \frac{6}{20}$ and $p(S) = \frac{4}{20}$ and $p(T \cap S) = \frac{1}{20}.$

This means that $p(T \cup S) = \frac{6}{20} + \frac{4}{20} - \frac{1}{20} = \frac{9}{20}.$

EXAMPLE

If $p(A) = 0.6$, $p(B) = 0.3$ and $p(A \cap B) = 0.2$, find

(a) $p(A \cup B)$ (b) $p(B')$ (c) $p(A \cap B')$

SOLUTION

(a) Using the addition formula we have, $p(A \cup B) = p(A) + p(B) - p(A \cap B)$
$$\Rightarrow p(A \cup B) = 0.6 + 0.3 - 0.2 = 0.7$$

(b)   Using the complementary formula, we have $p(B') = 1 - p(B) = 1 - 0.3 = 0.7$.

(c)   To determine $p(A \cap B')$, we need to use a Venn diagram:

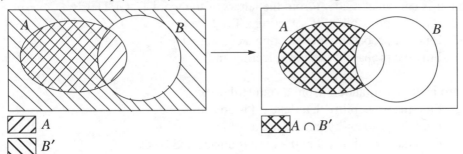

$\boxed{\diagdown}$ A

$\boxed{\diagdown}$ B'

Using the second Venn diagram we are now in a position to form a new formula;
$$p(A \cap B') = p(A) - p(A \cap B).$$
Therefore, $p(A \cap B') = 0.6 - 0.2 = 0.4$.

EXAMPLE

A coin is tossed three times. Find the probability of
(a)   obtaining three tails
(b)   obtaining at least one head.

SOLUTION

We begin by drawing a tree diagram to describe the situation:

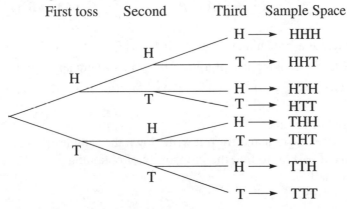

From the tree diagram we have a sample space made up of eight possible outcomes:
{HHH, HHT, HTH, HTT, THH, THT, TTH, TTT}

(a)   Let X be the event "Obtaining three tails.", so $X = \{TTT\}$. Therefore $p(X) = \dfrac{1}{8}$.

(b)   Although we can answer this question by using the tree diagram, we make use of complementary events to solve this problem.
Notice that "At least one head." is the complement of no heads (or "Three tails").

Therefore, $p(\text{At least one head}) = p(X') = 1 - p(X) = 1 - \dfrac{1}{8} = \dfrac{7}{8}$.

EXERCISE 12.2

1. A letter is chosen at random from the letters of the word TOGETHER.
   (a) Find the probability of selecting a T
   (b) Find the probability of selecting a consonant
   (c) Find the probability of not selecting an E.

2. A card is drawn at random from a standard deck.
   (a) Find the probability that the card is an ace.
   (b) Find the probability that the card is black.
   (c) Find the probability that the card is an ace and black.
   (d) Find the probability that the card is an ace or black.

3. A letter is selected at random from the alphabet. Find the probability that the letter is a vowel or comes from the word 'helpful'.

4. The events A and B are such that $p(A) = 0.5$, $p(B) = 0.7$ and $p(A \cap B) = 0.2$. Find
   (a) $p(A \cup B)$ (b) $p(B')$ (c) $p(A' \cap B)$

5. The events A and B are such that $p(A) = 0.35$, $p(B) = 0.5$ and $p(A \cap B) = 0.15$. Making use of a Venn diagram (where appropriate) find:
   (a) $p(A')$ (b) $p(A \cup B)$ (c) $p(A \cup B')$.

6. The events A and B are such that $p(A) = 0.45$, $p(B) = 0.7$ and $p(A \cap B) = 0.20$. Making use of a Venn diagram (where appropriate) find:
   (a) $p(A \cup B)$ (b) $p(A' \cap B')$ (c) $p((A \cap B)')$.

7. A coin is tossed three times.
   (a) Draw a tree diagram and from it write down the sample space.
   Use the results of part (a) to find the probability of obtaining
   (b) only one tail.
   (c) at least 2 tails,
   (d) 2 tails in succession
   (e) 2 tails.

8. In a class of 25 students it is found that 6 of the students play both tennis and chess, 10 play tennis only and 3 do not participate in any acitivies at all. A student is selected at random from this group. Using a Venn diagram, find the probability that the student:
   (a) plays both tennis and chess
   (b) plays chess only
   (c) does not play chess.

9. A blue and a red die are rolled together (both numbered one to six).
- (a) Draw a lattice diagram that best represents this experiment.
- (b) Find the probability of observing an odd number.
- (c) Find the probability of observing an even number with the red die.
- (d) Find the probability of observing a sum of 7
- (e) Find the probability of observing a sum of 7 or an odd number on the red die.

10. A card is drawn at random from a standard deck of 52 playing cards. Find the probability that the card drawn is
- (a) a diamond
- (b) a club or spade
- (c) a black card or a picture card
- (d) a red card or a queen

11. A and B are two events such that $p(A) = p$, $p(B) = 2p$ and $p(A \cap B) = p^2$.
- (a) Given that $p(A \cup B) = 0.4$, find p.

Hence, use a Venn Diagram to find the following:
- (b) $p(A' \cup B)$ (c) $p(A' \cap B')$.

12. In a group of 30 students 20 hold an Australian passport, 10 hold a Malaysian passport and 8 hold both passports. The other students hold only one passport (that is neither Australian nor Malaysian). A student is selected at random.
- (a) Draw a Venn diagram which describes this situation.
- (b) Find the probability that this student has both passports.
- (c) Find the probability that the student holds neither passport.
- (d) Find the probability that the student holds only one passport.

12.3 CONDITIONAL PROBABILITY

Conditional probability works in the same way that simple probability does. The only difference is that we are provided with some prior knowledge (or some extra condition about the outcome). So rather than considering the whole sample space, U, given some extra information about the outcome of the experiment, we only need to concentrate on part of the whole sample space, U^*. This means that the sample space is reduced from U to U^*. Before formalising this section, we use an example to highlight the basic idea.

EXAMPLE
(a) In the toss of a die, find the probability of obtaining a 'Two'.
(b) After tossing a die, it is noted that an even number appeared, what is the probability that it is a 'Two' ?

SOLUTION
(a) This part is straight forward: $U = \{ 1, 2, 3, 4, 5, 6\}$, and so $\Pr(\text{'Two'}) = \dfrac{1}{6}$.

(b) This time, because *we know that an even number has occured*, we have a new sample space, namely $U^* = \{2, 4, 6\}$. The new sample size is $n(U^*) = 3$.

Therefore, Pr('Two' *given that an even number showed up*) $= \dfrac{1}{3}$.

FORMAL DEFINITION OF CONDITIONAL PROBABILITY

If A and B are two events, then **the conditional probability of event A given event B is** found using

$$p(A|B) = \frac{p(A \cap B)}{p(B)}, \; p(B) \neq 0$$

Note 1.   If A and B are mutually exclusive then $p(A|B) = 0$.

      2.   From the above rule, we also have the general **Multiplication rule**: That is,

$$p(A \cap B) = p(A|B) \times p(B)$$

It should also be noted that usually $p(A|B) \neq p(B|A)$.

EXAMPLE

Two dice numbered one to six are rolled onto a table. Find the probability of obtaining a sum of five given that the sum is seven or less.

SOLUTION

We first draw a lattice diagram:

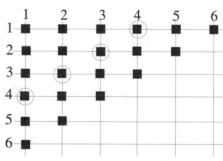

From the diagram we see that the new sample space is made up of 21 outcomes (black boxes) and the event we want (circled) consists of 4 outcomes.

We then have that

$$p((X=5) \cap (X \le 7)) = \frac{4}{36} \text{ and } p(X \le 7) = \frac{21}{36}.$$

Therefore, $p(X=5 | X \le 7) = \dfrac{\frac{4}{36}}{\frac{21}{36}} = \dfrac{4}{21}$.

EXAMPLE

A box contains 2 red cubes and 4 black cubes. If two cubes are chosen at random, find the probability that both cubes are red given that
(a)   the first cube is not replaced before the second cube is selected,
(b)   the first cube is replaced before the second cube is selected.

SOLUTION

Let A be the event "the first cube is red" and B be the event "the second cube is red".

This means that the event $A \cap B$ must be "both cubes are red".

Now, $p(A) = \dfrac{2}{6} = \dfrac{1}{3}$ (as there are 2 red cubes from a total of 6 cubes in the box).

The value of $p(B)$ depends on whether the selection is carried out with or without replacement.

(a) If the first cube selected is red and it is not replaced, then we only have 1 red cube left (in the box) out of a total of five cubes.

So, the probability that the second cube is red given that the first is red is $\dfrac{1}{5}$.

That is $\quad p(B|A) = \dfrac{1}{5} \Rightarrow p(A \cap B) = p(B|A) \times p(A) = \dfrac{1}{5} \times \dfrac{1}{3} = \dfrac{1}{15}$.

(b) This time, because the cube is replaced, the probability that the second cube is red given that the first one is red is still $\dfrac{1}{3}$.

So that, $\quad p(B|A) = \dfrac{1}{3} \Rightarrow p(A \cap B) = p(B|A) \times p(A) = \dfrac{1}{3} \times \dfrac{1}{3} = \dfrac{1}{9}$.

EXAMPLE

Two events A and B are such that $p(A) = 0.5, p(B) = 0.3$ and $p(A \cup B) = 0.6$. Find

(a) $p(A|B)$.   (b) $p(B|A)$ (c) $p(A'|B)$

SOLUTION

(a) $p(A|B) = \dfrac{p(A \cap B)}{p(B)}$, therefore we need to find $p(A \cap B)$.

Using the addition rule we have $p(A \cup B) = p(A) + p(B) - p(A \cap B)$

$$0.6 = 0.5 + 0.3 - p(A \cap B)$$

$$\therefore p(A \cap B) = 0.2$$

Therefore, $p(A|B) = \dfrac{p(A \cap B)}{p(B)} = \dfrac{0.2}{0.3} = \dfrac{2}{3}$

(b) $p(B|A) = \dfrac{p(B \cap A)}{p(A)} = \dfrac{0.2}{0.5} = 0.4$.

(c) $p(A'|B) = \dfrac{p(A' \cap B)}{p(B)} = \dfrac{p(B) - p(A \cap B)}{p(B)} = \dfrac{0.3 - 0.2}{0.3} = \dfrac{1}{3}$

INDEPENDENCE

The events A and B are said to be statistically independent if the probability of event B occuring was not influenced by the occurence of event A.

Therefore we have the mathematical definition:

Two events *A* **and** *B* **are independent if, and only if,**
$$p(A|B) = p(A) \text{ and } p(B|A) = p(B)$$
However, a more convenient definition for independence can be given as follows:

A and B are independent if, and only if $p(A \cap B) = p(A) \times p(B)$

This definition can be used as a test to decide if two events are independent. However, as a rule of thumb, if two events are 'physically independent' then they will also be statistically independent.

There are a few points that should always be considered when dealing with independence:

1. Never assume that two events are independent unless you are absolutely certain that they are independent.

2. How can you tell if two events are independent ?
A good rule of thumb is:
If they are physically independent, they are mathematically independent.

3. Make sure that you understand the difference between mutually exclusive events and independent events.
Mutually exclusive means that the events *A* and *B* have nothing in common and so there is no intersection. i.e., $A \cap B = \emptyset \Rightarrow p(A \cap B) = 0$.
Independent means that the outcome of event A will not influence the outcome of event B i.e., $p(A \cap B) = p(A) \times p(B)$.

4. Independence need not only be for two events, it can be extended, i.e., if the events *A*, *B* and *C* are each independent of each other then
$$p(A \cap B \cap C) = p(A) \times p(B) \times p(C)$$

5. Showing that two events, *A* and *B* are independent, requires two steps:
Step 1 Evaluate the product $p(A) \times p(B)$.
Step 2 Determine the value of $p(A \cap B)$ using any means (other than step 1) i.e., use grids, tables, Venn diagrams, . . .
That is, you must not assume anything about A and B.
Step 3 If the answer using Step 1 is equal to the answer obtained in Step 2, then and only then will the events be independent. Otherwise, they are not independent.
Notice that not being independent does not therefore mean that they are mutually exclusive, they simply aren't independent, that's all.

6. Do not confuse the multiplication principle with the the rule for independence;
Multiplication principle is $p(A \cap B) = p(A|B) \times p(B)$
Independence is given by $p(A \cap B) = p(A) \times p(B)$

EXAMPLE

Two fair dice are rolled. Find the probability that two even numbers will show up.

SOLUTION

Let the E_1 and E_2 denote the events "An even number on the first die." and "An even number on the second die." respectively.

In this case, the events are physically independent, i.e., the outcome on one die will not influence the outcome on the other die, and so we can confidently say that E_1 and E_2 are independent events.

Therefore, we have $p(E_1 \text{ and } E_2) = p(E_1 \cap E_2) = p(E_1) \times p(E_2) = \dfrac{1}{2} \times \dfrac{1}{2} = \dfrac{1}{4}$.

EXAMPLE

Debra has a chance of 0.7 of winning the 100 m race and a 60% chance of winning the 200 m race.

(a)   Find the probability that she only wins one race

(b)   Find the probability that she wins both races.

SOLUTION

Let W_1 denote the event "Debra wins the 100 m race." and W_2, the event "Debra wins the 200 m race.".

(a)   If Debra wins only one race she must either

win the 100 m **and** lose the 200 m **or**

win the 200 m **and** lose the 100 m.

That is, we want $p(W_1 \cap W_2') = p(W_1) \times p(W_2') = 0.7 \times 0.4 = 0.28$ or

$p(W_2 \cap W_1') = p(W_2) \times p(W_1') = 0.6 \times 0.3 = 0.18$.

Therefore, the required probability is $0.28 + 0.18 = 0.46$

We can multiply the probabilities because the events are independent.

We also notice that if W_1 and W_2 are independent, then so too are their complements.

(b)   Winning both races means that Debra will win the 100 m **and** 200 m race.

Therefore, we have $p(W_1 \cap W_2) = p(W_1) \times p(W_2) = 0.7 \times 0.6 = 0.42$

Notice how we have made repeated use of the word '**and**', this emphasizes the fact that we are talking about the intersection of events.

EXAMPLE

Four seeds are planted, each one having an 80% chance of germinating.

Find the probability that

(a)   all four seeds will flower

(b)   at least one seed will flower.

SOLUTION

(a)   Let G_i denote the event that the i th seed germinates.

This means that $p(G_1) = p(G_2) = p(G_3) = p(G_4) = 0.8$

It is reasonable to assume that each seed will germinate independently of the other.

Therefore, p(All four seeds germinate) $= p(G_1 \cap G_2 \cap G_3 \cap G_4)$

$$= p(G_1) \times p(G_2) \times p(G_3) \times p(G_4)$$

$$= (0.8)^4$$

$$= 0.4096$$

(b)   Now, p(At least one seed will flower) $= 1 - p$(No seeds germinate).

p(Any **one** seed does not germinate) $= p(G_i') = 0.2$

Therefore, p(At least one seed will flower) $= 1 - (p(G_i'))^4 = 1 - (0.2)^4 = 0.9984$.

EXAMPLE

A bag contains 5 white balls and 4 blue balls. Two balls are selected in such a way that the first ball drawn is not replaced before the next ball is drawn.
Find the probability of selecting one white ball.

SOLUTION

We begin by drawing a diagram of the situation:

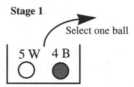

Stage 1   Select one ball

Stage 2
After the first selection the bag would contain one of the situations shown:

From our diagram we quickly notice that there are two possible sample spaces for the second selection.

As an aid, we make use of a tree diagram, where W_i denotes the event "A white ball is selected on the ith trial" and B_i denotes the event "A blue ball is selected on the ith trial".

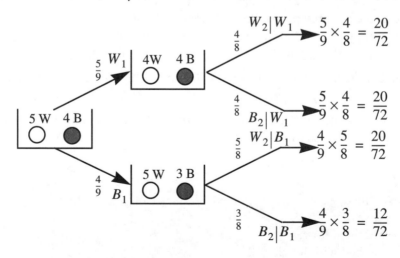

The event "Only one white" occurs if the first ball is white **and** the second ball is blue, **or** the first ball is blue **and** the second ball is white.

$$p(\text{One White ball}) = p(W_1 \cap B_2) + p(B_1 \cap W_2)$$
$$= p(B_2 | W_1) \times p(W_1) + p(W_2 | B_1) \times p(B_1)$$
$$= \frac{4}{8} \times \frac{5}{9} + \frac{5}{8} \times \frac{4}{9}$$
$$= \frac{5}{9}$$

EXERCISE 12.3

1. Two events A and B are such that $p(A) = 0.6$, $p(B) = 0.4$ and $p(A \cap B) = 0.3$, find the probability of the following events:
   (a) $A \cup B$ (b) $A | B$ (c) $B | A$
   (d) $A | B'$

2. A and B are two events such that $p(A) = 0.3$, $p(B) = 0.5$ and $p(A \cup B) = 0.55$. Find the probability of the following events:
   (a) $A | B$ (b) $B | A$ (c) $A | B'$
   (d) $A' | B'$

3. Urn A contains 9 cubes of which 4 are red. Urn B contains 5 cubes of which 2 are red. A cube is drawn at random and in succesion from each urn.
   (a) Draw a tree diagram representing this process.
   (b) Find the probability that both cubes are red.
   (c) Find the probability that only 1 cube is red.
   (d) If only 1 cube is red, find the probability that it came from urn A.

4. A box contains 5 red, 3 black, and 2 white cubes. A cube is randomly drawn and has its colour noted. The cube is then replaced, together with 2 more of the same colour. A second cube is then drawn.
   (a) Find the probability that the first cube selected is red.
   (b) Find the probability that the second cube selected is black.
   (c) Given that the first cube selected was red, what is the probability that the second cube selected is black?

5. A fair coin, a double-headed coin and a double-tailed coin are placed in a bag. A coin is randomly selected. The coin is then tossed.
   (a) Draw a tree diagram showing the possible outcomes.
   (b) Find the probability that the coin lands with a tail showing uppermost.
   (c) In fact, the coin falls "heads", find the probability that it is the "double-headed" coin.

6. Two unbiased coins are tossed together. Find the probability that they both display heads given that at least one is showing a head.

7. A money box contains 10 discs, 5 of which are yellow, 3 of which are black and 2 green. Two discs are selected in succession, the first disc not being replaced before the second is selected.
    (a)   Draw a tree diagram representing this process.
    (b)   Hence find the probability that the discs will be of a different colour
    (c)   Given that the second disc was black, what is the probability that both were black?

8. Two dice are rolled. Find the probability that the faces are different given that the dice show a sum of 10.

9. Given that $p(A) = 0.6$, $p(B) = 0.7$ and that A and B are independent events. Find the probability of the event
    (a) $A \cup B$ (b) $A \cap B$ (c) $A|B'$ (d) $A' \cap B$

10. The probability that an animal will still be alive in 12 years is 0.55 and the probability that its mate will still be alive in 12 years is 0.60.
    Find the probability that
    (a)   both will still be alive in 12 years
    (b)   only the mate will still be alive in 12 years
    (c)   at least 1 will still be alive in 12 years
    (d)   the mate is still alive in 12 years given that only one is still alive in 12 years.

11. Tony has a 90% chance of passing his maths test, whilst Tanya has an 85% chance of passing the same test. If they both sit for the test, find the probability that
    (a)   only one of them passes
    (b)   at least one passes the test
    (c)   Tanya passed given that at least one passed.

12. The probability that Rory finishes a race is 0.55 and the probability that Millicent finishes the same race is 0.6. Because of team spirit, there is an 80% chance that Millicent will finish the race if Rory finishes the race.
    Find the probability that
    (a)   both will finish the race
    (b)   Rory finishes the race given that Millicent finishes

13. If the events A and B are independent events. Show that their complementary events are also independent events.

14. A student runs the 100 m, 200 m and 400 m races at the school athletics day. He has an 80% chance of winning any one given race. Find the probability that he will
    (a)   win all 3 races,
    (b)   win the first and last race only,
    (c)   win the second race given that he wins at least two races.

EXAMINATION STYLE QUESTIONS

1. The frequency distribution for how long (in minutes) customers stayed at a bistro is shown below:

Time customer stayed in bistro	Frequency
1-10	11
11-20	8
21-30	9
31-40	7
41-50	13
51-60	2

(a) What is the probability that a customer stayed between 11–20 minutes.
(b) What is the probability that a customer stayed no more than 40 minutes
(c) What is the probability that a customer stayed between 21–50 minutes.

2. A box containing small cardboard squares numbered 1 to 10 has one of the cardboarb pieces randomly selected.

What is the probability that the number selected is

(a) even?
(b) greater than 3?
(c) a prime number?
(d) a prime number and at least 5.

3. A class of 40 students consist of 24 studying History, 22 studying Economics and 15 studying both these subjects.
(a) Illustrate this information using a Venn diagram.
(b) Use your diagram to find the probability that a student studies
    (i) both subjects.
    (ii) History only.
    (iii) Exactly one subject.
    (iv) neither subject.

4. A student runs the 100 m, 200 m and 400 m races at the school athletics day. He has an 70% chance of winning any one given race. Find the probability that he will
(a) win all 3 races,
(b) win the first and last race only,
(c) win the second race given that he wins at least two races.

SELF ASSESSMENT TEST (45 MINUTES)

1. In a group of 70 people, 42 have fair hair, 34 do not have blue eyes and 23 have fair hair but do not have blue eyes.

(i) Find the number of students that have both blue eyes and fair hair.

(ii) Find the probability that a randomly chosen student has neither blue eyes nor fair hair.

(iii) If a person with blue eyes is chosen at random from the group, what is the probability that this person has fair hair?

(iv) Is the characteristic of having blue eyes independent of the characteristic of having fair hair? Justify your answer.

[9 marks]

2. A bowl contains 8 red balls and 4 green balls. A ball is selected at random from the bowl, its colour noted and it is then replaced. A second ball is drawn and its colour is also noted.

(i) What is the probability that both balls are green?

(ii) What is the probability that the balls are of different colours?

(iii) If the first ball drawn is red, what is the probability that the second is also red?

[4 marks]

3. Two events A & B are exclusive. Prove that if $p(A) > 0$ and $p(B) > 0$ then the events are dependent.

[3 marks]

4. Dale and Kritt are trying to solve a physics problem. The chances of solving the problem are Dale—65% and Kritt— 75%. Find the probability that

(a) only Kritt solves the problem

(b) Kritt solves the problem

(c) both solve the problem

(d) Dale solves the problem given that the problem was solved

[7 marks]

5. A coin which is weighted in such a way that the there is a 70% chance of it landing heads. The coin is tossed three times in succession find the probability of observing

(a) three tails

(b) two heads

(c) two heads given that at least one head showed up.

[6 marks]

FUNCTIONS & RELATIONS

13

Chapter contents

- Idea of a relation
- Idea of function.
- Domain and range.
- Mapping notation.
- Piecewise linear function.
- Step function.

13.1 RELATIONS

Consider the relationship between the weight of five students and their ages as shown in the table below:

Age (years)	Weight (kg)
10	31
12	36
14	48
16	53
18	65

We can represent this information as a **set of ordered pairs**. An age of 10 years would correspond to a weight of 31kg, and, an age of 16 years would correspond to a weight of 53kg. This type of information represents a **relation** between two sets of data. The information given in the table would be represented as

$\{(10, 31), (12, 36), (14, 48), (16, 53), (18, 65)\}$

The **set of all first elements** of the ordered pair is called the **domain** of the relation and is referred to as the **independent variable**. The **set of all second elements** is called the **range** and is referred to as the **dependent variable**.

For the above example, the domain = $\{10, 12, 14, 16, 18\}$,and,

the range = $\{31, 36, 48, 53, 65\}$.

Notice that $(10, 31) \neq (31,10)$! This is clearly the case as the ordered pair

$(10, 31)$ provides the correct relation between age and weight, i.e., at age 10 years the weight of the student is 31kg. On the other hand, the ordered pair $(31,10)$ would indicate that at age 31 years the weight of the student is 10kg!

EXAMPLE

Determine the domain and range for each of the following relations:
(a) $\{(0,0), (1,1), (2,4), (3,9), (4,16), (5,25)\}$
(b) $\{(-3,4), (-1,0), (2,-2), (-2,2)\}$

SOLUTION

(a)   The domain is the set of all first elements; i.e., $\{0, 1, 2, 3, 4, 5\}$.
        The range is the set of all second elements; i.e., $\{0, 1, 4, 9, 16, 25\}$.
(b)   The domain is the set of all first elements; i.e., $\{-3, -1, 2, -2\}$.
        The range is the set of all second elements; i.e., $\{4, 0, -2, 2\}$

The letter 'X' is often used to denote the domain and the letter 'Y' to denote the range. For part (b) in the above example, we have X = $\{-3, -1, 2, -2\}$ and Y = $\{4, 0, -2, 2\}$. This is simply a convention, nothing more.

In many instances a relation is specified in terms of a **rule** that provides information as to how the elements in the range relate to the elements in the domain.

EXAMPLE

A relation is defined by the rule $y = x + 2$, where $x \in \{0, 1, 2, 3, 4\}$.
(a)   Determine the range of this relation.
(b)   Express this relation as a set of ordered pairs.

SOLUTION

(a)   The domain of this relation is given by the x values, i.e., $\{0, 1, 2, 3, 4\}$. We can therefore substitute these values into the equation $y = x + 2$ and determine their corresponding y–values. This will provide the range of the relation.

Substituting we have,

$$x = 0 \Rightarrow y = 0 + 2 = 2$$
$$x = 1 \Rightarrow y = 1 + 2 = 3$$
$$x = 2 \Rightarrow y = 2 + 2 = 4, \text{ and so on.}$$

This produces a set of y–values $\{2, 3, 4, 5, 6\}$ that defines the range.

(b)   The set of ordered pairs would be $\{(0, 2), (1, 3), (2, 4), (3, 5), (4, 6)\}$.

Notice that we can describe the set of ordered pairs more formally as:

$$\{(x,y) : y = x + 2, x \in \{0, 1, 2, 3, 4\}\}.$$

which is read as;

"The set of ordered pairs x and y, such that $y = x + 2$, where x is an element of the set of values $\{0, 1, 2, 3, 4\}$."

Such information can also be displayed visually.

MAPPING DIAGRAMS

A mapping diagram as shown below can be used to graph the relation $\{(0, 2), (1, 3), (2, 4),(3, 5), (4, 6)\}$:

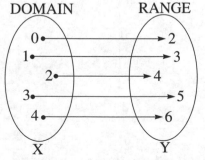

CARTESIAN PLANE

The Cartesian plane can also be used to graph this relation

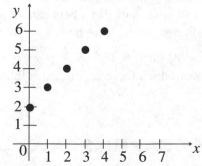

Notice that we do not join the points together as the domain specifies that the only values of x that can be used must be from the set $\{0, 1, 2, 3, 4\}$, and so a value such as $x = 2.4$ cannot be used.

Functions and relations

Both these visual representations are very useful when describing a relation, however, we will mainly consider the Cartesian plane when providing a graphical representation of relations.

We will now look at some further examples:

EXAMPLE

Determine the domain and range of the following relations

(a) $y = 1 - x^2, x \geq 0$ (b) $y > 2 - x, x \in \mathbb{R}$ (c) $x^2 + y^2 = 4$

SOLUTION

(a) For this relation the domain is specified as $\{x:x \geq 0\}$, and so we can only sketch the graph of $y = 1 - x^2$, for these values of x. Using the graph we can see that the range is $\{y:y \leq 1\}$.

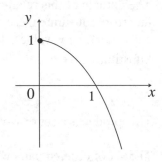

(b)

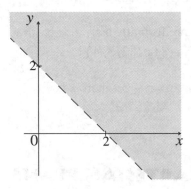

This time we have a shaded half–plane. The domain of this relation is $\mathbb{R}$. Similarly, the range is also $\mathbb{R}$, the set of real numbers.

(c) The relation $x^2 + y^2 = 4$ represents a circle of radius 2 units with its centre at the origin. Note that we can only use values of x between –2 and 2. For example, if we have $x = 3$, then we must have $9 + y^2 = 4 \Rightarrow y^2 = -5$. for which there are no real solutions.

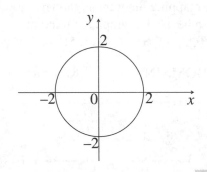

THE GRAPHICS CALCULATOR

The new course allows the use of graphic calculators, so we will consider their use when determining the properties of relations. Although in this text we use the TI–83 and TI–82, other graphic calculators could be used.

NB: On most graphic calculators, the display screen is two thirds as high as it is wide. Because of this, when we graph a relation that describes a circle we obtain a diagram that is not a true geometric representation. To obtain a true geometric representation we need to use a window that produces a square setting. This is done by using the fact that $\dfrac{Y_{max} - Y_{min}}{X_{max} - X_{min}} = \dfrac{2}{3}$.

For example, this window shows such a setting:

$$\frac{Y_{max} - Y_{min}}{X_{max} - X_{min}} = \frac{4 - (-4)}{6 - (-6)} = \frac{8}{12} = \frac{2}{3}$$

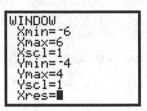

These settings enable us to obtain a true geometric representation of the circle with equation $x^2 + y^2 = 16$. We first re–arrange the given equation so that y is the subject.

That is, $x^2 + y^2 = 16 \Rightarrow y = \pm\sqrt{16 - x^2}$. We can now graph the equations $y = \sqrt{16 - x^2}$ and $y = -\sqrt{16 - x^2}$.

We begin by typing in the equation and then the negative of the equation. Use the VARS and arrow keys, and then the above window settings. Now press the GRAPH function to sketch the circle:

  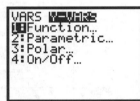

The final output is:

 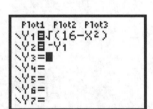 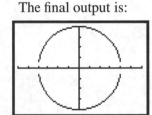

Using the window setting shown below, a distorted graph is the result as shown here:

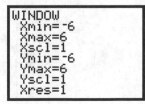 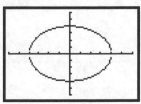

EXERCISE 13.1

1. State the domain and range of the following relations:
  (a) $\{(2,4), (3,-9), (-2,4), (3,9)\}$
  (b) $\{(1,2), (2,3), (3,4), (5,6), (7,8), (9,10)\}$
  (c) $\{(0,1), (0, 2), (1,1), (1,2)\}$

2. Find the range for each of the following
  (a) $\{(x,y):y = x + 1, x \in \mathbb{R}^+\}$
  (b) $\{(x,y):y \geq x, x \geq 0\}$
  (c) $y = x^2 + 2x + 1, x > 2$
  (d) $y = 2x - x^2, x \in \mathbb{R}$
  (e) $x^2 + y^2 = 9, -3 \leq x \leq 3$
  (f) $x^2 - y^2 = 9, x \geq 3$
  (g) $y = x - 1, 0 < x \leq 1$
  (h) $y = 4 - x^2, -2 \leq x < 1$
  (i) $y = \sqrt{x}, x \geq 0$
  (j) $y = \sqrt{x}, 1 \leq x \leq 25$
  (k) $y = \dfrac{4}{x + 1}, x > 0$
  (l) $\{(x,y):y^2 = x, x \geq 1\}$

3. State the range and domain for each of the following relations:

(a)
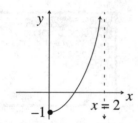

(b)
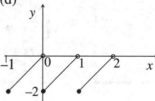

(c)
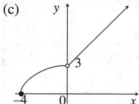

(d)
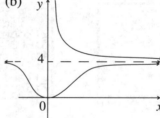

(e)
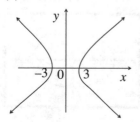

(f)
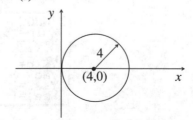

13.2 FUNCTIONS

A relation describes any set of ordered pairs. However, of all these relations there is a special group which are known as **functions**. They have the following definition:

> A function is a relation in which no two of the ordered pairs have the same first element.

That is, every set of ordered pairs is a relation, but **every relation is not a function**. So that, in fact, functions make up a subset of all relations.

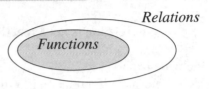

Relations

Functions

Another approach to determine if a relation is a function is to use the **vertical line test**. The method is quite simple:

Step 1   Sketch the graph of the relation.
Step 2   Make a visual check of the number of times a vertical line would cut the graph.
Step 3   If the vertical line only ever cuts at one place, the relation is a function. If the vertical line cuts at two or more places (for the same x–value), then the relation is not a function.

EXAMPLE

Which of the following defines a function?

(a) $\{(0,2), (1,2), (2,1)\}$ (b) $\{(x, y):y = x^3 + 1, x \in \mathbb{R}\}$

(c) $y^2 = x, x \geq 0$ (c) $\{(x,y):x^2 + y^2 = 16\}$

SOLUTION

(a)   Clearly, we have every first element of the ordered pairs different. This means that this relation is also a function.

(b)   Using the TI–83 to provide a visual check:

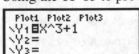

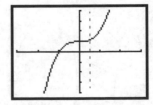

From the graph shown, a vertical line anywhere on the domain for which the relation is defined will cut the graph at only one place (for the same x-value). This relation is therefore a function.

(c) Again we make use of a visual approach to determine if the relation is a function. First we write the relation in a form that will enable us to enter it into the TI–83:

$$y^2 = x \Rightarrow y = \pm\sqrt{x}$$

We can therefore define the relation

$$Y_1 = \sqrt{X} \text{ and } Y_2 = -\sqrt{X}$$

and sketch both of them on the same set of axes. Placing a vertical line over sections of the domain clearly shows that the line cuts the graph in two places.
Therefore this relation is not a function.

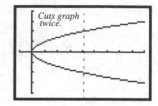

Algebraic proof
We can determine if a relation is a function by algebraic means.

Begin by choosing a value of x that lies in the domain. For example $x = 4$. This gives the following equation:

$$y^2 = 4 \Rightarrow y = \pm\sqrt{4}$$

From which we can say that when $x = 4$, $y = 2$ **and** $y = -2$, so that there are two ordered pairs, $(4,2)$ and $(4, -2)$. This is a breach of the definition of a function, as we have two different y-values for one x-value.

(d) This relation describes the equation of a circle with radius 4 units and centre at the origin. The graph of this relation is shown earlier in this chapter.
This graph would therefore fail the vertical line test, and so is not a function.

MAPPING AND FUNCTION NOTATION

A relation is also called a mapping if, for example, every element of a set X is related to exactly one element of a second set Y.
Such mappings are often called *functional relations*, or simply *functions*. So that in fact, a function is really another name for a mapping.

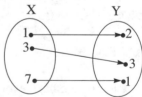

DEFINITION

A function f, (or a mapping f), from a set X to a set Y is a relation which assigns to each element x of the set X a unique element y of the set Y, the **co-domain**.

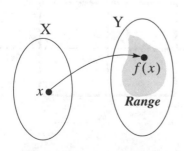

The set X is called the domain of f. The element y is called the **image** of x under f and we denote this image by $f(x)$ (read as; f of x) the value of the function f at x. We write $f: x \mapsto f(x)$.
We can also write these expressions as follows

1. $f: X \mapsto Y$, where $y = f(x)$

2. $f:X\longmapsto Y, y = f(x)$

3. $y = f(x), x \in X$

The range of f is not necessarily the set Y. The **range** of f is actually a subset of Y (or it could be equal to Y). Set Y describes the types of numbers that will be produced when f is applied to different x-values — not necessarily which numbers we will end up with! So that the range of f is given by the values of $f(x)$.

Notice that f describes not only the rule, $f(x)$, but also the domain, X, and sometimes the co-domain, Y

EXAMPLE

Determine the range of the function $f:\{x:x \geq 0\}\longmapsto \mathbb{R}, y = x+1$.

SOLUTION

First note that the co-domain is given by $\mathbb{R}$, the set of real numbers. To determine the range of this function, sketch its graph.

From the graph shown, it is clear that the only possible values of y are those for which $y \geq 1$.
In this case we have a closed circle at the end point and so we include that y–value as part of the range.
Therefore the range of f is $\{y:y \geq 1\}$.

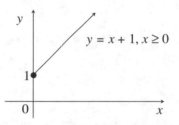

EXAMPLE

For the function $f(x) = x^3 + 1, x \in \mathbb{R}$ find
(a) $f(-1), f(2)$,
(b)   the element of the domain that has 28 as its image.

SOLUTION

(a) $f(x) = x^3 + 1, x \in \mathbb{R} \Rightarrow f(-1) = (-1)^3 + 1 = -1 + 1 = 0$.

Similarly, $f(2) = 2^3 + 1 = 9$.

(b)   If the image is 28, then we want the value of x for which $f(x) = 28$.

We then have, $f(x) = 28 \Rightarrow x^3 + 1 = 28$

$\Leftrightarrow$ $x^3 = 27$

$$\Leftrightarrow \qquad x = 3 \quad \text{\textit{(Taking the cube root of both sides)}}$$

Therefore, the element of the domain that has an image of 28 is 3.

EXAMPLE

For the function $f(x) = x^2 - 3$, $x \in \mathbb{R}$ find

(a) $f(6)$

(b) $f(x+1)$

(c) $f(x+h) - f(x)$

SOLUTION

(a) To determine the value of $f(6)$, we 'replace' the x–term in the rule of $f(x)$ with

the number '6': $\qquad f(6) = (6)^2 - 3 = 36 - 3$

$$= 33$$

(b) This time we 'replace' the x–term in the rule of $f(x)$ with '$x + 1$':

$$f(x+1) = (x+1)^2 - 3 = x^2 + 2x + 1 - 3$$

$$= x^2 + 2x - 2$$

(c) $f(x+h) - f(x) = (x+h)^2 - 3 - (x^2 - 3)$

$$= (x^2 + 2xh + h^2) - \cancel{3} - \cancel{x^2} + \cancel{3}$$

$$= 2xh + h^2$$

EXAMPLE

Consider the function $g:\{x: -1 \le x \le 2\} \mapsto \mathbb{R}$, where $g(x) = x^2 + 2$,

(a) Find $g(-1)$, $g(0)$, and $g(2)$.

(b) Determine the range of g.

SOLUTION

(a) $g(-1) = (-1)^2 + 2 = 3$.

$g(0) = (0)^2 + 2 = 2$

$g(2) = (2)^2 + 2 = 6$

(b) To determine the range of the function g, we need to sketch its graph:

To sketch this graph we begin by sketching the graph of $y = x^2 + 2$ for all real values of x.

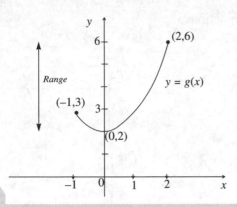

However, the domain is given by $x \in [-1, 2]$. This means that we 'remove' the parts of the graph that are not allowed, leaving the required part of the graph.

From the graph of g, the range of this function is $\{y: 2 \leq y \leq 6\}$.

EXERCISE 13.2

1. A function is defined as follows, $f: x \mapsto 2x + 3, x \geq 0$.
   (a) Find the value of $f(0), f(1), f(-2)$.
   (b) Evaluate the expressions   i. $f(x + a)$
       ii. $f(x + a) - f(x)$
   (c) Find $\{x: f(x) = 9\}$.

2. Given that $f(x) = \dfrac{x}{x + 1}, x \in [0, 10]$, find

   (a) $f(0), f(10)$.
   (b) $\{x: f(x) = 5\}$.

   (c)   the range of $f(x) = \dfrac{x}{x + 1}, x \in [0, 10]$.

3. For the mapping $x \mapsto 2 - \dfrac{1}{2}x^2, x \in \mathbb{R}$, find   (a) $f(x + 1), f(x - 1)$,

        (b) a, given that $f(a) = 1$,
        (c) b, given that $f(b) = 10$.

4. A function is defined as follows, $y = x^3 - x^2, x \in [-2, 2]$.
   (a) Find the value(s) of x such that $y = 0$.

   (b) Sketch the graph of $y = x^3 - x^2, x \in [-2, 2]$ and determine its range.

5. The function f is defined as $f: (-\infty, \infty) \mapsto \mathbb{R}$, where $f(x) = x^2 - 4$.
   (a) Sketch the graph of   i. f
       ii. $y = x + 2, x \in (-\infty, \infty)$
   (b) Find   i. $\{x: f(x) = 4\}$ ii. $\{x: f(x) = x + 2\}$

6. Which of the following relations are also functions?

(a)

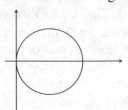

(b)

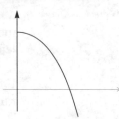

(c)

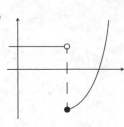

(d)

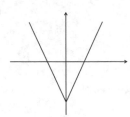

(e)

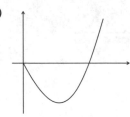

(f)

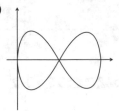

7. Use both *visual tests* and *algebraic tests* to show that the following relations are also functions.

(a) $x \mapsto x^3 + 2, x \in (0,5)$

(b) $x \mapsto \sqrt{x} + 1, x \in [0, 9)$

(c) $\{(x,y): y^3 = x + 1, x \in \mathbb{R}\}$

(d) $\{(x,y): y = x^2 + 1, x \in \mathbb{R}\}$

8. Use an algebraic method to decide which of the following relations are also functions.

(a) $f: x \mapsto \dfrac{1}{x}, x \in \mathbb{R}\backslash\{0\}$

(b) $\{(x,y): y^2 - x = 9, x \geq -9\}$

(c) $\{(x,y): y^2 - x^2 = 9, x \geq -9\}$

(d) $f(x) = \dfrac{1}{x^2} + 1, x \neq 0$

(e) $f(x) = 4 - 2x^2, x \in \mathbb{R}$

(f) $f: x \mapsto \dfrac{4}{x + 1}, x \in \mathbb{R}\backslash\{-1\}$

9. Sketch the graph of $f: x \mapsto \dfrac{x^2}{x^2 + 2}, x \in \mathbb{R}$ and use it to

(a) show that f is a function,
(b) determine its range.

10. A function is defined by $f: x \mapsto \dfrac{x + 10}{x - 8}$, where $x \geq 0$.

(a) Determine the range of f.
(b) Find the value of a such that $f(a) = a$.

13.3 MORE LINEAR FUNCTIONS

In Chapter 8 we worked with straight lines of the form $ax + by + c = 0$ and $y = mx + c$. In this chapter we formalised the notion of a function and introduced the mapping notation, so that for a straight line, we can express the equations $ax + by + c = 0$ and $y = mx + c$ more formally by writing it as $f : x \mapsto mx + c$. The important thing is that it is only a notational change, nothing else. All the properties that we have already dealt with remain unchanged.

PIECEWISE LINEAR FUNCTIONS

Some functions are made up of several different rules for different subsets of their domains. Such functions are often refered to as hybrid functions. A special case of hybrid functions is when each rule is a linear function, in this case we have what is known as a **piecewise linear function**. An example of such an example is

$$f(x) = \begin{cases} x - 2 & \text{if } x > 4 \\ 2x - 6 & \text{if } x \le 4 \end{cases}$$

To sketch this graph we simply sketch the graph of
$$y = x - 2 \text{ for } x > 2 \text{ and then}$$
sketch the graph of
$$y = 2x - 6 \text{ for } x \le 4 :$$

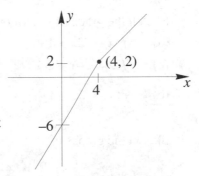

Notice then, that because the two line meet at the point (4, 2), the resulting function is called a **piecewise continuous linear function**.

Hint: The easiest way to sketch these graphs (other than using a graphics calculator) is to simply sketch each straight line as if there were no restrictions and then rub out those sections that are not required.

On the TI–82 or TI–83 graphics calculator, we can sketch the above function as follows: After entering the equation editor, i.e., **Y =** screen, type the following:

$$\mathbf{Y = (X - 2)(X > 4) + (2x - 6)(X \le 4)}$$

The expressions (X > 4) and (X ≤ 4) are found under the TEST/ LOGIC window. To access this window press **2nd MATH**. i.e., type (**X 2nd MATH** [then use the arrow key to select >, press ENTER] **4**) + (**2 X − 6**)(**X 2nd MATH** [then use the arrow key to select ≤, press ENTER] **4**) and then press **GRAPH**.

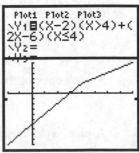

GREATEST INTEGER FUNCTION

Another type of piecewise linear function is the
greatest integer function (y = [x]) or the **step function**.

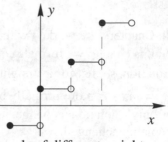

These graphs are made up of discontinuous
horizontal lines (segments) that end up resembling a stair
case.

Such graphs are useful when modelling the cost of mailing parcels of different weights.

For example, if it costs $3.00 to send parcels
weighing between at least 1kg but less than 3 kg,
$ 7.00 for parcels weighing at least 3 kg but less
that 5 kg, $ 13.00 for parcels weighing at least 5 kg
but less that 8 kg and so on, we have the following graph:

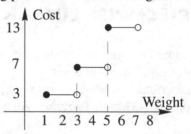

EXERCISE 13.3

1. Sketch the graph of the following functions

   (a) $f : x \mapsto 2x + 1$

   (b) $f : x \mapsto 3x - 2$

   (c) $f : x \mapsto -x + 2$

   (d) $f : x \mapsto 3 - 2x$

   (e) $f : x \mapsto 5 - \dfrac{1}{2}x$

   (f) $f : x \mapsto 2 - \dfrac{1}{5}x$

2. Sketch the graphs of

   (a) $f(x) = \begin{cases} x - 2 & \text{if } x > 2 \\ 2x - 6 & \text{if } x \le 2 \end{cases}$

   (b) $f(x) = \begin{cases} 2x - 1 & \text{if } x > 1 \\ -x + 2 & \text{if } x \le 1 \end{cases}$

   (c) $f(x) = \begin{cases} 3x - 1 & \text{if } x > 3 \\ x + 5 & \text{if } x \le 3 \end{cases}$

   (d) $f(x) = \begin{cases} x + 2 & \text{if } x > 2 \\ x - 2 & \text{if } x \le 2 \end{cases}$

   (e) $f(x) = \begin{cases} 4 - x & \text{if } x > 4 \\ 2x - 8 & \text{if } x \le 4 \end{cases}$

   (f) $f(x) = \begin{cases} \dfrac{1}{2}x + 1 & \text{if } x > 2 \\ 2x - 2 & \text{if } x \le 2 \end{cases}$

3. Sketch each of the functions in Question 2 using a graphics calculator.

4. A piecewise linear function is defined by $f(x) = \begin{cases} 2x + a & \text{if } x > 2 \\ 4 - x & \text{if } x \le 2 \end{cases}$.

   Find a if the graph is to be continuous.

EXAMINATION STYLE QUESTIONS

1.   A relation is given by $f:x \mapsto \dfrac{2x}{3} + 1$, for $0 \le x \le 3$.

   (a)   Is this relation a function?
   (b)   Sketch the graph of f.
   (c)   For f, state   (i)   the domain   (ii)   the range.
   (d)   For what value of x will the image of f be 9?

2.   The displacement, s m, of an object from a fixed point O after being in motion for t

   seconds is given by the function $s:t \mapsto t^2 + 2$, where $t \ge 0$.
   (a)   Find the object's initial displacement.
   (b)   How far from the origin will the object be after travelling for 8 seconds?
   (c)   Sketch the graph representing the object's displacement at any time t seconds.

3.   The function $f:x \mapsto a(x-3)^2 - b$ is shown
   in the figure alongside.

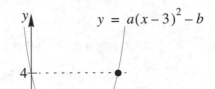
$y = a(x-3)^2 - b$

   (a)   State the range of the function.
   (b)   State the coordinates of
           (i)   the y-intercept(s).
           (ii)   the x–intercept(s).
   (c)   Find the values of a and b.

4.   Sketch the function defined as $f(x) = \begin{cases} \dfrac{1}{2}x + 1 & \text{if } x > 2 \\ x & \text{if } x \le 2 \end{cases}$

5.   The temperature, T°C of kettle, t minutes after it is removed from the stove is
   thought to to be given by

   $$T(t) = 28 + \frac{64}{t}, t > 0$$

   (a)   Complete the table below

t min	2	4	8	16	32
T °C					

   (b)   Use your results of (a) to plot the graph of $T(t) = 28 + \dfrac{64}{t}, t > 0$.

   (c)   What will the eventual temperature of the kettle be?
   (d)   How long will it take the kettle to reach a temperature of 40°C?

SELF ASSESSMENT TEST (60 MINUTES)

1. If $f: x \mapsto x^2 - x + 1$, (i)   find $f(2)$

                                      (ii) a given that $f(a) = -1$

                                                                                  [4 marks]

2. The point $(1, 6)$ and $(-1, 0)$ lie on the curve $y = x^2 + bx + c$.

    (a)   Show that $b + c = 5$ and $-b + c = -2$.

    (b)   Using (a) solve for b and c.

                                                                                 [6 marks]

3. A function is defined by $f: \mathbb{R} \mapsto \mathbb{R}, \; x \mapsto 7 - x^2$. Find the range of this function. Classify the function as one:one or many:one.

                                                                                 [2 marks]

4. Sketch the graph of the linear piecewise function $f(x) = \begin{cases} x - 1 & \text{if } x \geq 3 \\ -x + 5 & \text{if } x < 3 \end{cases}$

                                                                                 [3 marks]

5. A function is defined by $f(x) = 2x + 1 \; x \in \mathbb{R}$. Find the value(s) of x for which $f(2x) = f(x + 1)$.

                                                                                 [3 marks]

6. A sheet of paper of dimension 12 cm by 8cm has four equal squares of side length x cm cut out from its corners.

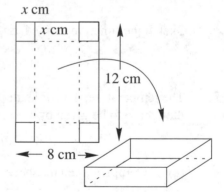

    (a)   Show that the volume, V(x) cm^3 of the box is given by

$$V(x) = 4x(6 - x)(4 - x)$$

    (b)   Complete the table below

x cm	0	1	2	3	4
V cm^3					

    (c)   Estimate, to one decimal point, the maximum volume this box can have.

                                                                                  [6 marks]

TRIGONOMETRIC FUNCTIONS

1 4

Chapter contents

Key Formulae

- $f(x) = a\sin bx + c$

- $f(x) = a\cos bx + c$

- $\tan\theta = \dfrac{\sin\theta}{\cos\theta}$

14.1 TRIGONOMETRIC FUNCTIONS

Chapter 7 mainly dealt with acute angles and the similar triangle definition given at the start of that chapter. There were, however, occasions on which it was presumed that the trigonometric ratios of obtuse angles exist and can be found using a calculator. The time has come to consider the trigonometric ratios of all angles. This is done using a unit circle.

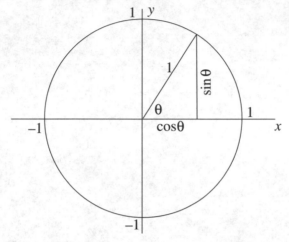

The angle θ is measured anti-clockwise from the positive direction of the x-axis. Negative angles can be opened clockwise from the positive direction of the x-axis. To find the trigonometric ratios of an angle such as $210°$, find the appropriate position for the radius and then find the coordinates of the point on the unit circle.

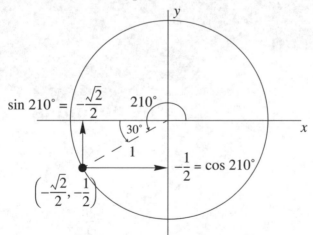

The results of this diagram are that: $\sin(210°) = -\dfrac{1}{2}$, $\cos(210°) = -\dfrac{\sqrt{2}}{2}$. It is also important to recognise that this diagram gives the ratios for many other angles. That is,

$$\sin(210°) = \sin(-150°) = \sin(210 \pm 360)° = \sin(210 \pm 720)° = \ldots = -\frac{1}{2}$$

and $\cos(210°) = \cos(-150°) = \cos(210 \pm 360)° = \cos(210 \pm 720)° = \ldots = -\dfrac{\sqrt{2}}{2}$

There is an infinite set of angles all of which give these values for the main trigonometric ratios. These are all separated by one complete turn or 360°. This is known as **periodic** behaviour. Many real world phenomena are periodic in the sense that the same patterns repeat over time. The trigonometric functions are often used to model such phenomena which include sound waves, light waves, alternating current electricity and other more approximately periodic events such as tides and even our moods.

It should be noted that when the trigonometric functions are used for these purposes, the angles are almost always measured in **radians** (which is a different way of measuring angles). However for the remainder of this chapter will use degrees.

WHAT DO TRIGONOMETRIC FUNCTIONS LOOK LIKE?

As we have seen, the sine and cosine values have a periodic nature about them. This means that if we were to plot a graph of the sine values versus its angles or the cosine values versus its angles, we could expect their graphs to demonstrate a periodic nature. Such graphs are easily obtained by plotting points:

THE SINE FUNCTION:

θ	0	30	45	60	90	120	135	150	180	...	330	360
$\sin\theta°$	0.0	0.5	0.71	0.87	1.0	0.86	0.71	0.5	0.0	...	−0.5	0.0

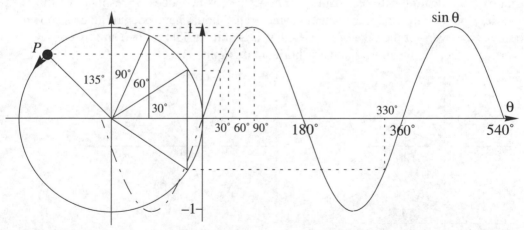

We also notice that as the sine of angle θ corresponds to the y–value of a point P on the unit circle, as P moves around the circle in an anti–clockwise direction, we can measure the y–value and plot it on a graph as a function of θ (as shown above).

Feature of sine graph: (a) Maximum value = 1, Minimum value = −1

(b) Period = 360° (i.e., graph repeats itself every 360°)

(c) If P moves in clockwise direction, y–values continue in their periodic nature (see dashed part of graph).

THE COSINE FUNCTION:

θ	0	30	45	60	90	120	135	150	180	...	330	360
cos θ°	1.0	0.87	0.71	0.5	0.0	–0.5	–0.71	–0.87	–1.0	...	0.87	1.0

Plotting these points on a cos θ° versus θ –axis, we have:

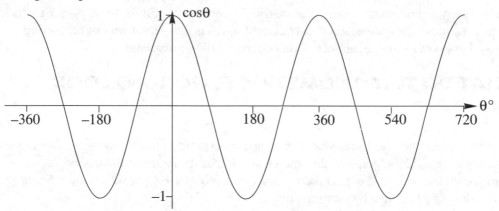

Feature of cosine graph:
    (a)   Maximum value = 1, Minimum value = –1
    (b)   Period = 360° (i.e., graph repeats itself every 360°)
    (c)   If P moves in clockwise direction, x–values continue in their periodic nature.

There is a note to be made about using the second method (that was used to obtain the sine graph) when dealing with the cosine graph. As the cosine values correspond the the x–values on the unit circle, the actual cosine graph should have been plotted as shown below. However, for the sake of consistency, it is quite alright to then simply convert the 'vertical graph' to the more standard 'horizontal graph':

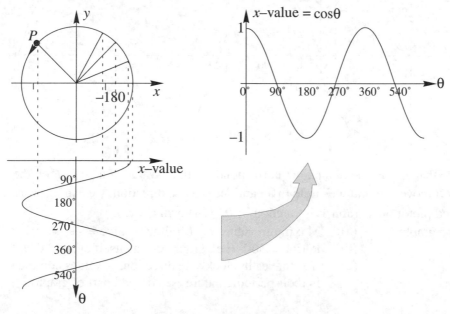

To summarise these two graphs we have that the **period** of each of these functions is $360°$. This is the distance on the θ-axis between identical places on the graph (such as successive peaks). The **amplitude** of the functions is the distance between the centre line (in this case the θ-axis) and one of the maximum points. In this case, the amplitude is 1. The sine and cosine functions are useful for modelling wave phenomena such as sound, light, water waves etc.

The third trigonometric function (tangent) [**which is not on the syllabus**] is defined as $\tan\theta = \dfrac{\sin\theta}{\cos\theta}$ and so is defined for all angles for which the cosine function is non-zero.

The angles for which the tangent function are not defined correspond to the x-axis intercepts of the cosine function which are $\pm 90°, \pm 270°, \pm 450°, \dots$. At these points the graph of the tangent function has vertical asymptotes.

The period of the tangent function is $180°$, which is half that of the sine and cosine functions. Since the tangent function has a vertical asymptote, it cannot be said to have an amplitude. It is also generally true that the tangent function is less useful than sine and cosine for modelling applications.

The graph of the basic tangent function is:

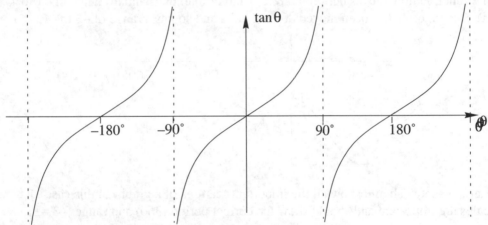

SKETCHING SINE AND COSINE GRAPHS

We now consider some of the possible transformations that can be applied to the standard sine and cosine function and look at how these transformations effect the basic properties of both these graphs

TRANSLATIONS

Functions of the type $y = \sin(x) + c$ (or in mapping notation $x \mapsto \sin(x) + c, x \in \mathbb{R}$) nvolve vertical translations. Mapping notation is discussed in detail in Chapter 13. For this chapter, we will use the cartesian notation $y = \sin(x) + c$. You should, however, realise that this is interchangeable with the mapping notation $x \mapsto \sin(x) + c, x \in \mathbb{R}$ and with the functional notation $f(x) = \sin(x) + c$.

Adding or subtracting a fixed amount to a trigonometric function translates the graph parallel to the y-axis.

EXAMPLES

Sketch the graphs of the functions for x values in the range $-360°$ to $720°$.

(i) $y = \sin(x) + 1$ (ii) $y = \cos(x) - 2$

SOLUTIONS

(i)

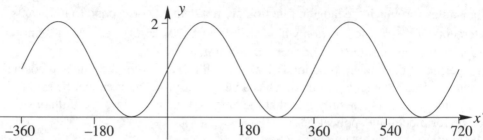

The function now moves between 0 & 2, 1 larger than the standard range of -1 to 1.

(ii) This function has been moved down 2 units and so has a range of -3 to -1.

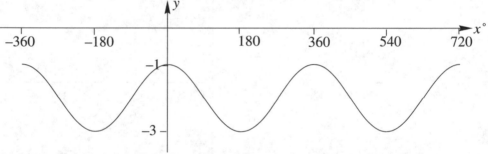

A graph sketch should show all the important features of a graph. In this case, the axes scales are important and should show the correct period (360) and range $[-3, -1]$.

DILATIONS

Functions of the form $y = a\sin x$ etc. are dilated parallel to the y-axis. In the case of the sine and cosine functions, **the amplitude becomes 'a' and not 1**. This dilation does not affect the shape of the graph.

EXAMPLES

Sketch the graphs of the following functions for x values in the range $-360°$ to $720°$.

(i) $y = 2\cos x$ (ii) $y = \dfrac{1}{3}\sin x$

SOLUTIONS

(i)   This is the cosine graph (broken line) with an amplitude of 2.

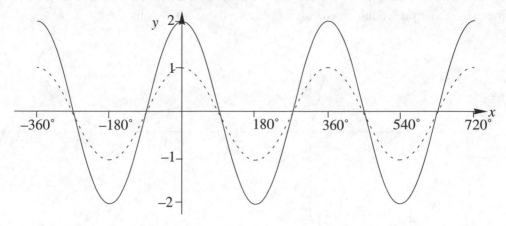

(ii)   This is the sine graph (broken line) with an amplitude of $\frac{1}{3}$.

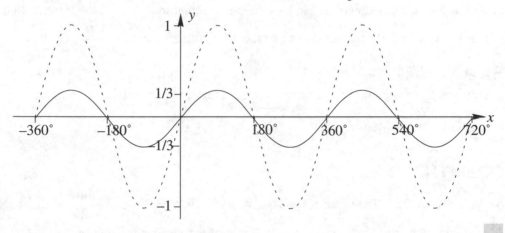

REFLECTIONS AND DILATIONS

$y = -\cos x$ is the basic cosine graph (broken line) reflected in the **x-axis**. This is because the y values will be reversed in sign from those calculated for the cosine graph.

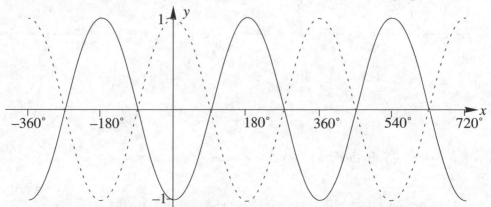

By contrast $y = \sin(-x)$ is the basic sine graph reflected in the **y-axis**. A table of values for these functions should make the reasons for these reflections clear.

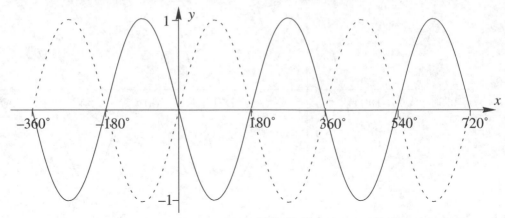

Functions of the form $y = \cos(nx)$ are dilated parallel to the x-axis. This means that the period of the graph is altered. It can be valuable to remember and use the formula that relates the value of n to the period (τ) of the dilated function: $\tau = \dfrac{360°}{n}$.

EXAMPLES

Sketch graphs of the following functions for x values in the range $-360°$ to $720°$.

   (i) $y = \sin(2x)$ (ii) $y = \cos\left(\dfrac{x}{2}\right)$

SOLUTIONS

(i) $y = \sin(2x)$. The value of n is 2 so the period is $\tau = \dfrac{360°}{n} = \dfrac{360°}{2} = 180°$. Note

that this means that the period is **half** that of the basic sine function.

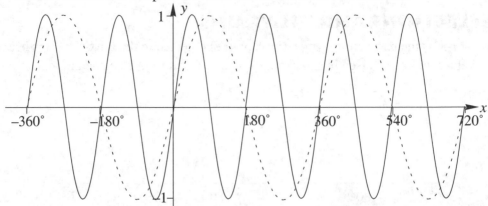

(ii) $y = \cos\left(\dfrac{x}{2}\right)$. In this case the value of $n = \dfrac{1}{2}$ and the period $\tau = \dfrac{360°}{n} = \dfrac{360°}{1/2}$

$$= 720°.$$

The graph is effectively stretched to twice its original period.

272

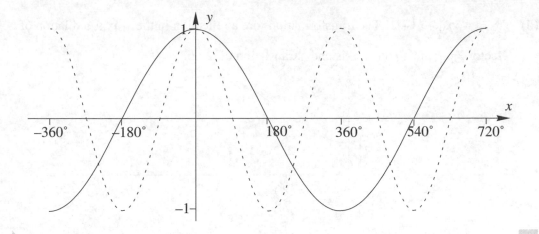

COMBINED TRANSFORMATIONS

You may be required to combine some or all of these transformations in a single function. The general function of the type

$$y = a\sin(bx) + c \ \& \ y = a\cos(bx) + c \text{ has:}$$

an amplitude of 'a'

a period of $\dfrac{360°}{b}$

a translation of 'c' units upwards.

EXAMPLES

Sketch graphs of the following functions for x values in the range $-360°$ to $720°$.

(i) $y = 2\sin(2x) + 1$ $\qquad$ (ii) $y = -\cos\left(\dfrac{1}{2}x\right) + 2$

SOLUTIONS

(i) $y = 2\sin(2x) + 1$ This graph has an amplitude of 2, a period of π and a vertical translation of 1 unit up.

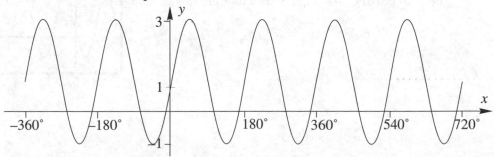

(ii) $y = -\cos\left(\frac{1}{2}x\right) + 2$. The transformations are a reflection in the x-axis, a dilation of

factor 2 parallel to the x-axis and a translation of 2 up.

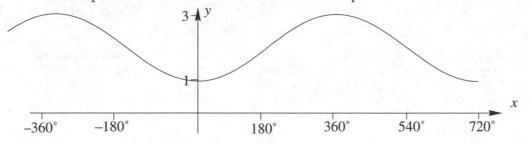

USING A GRAPHICS CALCULATOR

The first of the above examples could be sketched as follows:

Step 1. Make sure that the calculator is in degree mode.
Failure to do this could be disastrous!

Step 2. Enter the function rule. Remember to use the π key
where necessary. Do not use approximations such as
3.14

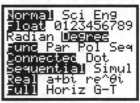

Step 3. Select an appropriate range. using the WINDOW

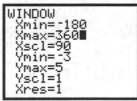

In this case, the viewing window is suitable.
This will provide an adequate sketch of the function.

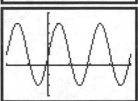

EXERCISE 14.1

1. Find the period and the amplitude of the following functions.

(i) $y = 2\sin x$ (ii) $y = 3\cos\dfrac{x}{3}$

(iii) $y = -4\sin(2x) + 1$ (iv) $y = 2 - 3\cos(2x)$

(v) $y = \dfrac{1}{4}\cos(3x) + 5$ (vi) $y = -\dfrac{2}{3}\cos\left(\dfrac{3}{4}x\right) + 5$

2. Sketch graphs of the following functions for x values in the interval $[-360°, 360°]$.

(i) $y = \sin(2x)$ (ii) $y = -\cos\left(\dfrac{x}{2}\right)$

(iii) $f(x) = 2\sin(x)$ (iv) $y = 1 - 2\sin(2x)$

(v) $y = -2\cos\left(\dfrac{x}{2}\right)$ (vi) $y = 3\cos(x)$

(vii) $y = 2\cos\left(\dfrac{1}{3}x\right) - 1$ (viii) $f(x) = 4\sin\left(\dfrac{x}{2}\right)$

(ix) $y = 2 - \sin\left(\dfrac{2x}{3}\right)$ (x) $y = 5 + 15\sin(2x)$

(xi) $f(x) = 8 - 4\cos\left(\dfrac{1}{2}x\right)$ (xii) $f(x) = 12.5 + 2.5\sin(4x)$

3. Sketch graphs of the following functions for x values in the interval $[0,4]$.

(i) $y = 2\cos(360x)$ (ii) $f(x) = 2 + \cos(180x)$

(iii) $y = \sin(360x) - 1$ (iv) $y = 12 + 1.5\sin(180x)$

(v) $f(x) = 8 - 4\sin(60x)$ (vi) $f(x) = 4.5 - 1.5\cos(360x)$

14.2 APPLICATIONS

Functions of the type considered in the previous section are useful for modelling periodic phenomena. These sorts of applications usually start with data that has been measured in an experiment. The next task is to find a function that 'models' the data in the sense that it produces function values that are similar to the experimental data. Once this has been done, the function can be used to predict values that are missing from the measured data (interpolation) or values that lie outside the experimental data set (extrapolation).

EXAMPLE

The table shows the depth of water at the end of a pier at various times (measured, in hours after midnight on the first day of the month.

t hours	0	3	6	9	12	151
D metres	16.20	17.49	16.51	14.98	15.60	17.27

t hours	8	21	24	27	30	33
D metres	17.06	15.34	15.13	16.80	17.42	15.89

Plot the data as a graph. Use your result to find a rule that models the depth data. Use your model to predict the time of the next high tide.

SOLUTION

The graph is

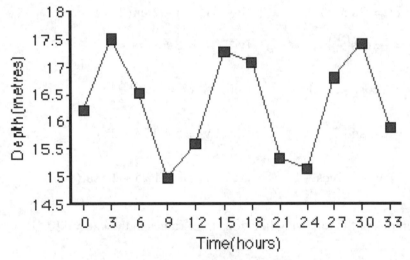

This does suggest that the depth is varying periodically. It appears that the period is approximately 13 hours. This is found by looking at the time between successive high tides. This is not as easy as it sounds as the measurements do not appear to have been made exactly at the high tides. This means that an estimate will need to be made based upon the observation that successive high tides appear to have happened after 3, 16 and 32 hours. Next, the amplitude and vertical translation. Again, because we do not have exact readings at high and low tides, these will need to be estimated. The lowest tide recorded is 14.98 and the highest is 17.49. A first estimate vertical translation is

$\dfrac{17.49 + 14.98}{2} = 16.235$ and the amplitude is $17.7 - 16.235 = 1.465$. Since the graph

starts near the mean depth and moves up it seems likely that the first model to try might be:

$$y = 1.465 \times \sin\left(\frac{360t}{13}\right) + 16.235$$

Notice that the dilation factor (along the x–axis) is found by using the result that if

$$\tau = 13 \Rightarrow \frac{360}{n} = 13 \therefore n = \frac{360}{13}.$$

The model should now be 'evaluated' which means testing how well it fits the data. This can be done by making tables of values of the data and the values predicted by the model and working to make the differences between these as small as possible. This can be done using a scientific or graphic calculator. A particularly useful technological tool to help with a task such as this is a spreadsheet. The following spreadsheet is one way of finding periodic data models:

A	A	B	C	D	E	F	G
1	t	D	Model	Error			
2	0	16.20	16.24	0.03		Model Parameters	
3	3	17.49	17.69	0.20		Amplitude	1.465
4	6	16.51	16.59	0.07		Period	13
5	9	14.98	14.87	-0.12		Horizontal	0
6	12	15.60	15.55	-0.04		Vertical	16.235
7	15	17.27	17.44	0.17			
8	18	17.06	17.21	0.14			
9	21	15.34	15.26	-0.07			
10	24	15.13	15.03	-0.10			
11	27	16.80	16.92	0.11			
12	30	17.42	17.60	0.19			
13	33	15.89	15.88	-0.00			

Column A contains the times and column B the depths. Column C contains the trigonometric function being used to model the data. Column D contains the errors for each piece of data. The parameters used to produce the model are stored in cells G3 to G6. The formulas in column C use a mixture of relative cell addresses (e.g. A2) which are updated when they are copied and absolute addresses (e.g. G$3) which are copied unchanged. These are used for the parameters.

The model shown is quite good in that the errors are small with some being positive and some negative.

The function used is: $D = 1.465 \times \sin\left(\frac{360t}{13}\right) + 16.235$ and this can now be used to

predict depths for times that measurements were not made.

The graph of the modelling function can also be added to the graph of the data. Based on this graph we see that our model approximates the data well.

:

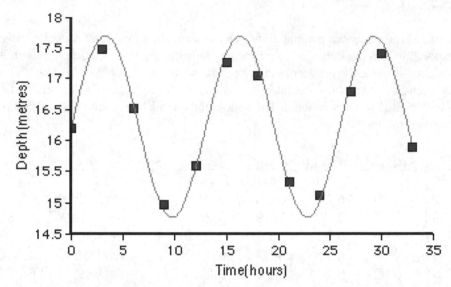

The modelling function can also be used to predict depths into the future (extrapolation). The next high tide, for example can be expected to be 13 hours after the high tide at about 29.3 hours. This is after 42.3 hours.

EXERCISE 14.2

1. The table shows the temperature in an office block over a 36 hour period.

h (hours)	0	3	6	9	12	15	18	21	24	27	30	33	36
T°C	19.0	22.5	24.0	22.5	19.0	15.5	14.0	15.5	19.0	22.5	24.0	22.5	19.0

(i) Estimate the amplitude, period, horizontal and vertical translations.
(ii) Accurately plot a graph of T°C vs h (hours) and use it to find a rule that models the data.
(iii) Use your rule to predict the temperature after 40 hours.

2. The table shows the light level (L) during an experiment on dye fading.

t (sec)	0	1	2	3	4	5	6	7	8	9	10
L	7.0	10.0	7.5	4.1	6.1	9.8	8.3	4.4	5.3	9.3	9.0

(i) Estimate the amplitude, period, horizontal and vertical translations.
(ii) Accurately plot a graph of L vs t (hours) and use it to find a rule that models the data.

3. The table shows the value in $s of an industrial share over a 20 month period.

Month	0	2	4	6	8	10	12	14	16	18	20
Value	7.0	11.5	10.8	5.6	2.1	4.3	9.7	11.9	8.4	3.2	2.5

    (i)   Estimate the amplitude, period, horizontal and vertical translations.
    (ii)   Accurately plot a graph of Value vs Month and use it to find a rule that models the data.

4. The table shows the population (in thousands) of a species of fish in a lake over a 22 year period.

Year	0	2	4	6	8	10	12	14	16	18	20	22
Pop.	12.0	12.9	12.8	11.7	11.0	11.5	12.5	13.0	12.3	11.2	11.0	12.0

    (i)   Estimate the amplitude, period, horizontal and vertical translations.
    (ii)   Accurately plot a graph of Pop vs Year and use it to find a rule that models the data.

5. The table shows the average weekly sales (in thousands of $s) of a small company over a 15 year period.

time	0	1.5	3	4.5	6	7.5	9	10.5	12	13.5	15
Sales	3.5	4.4	7.7	8.4	5.3	3.3	5.5	8.5	7.6	4.3	3.6

    (i)   Estimate the amplitude, period, horizontal and vertical translations.
    (ii)   Accurately plot a graph of Sales vs time and use it to find a rule that models the data.

6. The table shows the average annual rice production, P, (in thousands of tonnes) of a province over a 10 year period.

t	0	1	2	3	4	5	6	7	8	9	10
P	10.7	10.5	11.5	11.3	10.4	11.0	11.6	10.7	10.5	11.6	10.7

    (i)   Estimate the amplitude, period, horizontal and vertical translations.
    (ii)   Accurately plot a graph of P vs t and use it to find a rule that models the data.

14.3 EQUATIONS

If θ is an acute angle, it is quite easy to prove two simple statements that are true for every value of θ.

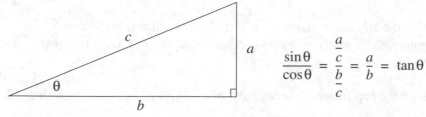

$$\frac{\sin\theta}{\cos\theta} = \frac{\frac{a}{c}}{\frac{b}{c}} = \frac{a}{b} = \tan\theta$$

In addition, there are some 'special angles' that are derived from two triangles:

This triangle gives the basic set of trigonometric ratios:

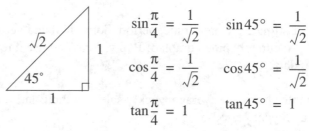

$$\sin\frac{\pi}{4} = \frac{1}{\sqrt{2}} \qquad \sin 45° = \frac{1}{\sqrt{2}}$$

$$\cos\frac{\pi}{4} = \frac{1}{\sqrt{2}} \qquad \cos 45° = \frac{1}{\sqrt{2}}$$

$$\tan\frac{\pi}{4} = 1 \qquad \tan 45° = 1$$

and the equilateral triangle: Which gives these ratios:

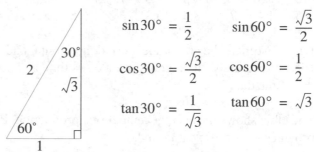

$$\sin 30° = \frac{1}{2} \qquad \sin 60° = \frac{\sqrt{3}}{2}$$

$$\cos 30° = \frac{\sqrt{3}}{2} \qquad \cos 60° = \frac{1}{2}$$

$$\tan 30° = \frac{1}{\sqrt{3}} \qquad \tan 60° = \sqrt{3}$$

Similar exact values for angles such as $30° + 360° = 390°$ exist. These can be found either using the graphs of the functions or the unit circle.

EXAMPLES

Solve the following equations giving all the solutions in the intervals indicated:

(i) $\sin\theta = \frac{1}{2}, 0° \le \theta \le 360°$ (ii) $2\cos\theta = -\sqrt{3}, -180° \le \theta \le 180°$

SOLUTIONS

(i) $\sin\theta = \frac{1}{2}, 0° \le \theta \le 360°$

METHOD 1:

The **principal value** or first solution to this equation can be found using a calculator. Firstly, the calculator must be in degree mode. This is because the range given for the solutions is stated in degrees. The principal value of the equation is found using the inverse sine function (usually 2nd sin). The value that results is 30°.

This is not the only angle that is a solution to the equation in the range stated. The other angles can be found either by considering the graph of the sine function or the unit circle diagram shown. The principal solution is shown. Since the sine is defined as the vertical displacement of the point, any angle that results in a vertical displacement of $\frac{1}{2}$

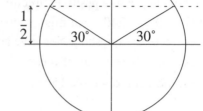

will be a solution of the equation.

The other solutions are (in the second quadrant) $180° - 30° = 150°$ and any other angle that, when opened anti-clockwise from the positive direction of the x-axis, has a vertical displacement of 0.5.

These can be generated using the fact that the sine function has a period of 360° and are $30° \pm 360°$, $150° \pm 360°$, $30° \pm 2 \times 360°$, $150° \pm 2 \times 360°$…. Only some of these lie in the range specified in the question. These are 30° and 150°. Whilst a calculator will not give you the second of these solutions, it will be able to confirm that it is correct by evaluating sin150° to get 0.5.

METHOD 2:

This method makes use of an accurate sketch (or plot) of the graph. So that all we need to do is read–off the values directly from the graph.

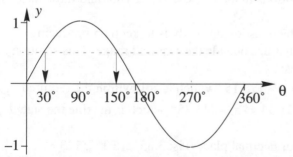

It must be noted that this method relies on the accuracy of the graph.

With the TI–83, we can make use of the **TRACE** function to help us obtain these solutions or even use the **TABLE** display:

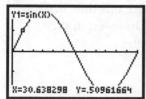

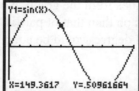

X	Y1
25	.42262
26	.43837
27	.45399
28	.46947
29	.48481
30	.5
31	.51504

Y1=.5

X	Y1
145	.57358
146	.55919
147	.54464
148	.52992
149	.51504
150	.5
151	.48481

Y1=.5

(ii) $2\cos\theta = -\sqrt{3}, -180° \le \theta \le 180°$ must first be rearranged to $\cos\theta = -\dfrac{\sqrt{3}}{2}$

    Using a calculator we have that $\cos^{-1}\left(-\dfrac{\sqrt{3}}{2}\right) = 150°$.

The other angles are found using the graph of the cosine function or the unit circle.

The next angle in a positive direction is:
$270° - 30° = 240°$, but this is outside the range specified in the question. Negative angles open clockwise. There is one of these: $-150°$.
The solutions are $-150°, 150°$.

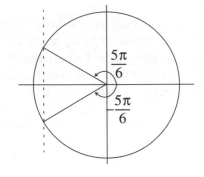

(iv) $\sin 3x = 0.2, 0 \le x \le 180$

    The principal solution of the basic equation $\sin\theta = 0.2$ is $\sin^{-1} 0.2 \approx 11.54°$.
    The remaining solutions are:
    $180° - 11.54° \approx 168.46°$
    $360° + 11.54° \approx 371.54°$ etc.
    This leads to the sequence of solutions:

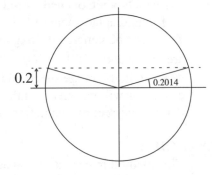

    $3x \approx 11.54° \Rightarrow x \approx 3.85°$

    $3x \approx 168.46° \Rightarrow x \approx 15.15°$

    $3x \approx 371.54° \Rightarrow x \approx 123.85°$
    The next consideration is, how many solutions should we generate?
    The question requires all the solutions in the range $0° \le x \le 180°$ and these have not necessarily all been found yet.
    All that is necessary to answer the question correctly is to keep on producing solutions until one is produced that lies outside the required range. This solution set is not yet complete and continues:
    $3x \approx 540° - 11.54 = 528.46 \Rightarrow x \approx 176.15°$ which is still within the required range, $3x = 720° + 11.54° \approx 731.54 \Rightarrow x \approx 243.85°$ which is outside the stated range.
    The complete solution set (to four decimal places) is: 3.85°, 15.15°, 123.85°, 176.15°.

However, as in the last example, we can make use of the graph of $f(x) = \sin(3x)$ and then read simply reaad off the required values from the graph. Notice this time that the solutions require a much more accurate graph than that of part(i). However, in such situations, an answer correct to the nearest degree would be adequate.

EXAMPLE

The height of the tide is h metres at time t hours, where $h = 4.5 + 2.5\sin 30t°$.

(a)   Copy and complete the table below

t hours	0	4	8	12	16	20	24
h metres							

(b)   On a set of axes draw the graph of $h = 4.5 + 2.5\sin 30t°$.

(c)   Find the height of the tide at the following times
       (i)   3 hours   (ii)   7.5 hours.

(d)   Find all the times in the first 24 hours when the height is 6.5 m.

SOLUTION

(a)   When $t = 0$, $h = 4.5 + 2.5\sin(30 \times 0)° = 4.5 + 0 = 4.5$

When $t = 4$, $h = 4.5 + 2.5\sin(30 \times 4)° = 4.5 + 2.5\sin 120° \approx 6.67$

Continuing in this manner we can complete the table of values:

t hours	0	4	8	12	16	20	24
h metres	4.5	6.67	2.33	4.5	6.67	2.33	4.5

Or we could use the TI–83: Notice that it is important to have the TABLE SET UP correctly, so that in this case we have that t starts at 0 and it increases by 4 each time.

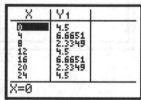

(b)   Although such a graph can be sketched on graph paper accurately, we will make use of the TI–83 in this instance:

Enter equation:

Use an appropriate WINDOW setting:

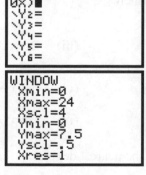

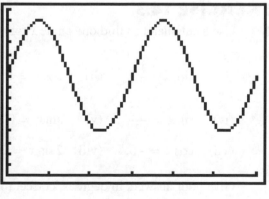

(c)   (i)   When $t = 3$, $h = 4.5 + 2.5\sin(30 \times 3)° = 4.5 + 2.5 \times 1 = 7.0$

(ii)   When $t = 7.5$, $h = 4.5 + 2.5\sin(30 \times 7.5)° = 2.73$

Again, we can make use of the CALC function on the TI–83, from which these values can then be obtained:

i.e., press **2nd TRACE**, **ENTER** and then simply type in the value of t, (at the X = prompt) this will produce a graph, where the value is on the graph and what the value of h is.

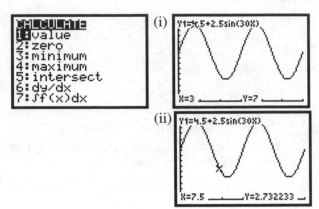

(d)   In this case we simply use the graph we have and read the values from it:

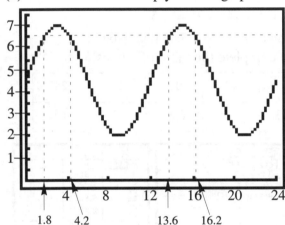

From the graph, the first time $h = 6.5$ is approximately when $t = 1.8$.
The second time $t \approx 4.2$.
Similarly, the next two times are,
$t \approx 13.8, 16.2$

EXERCISE 14.3

1.   Use a calculator to find one angle x for which:

(i) $\sin x = \dfrac{1}{2}$ (ii) $\cos x = 0$ (iii) $2\cos x = -1$

(iv) $\sin x = \dfrac{\sqrt{3}}{2}$ (v) $\sin x = 0.8$ (vi) $\cos x = -\dfrac{1}{3}$

(vii) $\cos x = -0.4$ (viii) $2\sin x = 3$ (ix) $\cos x = -0.46$

Give your answers in degrees, correct to the nearest degree

2. Solve the following equations giving all solutions in the intervals indicated. Where possible, give exact solutions. If exact solutions do not exist, give degrees correct to the nearest degree.

(i) $2\cos x = 1, -360° \le x \le 360°$ (ii) $2\sin x = \sqrt{3}, 0° \le x \le 360°$

(iii) $\sin 2x = 0.3, 0° \le x \le 360°$ (iv) $\sin 2x = 0.35, 0° \le x \le 180°$

(v) $3\cos 2x + 1 = 0, 0° \le x \le 180°$

3. The population (in thousands) of a species of butterfly in a nature sanctuary is modelled by the function:

$$P = 3 + 2\sin(45t)°, 0 \le t \le 12$$

where t is the time in weeks after scientists first started making population estimates.

(i) What is the intial population?
(ii) What are the largest and smallest populations?
(iii) When does the population first reach 4 thousand butterflies?

4. A water wave passes a fixed point. As the wave passes, the depth of the water (D metres) at time t seconds is modelled by the function:

$$D = 7 + \frac{1}{2}\cos(72t)°, t > 0$$

(i) What are the greatest and smallest depths?
(ii) Find the first two times at which the depth is 6.8 metres.

EXAMINATION STYLE QUESTIONS

1. On the same set of axes sketch the graphs of

    (a) $f(x) = 2\sin x°$, $0 \le x \le 360$.

    (b) $g(x) = \cos(3x)$, $0° \le x \le 360°$.

2.   (a)   Sketch the graph of $f: x \mapsto \sin 2x$ where $-180° \le x \le 180°$.

    (b)   Hence, find the two smallest positive values of x for which $f(x) = 0.5$.

3. The height of the tide is h metres at time t hours, where $h = 5 + 2\sin 30t°$.

    (a)   Copy and complete the table below

t hours	0	4	8	12	16	20	24
h metres							

    (b)   On a set of axes draw the graph of $h = 5 + 3\sin 30t°$.

    (c)   Find the height of the tide at the following times

        (i)   3 hours   (ii)   5.5 hours.

    (d)   Find all the times in the first 24 hours when the height is 3.0 m.

4. The height, h metres, above ground of a chair in a big wheel is found to be modelled by the equation

$$h(t) = 5.8 - 4.6\cos 6t°$$

Where the chair is initially at its lowest point.

    (a)   How long does it take for the chair to come back to its initial position?

    (b)   Copy and complete the table below

t hours	0	12	24	36	48	60	72
h metres							

    (c)   Sketch the graph showing the height of the chair against time.

    (d)   When will the chair first reach a height of 8.0 m?

5. For the function with equation $f: x \mapsto 5\cos 3x° - 2$

    (a)   state

        (i)   its amplitude

        (ii)   its period

        (iii)   its maximum value.

    (b)   Find the smallest positive value for which $f(x) = 0.5$.

SELF ASSESSMENT TEST (30 MINUTES)

1. State (a) the period
(b) the amplitude
of the functions

    (i) $2\cos 3x°$.
    (ii) $-4\sin\frac{1}{2}x°$

[2 marks]

2. Determine the maximum value of the function $x \mapsto 4 - 2\sin(2x)$.

[1 mark]

3. Sketch the graphs of the functions:

    (i) $y = 2\sin\left(\frac{x}{2}\right), 0° \leq x \leq 360°$
    (ii) $y = 2 - 3\cos(90x°), 0 \leq x \leq 8$

[7 marks]

4. When a person is at rest, the blood pressure P millimetres of mercury at any time t seconds can be modelled approximately by the equation
$$P(t) = -20\cos(300t)° + 100, t \geq 0.$$
    (a)   Determine the amplitude and period of P.
    (b)   What is the maximum blood pressure reading that can be recorded?
    (c)   Sketch the graph of $P(t)$, showing two full cycles.
    (d)   Find the first two times when the pressure reaches a reading of 110.
    (e)   For what percentage of time will the pressure be in excess of 110?

[10 marks]

FUNCTIONS 3

EXPONENTIAL FUNCTIONS

1 5

Chapter contents

– Domain and range.
– Exponential function.
– Applications
– Exponential equations

Key Formulae

- $f(x) = a^x, a > 0$

15.1 THE EXPONENTIAL FUNCTION

GRAPHS AND PROPERTIES OF EXPONENTIAL FUNCTIONS

The **exponential function** takes the form $f(x) = a^x, x \in \mathbb{R}, a > 0, a \neq 1$.

GRAPHS WITH $a > 1$

An example of an exponential function is $f(x) = 2^x, x \in \mathbb{R}$. So, how does the graph of $f(x) = 2^x$ compare to that of $f(x) = x^2$?

We know that the graph of $f(x) = x^2$ represents a parabola with its vertex at the origin, and is symmetrical about the x–axis. To determine the properties of the exponential function we set up a table of values and use those values to sketch a graph of $f(x) = 2^x$.

x	-3	-2	-1	0	1	2	3	4	5
$y = x^2$	9	4	1	0	1	4	9	16	25
$y = 2^x$	2^{-3}	2^{-2}	2^{-1}	2^0	2^1	2^2	2^3	2^4	2^5
	$= \frac{1}{8}$	$= \frac{1}{4}$	$= \frac{1}{2}$	$= 1$	$= 2$	$= 4$	$= 8$	$= 16$	$= 32$

We can now plot both graphs on the same set of axes and compare their properties:

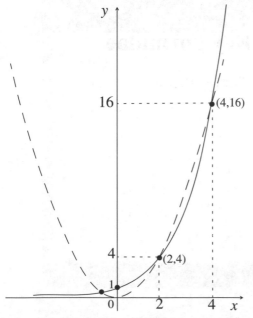

Properties

For the exponential graph we have that;

1. The function increases for all values of x (i.e., as x increases so too do the values of y).

2. The function is always positive (i.e., it lies above the x-axis).

3. As $x \rightarrow \infty$ then $y \rightarrow \infty$

    $x \rightarrow -\infty$ then $y \rightarrow 0$.

    That is, the x-axis is an asymptote.

4. For values of

    $x > 0$ then $y > 1$,

    $x = 0$ then $y = 1$

    and $x < 0$ then $0 < y < 1$.

Notice how different the graphs of the two functions are, even though their rules appear similar. The difference being that for the quadratic function, the variable x is the base, whereas for the exponential, the variable x is the power.

We can now investigate the exponential function for different bases.

To do this we make use of the TI–83. Consider the exponential functions $f(x) = 3^x$ and $f(x) = 4^x$:

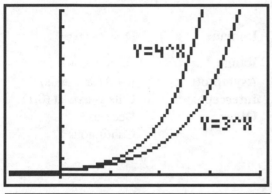

From the graphs we can see that the graph of $f(x) = 4^x$ increases much faster that the graph of $f(x) = 3^x$. However, to observe the behaviour of the two graphs in the region $-1 \leq x \leq 1$, we will need to zoom in on that region.

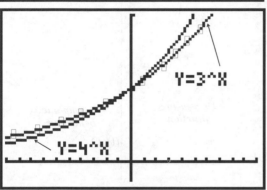

From their graphs we can see that for values of x less than zero, the graph of $f(x) = 3^x$ lies above that of $f(x) = 4^x$. Whereas for values of x greater than zero, then the graph of $f(x) = 4^x$ lies above that of $f(x) = 3^x$.

Notice then that at $x = 0$, both graphs pass through the point $(0, 1)$.

Functions that display these properties are referred to as **exponential growth** functions.

WHAT HAPPENS WHEN 0 < a < 1?

Again, we make use of the TI–83 to investigate any changes that occur. We consider the case where $a = \frac{1}{2}$.

The general shape of the graph remains the same, except that it has been **reflected** about the y-axis.

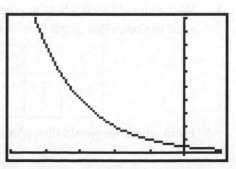

We can summarise the exponential function as follows:

$x \mapsto a^x, a > 1, x \in \mathbb{R}$ $x \mapsto a^x, 0 < a < 1, x \in \mathbb{R}$

e.g., $f(x) = 2^x$, $f(x) = 3^x$ e.g., $f(x) = \left(\dfrac{1}{2}\right)^x$, $f(x) = \left(\dfrac{1}{3}\right)^x$

Properties   ### Properties

Domain	:	$\mathbb{R} = (-\infty, \infty)$
Range	:	$\mathbb{R}^+ = (0, \infty)$
Asymptote	:	$y = 0$ (or x–axis)
Intercepts	:	Cuts y–axis at $(0,1)$
Other	:	Increases
		Continuous

Domain	:	$\mathbb{R} = (-\infty, \infty)$
Range	:	$\mathbb{R}^+ = (0, \infty)$
Asymptote	:	$y = 0$ (or x–axis)
Intercepts	:	Cuts y–axis at $(0,1)$
Other	:	Decreases
		Continuous

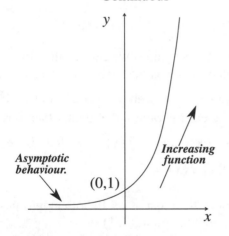

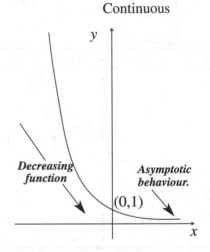

EXAMPLE

Sketch the graphs of   (a) $f(x) = 3^x$

                              (c) $f(x) = 3^x + 2$

SOLUTION

(a)   We've already seen what the graph of $f(x) = 3^x$ looks like. However, should we need to sketch this graph from scratch, we would simply set up a table of values

x	–2	–1	0	1	2	3
$f(x)$	$\dfrac{1}{9}$	$\dfrac{1}{3}$	1	3	9	27

From which we would then plot the points on a set of axes:

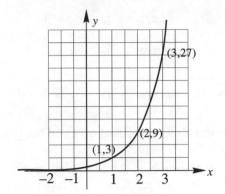

(b)   The graph of $f(x) = 3^x + 2$ is simply the same as that of $f(x) = 3^x$ except that this time the graph has been moved up 2 units.

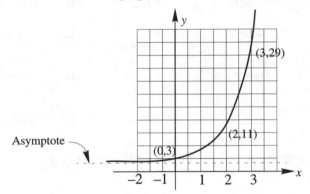

EXERCISE 15.1

1.   On separate sets of axes sketch the graphs of the following functions for $x \in \mathbb{R}$ and determine the range of each function.

(a) $f(x) = 4^x$ (b) $f(x) = 3^x$ (c) $f(x) = 5^x$

(d) $f(x) = (2.5)^x$ (e) $f(x) = (3.2)^x$ (f) $f(x) = (1.8)^x$

(g) $f(x) = \left(\frac{1}{2}\right)^x$ (h) $f(x) = \left(\frac{1}{3}\right)^x$ (i) $f(x) = \left(\frac{1}{5}\right)^x$

(j) $f(x) = \left(\frac{3}{4}\right)^x$ (k) $f(x) = \left(\frac{5}{8}\right)^x$ (l) $f(x) = (0.7)^x$

2.   Describe the effect of changing c on the following graphs

(a) $f(x) = 2^x + c$ where   i. $c = 1$ ii. $c = 2$

(b) $f(x) = 3^x + c$ where   i. $c = 1$ ii. $c = -2$

(c) $f(x) = 5^x + c$ where   i. $c = 3$ ii. $c = -1$

(d) $f(x) = \left(\dfrac{1}{2}\right)^x + c$ where   i. $c = \dfrac{1}{2}$ ii. $c = -\dfrac{1}{2}$

(e) $f(x) = \left(\dfrac{1}{4}\right)^x + c$ where   i. $c = 4$ ii. $c = -\dfrac{1}{4}$

Make a general statement about the effect of 'c' on the graph of $f(x) = a^x + c$.

3. Describe the effect of changing b on the following graphs

(a) $f(x) = b \times 2^x$ where   i. $b = 3$ ii. $b = 5$

(b) $f(x) = b \times 3^x$ where   i. $b = 2$ ii. $b = -2$

(c) $f(x) = b \times 5^x$ where   i. $b = \dfrac{1}{2}$ ii. $b = -1$

(d) $f(x) = b \times \left(\dfrac{1}{2}\right)^x$ where   i. $b = 3$ ii. $b = -2$

(e) $f(x) = b \times \left(\dfrac{1}{4}\right)^x$ where   i. $b = 4$ ii. $b = -5$

Make a general statement about the effect of 'b' on the graph of $f(x) = b \times a^x$.

4. (a) For the function $f : x \mapsto 2^{kx}$, $x \in \mathbb{R}$, sketch the graph of f for

    i. $k = 1, 2, 3, 4$

    ii. $k = \dfrac{1}{2}, \dfrac{1}{3}, \dfrac{1}{4}, \dfrac{1}{5}$

(b) For the function $f : x \mapsto 3^{kx}$, $x \in \mathbb{R}$, sketch the graph of f for

    i. $k = 1, 2, 3, 4$

    ii. $k = \dfrac{1}{2}, \dfrac{1}{3}, \dfrac{1}{4}, \dfrac{1}{5}$.

(c) For the function $f : x \mapsto 5^{kx}$, $x \in \mathbb{R}$, sketch the graph of f for

    i. $k = 1, 2, 3, 4$

    ii. $k = \dfrac{1}{2}, \dfrac{1}{3}, \dfrac{1}{4}, \dfrac{1}{5}$.

(d) For the function $f : x \mapsto \left(\dfrac{1}{2}\right)^{kx}$, $x \in \mathbb{R}$, sketch the graph of f for

    i. $k = 1, 2, 3, 4$

    ii. $k = \dfrac{1}{2}, \dfrac{1}{3}, \dfrac{1}{4}, \dfrac{1}{5}$.

Make a general statement about the effect of 'k' on the graph of $f(x) = a^{kx}$.

5. On the same set of axes sketch the following graphs

(a) $f(x) = 3^x, x \in \mathbb{R}$ and $f(x) = 3^{-x}, x \in \mathbb{R}$.

(b) $f(x) = 5^x, x \in \mathbb{R}$ and $f(x) = 5^{-x}, x \in \mathbb{R}$.

(c) $f(x) = 10^x, x \in \mathbb{R}$ and $f(x) = 10^{-x}, x \in \mathbb{R}$.

(a) $f(x) = \left(\dfrac{1}{3}\right)^x, x \in \mathbb{R}$ and $f(x) = \left(\dfrac{1}{3}\right)^{-x}, x \in \mathbb{R}$.

How does the graph of $f(x) = a^{-x}$ compare to the graph of $f(x) = a^x$?

6. Based on your findings in Questions 5–8, describe the effects of b, c and k for the function $f(x) = b \times a^{kx} + c$.

7. Find the range of the following functions:

(a) $f:[0,4] \mapsto \mathbb{R}$, $y = 2^x$ (b) $f:[1,3] \mapsto \mathbb{R}$, $y = 3^x$

(c) $f:[-1,2] \mapsto \mathbb{R}$, $y = 4^x$ (d) $f:[-1,2] \mapsto \mathbb{R}$, $y = 2^x$

(e) $f:[-1,3] \mapsto \mathbb{R}$, $y = 3^x$ (f) $f:[-2,2] \mapsto \mathbb{R}$, $y = 4^x$

(g) $f:[-1,2] \mapsto \mathbb{R}$, $y = \left(\dfrac{1}{4}\right)^x$ (h) $f:[-2,0] \mapsto \mathbb{R}$, $y = \left(\dfrac{1}{3}\right)^x$

(i) $f:[2,3] \mapsto \mathbb{R}$, $y = \left(\dfrac{1}{2}\right)^x$ (j) $f:[-1,1] \mapsto \mathbb{R}$, $y = \left(\dfrac{1}{10}\right)^x$

15.2 SOLVING EQUATIONS

Solving exponential equations can carried out by

(a) plotting an accurate graph and reading solution from the graph
(b) using an algebraic solution (which is beyond the scope of this course).
(c) using a graphics calculator.

We illustrate methods (a) and (c) by looking at two specific examples.

EXAMPLE

Solve each of the following equations

(a) $2^x = 10$

(b) $2 \times 3^x + 1 = 40$

SOLUTION

(a) To start with we need to plot a graph of the function $f(x) = 2^x$, from where we will then simply read the solution from the graph (i.e., along the *x*–axis).

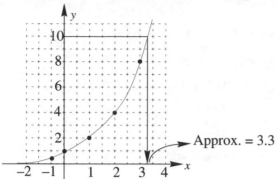

From our graph we therefore have
that if $2^x = 10$ then $x \approx 3.3$.

Approx. = 3.3

(b)   To solve the equation $2 \times 3^x + 1 = 40$ using the TI–83, all we need to do is use the **solve(** function: Press **2nd 0** [CATALOG] **ALPHA LN** [S] **ALPHA LN** [S]
Then use the arrow key to move cursor to **solve(** function:
Press ENTER, type in the equation in the form **Equation = 0**,

(this means that the equation $2 \times 3^x + 1 = 40$ must first be

transposed to the equation $2 \times 3^x + 1 - 40 = 0$) next type X,
then provide an initial guess (2 in this case), close the
parenthesis and then press ENTER:

```
solve(2*3^X+1-40
,X,2)
        2.703787766
```

Note, applying this method to the first example gives:

```
solve(2^X-10,X,2
)
        3.321928095
```

EXERCISE 15.2

1.   Solve the following equations using
(a)   a graphical solution.
(b)   a graphics calculator.

(i) $2^x = 8$	(ii) $3^x = 27$	(iii) $4^x = 16$
(iv) $2^x = 15$	(v) $3^x = 25$	(vi) $4^x = 10$
(vii) $3^x - 2 = 12$	(viii) $5^x + 2 = 19$	(ix) $2^x - 3 = 15$
(x) $2^{-x} = 8$	(xi) $3^{-x} = 27$	(xii) $4^{-x} = 16$
(xiii) $2^{-x} = 10$	(xiv) $3^{-x} + 2 = 3$	(xv) $8 - 2^{-x} = 3$

2.   Solve the following equations using
(a)   a graphical solution.
(b)   a graphics calculator.

296

(i) $2 \times 3^x + 4 = 16$ (ii) $3 \times 2^x - 1 = 9$

(iii) $5 \times 2^x - 4 = 21$ (iv) $8 \times 3^x + 4 = 68$

15.3 APPLICATIONS

EXAMPLE

A radioactive element decays in such a way so that the amount present each year is 0.95 of the amount present the previous year. At the start of 1990, there were 50 mg of the element present.

(a)   Produce a table of values showing how much of the element is present at the start of each year from 1990 to 1998.

(b)   The rule for this situation is given by $N = k \times a^t$, where N mg is the amount of element present t years after the start of 1990. Find the value of a and k.

(c)   Sketch the graph of $N = k \times a^t$.

(d)   How long will it be before there is 25 mg of this element remaining?

SOLUTION

(a)   Initially there is 50 mg of the element present. At the start of the following year there will be 95% of that left over, i.e., there will be $0.95 \times 50 = 47.5$ mg left over. At the start of the year after there will be 95% of 47.5 mg left over. i.e., the will be $0.95 \times 47.5 = 45.125$ mg, and so on. Continuing in this manner we can complete the table of values:

t	0	1	2	3	4	5	6	7	8
N	50	47.5	41.13	42.87	40.73	38.69	36.75	34.92	33.17

(b)   The initial amount is 50 mg, therefore, $k = 50$. The quantity is decreasing by 95% each time, therefore, $a = 0.95$.

(c)   Using the T^–83, we have:

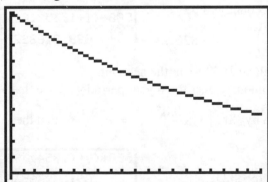

(d) Using the TI–83 we are solving the equation $25 = 50 \times (0.95)^t$ or (as is required for the TI–83), we need to solve the equation

$$50 \times 0.95^t - 25 = 0:$$

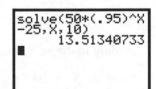

That is, it takes 13.51 years for this amount of radioactive element to halve.

THE NATURAL EXPONENTIAL FUNCTION

A special base is the number $e = \lim_{n \to \infty}\left(1 + \frac{1}{n}\right)^n = 2.718\ldots$.

As $e > 1$, the properties of the functions $x \mapsto e^x, x \in \mathbb{R}$ and $x \mapsto e^{-x}, x \in \mathbb{R}$ are identical

to those of the function $x \mapsto a^x, a > 1, x \in \mathbb{R}$ and $x \mapsto a^{-x}, a > 1, x \in \mathbb{R}$
Using the TI–83 we display both graphs:

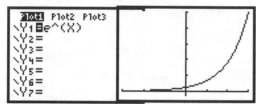
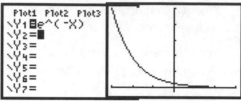

Note: **work using base 'e' is not examinable**. It is included here as a discussion point.

EXAMPLE

Five hundred dollars is deposited into a bank account that pays 5.40% interest per annum.
(a)   How much money will there be in the account at the end of 6 years if
   (i)   the interest is compounded quarterly?
   (ii)   the interest is compounded continuously?
(b)   Under continuous compounding, how long will it be before the money in the account is doubled?
(c)   Show the behaviour of continuous compounding using a graph.

SOLUTION

Let the amount of money in the account after t years be $\$A(t)\,, t \geq 0$.
(a)   (i)   Because interest is compounded quarterly, we need to first determine the interest per quarter, i.e., $5.4 \div 4 = 1.35$. Next, over a period of 6 years the interest would have been compounded $6 \times 4 = 24$ times.
Therefore, the amount in the account will be

given by $A = 500 \times \left(1 + \frac{1.35}{100}\right)^{24} = 689.826\ldots$

```
500*(1+1.35/100)
^24
          689.8268225
```

That is, after six years there will be $689.83 in the account.
   (ii)   For interest compounded continuously over the 6 year period we have that

the compounding term is given by $\lim_{n \to \infty}\left(1 + \frac{0.054}{n}\right)^n = e^{0.054}$ so that the

amount in the account is

given by $A = 500(e^{0.054})^6 = 691.323\ldots$

```
500*(e^(.054))^6
          691.3236536
```

That is, after six years there will be $691.32 in the account.
(b)   Initially there is $500 in the account, meaning that we want to find the time taken for the amount to reach $1000 (assuming continuous compounding). That is, we want

the value of t such that $1000 = 500e^{0.054t}$.
Using the TI–83, we have that $t = 12.84$

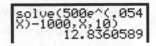

That is, it will take approximately 12.84 years.

(c) To display the behaviour of the amount of money in the account, we simply need to sketch the graph of the exponential function

$A(t) = e^{0.054t}, t \geq 0$

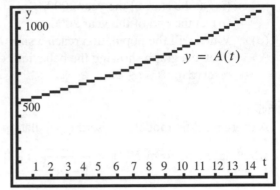

EXERCISE 15.3

1. The charge Q coulombs stored at the plates of a leaky capacitor after time t seconds is determined by the equation $Q(t) = Q_0 \times (1.122)^{-t}, t \geq 0$, where Q_0 is the initial charge.

   (a) If the charge on the plates is 250 coulombs after 5 seconds, determine the original charge.
   (b) What proportion of the original charge remains after 10 seconds?
   (c) How long will it take the charge to reduce by half?
   (d) Sketch the graph of the charge remaining on the plates for $t \geq 0$.

2. The number of bacteria in a culture, N, has been modelled by the exponential function $N(t) = 1200 \times (1.148)^t, t \geq 0$, where t is measured in days.

   (a) Find the initial number of bacteria in this culture.
   (b) How many bacteria (to the nearest hundred) will there be after
       (i) 5 days?   (ii) 10 days?
   (c) How long will it take for the number of bacteria to reach 5000?
   (d) Sketch the graph showing the number of bacteria for $t \geq 0$.

3. A population of 120 mammals from an endangered species were introduce onto an enclosed reserve at the start of 1990. By the start of 1995 the population had increased to 300.

   It is believed that a model of the form $N(t) = N_0(2.718)^{kt}, t \geq 0$ (where $N(t)$ represents the number of mammals present at time t years since their introduction onto the reserve) adequately approximates the population size of this mammal.

    (a)   State the value of N_0. What does it represent?

    (b)   Determine the value of k to 4 decimal places.

    (c)   Find the population size

        (i) at the start of the year 2000.

        (ii) at the end of the year 2000.

    (d)   When will the population reach a size of 1000?

    (e)   Sketch a graph showing the behaviour of the mammal population on the reserve for $0 \leq t \leq 20$.

[Extension]

4.   A more realistic model to describe population growth is known as a logistic model which takes the form $N(t) = \dfrac{a}{1 + be^{-kt}}$, $t \geq 0$, a, b and k are all positive constants.

    (a)   Sketch the graph of $W(t) = 1 + be^{-kt}$, $t \geq 0$, for positive values of b and k.

    (b)   (i)   Use your graph in (a) to sketch the graph of $y = \dfrac{1}{W(t)}$, $t \geq 0$.

         (ii)   Hence, sketch the graph of $y = \dfrac{a}{W(t)}$, $t \geq 0$.

    (c)   Investigate the behaviour of $y = N(t)$, $t \geq 0$ for different values of a, b and k.

EXAMINATION STYLE QUESTIONS

1. On the same set of axes, sketch the graphs of

   (a) $f(x) = 3^x + 1$

   (b) $g(x) = \left(\dfrac{1}{2}\right)^x$

Hence, find the value of x, to one decimal place, where $f(x) = g(x)$.

2. The graph with equation $f(x) = 2^x + c$ passes through the point $(1, 3)$.

   (a) Find the value of c.

   (b) Hence, solve for x, where $f(x) = 9$.

3. A bacteria culture is placed under a strict controlled environment. Under these conditions, the bacteria is allowed to double in number every hour. Initially there were 8 bacteria.

   (a) Complete the following table

t, time in hours	0	1	2	3	4	5
N, number of bacteria	8					

   (b) Using an appropriate scale, draw a graph with N, the number of bacteria, on the vertical axis and t, the number of hours, on the horizontal axis.

   (c) Using your graph in (b), estimate

     (i) the number of bacteria after 2.5 hours.

     (ii) after how many hours would there be 100 bacteria.

4. The population of a nest of ants, t weeks after it was located is thought to follow the exponential model defined by

$$N = 400 \times (1.12)^t, \ t \geq 0.$$

   (a) How many ants were there when the nest was discovered?

   (b) How many ants were there in the nest after

     (i) 5 weeks.

     (ii) 10 weeks.

   (c) Using an appropriate scale, draw a graph with N, the number of ants, on the vertical axis and t, the number of weeks, on the horizontal axis.

   (d) Using your graph in (c), estimate after how many weeks would there be 2000 ants.

5. The current, I amps, flowing through a circuit, once switched off, dies away according to the rule $I(t) = 20 \times (0.25)^t$, where t is measured in seconds.

   (a) Draw a graph of I, for $0 \leq t \leq 4$.

   (b) Estimate how long it takes for the current to reach 10 amps.

SELF ASSESSMENT TEST (30 MINUTES)

1. On the same set of axes, sketch the graphs of

(a) $f(x) = 2^x + 3$, $-1 \le x \le 3$, stating its range.

(b) $g(x) = \left(\frac{1}{3}\right)^x - 1$, $-1 \le x \le 3$, stating its range.

[6 marks]

2. Solve the equations

(a) $3^x + 2 = 11$

(b) $4 - \left(\frac{1}{2}\right)^x = 2$

[4 marks]

3. The exponential function $f(x) = k \times 2^x + c$ is shown in the diagram.
Find k and c.

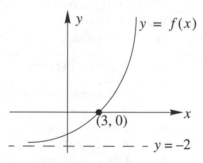

[4 marks]

4. A bacteria culture is placed under a strict controlled environment. Under these conditions, the bacteria is allowed to double in number every hour. Initially there were 10 bacteria.

(a) Complete the following table

t, time in hours	0	1	2	3	4	5	6	7
N, number of bacteria	10							

(b) Using a scale of 1 cm to represent 1 hour and 1 cm to represent 100 bacteria, draw a graph with N, the number of bacteria, on the vertical axis and t, the number of hours, on the horizontal axis.

(c) Using your graph in (b), estimate

(i) the number of bacteria after 2.5 hours.

(ii) after how many hours would there be 500 bacteria.

[10 marks]

FINANCIAL MATHEMATICS 1

FINANCE

16

Chapter contents

– Currency conversion.
– Simple interest.
– Compound interest
– Loan tables

Key Formulae

- $I = \dfrac{Crn}{100}$

- $I = C\left(1 + \dfrac{r}{n}\right)^n - C$

16.1 CURRENCY CONVERSIONS

Most currencies in the modern world are decimalised. This usually means that there is a unit of currency such as the dollar, pound, kroner etc. This basic unit is often divided into smaller parts (often one hundredth of the main unit) such as the cent, penny, ore etc. This means that most currency calculations can be carried out using normal decimal arithmetic and normal calculators and computers. This was not always the case. For example, many countries used a system derived from that of the Roman Empire in which the main unit was the pound. This was divided into twenty shilling which were, in turn, each divided into twelve pennies (originally denarii). This was a system in which it was difficult to perform even simple calculations such as addition. Such non-decimal currency systems are now rare, which is fortunate for accountants! The remainder of this unit will assume a decimalised currency.

BASIC CONVERSIONS

The currencies of different countries are not all of equivalent value. This means that one German Mark does not have the same buying power as, for example, one Japanese Yen. The conversion rate between these currencies is decided by a complex set of market forces. The most powerful of these are connected with currency trading in which dealers buy and sell investments in various countries. Also, the general strength and success of a country's economy will have an effect on the value of it's currency. Econonmically successful countries generally have strong currencies. There is, however, a control mechanism that prevents the currencies of economically strong countries from growing in value without limit. The more a country's currency grows in value, the more expensive an export item becomes in other countries. This means that the economy will not grow as rapidly, tending to reduce the value of the currency. It is not important to understand all these forces for this course. That is the area covered by economics.

In simple terms, whilst the values of currencies might fluctuate, it is generally the case that if a kettle costs $40 in Utopia and 10 Marks in Floria, the same ratio (4:1) will operate for other items so a $600 mower might be expected to cost about $\frac{600}{4}$ = 150 Marks:

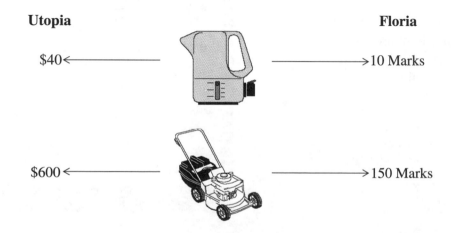

Utopia		**Floria**
$40 ←		→ 10 Marks
$600 ←		→ 150 Marks

This is a very general observation and is only approximately true in valuing items in different countries.

In the above example, we might say that 1 Florian Mark is worth $4 in the Utopian currency. This is said the be the **exchange rate** between the two currencies. Such exchange rates which, as we have already observed are determined by many factors, but can generally be found in the business sections of daily papers. They are also displayed in banks and other financial institutions.

EXAMPLES
The currency conversion rates between five countries are shown.

US	Aus	Sterling	Yen	Mark
1	1.633	0.610	139.490	1.782

Convert:

1. $50 US to Japanese Yen
2. £15 Sterling to $US
3. $1500 Australian to Marks
4. 125 Yen to Sterling.

SOLUTIONS

1. From the table, $1 US is equivalent to 139.490 Yen. Thus $50 US are worth $50 \times 139.490 = 6974.5$ Yen. The diagram shows how this calculation should look on a TI-83 graphic calculator.

2. $1 US is equivalent to £0.61 Sterling. It follows that £1 Sterling must be equivalent to $\dfrac{1}{0.61} = 1.6393443$ dollars.

£15 Sterling is equivalent to $15 \times 1.6393443 \approx 24.59016$ or $24.59. A simple alternative is $\dfrac{15}{0.61} \approx 24.59016$ which gives the answer in one step. Note the use of the automatic answer memory in this example.

3. $1500 Australian to Marks requires us to make the appropriate conversion. From the table, $1.633 Australian is equivalent to 1.782 marks. $1 is equivalent to $\dfrac{1.782}{1.633} \approx 1.0912431$. $1500 is equivalent to

Financial Mathematics

$1500 \times 1.0912431 \approx 1636.86$ Marks. In on step, this is $\dfrac{1.782}{1.633} \times 1500 \approx 1636.86$

4. 125 Yen to Sterling needs the value of 1 Yen to be expressed in £ Sterling. This is $\dfrac{0.610}{139.490} \approx 0.00437307$.

Thus 125 Yen is equivalent to

$0.00437307 \times 125 \approx 0.5466$ or $\dfrac{0.610}{139.490} \times 125 \approx 0.5466$.

This is about £0.56

EXERCISE 16.1

1. $1 Canadian is equivalent to 4.092 French francs. Convert the following Canadian dollar amounts to French francs, giving your answers to the nearest franc.

a.	$205	b.	$138	c.	$126
d.	$100	e.	$183	f.	$95

2. 1 Swiss franc is equivalent to 3.473 South African rand. Convert the following Swiss franc amounts to South African rand, giving your answers to the nearest rand.

a.	366	b.	165	c.	320
d.	474	e.	144	f.	140

3. 1 German mark is equivalent to 23.261 Indian rupees. Convert the following German mark amounts to Indian rupees, giving your answers to the nearest rupee.

a.	75	b.	17	c.	77
d.	74	e.	56	f.	79

4. $1 US is equivalent to 1740 Italian lire. Convert the following **Italian lire** amounts to $US, giving your answers to the nearest US cent.

a.	54329	b.	49550	c.	988
d.	34902	e.	47351	f.	59876

5. $1 Australian is equivalent to 3.5138 French francs and to 3.0274 South African rand. Convert the following amounts in South African rand to French francs, giving your answers to the nearest franc.

a.	77	b.	18	c.	33
d.	103	e.	144	f.	63

COMMISSION

It is generally the case that agents who change money between currencies will charge for this service. These charges are often called **commission**. There are two main ways in which agents charge such a commision. These are illustrated in the following two examples:

EXAMPLE

An agent offers to exchange $US to other currencies at the published daily rate. Their commission is $5 per transaction or 1%, whichever is the greater with the commission being paid in $UD. Three customers wish to convert the following amounts of $US to Italian lire on a day when the exchange rate was 1760 lire to the dollar:

    a. $20   b. $200   c. $20 000

Find the numbers of lire that each will receive after the commission has been charged.

SOLUTION

a.   The commission is either $5 or 1% of the sum to be exchanged. In this case the 1% commission would be 1% of $5 $= \dfrac{1}{100} \times 5 \ = \ 0.05$ or 5 cents. This is much less than the $5 minimum commission. The exchange will, therefore, attract a commission of $5. This means that the customer will only have $20 – $5 = $125 to exchange.

    This will yield $1760 \times 15 \ = \ 26400$ lire.

    In this case, the customer has paid a comparatively large proportion of the money (one quarter) in commission. This is a thing to look out for when you are travelling!

b.   Again the commission is $5 as 1% of the amount to be exchanged ($200) is $2 and this is the smaller amount. This leaves $195 to be exchanged. The amount that the customer will receive is $1760 \times 195 \ = \ 343200$ lire. This customer has paid a much smaller proportion of the money in commission than the first.

c.   If $20 000 is to be exchanged, the 1% commision is 1% of $20 000 = $200. This leaves $20 000 – $200 = $19 800.

    When converted to lire this becomes $1760 \times 19800 \ = \ 34848000$ lire.

The second way in which commissions can be charged is to use a slightly different rate when buying or selling a different currency.

Financial Mathematics

EXAMPLE

A bank offers the following exchange rates for $1 Australian in relation to the French franc: 'We buy: 3.5959, we sell: 3.5138'. A customer wishes to exchange $1200 Australian for francs. How many francs will the customer receive? If the customer then immediately exchanges these francs for Australian dollars, how much will she receive? What is the effective exchange rate? Assume that all currency amounts are rounded to the nearest whole number to complete each transaction.

SOLUTION

The bank is selling francs to the customer so the rate for the first transaction is the 'selling rate' of 3.5138.

The customer receives: $3.5138 \times 1200 = 4216.56$ or 4217 when rounded to the nearest franc.

If the customer immediately reconverts this amount back to Australian dollars, the bank will use the 'buying rate' of 3.5959 and she will receive: $\dfrac{4217}{3.5959} = 1172.7245$. This amount rounds to $1173 Australian.

This amounts to a commission of $1200 - 1173 = \$27$ on the two transactions.

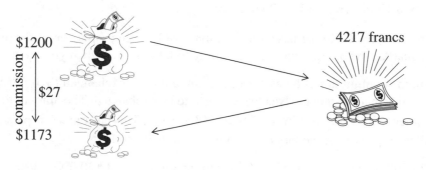

EXERCISE 16.2

1. A bank offers the following exchange rates for $1 US in relation to the Japanese yen: 'We buy: 145.7, we sell: 143.1'. If a customer wishes to exchange the following amounts, find:

    i.   the number of yen the customer receives, correct to the nearest whole number.

    ii.   the number of $US that will result if the amount in i. is immediately returned to $US.

    iii.   the effective commission on the two transactions in $US.

a.	1000	b.	1281	c.	1513
d.	1356	e.	1283	f.	1595

2. A bank offers the following exchange rates for 1 German mark in relation to the Italian lire: 'We buy: 1033, we sell: 1019'. If a customer wishes to exchange the following amounts, find:

i. the number of Italian lire the customer receives, correct to the nearest whole number.

ii. the number of German marks that will result if the amount in i. is immediately returned to German marks.

iii. the effective commission on the two transactions in German marks.

a.	1000	b.	1608	c.	1359
d.	1468	e.	1606	f.	1217

3. A bank offers the following exchange rates for Swiss francs in relation to the Indian rupee: 'We buy: 33.7, we sell: 31.9'. If a customer wishes to exchange the following amounts, find:

i. the number of Indian rupees the customer receives, correct to the nearest whole number.

ii. the number of Swiss francs that will result if the amount in i. is immediately returned to Swiss francs.

iii. the effective commission on the two transactions in Swiss francs.

a.	900	b.	1433	c.	1404
d.	1390	e.	1334	f.	1488

4. A bank offers the following exchange rates for $1 US in relation to the South African rand: 'We buy: 6.26, we sell: 6.09'. If a customer wishes to exchange the following amounts, find:

i. the number of South African rand the customer receives, correct to the nearest whole number.

ii. the number of $US that will result if the amount in i. is immediately returned to $US.

iii. the effective commission on the two transactions in $US.

a.	6627	b.	7491	c.	7358
d.	7472	e.	6201	f.	7030

16.2 SIMPLE INTEREST

When money is borrowed or lent, the borrower usually pays the lender for the service. The amount charged is usually called **interest**. There are two common methods of calculating this interest: simple interest and compound interest.

Simple interest is usually calculated as a percentage of the amount borrowed (the **principal**).

EXAMPLE

A family invests $1250 in an account that pays 6% annual simple interest for 7 years. Find the amount of interest paid over this period.

SOLUTION

The interest is 6% of the principal ($1250) each year.

This amount is $\frac{6}{100} \times 1250 = \$75$. Since this is paid in each of the 7 years, the total amount of interest is: $6 \times 75 = \$450$.

The above example could have been solved using the simple interest formula:

$$I = \frac{PRT}{100}$$

I = interest paid, P = the amount invested (or borrowed), known as the principal, R = the interest rate (%) and T is the number of time periods that the loan or investment lasts. R and T must refer to the same period of time. For example, if the time period is a year, the interest rate must be 'per year' (also known as per annum).

It is also possible to transform the formula to use it to solve problems in which quantities other than the interest are unknown.

EXAMPLES

1. If $600 is invested in an account and earns $136.50 simple interest over a 3.,5 year period, find the annual interest rate.

2. If 1450 crowns are invested at a monthly interest rate of 0.08% and earn 8.12 crowns simple interest, find the number of months of the investment.

SOLUTIONS

1. The unknown in this question is R. If the subject of the formula is changed to R it

becomes: $R = \frac{100I}{PT}$. Substitution gives: $R = \frac{100 \times 136.50}{600 \times 3.5} = 6.5\,\%$.

2. Changing the subject of the formula to T, the unknown of this problem gives:

$$T = \frac{100I}{PR}.$$

The rate in this question is 'per month' and so is the time. If the time periods are not the same, then they must be made so. So, for example, a time of 2 years would have to become 24 months if the rate was quoted in % per month.

Substituting gives: $T = \dfrac{100 \times 8.12}{1450 \times 0.08} = 7$ months.

EXERCISE 16.3

1. For the following loans, calculate the simple interest earned:

	Principal	Rate (% per annum)	Time (years)
a.	$1,340.00	10	6
b.	$1,562.00	9	4
c.	$780.00	4	7
d.	$1,550.00	6	3
e.	$10,200.00	8	8
f.	$6,250.00	6.5	2

2. For the following loans, calculate the simple interest earned, noting that the time periods are given in months:

	Principal	Rate (% per annum)	Time (months)
a.	$1,340.00	12	24
b.	$1,562.00	11	36
c.	$780.00	4	18
d.	$1,550.00	5	15
e.	$10,200.00	7.5	3
f.	$6,250.00	4.5	8

3. For the following loans, calculate the interest rate (% per annum):

	Principal	Interest	Time (years)
a.	$120.00	$50.40	6
b.	$568.00	$51.12	3
c.	$890.00	$569.60	8
d.	$1,650.00	$396.00	2
e.	$125.00	$132.75	9
f.	$6,250.00	$1,743.75	3

Financial Mathematics

4. For the following loans, calculate the principal (in marks):

	Rate (% per annum)	Interest (marks)	Time (years)
a.	3	63.00	7
b.	7	165.90	3
c.	6	960.00	8
d.	9	65.70	2
e.	2	245.16	9
f.	9	813.15	1

5. For the following loans, calculate the time of the loan (in years):

	Principal (crowns)	Interest (crowns)	Rate (% per annum)
a.	1560	546.00	7
b.	200	42.00	3
c.	2570	411.20	8
d.	2030	324.80	2
e.	700	693.00	9
f.	950	34.20	1

6. For the following loans, calculate the time of the loan (in months):

	Principal (dinars)	Interest (dinars)	Rate (% per annum)
a.	3000	210.00	7
b.	5600	98.00	3
c.	1290	17.20	8
d.	3400	45.33	2
e.	780	64.35	9
f	2700	8.10	1

7. Helen has 6000 Swiss francs. She wishes to invest this money over a period of 5 years. She has two choices:

EITHER: Invest in a Swiss bank that offers 7.3% annual simple interest. OR:

Convert the money to Japanese yen at an exchange that offers 'We buy: 155.7, we sell: 153.1'. Then invest with an institution that offers 7.4% annual simple interest. After the investment period, find the number of Swiss francs that Helen will get when she re-converts her investment.

16.3 COMPOUND INTEREST

The calculation of simple interest described in the previous section implies that everytime interest is paid, it is withdrawn by the investor. This leaves the principal untouched throughout the period of the loan. This may be the case, however, it is much more usual for investors to add (or **compound**) the interest to the principal so that the principal grows during the term of the investment. It is possible to follow the progress of such a loan period by period as in the following example.

EXAMPLE

Boris invests $560 at 6% annual interest compounded annually over a period of 10 years. Compare the results of this with the simple interest alternative.

SOLUTION

The calculation of the interest due at the end of each year is done using the simple interest formula: $I = \dfrac{PRT}{100}$. For the first year, $I = \dfrac{560 \times 6 \times 1}{100} = 33.6$ or $33.60.

This amount is compounded so that the new principal that operates over the second year is: $560 + $33.60 = $593.60.

In the second year the interest is: $I = \dfrac{593.6 \times 6 \times 1}{100} = 35.612$ or $35.62 rounded to the nearest cent. This means that at the end of the second year the amount in the account will be $593.60 + $35.62 = $629.22. In the third year, the interest will be larger again because it is based on a larger principal.

The complete set of results are:

	Year	Principal	Interest
	Start	$560.00	$33.60
After year -	1	$593.60	$35.62
	2	$629.22	$37.75
	3	$666.97	$40.02
	4	$706.99	$42.42
	5	$749.41	$44.96
	6	$794.37	$47.66
	7	$842.03	$50.52
	8	$892.55	$53.55
	9	$946.11	$56.77
	10	$1,002.87	

Thus after ten years of interest the amount in the account is $1,002.87. The total interest paid is $1,002.87 − $560 = $442.87.

This compares with the simple interest that might be paid of $\dfrac{560 \times 6 \times 10}{100} = \$336$, a significantly smaller amount.

Step by step calculations of compound interest are best done by using a calculating device. If using a graphic calculator the steps are:

1. Type in the principal and then press ENTER. This places the principal in the automatic memory location called 'Ans'. Every time the calculator performs a calculation the answer is placed in this memory.

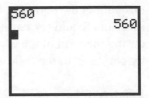

2. Press × 1.06 followed by ENTER. 1.06 is $1 + \dfrac{6}{100}$ and is the factor that will increase the principal by 6%. Note that this keying sequence will result in the calculator automatically bringing up the 'Ans' memory of the principal.

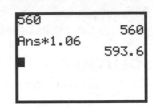

3. Next, press ENTER again. The calculator will repeat the previous calcuation (Ans×1.06) with the new pincipal (593.6). All that is necessary to calculate the amounts in successive years is to continue to press ENTER.

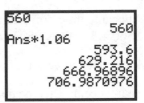

An alternative is to use a spreadsheet. An example of the formulas that could be used is:

A	A	B	C
1	Year	Principal	Interest
2	Start	560	+B2*6/100
3	1	+B2+C2	+B3*6/100
4	2	+B3+C3	+B4*6/100
5	3	+B4+C4	+B5*6/100
6	4	+B5+C5	+B6*6/100
7	5	+B6+C6	+B7*6/100
8	6	+B7+C7	+B8*6/100
9	7	+B8+C8	+B9*6/100

The interst for each year is calculated in column C using the simple interest formula. This is then added to the amount in column B.

Compound interest is most commonly calculated using the formula: $A = P\left(1 + \dfrac{R}{100}\right)^n$

where P is the principal, R is the interest rate, n is the number of compunding periods and A is the amount in the account. As with simple interest, the same calculation can be used to follow both loans and investments.

EXAMPLES

1. $1200 is placed in a savings account that pays 8% annual interest compounded annually. Find the amount in the account and the interest paid after 10 years.

2. Find the interest earned over a 5 year period if 1500 marks is invested in a savings account that pays 6% annual interest compounded monthly.

SOLUTIONS

1. In this case $P = 1200$, $R = 8$ and $n = 10$.

Using the formula: $A = 1200\left(1 + \dfrac{8}{100}\right)^{10} = 2590.71$.

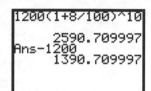

The account will contain $2590.71 after 10 years. The interest is $2590.71 − $1200 = $ 1390.71

2. In this case the interest rate is annual but the interest is calculated monthly. Before using the formula we must express the interest rate as % per month by dividing it by 12 to get $R = 0.5\%$. The number of interest periods must also be expressed in months ($n = 60$ months).

Using the formula: $A = 1500\left(1 + \dfrac{0.5}{100}\right)^{60} = 2023.2752$

or 2023 marks.

The interest paid is 2023 − 1500 = 523 marks.

EXERCISE 16.4

1. Find the amounts that will result if the following principals (in yen) are invested at the rates and for the times given.

	Principal (yen)	Rate % per annum	Time years
a.	2300	4	12
b.	600	14	20
c.	4200	8	20
d.	1300	4	4
e.	4300	2	16
f.	800	12	12

2. Find the amounts that will result if the following principals (in marks) are invested at the rates and for the times given.

	Principal (marks)	Rate % per annum	Time years
a.	4800	8	12
b.	88800	6	4
c.	79700	2	24
d.	75300	6	12
e.	75800	4	24
f.	26000	4	16

3. Find the amounts that will result if the following principals (in francs) are invested at the rates and for the times given.

	Principal (franks)	Rate % per annum	Time months
a.	14900	2	3
b.	30900	4	2
c.	29700	8	2
d.	31200	14	4
e.	39000	6	1
f.	27000	14	3

4. Find the amounts that will result if the following principals (in yen) are invested at the rates and for the times given.

	Principal (yen)	Rate % per annum	Time months
a.	21700	8	3
b.	28700	0	5
c.	23100	4	7
d.	30000	12	4
e.	28000	8	6
f.	1600	4	3

5. If a choice has to be made between investing $1500 for 5 years between the following options, which should the investor choose and why?

Account A: offers 10% per annum calculated annually.

Account B: offers 9.7% per annum calculated monthly.

Account C: offers 9.5% per annum calculated daily.

16.4 FINANCIAL TABLES

There are a number of financial calculations that are often performed using tables. These are generally used to save calculation.

INVESTMENTS AND SAVINGS

The following table shows the compound interest amounts produced by $1000 compounded monthly over various periods.

Rate(%) Month	2	2.5	3	3.5	4	4.5	5	5.5
1	$1,001.67	$1,002.08	$1,002.50	$1,002.92	$1,003.33	$1,003.75	$1,004.17	$1,004.58
2	$1,003.34	$1,004.17	$1,005.01	$1,005.84	$1,006.68	$1,007.51	$1,008.35	$1,009.19
3	$1,005.01	$1,006.26	$1,007.52	$1,008.78	$1,010.03	$1,011.29	$1,012.55	$1,013.81
4	$1,006.68	$1,008.36	$1,010.04	$1,011.72	$1,013.40	$1,015.08	$1,016.77	$1,018.46
5	$1,008.36	$1,010.46	$1,012.56	$1,014.67	$1,016.78	$1,018.89	$1,021.01	$1,023.13
6	$1,010.04	$1,012.57	$1,015.09	$1,017.63	$1,020.17	$1,022.71	$1,025.26	$1,027.82
7	$1,011.73	$1,014.67	$1,017.63	$1,020.60	$1,023.57	$1,026.55	$1,029.53	$1,032.53
8	$1,013.41	$1,016.79	$1,020.18	$1,023.57	$1,026.98	$1,030.40	$1,033.82	$1,037.26
9	$1,015.10	$1,018.91	$1,022.73	$1,026.56	$1,030.40	$1,034.26	$1,038.13	$1,042.01
10	$1,016.79	$1,021.03	$1,025.28	$1,029.55	$1,033.84	$1,038.14	$1,042.46	$1,046.79
11	$1,018.49	$1,023.16	$1,027.85	$1,032.56	$1,037.28	$1,042.03	$1,046.80	$1,051.59
12	$1,020.18	$1,025.29	$1,030.42	$1,035.57	$1,040.74	$1,045.94	$1,051.16	$1,056.41
13	$1,021.88	$1,027.42	$1,032.99	$1,038.59	$1,044.21	$1,049.86	$1,055.54	$1,061.25
14	$1,023.59	$1,029.56	$1,035.57	$1,041.62	$1,047.69	$1,053.80	$1,059.94	$1,066.11
15	$1,025.29	$1,031.71	$1,038.16	$1,044.65	$1,051.18	$1,057.75	$1,064.36	$1,071.00
16	$1,027.00	$1,033.86	$1,040.76	$1,047.70	$1,054.69	$1,061.72	$1,068.79	$1,075.91
17	$1,028.71	$1,036.01	$1,043.36	$1,050.76	$1,058.20	$1,065.70	$1,073.24	$1,080.84
18	$1,030.43	$1,038.17	$1,045.97	$1,053.82	$1,061.73	$1,069.70	$1,077.72	$1,085.79
19	$1,032.15	$1,040.33	$1,048.58	$1,056.90	$1,065.27	$1,073.71	$1,082.21	$1,090.77
20	$1,033.87	$1,042.50	$1,051.21	$1,059.98	$1,068.82	$1,077.73	$1,086.72	$1,095.77
21	$1,035.59	$1,044.67	$1,053.83	$1,063.07	$1,072.38	$1,081.77	$1,091.24	$1,100.79
22	$1,037.32	$1,046.85	$1,056.47	$1,066.17	$1,075.96	$1,085.83	$1,095.79	$1,105.84
23	$1,039.04	$1,049.03	$1,059.11	$1,069.28	$1,079.54	$1,089.90	$1,100.36	$1,110.91
24	$1,040.78	$1,051.22	$1,061.76	$1,072.40	$1,083.14	$1,093.99	$1,104.94	$1,116.00

This table can be used directly to find the amounts that will result from investing $1000. It can also be used to find the results of investing other amounts.

EXAMPLES

1. $1000 is placed in a savings account that pays 4.5% annual interest compounded monthly. Find the amount in the account and the interest paid after 8 months.

2. Find the interest earned over a 1 year period if 1500 marks is invested in a savings account that pays 3% annual interest compounded monthly.

SOLUTIONS

1. Directly from the table, reading the approprite row and column:

Rate(%) Month	2	2.5	3	3.5	4	4.5	5	5.5
....								
6	$1,010.04	$1,012.57	$1,015.09	$1,017.63	$1,020.17	$1,022.71	$1,025.26	$1,027.82
7	$1,011.73	$1,014.67	$1,017.63	$1,020.60	$1,023.57	$1,026.55	$1,029.53	$1,032.53
8	$1,013.41	$1,016.79	$1,020.18	$1,023.57	$1,026.98	**$1,030.40**	$1,033.82	$1,037.26
9	$1,015.10	$1,018.91	$1,022.73	$1,026.56	$1,030.40	$1,034.26	$1,038.13	$1,042.01
....								

The amount is $1030.40.

2. Again from the the table:

Rate(%) Month	2	2.5	3	3.5	4	4.5	5	5.5
....								
11	$1,018.49	$1,023.16	$1,027.85	$1,032.56	$1,037.28	$1,042.03	$1,046.80	$1,051.59
12	$1,020.18	$1,025.29	**$1,030.42**	$1,035.57	$1,040.74	$1,045.94	$1,051.16	$1,056.41
13	$1,021.88	$1,027.42	$1,032.99	$1,038.59	$1,044.21	$1,049.86	$1,055.54	$1,061.25

1000 marks will amount to 1030.42.

1500 marks will amount to $\dfrac{1500}{1000} \times 1030.42 = \$1545.63$

EXERCISE 16.5

1. Use the above table to find the amount that 1000 yen will amount to after 10 months in an account that pays 4% annual interest compounded monthly.

2. Use the table to find the amount that 20 000 rupees will amount to after 18 months in an account that pays 3.5% annual interest compounded monthly.

3. Use the table to find the amount that $150 will amount to after 16 months in an account that pays 4.5% annual interest compounded monthly.

4. Use the table to find the amount that 120 000 lire will amount to after 20 months in an account that pays 2.5% annual interest compounded monthly.

5. Use the table to find the amount that 250 000 crowns will amount to after 2 months in an account that pays 5.5% annual interest compounded monthly.

LOAN REPAYMENTS

When a consumer takes out a loan it is common for the interest on the loan to be calculated on the balance at each stage of the loan. As the debt decreases, so does the interest. The is known as **decreasing balance** interest. This makes the calculation much hardr to follow than the simple interest method.

A good way to follow such a loan is to use a spreadsheet. The following example shows this.

EXAMPLE

Frieda borrows 12 000 Swiss francs to help her buy a car. The company that issues the loan charges 9% annual interest calculated monthly. The repayments are monthly and the loan is to last 5 years. Write a spreadsheet that will track this loan and find the repayment that will discharge the loan in 5 years.

SOLUTION

The diagram shows the result of fixing the payment at 300 Swiss francs.

A	A	B	C	D	E	F
1	Ann rate	9				
2	Principal	12000				
3	Payment	300			Final bal:	-3839
4						
5	Month	Loan	Interest	Payment		
6	0	12000	90	300		
7	1	11790	88	300		
8	2	11578	87	300		
9	3	11365	85	300		

The sheet extends below this diagram. The formulas used are:

A	A	B	C	D	E	F
1	Ann rate	9				
2	Principal	12000				
3	Payment	300			Final bal:	+B66
4						
5	Month	Loan	Interest	Payment		
6	0	+B2	+B6*$B$1/1200	+$B$3		
7	+A6+1	+B6+C6-D6	+B7*$B$1/1200	+$B$3		
8	+A7+1	+B7+C7-D7	+B8*$B$1/1200	+$B$3		
9	+A8+1	+B8+C8-D8	+B9*$B$1/1200	+$B$3		

Column A uses a formula to write a column of sequential numbers to represent the months of the loan. Column C calculates the simple interest due on the balance of the loan at the beginning of each month. The denominator of the interest formula is 1200, not 100, because the quoted interest rate is annual but the interest is charged monthly. The formula that calculates this uses an 'absolute cell reference'. $B$1. The effect of the '$' signs is to make sure that this part of the formula is reproduced exactly when the formula is copied.

Cell references that do not have the '$' sign are updated when they are copied. Column C calculates the new debt as the old debt + interst – payment. Cell F3 records the debt after 60 months (5 years) so that the user of the spreadsheet can change the key parameters of the problem: the interest rate in B1 the principal in B2 and the monthly payment in B3. The final balance is in cell B66, well off the home screen. To enable a user to change the main parameters of the problem (B1 to B3) and see the final debt immediately.

After a bit of trial and error, you should be able to arrive at the solution to the problem:

A	A	B	C	D	E	F
1	Ann rate	9				
2	Principal	12000				
3	Payment	249			Final bal:	8
4						
5	Month	Loan	Interest	Payment		
6	0	12000	90	249		
7	1	11841	89	249		
8	2	11681	88	249		

This shows that if the monthly repayment is set at 249 Swiss francs, the final debt will be 8 Swiss frances. This amounts to an almost complete discharge of the loan.

The above 'trial and error' method should be used to solve the following problems.

EXERCISE 16.6

Find the monthly payments necessary to discharge the following loans at the interest rates given in the periods specified.

	Loan (Crowns)	Rate	Period (months)
a.	3000	5	60
b.	6700	6	12
c.	2300	7	80
d.	7000	4	50
e.	3900	8	60
f.	12000	7	48
g.	3400	9	120
h.	15000	3	120

Rather than using 'trial and error', it is possible to use tables to find appropriate payments for reducing balance loans.

The following table shows the monthly payments needed to repay a loan of $10 000 over various

Rate	2	3	4	5	6	7	8	9
Months								
6	$1,676.40	$1,681.28	$1,686.17	$1,691.06	$1,695.95	$1,700.86	$1,705.77	$1,710.69
12	$842.39	$846.94	$851.50	$856.07	$860.66	$865.27	$869.88	$874.51
18	$564.39	$568.84	$573.31	$577.81	$582.32	$586.85	$591.40	$595.98
24	$425.40	$429.81	$434.25	$438.71	$443.21	$447.73	$452.27	$456.85
30	$342.01	$346.41	$350.83	$355.29	$359.79	$364.32	$368.88	$373.48
36	$286.43	$290.81	$295.24	$299.71	$304.22	$308.77	$313.36	$318.00
42	$246.72	$251.11	$255.55	$260.03	$264.56	$269.14	$273.77	$278.45
48	$216.95	$221.34	$225.79	$230.29	$234.85	$239.46	$244.13	$248.85
54	$193.80	$198.20	$202.66	$207.18	$211.77	$216.42	$221.12	$225.89
60	$175.28	$179.69	$184.17	$188.71	$193.33	$198.01	$202.76	$207.58
66	$160.13	$164.55	$169.04	$173.62	$178.26	$182.98	$187.78	$192.65
72	$147.50	$151.94	$156.45	$161.05	$165.73	$170.49	$175.33	$180.26
78	$136.83	$141.27	$145.81	$150.43	$155.14	$159.94	$164.83	$169.81
84	$127.67	$132.13	$136.69	$141.34	$146.09	$150.93	$155.86	$160.89
90	$119.75	$124.22	$128.79	$133.47	$138.25	$143.13	$148.12	$153.20
96	$112.81	$117.30	$121.89	$126.60	$131.41	$136.34	$141.37	$146.50
102	$106.69	$111.19	$115.81	$120.54	$125.39	$130.36	$135.44	$140.62
108	$101.25	$105.77	$110.41	$115.17	$120.06	$125.06	$130.19	$135.43
114	$96.39	$100.92	$105.58	$110.38	$115.29	$120.34	$125.51	$130.81
120	$92.01	$96.56	$101.25	$106.07	$111.02	$116.11	$121.33	$126.68
126	$88.06	$92.62	$97.33	$102.17	$107.16	$112.29	$117.56	$122.96
132	$84.46	$89.04	$93.77	$98.64	$103.67	$108.84	$114.15	$119.61
138	$81.18	$85.77	$90.52	$95.43	$100.49	$105.70	$111.06	$116.57
144	$78.17	$82.78	$87.55	$92.49	$97.59	$102.84	$108.25	$113.80
150	$75.40	$80.03	$84.83	$89.79	$94.92	$100.22	$105.67	$111.28

EXAMPLE

Find the monthly repayment needed to repay a loan of 200 000 marks over a 5 year period with 5% annual interest paid monthly on the reducing balance of the loan.

SOLUTION

The period is 60 months. From the table:

Rate	2	3	4	5	6	7	8	9
....								
54	$193.80	$198.20	$202.66	$207.18	$211.77	$216.42	$221.12	$225.89
60	$175.28	$179.69	$184.17	**$188.71**	$193.33	$198.01	$202.76	$207.58
66	$160.13	$164.55	$169.04	$173.62	$178.26	$182.98	$187.78	$192.65
....								

The repayment for a loan of 10 000 marks (the fact that the table refers to dollars does not matter) is $188.71. The repayment for a loan of 200 000 is 20×188.71 = 3774 marks

EXERCISE 16.7

Find the monthly payments needed to pay off the following loans (in francs) in the periods given.

	Loan	Rate (% p.a.)	Period (months)
1.	9700	4	12
2.	4100	4	24
3.	5100	3	78
4.	2600	2	18
5.	1300	5	6
6.	6800	8	18
7.	5300	3	102
8.	5100	5	60
9.	8200	8	12
10.	8800	4	108
11.	1000	4	90
12.	8200	5	24
13.	4500	3	24
14.	6900	2	78
15.	400	5	84
16.	8200	7	30
17.	3000	7	30
18.	900	5	24
19.	2900	7	84
20.	3700	7	84

INFLATION

Over recent years it has been generally true that wages and prices have risen steadily. This effect, known as **inflation**, does not generally make people more wealthy because rises in wages are offset by rises in prices. Such rises are often expressed as percentage rates

EXAMPLE

In a period when inflation is running at 5%, find the price of a television that originally cost $450, 4 years later.

SOLUTION

The price rises are cumulative (like compound interest).

Price after 4 years: $450\left(1 + \dfrac{5}{100}\right)^4 = 546.97781$ or $546.98

An alternative to the calculation above is to use an inflation table:

The table shows the price of a $100 article at various inflation rates after various periods.

Rate Year	2	2.5	3	3.5	4	4.5	5
1	$102.00	$102.50	$103.00	$103.50	$104.00	$104.50	$105.00
2	$104.04	$105.06	$106.09	$107.12	$108.16	$109.20	$110.25
3	$106.12	$107.69	$109.27	$110.87	$112.49	$114.12	$115.76
4	$108.24	$110.38	$112.55	$114.75	$116.99	$119.25	**$121.55**
5	$110.41	$113.14	$115.93	$118.77	$121.67	$124.62	$127.63
6	$112.62	$115.97	$119.41	$122.93	$126.53	$130.23	$134.01
7	$114.87	$118.87	$122.99	$127.23	$131.59	$136.09	$140.71
8	$117.17	$121.84	$126.68	$131.68	$136.86	$142.21	$147.75
9	$119.51	$124.89	$130.48	$136.29	$142.33	$148.61	$155.13
10	$121.90	$128.01	$134.39	$141.06	$148.02	$155.30	$162.89
11	$124.34	$131.21	$138.42	$146.00	$153.95	$162.29	$171.03
12	$126.82	$134.49	$142.58	$151.11	$160.10	$169.59	$179.59
13	$129.36	$137.85	$146.85	$156.40	$166.51	$177.22	$188.56
14	$131.95	$141.30	$151.26	$161.87	$173.17	$185.19	$197.99
15	$134.59	$144.83	$155.80	$167.53	$180.09	$193.53	$207.89

The table can be used to solve the previous example by selecting the entry in the 5% column and the 4 year row (bold). The price of a $450 television after 4 years at 5% inflation is $\frac{450}{100}(121.55) = 546.975$ or $546.98. Use of a table may result in small rounding errors over a calculator based solution.

EXERCISE 16.8

Find the prices of the following items at the inflation rates given after the periods indicated:

	Original price	Rate	Years
1.	$665	8	3
2.	$1282	5	8
3.	$983	1	4
4.	$548	10	1
5.	$204	4	13
6.	$197	10	13
7.	$911	10	5
8.	$90	9	6
9.	$499	6	2
10.	$1350	11	10
11.	$313	5	9
12.	$511	6	1.5
13.	$316	1	10
14.	$569	8	2.75
15.	$1487	6	13

EXAMINATION STYLE QUESTIONS

Process PLC is a small computer business. The main assets of this company are:
*   A deposit account that earns 5% annual interest calculated daily on the closing balance and credited at the end of each month.

*   A computer, worth $4500 at the end of May 1997, which depreciates at the rate of 22% per annum.

*   A current account. The charges are 70c per debit and 55c per credit on all transactions except bank charges.

*   A car worth $18000 at the end of May 1997, depreciating at 15% per annum.

The liabilities are:
*   A $15000 loan for the car (as at the end of May 1997). This loan charges 9% annual interest calculated monthly on the diminishing balance. The repayment is $360 per month.

*   a debt of $1500 owed to a supplier and which does not need to be paid until the end of June.

1. The tables show the activity in the two bank accounts over one month.

Current account

Date	Detail	Debit	Credit	Balance
1/5/97	Carried			$1263.65
5/5/97	Cheques		$647.45	
12/5/97	162345	$56.70		
17/5/97	162344	$126.30		
25/5/97	Transfer		$2300.00	
26/5/97	162347	$534.55		
31/5/97	Charges			

Deposit account

Date	Detail	Debit	Credit	Balance
1/5/97	Carried			$6500.45
10/5/97	Cheques		$1245.50	
31/5/97	Interest			

a. Complete the balance column for the current account, including the charges at the end of the month.
b. Complete the balance column for the deposit account, including the interest credit at the end of the month.

c. A company's equity is defined as the difference between its assets and liabilities. What is this company's equity at the end of May 1997?

[2 + 3 + 2 = 7 marks]

2. **a.** The computer's value changes with time. *Sketch* the graph of the computer's value against time.

b. Find the computer's value at the end of May 2000.

c. Process PLC intend to replace the computer as soon as it falls to half of its value at the end of May 1997. In which month will the computer be replaced?

[1 + 2 + 3 = 6 marks]

SELF ASSESSMENT TEST (30 MINS)

1. 1 German mark is equivalent to 23.261 Indian rupees.
    i.   Convert 150 marks to rupees.
    ii.   Convert 1250 rupees to marks.

[3 marks]

2. $1 New Zealand is worth 60 US cents. An exchange service charges a 3% fee to exchange money. How much will a traveller who wants to change $500 NZ to $US get?

[3 marks]

3. Find the simple interest on 60 000 lire invested at 5.6% p.a. simple interest for 6 years.

[2 marks]

4. Find the amount the 3500 Swiss francs will amount to after 5 years invested at 6.8% annual interest compounded annually.

[2 marks]

5. Find the amount the 1250 crowns will amount to after 7 years invested at 9% annual interest compounded monthly.

[3 marks]

FINANCIAL MATHEMATICS 2

LINEAR PROGRAMMING

17

Chapter contents

– Linear inequalities.
– Linear programming.

17.1 SIMULTANEOUS INEQUALITIES

Simultaneous inequalities can be solved using techniques similar to those used with simultaneous equations. The most useful way of depicting simultaneous inequalities is graphical.

EXAMPLE

Show (i) $2x + 3y \le 12$ and (ii) $x - 4y > 8$ graphically, using separate sets of axes.

SOLUTION

These problems are done in two stages. the first is to draw the graph of the related **equation**.

(i) Stage 1 is to draw the graph of $2x + 3y = 12$. This is probably best done by finding the intercepts: (0,4) & (6,0).

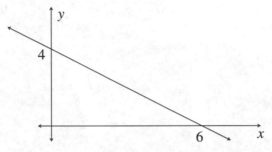

The line divides the cartesian plane into two regions. The points on one side of the line have coordinates that satisfy the inequality. The coordinates of the points on the other side of the line do not satisfy the inequality. Stage 2 is, therefore, to decide which side of the line is the correct side in the sense that its coordinates satisfy the inequality. The origin is often a good choice because it is easy to substitute zero into algebraic expressions. In the present case, the result is: $2 \times 0 + 3 \times 0 \le 12 \Rightarrow 0 \le 12$ which is true. This means that the origin is on the correct side of the line. If we shade the **incorrect** side of the line (i.e. 'shade out' the wrong side), we arrive at the following representation for the inequality:

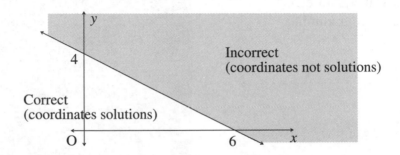

Every point in the unshaded region represents a solution to the inequality. The solution set is infinite. The points on the line represent solutions to the related equation $2x + 3y = 12$.

(ii)   The second problem has a similar solution except for the 'strict inequality' which means that the points on the boundary line:

$\left(x - 4y = 8 \Rightarrow 4y = x - 8 \Rightarrow y = \dfrac{x}{4} - 2 \right)$ are not included in the solution set. This is conventionally indicated by showing the boundary as a broken line:

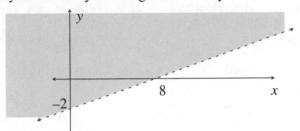

Simultaneous inequalities are solved by plotting the graphs and regions on the same set of axes.

EXAMPLE

Show these inequalities graphically: $x + 3y \geq 6$ $\qquad$ $2x - y \leq 4$.

SOLUTION

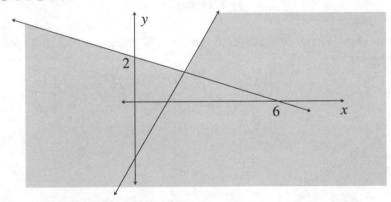

The open triangular region contains points whose coordinates satisfy both inequalities simultaneously. Points in the shaded region have coordinates that do **not** satisfy one or other or both of the inequalities.

In the above problems the unshaded (correct) region is often called the 'feasible region'. These problems also form the basis of the decision making technique known as 'Linear Programming' which will be covered later in this chapter.

EXERCISE 17.1

1. Show the following sets of simultaneous inequalities graphically. Shade the region which does **not** satisfy the set.

(i) $x + y \leq 4$ (ii) $y \geq 2x$ (iii) $x + 3y > 6$

(iv) $2x - y > 4$ (v) $y - \dfrac{x}{2} < 1$ (vi) $3x + \dfrac{y}{3} \leq 3$

(vii) $y \geq x$ (viii) $2x + y \geq 4$ (ix) $3x - 2y > 6$

         $x + y \leq 2$ $x - y \leq 3$ $x - 2y < 2$

(x) $x + 3y < 1$ (xi) $3x + 2y \leq 6$ (xii) $x + y \geq 2$

         $x - y > 2$ $x + 4y \geq 4$ $x + y \leq 5$

(xiii) $x + y < 3$ (xiv) $3x + 5y \leq 15$ (xv) $y \leq \dfrac{1}{2}x$

         $x \geq 0$ $4x + 3y \leq 12$

         $y \geq 0$ $x \geq 0$ $2x + 3y \leq 6$

         $x < y$ $y \geq 0$ $x \geq 0$

                                                             $y \geq 0$

2. For what value(s) of p do the following inequalities have no solutions?
$$x + y \geq 2$$
$$3x + 3y \leq p$$

3. The diagrams show sets of inequalities. Find the sets of inequalities that specify the unshaded regions.

(i) 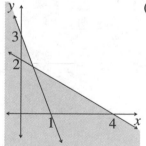   (ii)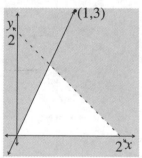

(iii) 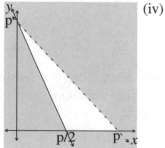   (iv)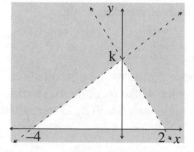

330

17.2 LINEAR PROGRAMMING

Linear programming was developed in the years immediately following the second world war. The first uses were in ensuring that scarce resources such as food and fuel were distributed as efficiently as possible. Today, linear programming is a commonly used method in business management in making decisions on operating procedures. We will consider a range of simplified linear programming problems.

There are several stages to solving a linear programming problem:

Stage 1: define the variables.

Stage 2: write the constraints of the problem as inequalities.

Stage 3: find the objective function.

Stage 4: plot graphs of the inequalities and identify the 'feasible region' for the problem.

Stage 5: use the objective function to find the optimal solution to the problem.

We will illustrate these various stages by the following examples:

EXAMPLE

1 metre of power cable costs $2 and 1 metre of coaxial cable costs $3. Menara has $60 to spend. Write the information as inequalities and show the feasible region as a graph. What is the largest amount of cable that Menara can afford to buy?

SOLUTION

Stage 1 is to identify the variables. In many cases the best way to do this is to look at the last part of the question. What are you asked to find? In this case it is the amount of each type of cable that Menara can afford to buy. These need to be given letter labels. It is best to use pronumerals that can easily be identified with what they represent. In this case let p = the number of metres of power cable that Menara buys and c = the number of metres of coaxial cable. You will probably find these easier to remember than x and y. Also, note that it is not necessary to know what coaxial cable is in order to answer this question!

Stage 2 is to set up the constraints. In this case, Menara cannot buy a negative amount of either type of cable so $p \geq 0, c \geq 0$. Also, there is a financial constraint. It can help to write the information as a table of costs:

Power cable p metres		Coaxial cable c metres		Total
$2 per metre		$3 per metre		$60
2p	+	3c	$\leq$	60

This leads to the third constraint $2p + 3c \leq 60$.

Stage 3 is to identify the 'objective function'. It can help to look at the question again to help identify this. In this case, Menara wants to buy as much cable of either type as possible. In mathematical trerms, Menara wants to maximise $A = p + c$ (the total length of cable bought is $p + c$). The objective function is not just an equation, but contains whether it is desired to maximise or minimise the function.

Stage 4 is to use the techniques developed in the previous section to graph the constraints.

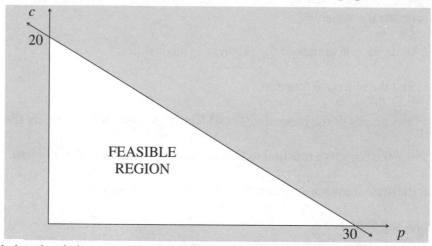

The unshaded region is known as the feasible region. Every point on the diagram represents an amount of each type of cable that Menara might try to buy. Points that are inside the feasible region (such as $p = 5$ and $c = 10$) represent amounts of cable that Menara can afford to buy (that is they are 'feasible'). Points that are in the shaded region represent amounts of cable that Menara cannot buy. For example, $p = 20$ and $c = 30$ is not a feasible solution as it represents buying 20 metres of power cable at a cost of $40 and 30 metres of coaxial cable at a cost of $60. The total cost is $100 and this is more than Menara can afford and so the solution is not feasible. The solution $p = -5$ and $c = 10$ is not feasible because Menara cannot buy a negative amount of cable (the constraint $p \geq 0$ is violated).

Stage 5. It is required to find the solution that gives the largest value of $A = p + c$, with the values of p and c taken from points in the feasible region. Since there are an infinite number of points in the feasible region, it seem that this will be a very long job. It is, fortunately, not necessary to try every point as the optimal solutions to linear programming problems always lie on the boundaries of the feasible region. More than this, the optimal solutions are almost always found at the vertices (corncrs) of the feasible region. For simple problems such as this, the optimal solution can be found by evaluating the objective function at each vertex. In this case, the vertices are $p = 0$, $c = 0$, $A = 0$ (the origin), $p = 30$, $c = 0$, $A = 30$ and $p = 0$, $c = 20$, $A = 20$. The largest value of the objective is 30 and the full solution is that Menara should buy 30 metres of power cable which will cost him $60. Remember to give an answer in terms of the original problem.

The previous problem was simple and could have been solved using common sense. Real linear programming problems may have thousands of variables with millions of vertices for the feasible region. In such cases, graphical solutions are not possible and checking the value of the objective function at every vertex is inefficient even when using a computer. In such cases methods based on matrices and computer algorithms are used. These are beyond the scope of this course, which is restricted to examples with only two variables.

EXAMPLE

A mining company produces three types of mineral ore: azurite, bauxite and cryolite. The company operates two mines, Newton and Gauss.

1 day of mining at Newton produces 3 tonnes of azurite, 1 tonne of bauxite and 6 tonnes of cryolite. 1 day of mining at Gauss produces 6 tonnes of azurite, 1 tonne of bauxite and 4 tonnes of cryolite. The costs of running each mine are $2000 per day at Newton and $3000 per day at Gauss.

The mining company has a single order for 18 tonnes of azurite, 5 tonnes of bauxite and 24 tonnes of cryolite. Find out how the company can fulfil this order for the smallest cost. Is there any surplus production?

SOLUTION

Stage 1: The variables are the numbers of days that the company works in each mine:

Let: n = the number of days worked in the Newton mine and g = the number of days worked in Gauss.

Stage 2: The information in this question is quite complex. A tabular display may help in finding the constraints:

	Newton (n)		Gauss (g)		Total
Azurite	$3n$	+	$6g$	$\geq$	18
Bauxite	$1n$	+	$1g$	$\geq$	5
Cryolite	$6n$	+	$4g$	$\geq$	24

In addition to these constraints, the company cannot operate either mine for a negative period of time so there are two additional constraints: $n \geq 0$ & $g \geq 0$. The complete set of constraints is: $n \geq 0$, $g \geq 0$, $3n + 6g \geq 18$, $n + g \geq 5$, $6n + 4g \geq 24$.

Stage 3: The objective is to minimise the cost (C) where $C = 2000n + 3000g$.

Stage 4: The constraints need to be plotted to get the feasible region. In this case it is better to use graph paper as it will be necessary to identify the vertices of the feasible region with a good level of accuracy.

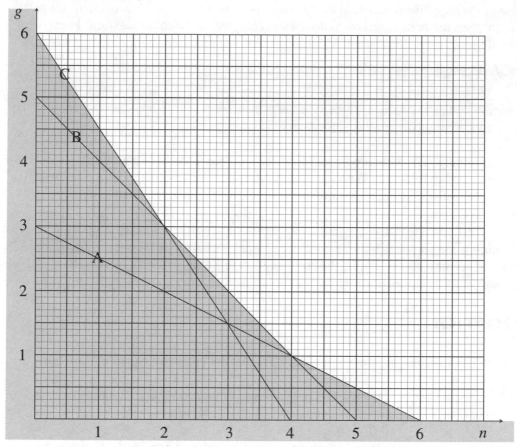

Stage 5: Selecting the solution vertex. The vertices are (0,6), (2,3), (4,1) & (6,0)

The costs of each vertex of the feasible region are:

n = days in Newton $2000 per day	g = days in Gauss $3000 per day	Cost
0	6	$18000
2	3	$13000
4	1	$11000
6	0	$12000

The best strategy is to work for 4 days in Newton and 1 day in Gauss for a cost of $9000. The production of the three ores is

Azurite: $3 \times 4 + 6 \times 1 = 18$, bauxite: $1 \times 4 + 1 \times 1 = 5$, both the correct amounts.

Cryolite: $6 \times 4 + 4 \times 1 = 28$ which has 4 tonnes over production.

EXAMPLE

A factory manufactures two types of electronic equipment. The 'Laser' tests the quality of optical fibre cable and the 'Joiner' tests the quality of the joins between lengths of the cable.

There are two major processes in the manufacture of these two products; wiring and assembly. One 'Laser' takes 5 worker hours for wiring and 6 worker hours for assembly. One 'Joiner' takes 6 worker hours for wiring and 3 worker hours for assembly. There are 30 worker hours per day available for wiring and 18 worker hours per day available for assembly. The company has also decided that it will make at least half as many 'Joiners' as 'Lasers'.

The profit made on each machine is $150.

(a)   How many of each machine should the company make to maximise their profit?

(b)   If the company can only make whole numbers of machines per day, what is the new optimal solution?

SOLUTION

Stage 1. The variables are l = the number of 'Lasers' made per day and j = the number of 'Joiners' made per day.

Stage 2. The constraints:

	Laser (l)		Joiner (j)		Total
Wiring	$5l$	+	$6j$	≤	30
Assembly	$6l$	+	$3j$	≤	18
Policy	$0.5l$	≤	j		

The first two constraints simplify to $5l + 6j \leq 30$, $2l + j \leq 6$. The third constraint needs care. It can be a good idea to think of it as an equation first. The statement ' it will make at least half as many 'Joiners' as 'Lasers'' can be simplified to ' it will make half as many 'Joiners' as 'Lasers''. This means that if the number of 'Lasers' is halved this will equal the number of 'Joiners'. As an example $l = 8$ and $j = 4$ fits the description. The equation that describes this is $j = 0.5 \times l$. The direction of the inequality sign also needs careful consideration. 'At least half as many 'Joiners' as 'Lasers' means that the number of 'Joiners' can be increased and that, for example, $l = 8$ and $j = 5$, fits the description and the the correct constraint is $j \geq 0.5l$.

Stage 3. The objective function is to maximise the profit where the profit function is:
$P = 150l + 150j$

Linear Programming

Stage 4. Graph the constraints and identify the feasible region:

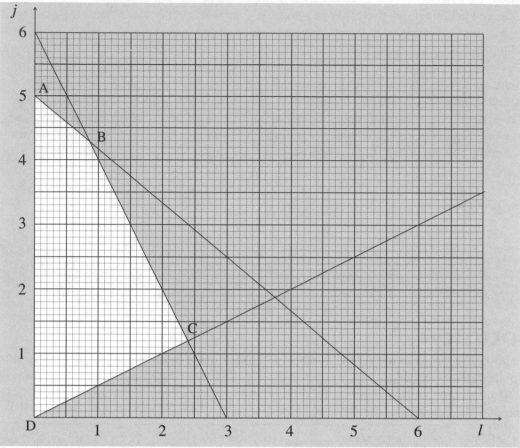

Stage 5. Find the coordinates of the vertices of the feasible region. These can often be read from the graph with sufficient accuracy. If more precision is desired, it can be achieved by solving simultaneous equations. The vertex A is the intercept of the constraint $5l + 6j \le 30$ with the j axis. This is the point (0,5). Vertex B would appear to have approximate coordinates (0.8,4.4). The exact coordinates are found by solving the equations related to the constraints $5l + 6j \le 30$, $2l + j \le 6$ simultaneously:

$$5l + 6j = 30...[1]$$
$$2l + j = 6...[2]$$
$$12l + 6j = 36...6 \times [2]$$
$$7l = 6...6 \times [2] - [1]$$
$$l = \frac{6}{7}$$

$$2 \times \frac{6}{7} + j = 6...[2]$$

$$j = \frac{30}{7}$$

The vertex is $\left(\frac{6}{7}, \frac{30}{7}\right)$ or $\left(\frac{6}{7}, 4\frac{2}{7}\right)$. This agrees with the approximate values read directly from the graph.

Similarly, vertex C is the intersection of the equations related to the constraints $j \geq \frac{1}{2}l$ and

$6l + 3j \leq 18$. The coordinates of this vertex are $(2.4, 1.2)$.
Finally, we must identify the optimal vertex:

Vertex	l	j	Profit
A	0	5	$750.00
B	$\frac{6}{7}$	$\frac{30}{7}$	$771.43
C	2.4	1.2	$540.00
D	0	0	$0.00

In the case of part (a), the best solution is to make $\frac{6}{7}$ ths of a 'Laser' and $\frac{30}{7}$ ths of a 'Joiner' per day for a profit of $771 (to the nearest dollar).

Part (b) allows only whole numbered points in the feasible region. This problem is known as an integer programming problem. In this case the feasible region is the set of points shown:

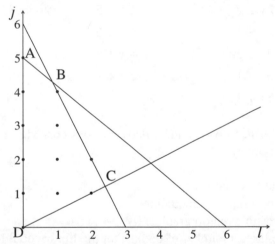

The optimal vertex is likely, but not inevitably, to be near to the optimal vertex of the linear programming problem. In this case it is probably best to check the vertices that are closest to the upper right hand boundary of the feasible region as these are the points that correspond to the largest production and hence the largest profit.

l	j	Profit
0	5	$750
1	4	$750
1	3	$600
2	2	$600

In this case there are two solutions that are equally good; to make no 'Lasers' and 5 'Joiners' or to make 1 'Laser' and 4 'Joiners' for a profit of $750.

EXERCISE 17.2

1. Solve the following problems. The variables are all elements of the real number set.

(i)   If $x, y \geq 0$ (ii)   If $x, y \geq 0$ (iii)   If $x, y \geq 0$

$$2x + 3y \leq 12 \qquad 2x + 5y \geq 10$$

$$x + y \leq 5 \qquad\qquad x + y \geq 4 \qquad\qquad y \leq \frac{3}{2}x$$

Maximise $7x + 8y$ Minimise $x + y$ $x + 2y \leq 8$

Maximise $x + 10y$

(iv)   If $x, y \geq 0$ (v)   If $x, y \geq 0$ (vi)   If $x, y \geq 0$

$$2y \leq 3x \qquad\qquad 5x + 4y \leq 20 \qquad\qquad 3x + 5y \leq 21$$

$$3x + 2y \leq 12 \qquad x + 4y \leq 8 \qquad\qquad 7x + 4y \leq 25$$

Maximise $2x + y$ Minimise $x + y$ Maximise $3x + 4y$

(vii)   If $x, y \geq 0$ (viii)   If $x, y \geq 0$

$$2y \geq x \qquad\qquad 1 \leq x \leq 5$$

$$y \leq 3x \qquad\qquad 2 \leq y \leq 6$$

$$5x + 4y \geq 20 \qquad\qquad x + y \geq 5$$

$$2x + 3y \leq 18 \qquad \text{Maximise } x + y$$

Maximise $5x + 2y$

2. Paperback books cost \$12 each and hardcover books cost \$18 each. A library has \$108 to spend on books.

     (a)   Define suitable variables.
     (b)   Write the contraints as inequalities.
     (c)   Show the feasible region graphically.
     (d)   What is the largest number of books that the library could buy?

3. A dietary supplement contains vitamins A and B. The two main sources of these vitamins are Xylol and Ylang. 1 gram of Xylol contains 6 units of vitamin A and 4 units of vitamin B. 1 gram of Ylang contains 5 units of vitamin A and 8 units of vitamin B. A bottle of the finished supplement must contain at least 30 units of vitamin A and 32 units of vitamin B. 1 gram of Xylol costs \$2 and one gram of Ylang costs \$3.

     (a)   Define suitable variables.
     (b)   Write the contraints as inequalities.
     (c)   Show the feasible region graphically.
     (d)   What is the smallest cost of ingredients to make one bottle of the supplement?

4. 'Aroma Oils Co.' are blending two essential oils to make a relaxing bath oil. The two main ingredients are Rose oil and Cedar oil which are added in small quantities to other much cheaper filler ingredients.

Every cu. cm. of Rose oil has 6 units of perfume and 4 units of moisturiser. Every cu. cm. of Cedar oil has 4 units of perfume and 8 units of moisturiser. The minimum requirements for one batch of bath oil are 24 units of perfume and 32 units of moisturiser. Rose oil costs $15 per cu. cm. and Cedar oil costs $12 per cu. cm.

(a)   Define suitable variables.
(b)   Write the contraints as inequalities.
(c)   Show the feasible region graphically.
(d)   What is the smallest cost of ingredients to make one batch of bath oil?

5. A company runs two trucks, 'Belinda' and 'Chloe'. On each trip 'Belinda' can carry cargo weighing 4 tonnes and with a volume of 7 cubic metres. 'Chloe' can carry cargo weighing 7 tonnes and with a volume of 5 cubic metres every trip. It costs $120 per trip to use 'Belinda' and $150 per trip to use 'Chloe'.

The company has to transport 28 tonnes of cargo with a volume of 35 cubic metres.

(a)   Define suitable variables.
(b)   Write the contraints as inequalities.
(c)   Show the feasible region graphically.
(d)   What is the smallest cost for which the cargo can be transported?

SELF ASSESSMENT TEST (30 MINS)

1. Solve: $2x + y = 6$

$3x - y = 14$

[3 marks]

2. Solve: $2x + 5y = -1.8$

$3x + 2y = 5$

[3 marks]

3. Admission prices to a concert are different for adults and children. The admission price for an adult is $6 more than the price for a child. A family of 2 adults and 3 chilren pay $72 for admission. Find the price of admission for an adult and the price for a child.

[3 marks]

4. Find the maximum value of $7x + 8y$ subject to the constraints:

$$x \geq 0$$
$$y \geq 0$$
$$3x + 2y \leq 12$$
$$4x + 5y \leq 23$$

[4 marks]

5. A manufacturing company makes two types of freezer, the 'Jumbo' and the 'Titan'. There are two main processes; assembly and finishing.

Each 'Jumbo' takes 7 worker hours to assemble and 3 worker hours to finish. Each 'Titan' takes 12 worker hours to assemble and 3 worker hours to finish. There are 84 worker hours per day available in the assembly area and 27 worker hours per day available in the finishing area. Each 'Jumbo' makes a profit of $120 and each 'Titan' makes a profit of $180.

(a) Formulate the problem, writing the constraints as inequalities.

(b) Assuming that the company can make fractional numbers of each model per day, find the exact coordinates of the vertex of the feasible region formed at the intersection of the assembly and finishing constraints.

(c) Find the profit made per day if the company uses the vertex calculated in part (b).

[6 marks]

MATRICES & GRAPH THEORY

OPTION

1 8

18.1 MATRICES

Matrices are in many senses similar to vectors except that whilst vectors are represented by columns of numbers, matrices are generally blocks of numbers. In their simplest form, matrices are often used to store information. Consider the following family shopping list:

	Mon	Tues	Wed	Thurs	Fri	Sat	Sun
Bread (loaf)	1	1	0	0	0	2	0
Milk (litre)	3	1	3	2	0	5	1
Eggs	6	6	0	0	6	6	0
Butter (100g)	2	0	1	0	0	3	1

If the family always makes the list in this way, that is beginning with Monday as far as the columns are concerned, and always recording the produce items in the same rows, then the headings become unnecessary and the information can be stored as a **matrix** (plural - matrices):

$$\begin{bmatrix} 1 & 1 & 0 & 0 & 0 & 2 & 0 \\ 3 & 1 & 3 & 2 & 0 & 5 & 1 \\ 6 & 6 & 0 & 0 & 6 & 6 & 0 \\ 2 & 0 & 1 & 0 & 0 & 3 & 1 \end{bmatrix}$$

This matrix has four rows and seven columns and is said to have an **order** of 4 by 7. To enter this matrix on the TI-82/3, press the MATRX key, select EDIT and matrix [A].

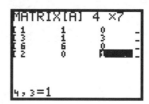

Next, enter the order of the matrix 4×7, and then enter the values given in the table. You can move from position to position by using the arrow keys. The screen is not large enough to display all the entries of this matrix. The other entries will 'scroll' into view when you use the right arrow.

Once the information has been stored in the matrix memory it can only be accessed using the MATRX, NAMES submenu. It is not sufficient to use ALPHA A which will only recall the contents of numeric memory A.

It is also useful to remember that spreadsheets are ideally suited to handle information in matrix form. Spreadsheets can generally handle larger matrices and do more with them, but you need a computer and these are not allowed in the exams (yet!). Spreadsheets will be considered later in this chapter.

TYPES OF MATRIX

There are several useful types of matrix.

1. A **row matrix** has only one row: $\begin{bmatrix} -3 & 4 & 5 \end{bmatrix}$.

2. A **column matrix** has only one column: $\begin{bmatrix} 4 \\ 0 \\ -1 \end{bmatrix}$.

3. A **diagonal matrix** is **square** with the elements on the leading diagonal (top left to bottom right) being the only non-zero entries: $\begin{bmatrix} 2 & 0 & 0 \\ 0 & -6 & 0 \\ 0 & 0 & \frac{1}{2} \end{bmatrix}$.

4. The **identity matrix** is a square matrix whose entries are all zero except for the leading diagonal whose entries are all 1: $\begin{bmatrix} 1 & 0 & 0 \\ 0 & 1 & 0 \\ 0 & 0 & 1 \end{bmatrix}$. The identity matrix play an important role in matrix arithmetic.

5. A **symmetric matrix** is a square matrix that is symmetric about its leading diagonal: $\begin{bmatrix} 1 & 2 & 3 \\ 2 & 6 & -5 \\ 3 & -5 & 1 \end{bmatrix}$.

6. The **transpose** of a matrix is obtained by exchanging the rows and columns. The transpose of $\begin{bmatrix} 2 & 5 & 3 \\ -1 & 7 & 0 \end{bmatrix}$ is sometimes written $\begin{bmatrix} 2 & 5 & 3 \\ -1 & 7 & 0 \end{bmatrix}^T$ and is: $\begin{bmatrix} 2 & -1 \\ 5 & 7 \\ 3 & 0 \end{bmatrix}$.

EXERCISE 18.1

Select a task that you perform regularly and which produces data that could be stored in matrix form. Examples could be:

*   Weekly shopping lists.

*   The test marks that you get in each of your subjects.

*   Your weekly expenses and the categories that you spend money on.

Keep records on your chosen subject and store the results as a matrix on either a spreadsheet or a graphic calculator.

18.2 MATRIX ARITHMETIC

If a second family makes a shopping list using the same row and column headings, they will also store their information in a matrix of order 4 by 7. Suppose that this second family want to buy the items indicated in this second matrix.

$$\begin{bmatrix} 1 & 1 & 2 & 0 & 0 & 2 & 0 \\ 3 & 0 & 1 & 2 & 0 & 5 & 1 \\ 6 & 2 & 0 & 1 & 2 & 6 & 0 \\ 2 & 1 & 1 & 0 & 1 & 3 & 1 \end{bmatrix}$$

If the two families wanted to place a single order, they would add the two matrices together. In this application, it would only make sense to add corresponding entries (top left to top left etc.

$$\begin{bmatrix} 1 & 1 & 0 & 0 & 0 & 2 & 0 \\ 3 & 1 & 3 & 2 & 0 & 5 & 1 \\ 6 & 6 & 0 & 0 & 6 & 6 & 0 \\ 2 & 0 & 1 & 0 & 0 & 3 & 1 \end{bmatrix} + \begin{bmatrix} 1 & 1 & 2 & 0 & 0 & 2 & 0 \\ 3 & 0 & 1 & 2 & 0 & 5 & 1 \\ 6 & 2 & 0 & 1 & 2 & 6 & 0 \\ 2 & 1 & 1 & 0 & 1 & 3 & 1 \end{bmatrix} = \begin{bmatrix} 1+1 & 1+1 & 0+2 & 0+0 & 0+0 & 2+2 & 0+0 \\ 3+3 & 1+0 & 3+1 & 2+2 & 0+0 & 5+5 & 1+1 \\ 6+6 & 6+2 & 0+0 & 0+1 & 6+2 & 6+6 & 0+0 \\ 2+2 & 0+1 & 1+1 & 0+0 & 0+1 & 3+3 & 1+1 \end{bmatrix}$$

$$= \begin{bmatrix} 2 & 2 & 2 & 0 & 0 & 4 & 0 \\ 6 & 1 & 4 & 4 & 0 & 10 & 2 \\ 12 & 8 & 0 & 1 & 8 & 12 & 0 \\ 4 & 1 & 2 & 0 & 1 & 6 & 2 \end{bmatrix}$$

Subtraction and other linear combinations are carried out in a similar way (also comparable to the methods used for vectors). It should be noticed that matrices of different orders cannot be combined in these ways.

EXAMPLES

Three matrices are defined as follows: $A = \begin{bmatrix} 2 & 3 & -4 \\ 1 & 0 & -2 \end{bmatrix}$ $B = \begin{bmatrix} 2 & 1 \\ 5 & 3 \\ 4 & 5 \end{bmatrix}$ $C = \begin{bmatrix} -1 & 3 & 0 \\ -3 & -1 & 6 \end{bmatrix}$

Evaluate:

    (i) $2B$ (ii) $-3C$ (iii) $A + C$
    (iv) $A + B$ (v) $2A + 3C$ (vi) $3A - 4C$

SOLUTIONS

(i) $2B = 2 \times \begin{bmatrix} 2 & 1 \\ 5 & 3 \\ 4 & 5 \end{bmatrix} = \begin{bmatrix} 4 & 2 \\ 10 & 6 \\ 8 & 10 \end{bmatrix}$

(ii) $-3C = -3 \times \begin{bmatrix} -1 & 3 & 0 \\ -3 & -1 & 6 \end{bmatrix} = \begin{bmatrix} 3 & -9 & 0 \\ 9 & 3 & -18 \end{bmatrix}$

(iii) $\begin{bmatrix} 2 & 3 & -4 \\ 1 & 0 & -2 \end{bmatrix} + \begin{bmatrix} -1 & 3 & 0 \\ -3 & -1 & 6 \end{bmatrix} = \begin{bmatrix} 2-1 & 3+3 & -4+0 \\ 1-3 & 0-1 & -2+6 \end{bmatrix} = \begin{bmatrix} 1 & 6 & -4 \\ -2 & -1 & 4 \end{bmatrix}$

(iv) $A + B$ cannot be calculated as the matrices are of different order.

(v) $2A + 3C = 2 \times \begin{bmatrix} 2 & 3 & -4 \\ 1 & 0 & -2 \end{bmatrix} + 3 \times \begin{bmatrix} -1 & 3 & 0 \\ -3 & -1 & 6 \end{bmatrix}$

$\qquad = \begin{bmatrix} 4 & 6 & -8 \\ 2 & 0 & -4 \end{bmatrix} + \begin{bmatrix} -3 & 9 & 0 \\ -9 & -3 & 18 \end{bmatrix}$

$\qquad = \begin{bmatrix} 1 & 15 & -8 \\ -7 & -3 & 14 \end{bmatrix}$

(vi) $3A - 4C = 3 \times \begin{bmatrix} 2 & 3 & -4 \\ 1 & 0 & -2 \end{bmatrix} - 4 \times \begin{bmatrix} -1 & 3 & 0 \\ -3 & -1 & 6 \end{bmatrix}$

$\qquad = \begin{bmatrix} 6 & 9 & -12 \\ 3 & 0 & -6 \end{bmatrix} + \begin{bmatrix} 4 & -12 & 0 \\ 12 & 4 & -24 \end{bmatrix}$

$\qquad = \begin{bmatrix} 10 & -3 & -12 \\ 15 & 4 & -30 \end{bmatrix}$

EXERCISE 18.2

1.   Two matrices are defined as: $P = \begin{bmatrix} 1 & 4 \\ -1 & 8 \end{bmatrix}, Q = \begin{bmatrix} 2 & -3 \\ -1 & 5 \end{bmatrix}$, evaluate:

   (i) $2P$ (ii) $-Q$ (iii) $3Q$
   (iv) $2P + Q$ (v) $3P + 2Q$ (vi) $Q - 4P$

2.   If $A = \begin{bmatrix} 1 & 1 & 2 \\ 0 & -6 & 9 \end{bmatrix}, B = \begin{bmatrix} 1 & 0 \\ 2 & 1 \\ 0 & -1 \end{bmatrix}, C = \begin{bmatrix} -3 & -5 \\ 0 & 1 \\ 3 & 2 \end{bmatrix}$, evaluate, where possible:

   (i) $-A$ (ii) $-2A$ (iii) $B + C$
   (iv) $2B$ (v) $2B - C$ (vi) $3(B + C)$

3.   If $X = \begin{bmatrix} 1 & 1 & 2 \\ 0 & 1 & 4 \\ 0 & 2 & 1 \end{bmatrix}, Y = \begin{bmatrix} -1 & -2 & 3 \\ 2 & 0 & 1 \\ 2 & 0 & -4 \end{bmatrix}$, evaluate:

   (i) $3X$ (ii) $2Y$ (iii) $X + Y$
   (iv) $X - Y$ (v) $3X + 2Y$ (vi) $2Y - X$

4. A stock control system stores the stocks of seven different products as the rows of a matrix. The company works a five day week and records the closing stocks as the columns of a matrix. What is the order of the matrix?

5. The diagram shows a spreadsheet used to store the sales of a small shop.

A	A	B	C	D	E	F	G	H	I	J	K	L	M
1	Week 1							Week 2					
2		Mon	Tues	Wed	Thurs	Fri			Mon	Tues	Wed	Thurs	Fri
3	Nuts	4	27	20	18	32		Nuts	45	4	44	4	53
4	Bolts	34	33	39	50	5		Bolts	11	10	10	48	8
5	Pegs	37	23	51	23	29		Pegs	23	10	39	51	9
6	Pins	0	48	45	10	23		Pins	36	22	44	5	38
7	Clips	49	21	55	17	25		Clips	53	17	56	28	11
8	Taps	53	10	49	9	49		Taps	8	16	33	47	26
9	Plugs	12	12	45	16	50		Plugs	46	33	0	25	9

(i) What was the number of sales of pins on Friday of Week 1?
(ii) Which item sold least on Thursday of Week 2?
(iii) Which item sold most on Monday of Week 1?
(iv) On what day were there no sales of Plugs?

A place on the spreadsheet at which the total sales in the two weeks will be calculated by formula is needed. What formula should be used to calculate the Monday sales of nuts? If this is copied to the cell immediately below, what will the formula read?

6. If $A = \begin{bmatrix} a & 1 \\ -1 & -a \end{bmatrix}$, $B = \begin{bmatrix} 2a & 2 \\ 1 & a \end{bmatrix}$, express $A + B$ as a matrix.

7. The zero matrix has entries that are all zero. Find the value(s) of a such that $P + Q$ is the zero matrix. $P = \begin{bmatrix} a & 2 \\ 5 & -3 \end{bmatrix}$, $Q = \begin{bmatrix} -3 & a-5 \\ -5 & a \end{bmatrix}$.

8. A diagonal matrix has all zero elements except for those on the top left to bottom right diagonal. Find the values of a such that the matrix $A + B$ is diagonal where:

$$A = \begin{bmatrix} 5 & 1 & a \\ 3 & 7 & -4 \\ -2 & a+2 & 2 \end{bmatrix} \qquad B = \begin{bmatrix} 3 & -1 & -2 \\ -3 & -2 & 2a \\ 2 & -4 & 3 \end{bmatrix}$$

MATRIX MULTIPLICATION

Matrix multiplication has a special definition that was developed because it appears to be the most practical. This definition can be useful in business applications, solving simultaneous equations and in transformation geometry. This last application has helped in the development of one of the newest branches of mathematics, fractal geometry.

The definition involves taking the rows of the left hand matrix and pairing these with the columns of the second matrix. If the problem is to find the product:

$$\begin{bmatrix} 2 & 5 & 0 \\ 1 & 0 & -2 \\ 1 & -3 & 1 \end{bmatrix} \times \begin{bmatrix} 1 & 3 & -1 \\ 0 & 2 & 0 \\ 1 & -3 & 1 \end{bmatrix}$$

the first step is to take the first row of the left hand matrix [2 5 0], write it as a column and

pair it up with the first column $\begin{bmatrix} 1 \\ 0 \\ 1 \end{bmatrix}$. The pairs are then multiplied and the products totalled

to give a single number:

$$2 \times 1 = 2$$
$$5 \times 0 = 0$$
$$0 \times 1 = 0$$
$$\overline{2}$$

This number is the result of combining the first row and the first column. It becomes the element in the first row and first column of the answer. The calculation must be completed for all the combinations of rows and columns. The nine calculations are:

$2 \times 1 = 2$	$2 \times 3 = 6$	$2 \times -1 = -2$
$5 \times 0 = 0$	$5 \times 2 = 10$	$5 \times 0 = 0$
$0 \times 1 = 0$	$0 \times -3 = 0$	$0 \times 1 = 0$
$\overline{2}$	$\overline{16}$	$\overline{-2}$
$1 \times 1 = 1$	$1 \times 3 = 3$	$1 \times -1 = -1$
$0 \times 0 = 0$	$0 \times 2 = 0$	$0 \times 0 = 0$
$-2 \times 1 = -2$	$-2 \times -3 = 6$	$-2 \times 1 = -2$
$\overline{-1}$	$\overline{9}$	$\overline{-3}$
$1 \times 1 = 1$	$1 \times 3 = 3$	$1 \times -1 = -1$
$-3 \times 0 = 0$	$-3 \times 2 = -6$	$-3 \times 0 = 0$
$1 \times 1 = 1$	$1 \times -3 = -3$	$1 \times 1 = 1$
$\overline{2}$	$\overline{-6}$	$\overline{0}$

In matrix form, this answer is: $\begin{bmatrix} 2 & 16 & -2 \\ -1 & 9 & -3 \\ 2 & -6 & 0 \end{bmatrix}$

It should be noted that matrix multiplication is not commutative. This means that the order in which the matrices are multiplied does matter. This is different from normal multiplication for which $a \times b = b \times a$ and which is commutative. In the case of the two matrices discussed above, the reversed product is:

$$\begin{bmatrix} 1 & 3 & -1 \\ 0 & 2 & 0 \\ 1 & -3 & 1 \end{bmatrix} \begin{bmatrix} 2 & 5 & 0 \\ 1 & 0 & -2 \\ 1 & -3 & 1 \end{bmatrix} = \begin{bmatrix} 4 & 8 & -7 \\ 2 & 0 & -4 \\ 0 & 2 & 7 \end{bmatrix}$$

It is not only square matrices that can be multiplied. All that is necessary is for the columns of the first matrix to match the number of rows in the second matrix.

EXAMPLES

For the matrices: $A = \begin{bmatrix} 1 & 0 \\ 2 & 6 \end{bmatrix}$, $B = \begin{bmatrix} 2 & -1 & -1 \\ 2 & 0 & -3 \end{bmatrix}$, $C = \begin{bmatrix} 2 & -1 \\ -3 & 2 \\ 1 & 4 \end{bmatrix}$, calculate, where possible:

(i) AB (ii) BC (iii) CA

(iv) BA (v) A^2 (vi) ABC

SOLUTIONS

(i) $AB = \begin{bmatrix} 1 & 0 \\ 2 & 6 \end{bmatrix} \begin{bmatrix} 2 & -1 & -1 \\ 2 & 0 & -3 \end{bmatrix} = \begin{bmatrix} 2 & -1 & -1 \\ 16 & -2 & -20 \end{bmatrix}$

Note that the result of multiplying a 2 by 2 matrix into a 2 by 3 matrix is a 2 by 3 matrix. In general, if an m by n matrix is multiplied by an n by p matrix (in that order), the result is an n by p matrix.

(ii) $BC = \begin{bmatrix} 2 & -1 & -1 \\ 2 & 0 & -3 \end{bmatrix} \begin{bmatrix} 2 & -1 \\ -3 & 2 \\ 1 & 4 \end{bmatrix} = \begin{bmatrix} 6 & -8 \\ 1 & -14 \end{bmatrix}$

(iii) $CA = \begin{bmatrix} 2 & -1 \\ -3 & 2 \\ 1 & 4 \end{bmatrix} \begin{bmatrix} 1 & 0 \\ 2 & 6 \end{bmatrix} = \begin{bmatrix} 0 & -6 \\ 1 & 12 \\ 9 & 24 \end{bmatrix}$

(iv) $BA = \begin{bmatrix} 2 & -1 & -1 \\ 2 & 0 & -3 \end{bmatrix} \begin{bmatrix} 1 & 0 \\ 2 & 6 \end{bmatrix}$ cannot be calculated as the orders are not compatible.

(v) $A^2 = \begin{bmatrix} 1 & 0 \\ 2 & 6 \end{bmatrix} \begin{bmatrix} 1 & 0 \\ 2 & 6 \end{bmatrix} = \begin{bmatrix} 1 & 0 \\ 14 & 36 \end{bmatrix}$

(vi) $ABC = \begin{bmatrix} 1 & 0 \\ 2 & 6 \end{bmatrix}\begin{bmatrix} 2 & -1 & -1 \\ 2 & 0 & -3 \end{bmatrix}\begin{bmatrix} 2 & -1 \\ -3 & 2 \\ 1 & 4 \end{bmatrix} = \begin{bmatrix} 1 & 0 \\ 2 & 6 \end{bmatrix}\begin{bmatrix} 6 & -8 \\ 1 & -14 \end{bmatrix} = \begin{bmatrix} 6 & -8 \\ 18 & -100 \end{bmatrix}$

There are two ways of calculating this triple product. The second is:

$ABC = \begin{bmatrix} 1 & 0 \\ 2 & 6 \end{bmatrix}\begin{bmatrix} 2 & -1 & -1 \\ 2 & 0 & -3 \end{bmatrix}\begin{bmatrix} 2 & -1 \\ -3 & 2 \\ 1 & 4 \end{bmatrix} = \begin{bmatrix} 2 & -1 & -1 \\ 16 & -2 & -20 \end{bmatrix}\begin{bmatrix} 2 & -1 \\ -3 & 2 \\ 1 & 4 \end{bmatrix} = \begin{bmatrix} 6 & -8 \\ 18 & -100 \end{bmatrix}$

This second method involves multiplying the first two matrices at the start, getting an answer and then multiplying this into the third. The order of the matrices has not been altered, just the way in which they have been grouped. This is called the **associative property** of matrix multiplication.

USING A GRAPHIC CALCULATOR AND SPREADSHEET

Matrices can be stored as described earlier in this chapter. The names can be recovered using the MATRX NAME command. To calculate AB in the example discussed above, enter the correct matrices and then draw out the two names to produce the result.

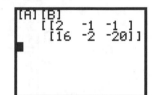

The two main groups of spreadsheets, EXCEL and LOTUS, handle matrix multiplication in a different way. In both cases, the matrices have to be entered into blocks of cells on the sheet. LOTUS then has a series of menu driven commands (/ DATA MATRIX MULTIPLY) which must be repeated each time the matrices are changed. Excel uses the MMULT array formula.

A spreadsheet for multiplying matrices is shown below. The first of the matrices to be multiplied is stored in cells A2 to B3 and the second in cells D2 to F3. The formula =MMULT(A2:B3,D3:F3) is entered by highlighting cells A6 to C7, typing the formula and pressing CTRL+SHIFT+ENTER if using Windows or COMMAND+RETURN if using Macintosh.

	A	B	C	D	E	F
1	A			B		
2	1	0		2	-1	-1
3	2	6		2	0	-3
4						
5	AB					
6	2	-1	-1			
7	16	-2	-20			

Once this Excel spreadsheet has been created, the matrix entries can be edited and the product is calculated automatically.

EXERCISE 18.3

1. Evaluate the following matrix products:

(i) $\begin{bmatrix} 2 & 3 \\ -1 & 0 \end{bmatrix}\begin{bmatrix} -2 & 1 \\ 3 & -2 \end{bmatrix}$

(ii) $\begin{bmatrix} 2 & -2 \\ 1 & 5 \end{bmatrix}\begin{bmatrix} 0 & 1 \\ -3 & 5 \end{bmatrix}$

(iii) $\begin{bmatrix} -6 & 5 \\ 0 & 3 \end{bmatrix}\begin{bmatrix} 2 & -2 \\ 1 & 1 \end{bmatrix}$

(iv) $\begin{bmatrix} -2 & 3 \\ -5 & 2 \end{bmatrix}\begin{bmatrix} 0 & 8 \\ -5 & 2 \end{bmatrix}$

(v) $\begin{bmatrix} \frac{1}{3} & 7 \\ 1 & \frac{3}{2} & \frac{3}{4} \end{bmatrix}\begin{bmatrix} -1 & 5 \\ \frac{1}{2} & 4 \end{bmatrix}$

(vi) $\begin{bmatrix} 1.5 & 2 \\ 3 & -1.5 \end{bmatrix}\begin{bmatrix} -1.6 & 1 \\ 2.5 & 2 \end{bmatrix}$

(vii) $\begin{bmatrix} 4 & -2 \\ 0 & -3 \end{bmatrix}\begin{bmatrix} 2 & -1 & 1 \\ -2 & 0 & 1 \end{bmatrix}$

(viii) $\begin{bmatrix} 5 & -1 \\ -2 & 0 \end{bmatrix}\begin{bmatrix} -2 & 1 & 1 \\ -1 & 2 & 3 \end{bmatrix}$

(ix) $\begin{bmatrix} 1 & 2 \\ 4 & 7 \end{bmatrix}\begin{bmatrix} \frac{1}{2} & -\frac{1}{2} & 3 \\ \frac{1}{3} & 1 & -\frac{1}{3} \end{bmatrix}$

(x) $\begin{bmatrix} 2 & 1 \\ -3 & 0 \end{bmatrix}\begin{bmatrix} 1.3 & 1.4 & 1.9 \\ -1 & -3.5 & 0 \end{bmatrix}$

(xi) $\begin{bmatrix} 1 & -2 & 0 \\ -2 & -3 & 1 \\ 3 & 0 & 1 \end{bmatrix}\begin{bmatrix} 1 & -2 \\ -5 & 0 \\ -2 & -1 \end{bmatrix}$

(xii) $\begin{bmatrix} 1 & 6 & -1 \\ 2 & -3 & -9 \\ 1 & 2 & 0 \end{bmatrix}\begin{bmatrix} 6 & 2 \\ 0 & 1 \\ -1 & 3 \end{bmatrix}$

(xiii) $\begin{bmatrix} 1 & 0 & 2 \\ 2 & 1 & 0 \\ 3 & 0 & 1 \end{bmatrix}\begin{bmatrix} 6 & 0 & 2 \\ 0 & 1 & 0 \\ 3 & 3 & 0 \end{bmatrix}$

(xiv) $\begin{bmatrix} -1 & 3 & -2 \\ 0 & -9 & 2 \\ -3 & -2 & 1 \end{bmatrix}\begin{bmatrix} 1 & -2 & -1 \\ 0 & 0 & 2 \\ 2 & -2 & 3 \end{bmatrix}$

(xv) $\begin{bmatrix} 1 & -1 & 5 \\ -1 & 0 & -8 \\ 2 & -3 & -2 \end{bmatrix}\begin{bmatrix} 0 & 0 & 1 \\ 2 & 3 & -2 \\ -1 & 1 & 2 \end{bmatrix}$

(xvi) $\begin{bmatrix} \frac{1}{2} & 2 & -3 \\ \frac{3}{4} & 5 & -2 \\ 0 & 1 & \frac{1}{2} \end{bmatrix}\begin{bmatrix} -1 & -\frac{2}{3} & 1 \\ -3 & -\frac{2}{3} & 1 \\ 2 & 5 & -\frac{1}{2} \end{bmatrix}$

(xvii) $\begin{bmatrix} 1 & x & x \\ 2 & x & 2x \\ -x & 1 & 2 \end{bmatrix}\begin{bmatrix} x & 1 \\ x & -x \\ 2x & 0 \end{bmatrix}$

(xviii) $\begin{bmatrix} a & 2x & -a \\ a & -2a & 0 \\ 0 & a & -x \end{bmatrix}\begin{bmatrix} 1 & 2 & 3 \\ x & 2 & -x \\ a & 0 & 1 \end{bmatrix}$

2. A matrix is defined by $M = \begin{bmatrix} -1 & 0 \\ 0 & -1 \end{bmatrix}$

   (i)   Find M^2

   (ii)   Find M^3, M^4, M^5

   (iii) Find a rule for M^n

3. The following information gives the numbers of journeys made by the delivery department of a small company:

From:→ To↓	A	B	C	D
A	0	3	4	2
B	1	0	0	6
C	1	2	0	2
D	4	3	0	0

The company has four different depots and the above table indicates that there was one journey made from depot A to depot B and three journeys made from B to A etc.

This second table gives the loading costs per load for goods leaving each depot.

Depot	Cost
A	$120
B	$105
C	$110
D	$100

It costs $120 to load for one trip at depot A etc.

   (i)   Write these two sets of information as matrices.

   (ii)   Find the product of the two matrices.

   (iii) Explain the meaning of the entries in the product matrix.

4. Two matrices are defined as follows: $A = \begin{bmatrix} \dfrac{1}{2} & -\dfrac{\sqrt{3}}{2} \\ \dfrac{\sqrt{3}}{2} & \dfrac{1}{2} \end{bmatrix}$, $B = \begin{bmatrix} \dfrac{\sqrt{3}}{2} & -\dfrac{1}{2} \\ \dfrac{1}{2} & \dfrac{\sqrt{3}}{2} \end{bmatrix}$

Find the product AB and hence find a value of n such that $(AB)^n = \begin{bmatrix} 1 & 0 \\ 0 & 1 \end{bmatrix}$.

DETERMINANT

The determinant of a 2 by 2 matrix is defined by $\det \begin{bmatrix} a & b \\ c & d \end{bmatrix} = ad - bc$. The determinant is a scalar. If a matrix has a non-zero determinant, it is said to be **non-singular**, and if the determinant is zero the matrix is said to be **singular**. We shall see that whether or not a matrix is singular is significant for some applications.

INVERSE

The inverse of a square matrix A is written A^{-1}. The product of a matrix and its inverse is the identity matrix, I, $AA^{-1} = A^{-1}A = I$. For 2 by 2 matrices, the inverse can be found by interchanging the top left and bottom right entries and changing the signs of the top right and bottom left entries. Finally, the inverse is found by dividing by the determinant. This can be done by dividing the matrix as a whole or by dividing each element separately.

$$\text{If } A = \begin{bmatrix} a & b \\ c & d \end{bmatrix}, \text{ then, } A^{-1} = \begin{bmatrix} \dfrac{d}{ad-bc} & \dfrac{-b}{ad-bc} \\ \dfrac{-c}{ad-bc} & \dfrac{a}{ad-bc} \end{bmatrix} = \frac{1}{ad-bc}\begin{bmatrix} d & -b \\ -c & a \end{bmatrix}$$

EXAMPLES

Find the determinant and, where possible, the inverses of these matrices:

(i) $\begin{bmatrix} 2 & 1 \\ 5 & 3 \end{bmatrix}$ (ii) $\begin{bmatrix} -3 & 2 \\ 0 & -1 \end{bmatrix}$ (iii) $\begin{bmatrix} 2 & 6 \\ 1 & 3 \end{bmatrix}$

SOLUTIONS

(i) $\det \begin{bmatrix} 2 & 1 \\ 5 & 3 \end{bmatrix} = 2 \times 3 - 1 \times 5 = 1$ so the matrix is non-singular. To find the inverse matrix, we interchange the 2 and 3 and reverse the signs of the other two elements.

Since the determinant is 1, this gives us the inverse matrix directly: $\begin{bmatrix} 3 & -1 \\ -5 & 2 \end{bmatrix}$. To check that this is correct, we calculate the products:

$$\begin{bmatrix} 2 & 1 \\ 5 & 3 \end{bmatrix}\begin{bmatrix} 3 & -1 \\ -5 & 2 \end{bmatrix} = \begin{bmatrix} 1 & 0 \\ 0 & 1 \end{bmatrix}, \begin{bmatrix} 3 & -1 \\ -5 & 2 \end{bmatrix}\begin{bmatrix} 2 & 1 \\ 5 & 3 \end{bmatrix} = \begin{bmatrix} 1 & 0 \\ 0 & 1 \end{bmatrix}.$$

In both cases, the product is the identity matrix confirming that the inverse is correct.

(ii) $\det \begin{bmatrix} -3 & 2 \\ 0 & -1 \end{bmatrix} = -3 \times -1 - 2 \times 0 = 3$ so the matrix is non-singular. The necessary

interchanges give the matrix $\begin{bmatrix} -1 & -2 \\ 0 & -3 \end{bmatrix}$ after dividing each element by the

determinant, the inverse is: $\dfrac{1}{3} \begin{bmatrix} -1 & -2 \\ 0 & -3 \end{bmatrix} = \begin{bmatrix} -\dfrac{1}{3} & -\dfrac{2}{3} \\ 0 & -1 \end{bmatrix}$.

The check gives: $\begin{bmatrix} -3 & 2 \\ 0 & -1 \end{bmatrix} \begin{bmatrix} -\dfrac{1}{3} & -\dfrac{2}{3} \\ 0 & -1 \end{bmatrix} = \begin{bmatrix} 1 & 0 \\ 0 & 1 \end{bmatrix}$, $\begin{bmatrix} -\dfrac{1}{3} & -\dfrac{2}{3} \\ 0 & -1 \end{bmatrix} \begin{bmatrix} -3 & 2 \\ 0 & -1 \end{bmatrix} = \begin{bmatrix} 1 & 0 \\ 0 & 1 \end{bmatrix}$ (correct).

(iii) $\det \begin{bmatrix} 2 & 6 \\ 1 & 3 \end{bmatrix} = 2 \times 3 - 6 \times 1 = 0$ so the matrix is singular. Because the calculation of

an inverse involves division by the determinant and division by zero is a forbidden process, singular matrices do not have inverses.

EXERCISE 18.4

1. Find the determinants of the following matrices:

(i) $\begin{bmatrix} 2 & 6 \\ 2 & 4 \end{bmatrix}$ (ii) $\begin{bmatrix} 3 & 0 \\ 2 & 3 \end{bmatrix}$ (iii) $\begin{bmatrix} -3 & 2 \\ 0 & -4 \end{bmatrix}$

(iv) $\begin{bmatrix} 4 & -2 \\ 1 & 0 \end{bmatrix}$ (v) $\begin{bmatrix} 3 & -3 \\ 4 & 1 \end{bmatrix}$ (vi) $\begin{bmatrix} \dfrac{1}{3} & -\dfrac{2}{3} \\ \dfrac{1}{3} & \dfrac{2}{3} \end{bmatrix}$

(vii) $\begin{bmatrix} 0.4 & -0.1 \\ -0.2 & 1.3 \end{bmatrix}$ (viii) $\begin{bmatrix} \dfrac{1}{\sqrt{2}} & -\dfrac{3}{\sqrt{2}} \\ \dfrac{1}{\sqrt{2}} & \dfrac{5}{\sqrt{2}} \end{bmatrix}$ (ix) $\begin{bmatrix} \cos\theta & -\sin\theta \\ \sin\theta & \cos\theta \end{bmatrix}$

(x) $\begin{bmatrix} x & 2 \\ 1 & x \end{bmatrix}$ (xi) $\begin{bmatrix} \sqrt{a} & a \\ 1 & \sqrt{a} \end{bmatrix}$ (xii) $\begin{bmatrix} \dfrac{\sqrt{3}}{2} & 1 \\ \dfrac{1}{2} & \sqrt{3} \end{bmatrix}$

2. Find the inverses of these matrices, where they exist.

(i) $\begin{bmatrix} -2 & 4 \\ 1 & 0 \end{bmatrix}$ (ii) $\begin{bmatrix} 3 & 2 \\ -4 & -2 \end{bmatrix}$ (iii) $\begin{bmatrix} -2 & -2 \\ 4 & -3 \end{bmatrix}$

(iv) $\begin{bmatrix} 1 & 0 \\ -2 & -4 \end{bmatrix}$ (v) $\begin{bmatrix} -4 & -1 \\ 1 & 0 \end{bmatrix}$ (vi) $\begin{bmatrix} 3 & 2 \\ 6 & 4 \end{bmatrix}$

(vii) $\begin{bmatrix} -1 & -3 \\ 4 & -3 \end{bmatrix}$ (viii) $\begin{bmatrix} 3 & -2 \\ 4 & -4 \end{bmatrix}$ (ix) $\begin{bmatrix} -0.2 & 0.2 \\ -0.2 & -0.8 \end{bmatrix}$

(x) $\begin{bmatrix} 0 & 1 \\ \dfrac{1}{3} & -\dfrac{1}{3} \end{bmatrix}$ (xi) $\begin{bmatrix} \dfrac{1}{4} & \dfrac{1}{4} \\ \dfrac{1}{6} & -\dfrac{1}{6} \end{bmatrix}$ (xii) $\begin{bmatrix} \dfrac{2}{9} & \dfrac{1}{3} \\ \dfrac{1}{9} & -\dfrac{1}{3} \end{bmatrix}$

(xiii) $\begin{bmatrix} 3 & 4 \\ 2 & 3 \end{bmatrix}$ (xiv) $\begin{bmatrix} x & 1 \\ 2x & 3 \end{bmatrix}$ (xv) $\begin{bmatrix} 2 & x \\ 3 & x \end{bmatrix}$

3. Find the value(s) of x such that $\begin{bmatrix} x & 2 \\ 2 & x \end{bmatrix}$ is singular.

4. Find the value(s) of x such that $\dfrac{1}{x}\begin{bmatrix} -3 & 4 \\ 3 & 4 \end{bmatrix}\begin{bmatrix} 4 & -4 \\ -3 & -3 \end{bmatrix} = \begin{bmatrix} 1 & 0 \\ 0 & 1 \end{bmatrix}$

5. If $\begin{bmatrix} 2 & 4 \\ 1 & 1 \end{bmatrix}\begin{bmatrix} a & 2 \\ -a & -1 \end{bmatrix} = \begin{bmatrix} 1 & 0 \\ 0 & 1 \end{bmatrix}$, find the value of a.

18.3 GRAPH THEORY

A **graph** (sometimes referred to as a **network**) is a representation of the way in which objects are connected. This is a very general idea and graph theory has been applied to problems as varied as making maps, managing transport systems and synchronising the construction of large buildings.

The first problem to have been studied using graph theory is said to have been the Königsberg bridge problem illustrated opposite. The two islands in the river were joined by the bridges shown. The inhabitants wanted to know if it was possible to walk across each bridge once and once only on a continuous walk that starts on either bank or either island.

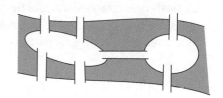

The problem was studied by the Swiss mathematician Leonhard Euler (1707-1783) who realised that the problem could be simplified to the diagram shown. This is an example of a graph in which the key points on the map are replaced by dots and the bridges by lines. In 1736 Euler used this simplified representation to prove that the citizens of Königsberg could not go on a continuous walk that crosses each bridge once and once only.

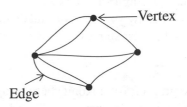

DEFINITIONS

A graph is made up of:
- Vertices (the plural of **vertex**). These are the dots on the above example.

- **Edges**, the lines joining the vertices.

There are some features that are commonly found on graphs:
- A **loop** is an edge that starts and finishes at the same vertex.

- A **multiple edge** occurs when more than one edge joins the same pair of vertices.

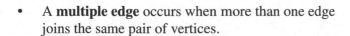

- A **directed edge** only allows us to pass along it in one direction. It is the graph equivalent of a 'one way street'.

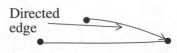

- Let G be a graph and let V and W be vertices in G. A **walk from V to W** is a finite alternating sequence of adjacent vertices and edges of G

- A **path** on a graph starts and finishes at a vertex and passes along connected edges. An **Eulerian path** is a path that uses each edge exactly once.

- A **circuit** on a graph is a path that starts and finishes at the same vertex. A **Hamiltonian circuit** is a circuit that passes through each vertex exactly once.

- The **degree** of a vertex is the number of edges incident (joining) it. The diagram shows the degrees of each vertex.

Euler discovered that Eulerian paths only exist for graphs that have:
- all vertices of even degree or
- two vertices of odd degree and the rest even.

Thus the graph shown does have an Eulerian path because the graph has two vertices of odd degree. In a case such as this, the path must start at one odd vertex and finish at the other.

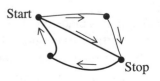

The graph for the Königsberg bridge problem has four vertices of odd degree and so does not have an Eulerian path.

TYPES OF GRAPH

We distinguish several different types of simple graph.

- **Connected** graphs are graphs that enable us to move from every vertex to every other vertex along a connected path.

- It is possibly easier to understand the idea of a connected graph by looking at a **disconnected** graph. In the example shown, it is not possible to move from vertex A to vertex B.

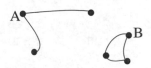

- A **complete** graph is one in which any two distinct vertices are joined by exactly one edge. The diagram shows the complete graph with four vertices.

- A **planar** graph can be drawn on a plane without any edges crossing over one another. The diagram shows a **non-planar** graph.

- A **tree** is a graph that has no circuits. Tree graphs do have the appearance of the branches of a tree.

- A **subgraph** is a part of a graph. That is, a subgraph is any subset of vertices and edges of a graph. The diagram shows one possible subgraph of the Königsberg bridge graph.

EXAMPLES

The diagram shows the towns of a small island and the roads connecting them.

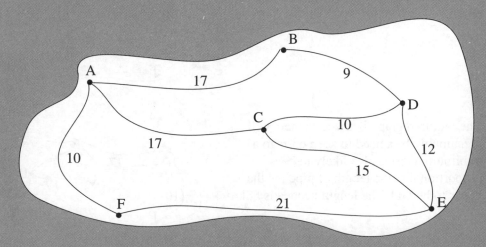

The numbers are the distances in kilometres.

1. A road inspection team wishes to travel along each road to check for holes. Can they do their inspection without travelling along any road more than once?

2. Chai has friends in each town. Can he visit them without passing through any town more than once?

3. A travelling salesman who lives at A wants to visit C, E & F. Show the sub-graph that the salesman should use.

4. Natural gas is to be imported to town E. The gas is to be distributed by a network of pipelines that, for service reasons, must follow the roads. Show the best graph for the pipelines.

SOLUTIONS

1. The path described is Eulerian. The degrees of the vertices are shown. Since there are 4 odd vertices, we can be certain that no Eulerian path exists.

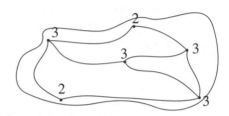

2. Chai needs a Hamiltonian circuit. There are several of these. The diagram shows an example. The distance covered in this circuit is 82 km.

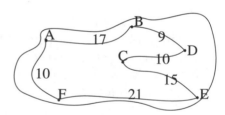

3. The diagram shows the shortest graph that the salesman should use is shown. The distance is 63km.

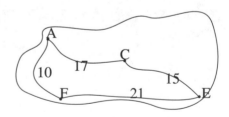

4. The required graph is a tree as there will presumably be a need to keep costs to a minimum. Cost is also likely to be proportional to the length of pipeline that needs to be laid. The length needed is 58km.

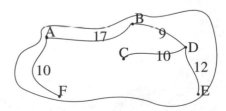

EXERCISE 18.5

1. The diagram shows three houses and three services. Each house must be connected to each service. Can the connections be made without crossing over at least two of the lines (i.e. is the graph planar)?

House 1 ●   ● Gas

House 2 ●   ● Electricity

House 3 ●   ● Telephone

2. Draw the three vertex complete graph.

3. The diagram shows the travel times (hours) between several towns. Draw the graph that gives the shortest travel time between A and E.

4. Which of the following graphs have Eulerian paths?

i.

ii.
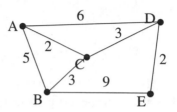

iii.

iv.

v.
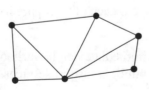

vi.
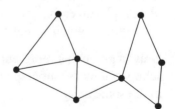

5. Is the complete five vertex graph planar?

6. What is the smallest number of edges that a four vertex connected graph can have?

7. The diagram shows a graph. Draw the subgraph that contains all the vertices but which has the smallest possible number of edges.

8. The diagram shows the network of a small regional airline. The numbers are the travel times in hours.

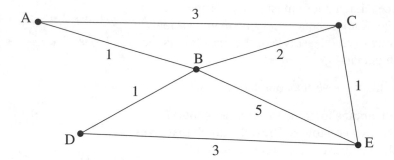

    i.   Find the shortest flying time between A & E.

    ii.   If the airline needs to reduce the number of different routes whilst still serving all the towns, what type of graph should it use?

9. What is the smallest number of bridges that the people of Königsberg would need to build so that they could cross each bridge once and once only on an afternoon walk?

10. Six people meet for a dinner party. Each shakes hands with every other guest.

    i.   Draw a graph that represents the handshakes.

    ii.   Find the sum of the degrees of the vertices.

    iii. How many handshakes are there for six guests?

    iv. How many handshakes are there for n guests?

11. What can be said about the sum of the degrees of a planar graph?

12. If the each member of your immediate family were to be represented by the vertices of a graph and each person were to be connected to each of their parents by an edge, what type of graph would be produced?

13. Draw a graph that represents the streets in the immediate neighbourhood of your school. Draw the subgraph that represents the public transport services that operate in the same area.

14. The diagram shows a cube and the planar graph that represents the same object.

    i.   Is it possible to travel in a continuous path that covers each edge of a cube once and once only?

    ii.   Repeat the analysis for the octahedron:

MATRIX REPRESENTATION

The type of simple graph discussed in the previous can be represented using matrices.
There are two ways of recording the information:

ADJACENCY MATRICES

The adjacency method of recording a graph is illustrated in this example:

EXAMPLE

Record the adjacency of the vertices in the graph shown.

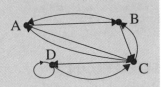

SOLUTION

The adjacency method of recording a graph involves setting up a square matrix with a row
and a column for each vertex.

	A	B	C	D
A	0	1	1	0
B	1	0	1	0
C	1	1	0	1
D	0	0	1	1

This can be written as the matrix: $\begin{bmatrix} 0 & 1 & 1 & 0 \\ 1 & 0 & 1 & 0 \\ 1 & 1 & 0 & 1 \\ 0 & 0 & 1 & 1 \end{bmatrix}$.

Since all the edges are 'two-way', the matrix is symmetric about the leading diagonal.

An adjacency matrix (A) of the type derived above gives us information about the number
of connections there are between vertices.

In this case, the square of A is: $A^2 = \begin{bmatrix} 0 & 1 & 1 & 0 \\ 1 & 0 & 1 & 0 \\ 1 & 1 & 0 & 1 \\ 0 & 0 & 1 & 1 \end{bmatrix} \begin{bmatrix} 0 & 1 & 1 & 0 \\ 1 & 0 & 1 & 0 \\ 1 & 1 & 0 & 1 \\ 0 & 0 & 1 & 1 \end{bmatrix} = \begin{bmatrix} 2 & 1 & 1 & 1 \\ 1 & 2 & 1 & 1 \\ 1 & 1 & 3 & 1 \\ 1 & 1 & 1 & 2 \end{bmatrix}$

The entries in this matrix tell us the number of two step connections that there are on the
graph. Thus, for example, there are three distinct ways of travelling from vertex C back to
vertex C in two steps. Can you identify them on the graph? There is one way of going from
A to B using two edges.

INCIDENCE MATRICES

An alternative to recording the adjacency of vertices is to record the edges and the vertices to which they are incident (joined).

EXAMPLE

Write an incidence matrix that records the graph shown.

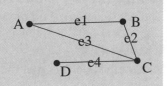

SOLUTION

We need to record that edge e1 is incident to vertex A but not to vertex D etc.

	A	B	C	D
e1	1	1	0	0
e2	0	1	1	0
e3	1	0	1	0
e4	0	0	1	1

EXERCISE 18.6

1. Write adjacency matrices for the graphs shown.

i.

ii.

iii.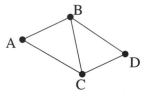

iv.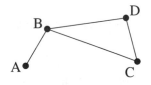

v.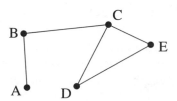

vi.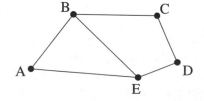

2. Draw the graphs represented by these adjacency matrices.

i. $\begin{bmatrix} 0 & 1 \\ 1 & 0 \end{bmatrix}$ ii. $\begin{bmatrix} 0 & 2 \\ 2 & 0 \end{bmatrix}$

iii. $\begin{bmatrix} 0 & 1 & 0 \\ 1 & 0 & 1 \\ 0 & 1 & 0 \end{bmatrix}$ iv. $\begin{bmatrix} 0 & 1 & 1 \\ 1 & 0 & 1 \\ 1 & 1 & 0 \end{bmatrix}$

3. Write incidence matrices for the following graphs.

i.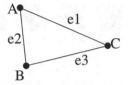

ii.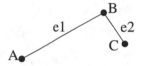

iii.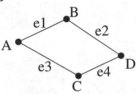

iv.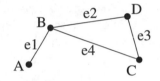

4. The graph shows the public transport routes between four towns.

Represent this as an adjacency matrix.

Calculate the square of this matrix and hence find the number of ways in which a person can travel from A to D in exactly two stages.

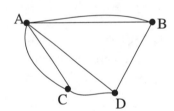

5. Represent the complete 5 vertex graph shown as an adjacency matrix.

Find the number of two stage routes that join adjacent vertices.

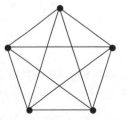

6. Use a graph theory method to find the number of different ways there are of travelling along exactly two edges of a cube and moving from one corner to the corner opposite it on the same face.

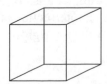

18.4 DIRECTED GRAPHS

The simplest category of directed graph very similar to the basic graphs discussed earlier but with some or all of the edges 'one way'.

EXAMPLE

The diagram shows the street map of a small town. The shaded areas are buildings and the unshaded areas are roads. At present all the roads are two way.

Represent the roads as a graph with the entries to the town and the road intersections as vertices and the roads as edges.

It is intended to turn the diagonal road into a pedestrian precinct and to create the one-way system shown. Represent this as a directed graph. Will the citizens be pleased with the new system? If not, recommend an improved system that has as many one way roads as possible.

SOLUTION

The graph required is shown.

With the one-way system in place, the graph becomes:

This is not a satisfactory system because, for example, it is not possible to pass from an intersection at the bottom left to one at the top right.

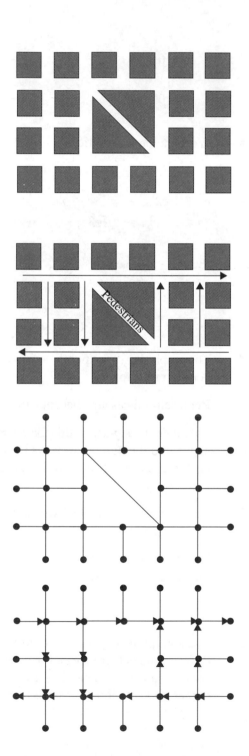

A better arrangement is shown:

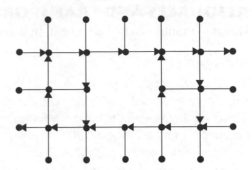

EXERCISE 18.7

1. The directed graph shown gives the travel times (hours) in the directions shown between several country towns. What is the shortest time for a trip from Amesville to Exton?

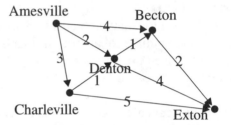

2. The graph shows the flows in a gas pipeline. The gas enters at the point marked 'entry' and leaves the network at the point marked 'exit'. In an attempt to simplify the network, the company wants to remove as many pipes as possible. Show one way in which this could be done whilst still leaving the entry point connected to the exit.

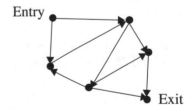

3. Draw a graph that represents the streets in your immediate neighbourhood. Show any one-way streets as directed edges. Design a one way system that still allows complete freedom of movement from one place to any other and which has all the benefits of one-way systems. Write a short justification of your design.

4. Directed graphs are sometimes used to represent the way in which money flows through the economic system. Think for a moment about what happens to the money that you spend each week. Can you represent the way in which this is spent as a directed graph? Remember that if you spend some money at a shop, some of it will go to the shop-keeper, some to the producer of the goods you buy and, almost certainly, some will go to the government in taxes. It may be that a small amount of this flows back to you as a student grant. As you may now see, this is a complex question. Keep your answer reasonably simple!

RESOURCES AND TRANSPORTATION GRAPHS

Directed graphs can be very useful in illustrating resources or skills.

EXAMPLE

The directed graph shows the skills of the
workforce of a small publishing company.
The company is about to accept a contract to
produce a small publicity leaflet. This
requires staff who can proofread, design,
typeset and print the product. The customer
will write the text and so this skill is not
required. If the company wants to use the
smallest number of its employees to fulfil
these tasks, who should it choose?

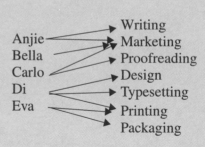

SOLUTION

The solution to small problems such as this can generally be found using commonsense.
There are a number of algorithms that have been developed to find the best solutions to
'real life' sized problems of this type. Some of these are quite complex and are beyond the
scope of this course.

In the present case, a good start is to remove
the skills that are not required for the present
project and to have a look at the graph that
results.

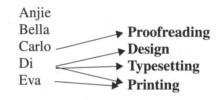

From this simplified graph it is obvious that
Carlo and Di should do the job.

Distribution problems can also be depicted using directed graphs.

EXAMPLE

The directed graph shows the warehouses and
retail outlets of a major clothing retailer. The
figures in brackets after the warehouse names
represent the current stocks of the new 'hot' style
of denims that are the company's best selling
item. The numbers in brackets after the store
names are the expected weekly sales of the
denims from that store. The directed edges show
the delivery routes and the costs (in crowns) of
delivering one pair of denims using that route.
What is the best way for the company to deliver
the required number of denims?

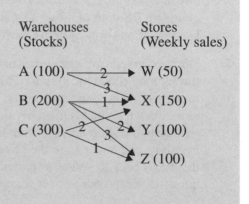

SOLUTION

As with the previous example, there are some sophisticated methods for finding the best solutions to 'real-sized' distribution problems of this sort. This is just as well as finding the best way of delivering goods is in everyone's interest as it will keep prices down, raise profits and save energy.

In the present case, we will again proceed using commonsense by seeing if it is possible to eliminate the more expensive routes and still supply the stores. The result is the graph shown. From this, the suggested solution is:
Send:
50 from A to W (cost 100 crowns)
100 from B to Y (cost 400 crowns)
50 from B to X (cost (50 crowns)
100 from C to X (cost 200 crowns)
100 from C to Z (cost 100 crowns)

Warehouses (Stocks)		Stores (Weekly sales)
A (100)	—2→	W (50)
B (200)	—1→	X (150)
C (300)	—2— 2→	Y (100)
	1	Z (100)

The total cost is 850 crowns.

EXERCISE 18.8

1. The graph shows the instruments played by a group of friends. They want to form a group that has a guitar, a bass guitar and drums. Who should play in the group?

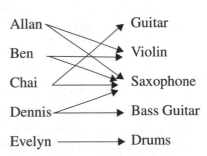

Allan
Ben
Chai
Dennis
Evelyn

Guitar
Violin
Saxophone
Bass Guitar
Drums

2. The graph shows the capabilities of the employees of a small gardening business. The business has one job that requires some planting on a plot that must then be surrounded with a fence which must also be painted. If the business requires that the job is to be done by the smallest possible group of its employees, who should they choose for the job?

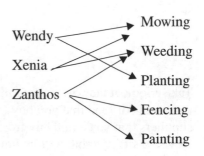

Wendy
Xenia
Zanthos

Mowing
Weeding
Planting
Fencing
Painting

3. A small translation service has four employees who are fluent in the languages indicated. If an employee is fluent in two languages, then they are considered to be capable of translating from one to another.

The service has a request to translate from Italian to Japanese. Who could they choose?

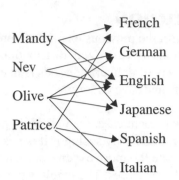

4. A small distributor of electronic goods has two factories and two shops. The daily output of each factory, the expected daily sales of each shop and the unit cost (marks) of delivery are shown. How should the company organise its distribution so that its costs are kept to a minimum?

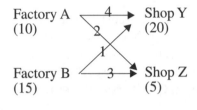

5. The graph shows the travelling expenses ($) that a company pays its sales staff to visit its various customers. If each sales person can visit at most two customers per day and each customer must be visited each day, who should visit each customer and what is the total daily expense?

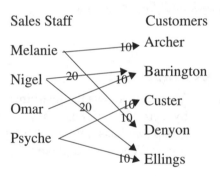

6. The graph shows the costs ($, 0000) of various sub-contracted services used by a news agency. The agency must have one supplier of each service. Who should the choose to minimise the costs (shown on the edges)?.

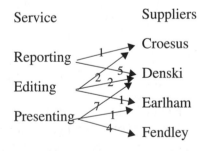

7. Take a look at the way your family chooses to buy its food supplies. List the main categories of food that you buy (vegetables, dairy, meat, fish etc.). List the main suppliers that you could buy from. How long does it take you to visit each supplier? Devise a strategy that will let your family do its food shopping in the shortest possible time.

SCHEDULING

Many complex tasks can be broken down into a set of much smaller parts. The problem of arranging these tasks in the appropriate order is known as a scheduling problem. Directed graphs can help in finding the best solutions to these problems.

EXAMPLE

When renovating their flat, Chai and Cara identify the following stages. Some they will do themselves and some will have to be done by trades people. They recognise that the tasks cannot be done all at once. For example, the plastering of the walls cannot be done until the rewiring is completed because the electrician needs to dig into the walls and would ruin any work done by the plasterer. We say that rewiring is a **pre-requisite** of plastering. They estimate that the times taken for these tasks will be:

Task	Label	Pre-requisite	Days
Design	A	None	1
Clearing carpets	B	A	2
Cleaning walls	C	A	1
Rewiring	D	B, C	5
Plumbing	E	B, C	3
Plastering	F	D, E	2
Painting	G	E, F	2
Tiling	H	E, F	1
Carpeting	I	G, H	1

Represent these tasks as a graph and find the order in which the tasks should be scheduled so that their renovations are completed in the shortest possible time.

SOLUTION

The graph must show the tasks in their correct order. Some tasks can be completed at the same time.

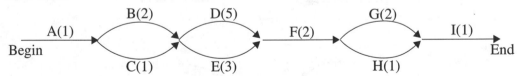

To decide when each task can begin, Chai and Clara must identify the path from the beginning of the project to the end that determines when the various tasks can start and finish. This is known as the **critical path** of the graph. This means choosing the longest of each of the tasks that can run at the same time.

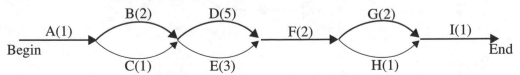

The reason for choosing B and not C as the task for the critical path is that both clearing carpets and cleaning wall must be completed before either the rewiring or plumbing can begin. This will take the 2 days of the longer task (B, clearing carpets). This now lets us identify the total time of the renovation and when Cara and Chai should book each tradesperson:

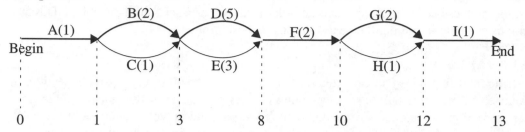

Thus the total renovation will take 13 days (provided that they have studied graph theory and do not take the 18 days of all the tasks!).

As with other graph theory problems discussed, real life problems are more complex than this (consider all the tasks involved in building a sky-scraper!). There are algorithms that allow us to find the critical paths of such complex problems. You might like to research some of these.

EXERCISE 18.9

1. For each of the following scheduling graphs, what are the critical paths and the shortest completion times?

i.

ii.

iii.

iv.

v.

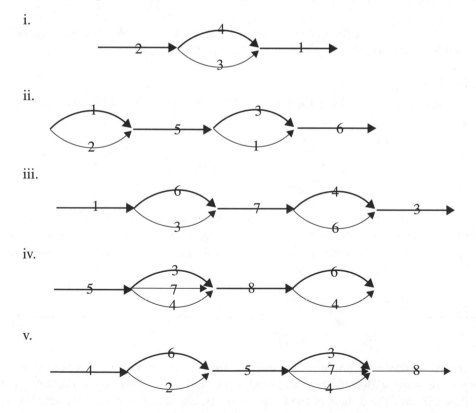

2. In the production of the school musical, the production team have identified the following tasks, associated times and pre-requisites. Show this information as a graph, identify the critical path and find the shortest possible completion time for the tasks.

Task	Label	Pre-requisite	Hours
Choosing title	A	None	2
Auditions (singers)	B	A	5
Selection of orchestra	C	A	5
Rehearsal of singers	D	B	7
Orchestra rehearsal	E	C	6
Dress rehearsal	F	D, E	3
Performances	G	F	8

3. The main tasks necessary for planning a party, associated times and pre-requisites are:

Task	Label	Pre-requisite	Hours
Decide venue	A	None	1
Make guest list	B	A	2
Design invitations	C	A	3
Write & send invitations	D	B, C	3
Hire DJ	E	B, C	1
Buy food	F	B, C	2
Buy drinks	G	B, C	2
Party!	H	E, F, G	6

4. In assembling an electronic test meter, the main steps, associated times and pre-requisites are:

Task	Label	Pre-requisite	Mins.
Drill cabinet	A	None	2
Fix transformer	B	A	3
Fix meter	C	A	2
Fix board	D	A	1
Wiring	E	B, C, D	4
Finishing	F	E	5
Testing	G	F	6
Packaging	H	G	1

5. Look at the problem of preparing a dinner party. Plan the courses and the various ingredients for each. Next, estimate the times taken for both preparation and cooking of each part of each course. Show all the tasks on a directed graph and prepare a set of instructions for the preparation of the dinner assuming that there is only one person who will undertake the task. Remember that, whilst a cook can peel potatoes whist the meat is roasting, most cooks cannot peel potatoes and pod peas at the same time!

18. 5 MARKOV CHAINS

One of the methods commonly used to solve probability problems is the tree diagram.

EXAMPLE

Tessa is keen to improve her fitness. She either trains for one or two hours per day. If she trains for one hour on a given day, there is an equal chance that she will train for one or two hours on the following day. If, however, she only trains for one hour, there is an 80% chance that she will train for two hours on the following day and a 20% chance that she will train for one hour.

Show Tessa's training habits as a tree (a directed graph) and as a matrix. What proportion of the days in a year is Tessa likely to train for 1 hour?

SOLUTION

The graph representation of Tessa's program (assuming that she trained for 1 hour on the previous day) is:

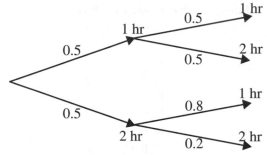

The graph can be represented by the matrix:

	1 hour	2 hours
1 hour	0.5	0.5
2 hours	0.8	0.2

or without the row and column headings: $\begin{bmatrix} 0.5 & 0.5 \\ 0.8 & 0.2 \end{bmatrix}$. The tree (assuming 1 hour of training

on the 1st) can be used to solve probability questions in the conventional way. Suppose Tessa starts to make records on the first day of the year. What is the probability that she will train for 2 hours on the 3rd day of the month?

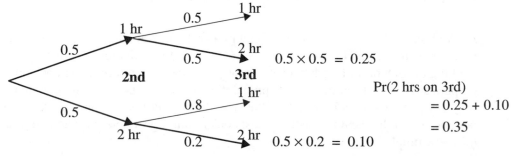

$$0.5 \times 0.5 = 0.25$$

Pr(2 hrs on 3rd)
$$= 0.25 + 0.10$$
$$= 0.35$$

$$0.5 \times 0.2 = 0.10$$

This means that if Tessa trained for 1 hour on the 1st, the probability that she will train for 2 hours on the 3rd is 0.35.

The same result could be achieved from the matrix representation:

$$\begin{bmatrix} 0.5 & 0.5 \\ 0.8 & 0.2 \end{bmatrix} \begin{bmatrix} 0.5 & 0.5 \\ 0.8 & 0.2 \end{bmatrix} = \begin{bmatrix} 0.65 & 0.35 \\ 0.56 & 0.44 \end{bmatrix}$$

The values in the final matrix are the complete set of results that could be found from the tree for the possibilities on the 3rd day of the month:
If she trained for 1 hour on the 1st Pr(1 hour on the 3rd) = 0.5×0.5+0.5×0.8 = 0.65
If she trained for 1 hour on the 1st Pr(2 hours on the 3rd) = 0.5×0.5+0.5×0.2 = 0.35
Not shown on the tree (which assumes 1 hour of training on the 1st)
If she trained for 2 hours on the 1st Pr(1 hour on the 3rd) = 0.8×0.5+0.2×0.8 = 0.56
If she trained for 2 hours on the 1st Pr(2 hours on the 3rd) = 0.8×0.5+0.2×0.2 = 0.44

If we want to look at the next day (the 4th) we could add an extra set of branches to the tree. This starts to get rather complicated. Instead we would do better to use the matrix representation of the problem. All we need to do is to multiply the matrix for the third by the basic matrix.

$$\begin{bmatrix} 0.5 & 0.5 \\ 0.8 & 0.2 \end{bmatrix} \begin{bmatrix} 0.65 & 0.35 \\ 0.56 & 0.44 \end{bmatrix} = \begin{bmatrix} 0.605 & 0.395 \\ 0.632 & 0.368 \end{bmatrix} \text{ or } \begin{bmatrix} 0.5 & 0.5 \\ 0.8 & 0.2 \end{bmatrix}^3 = \begin{bmatrix} 0.605 & 0.395 \\ 0.632 & 0.368 \end{bmatrix}$$

You should be able to do this sort of calculation either using pencil & paper or a graphic calculator. The calculator does, of course, save a lot of time.

The results of this matrix are interpreted in a similar way to those of the 3rd. Thus, if Tessa trained for 1 hour on the first, the probability that she trained for 1 hour on the 4th is 0.605.

We can now use this type of analysis to extend our predictions into the future. The matrices are:

Date	Matrices
5th	$\begin{bmatrix} 0.5 & 0.5 \\ 0.8 & 0.2 \end{bmatrix} \begin{bmatrix} 0.605 & 0.395 \\ 0.632 & 0.368 \end{bmatrix} = \begin{bmatrix} 0.6185 & 0.3815 \\ 0.6104 & 0.3896 \end{bmatrix}$
6th	$\begin{bmatrix} 0.5 & 0.5 \\ 0.8 & 0.2 \end{bmatrix} \begin{bmatrix} 0.6185 & 0.3815 \\ 0.6104 & 0.3896 \end{bmatrix} = \begin{bmatrix} 0.61445 & 0.38555 \\ 0.61688 & 0.38312 \end{bmatrix}$
7th	$\begin{bmatrix} 0.5 & 0.5 \\ 0.8 & 0.2 \end{bmatrix} \begin{bmatrix} 0.61445 & 0.38555 \\ 0.61688 & 0.38312 \end{bmatrix} = \begin{bmatrix} 0.615665 & 0.384335 \\ 0.614936 & 0.385064 \end{bmatrix}$
8th	$\begin{bmatrix} 0.5 & 0.5 \\ 0.8 & 0.2 \end{bmatrix} \begin{bmatrix} 0.615665 & 0.384335 \\ 0.614936 & 0.385064 \end{bmatrix} = \begin{bmatrix} 0.6153005 & 0.3846995 \\ 0.6155192 & 0.3844808 \end{bmatrix}$

It is becoming clear from this analysis (known as a Markov chain) that the probabilities are settling down to about 0.62 for Tessa training for 1 hour and 0.38 for her training for 2 hours on a day later in the month, irrespective of what she did on the first day of the month. To see this, note that the two rows of the matrix are becoming similar as we move to analyse the possibilities for days later in the month.

EXERCISE 18.10

1. If it has rained today, the chance that it will rain tomorrow is 70%. If it has not rained today, the chance that it will rain tomorrow is 40%. Write the matrix (M) that represents the data and by finding M^{10}, use it to predict the overall probability of rain on any day, correct to 3 decimal places.

2. Fiona is a 'form' tennis player. If she wins one match, she feels confident going into the next and expects to win 80% of the time. If she loses a match she will only win 30% of her following match. Express this as a matrix and use this matrix to find the chance that she will win the fifth match after a loss.

3. Ben has a difficult trip to work. If he has been on time one day then there is a 20% chance that he will be late the following day. If he is late one day then there is a 10% probability that he will be late on the next day. If Ben was late on Monday, what is the probability that he will be late on Friday?

4. The 'Striders' basketball team expect to win 60% of the games following a victory but if they are defeated, the train hard during the week and have a 70% chance of winning the next game. If they have just won the first game of the season, what is the probability that they will win:

    i.   the next game?
    ii.   the game after that?
    iii.   the tenth game in the series?

What is the proportion of games might they expect to win throughout a prolonged season?

5. Georgi plays the piano. He plays for either 1 or 2 hours each day. If he plays for 1 hour one day there is a probability of 0.9 that he will play for 2 hours the following day. If he plays for 2 hours on a particular day there is a probability of 0.4 that he will play for 2 hours on the following day. Use a Markov chain analysis to estimate the average time that Georgi will play per day.

6. Keep records (or use a newspaper archive or the internet) of the daily maximum temperature over a period of one month. Find:

    i.   the average daily maximum temperature.
    ii.   the proportion of days on which the daily maximum is exceeded on two successive days.

Use a Markov chain to analyse your data.

18.6 GAMES

The Theory of Games was developed by one of the 20th century's most inventive mathematicians, John von Neumann (1903-1957). Von Neumann was born in Hungary but worked in other European cities before moving to America.

Game theory looks at conflict of all types. In the truest sense of a conflict, there may be any number of 'players' (or combatants). We shall consider only games with two players. Further, there are many games in which one of the possibilities is for everyone to lose. An example of this is a nuclear conflict in which the most likely outcome is that everyone will lose everything! The most simple type of conflict or game is one in which one players gain is the other player's loss. Such a game is known as a two person zero sum game. This section will only consider this type of game.

ZERO SUM GAMES

Usually, a game involves each player in making a choice of moves. Depending upon the choice of each player, each will receive a 'payoff'. Such a payoff may be positive or negative.

EXAMPLE

Two players play a game. Each has a choice of two moves. Alan can choose move w or move x and Bea can choose move y or move z. The payoffs are sumarised in the following table:

Alan $\Downarrow$ Bea $\Rightarrow$	y	z
w	Alan (1) Bea (–1)	Alan (2) Bea (–2)
x	Alan (4) Bea (–4)	Alan (3) Bea (–3)

This means that if Alan choose move w and Bea chooses move z, Alan will win 2 points and Bea will lose 2 points. By contrast, if Alan chooses w and Bea chooses y, Alan will gain 1 and Bea lose 1. How should each play this game?

SOLUTION

One point to make at the start is that the payoffs can be represented as a single matrix. If we choose to look at Alan's payoffs this matrix is:

$$\begin{bmatrix} 1 & 2 \\ 4 & 3 \end{bmatrix}$$

Bea's payoffs can be deduced from this as the game is zero sum: $\begin{bmatrix} -1 & -2 \\ -4 & -3 \end{bmatrix}$. It is, however, possible to use Alan's matrix only, and the rest of this solution will do that.

Note that it is obvious at this stage that the game is not fair as Bea cannot possibly win. What she will seek to do is minimise her loss whilst Alan must try to maximise his gain. As far as Alan is concerned, he will probably argue as follows. If I choose move w, the worst thing that will happen is that I will win 1 point. This is found by looking at the first row of the payoff matrix and finding the smallest entry in it (1). If instead Alan chooses move x, the worst thing that will happen is that he will win 3. Move x is therefore better for Alan. Looking at the game from Bea's perspective, she will want to minimise her losses. Her moves are represented by the columns of the matrix. If she chooses move y, her worst result is a loss of 4 (the biggest number in the column; remember that these numbers represent losses for Bea and that a big number is bad for her). If, instead she chooses move z represented by the second column of the payoff matrix, the worst result for her is a loss of 3. This is the better option for Bea. The result of these thoughts for both players is that Alan will always play move x and Bea will always play move z with the result that Alan will win 3 and Bea lose 3 every time the game is played.

The matrix entry that corresponds to this solution is called a **saddle point** and the game is said to have a **stable solution**.

In summary, a zero sum game can be reduced to a single payoff matrix. To establish if the game has a saddle point and hence a stable solution, we find the smallest entry in each row and pick the largest of these. Also, we pick the largest entry in each column and pick the smallest of these. If these numbers are the same, the game has a stable solution.

EXAMPLE

Carmen and Don play a game. Each has a choice of three moves. The payoffs for each are given in the table below:

Carmen ⇓ Don ⇒	e	f	g
j	Carmen(1) Don(5)	Carmen(2) Don(4)	Carmen(2) Don(4)
k	Carmen(4) Don(2)	Carmen(4) Don(2)	Carmen(3) Don(3)
l	Carmen(3) Don(3)	Carmen(5) Don(1)	Carmen(1) Don(5)

Explain why this is a zero sum game. How should each of the players play the game?

SOLUTION

Each of the payoffs to the players add up to 6. There is, therefore, an effective bonus of 3 points to each for playing. If we remove this from both players, the payoffs become:

Carmen ⇓ Don ⇒	e	f	g
j	Carmen(−2) Don(2)	Carmen(−1) Don(1)	Carmen(−1) Don(1)
k	Carmen(1) Don(−1)	Carmen(1) Don(−1)	Carmen(0) Don(0)
l	Carmen(0) Don(0)	Carmen(2) Don(−2)	Carmen(−2) Don(2)

This is now a zero sum game as the payoffs in each cell add to zero. It is not uncommon for zero sum games to be of this type in which both players gain.

The payoff matrix for Carmen is: $\begin{bmatrix} -2 & -1 & -1 \\ 1 & 1 & 0 \\ 0 & 2 & -2 \end{bmatrix}$.

Looking at the row minima these are $\begin{bmatrix} -2 \\ 0 \\ -2 \end{bmatrix}$. The largest of these is 0. This process looks at

the worst thing that can happen for Carmen and shows that if she plays j she might lose 2 at worst, if she plays k the worst that can happen is a zero payoff and if she plays l she might lose 2.

Looking at the column maxima these are $\begin{bmatrix} 1 & 1 & 0 \end{bmatrix}$. These represent the losses for Don

(remember we are looking at the payoffs for Carmen and that a win for her means a loss for Don. Don will want to minimise his losses. If he chooses to play e he could lose 1, if he plays f he could also lose 1 whereas if he plays g the worst that can happen is a zero loss.

If both players look at this game, Carmen will play k and Don will play g. Each will receive a zero payoff in the modified game. Remember, however, that the original game gave each 3 points for playing. The true solution is: Carmen will play k and Don will play g. Each will get 3 points.

EXERCISE 18.11

1. Write the payoff matrix for player A in the game with these conditions:

A ⇓ B ⇒	e	f	g
j	A(5) B(5)	A(2) B(8)	A(4) B(6)
k	A(2) B(8)	A(2) B(8)	A(5) B(5)
l	A(6) B(4)	A(7) B(3)	A(1) B(9)

Does the game have a stable solution?

2. Find the solutions to the zero sum games with the following payoff matrices if the payoffs are stated for the 'row player':

i. $\begin{bmatrix} 2 & 5 \\ 3 & 3 \end{bmatrix}$ ii. $\begin{bmatrix} 6 & 4 \\ 5 & 2 \end{bmatrix}$ iii. $\begin{bmatrix} 1 & 1 \\ 1 & 0 \end{bmatrix}$

iv. $\begin{bmatrix} 2 & 3 & 6 \\ 1 & 1 & 4 \\ 2 & 5 & 2 \end{bmatrix}$ v. $\begin{bmatrix} 3 & 3 & 2 \\ 1 & 3 & 1 \\ 4 & 2 & 1 \end{bmatrix}$ vi. $\begin{bmatrix} 4 & 2 & 6 \\ 3 & 2 & 1 \\ 6 & 2 & 3 \end{bmatrix}$

3. The forces of Sir Tristram are besieging the castle of Sir Percival. The castle has two approaches; the gate and the moat. Sir Percival has to decide where to place the majority of his defensive forces and Sir Tristram has to choose which place to attack. If Sir Percival chooses to defend the gate, he estimates that he will lose 200 men if Sir Tristram attacks the gate and Sir Tristram will lose 600 men. If Sir Percival chooses to defend the gate, he estimates that he will lose 300 men if Sir Tristram attacks the moat and Sir Tristram will lose 500 men. If Sir Percival chooses to defend the moat, he estimates that he will lose 600 men if Sir Tristram attacks the gate and Sir Tristram will lose 200 men. If Sir Percival chooses to defend the moat, he estimates that he will lose 300 men if Sir Tristram attacks the moat and Sir Tristram will lose 500 men.

    i.   Is this a zero sum game?

    ii.   How should each knight command his soldiers?

MIXED STRATEGIES

Not every two person zero sum game has a stable solution. If this is the case, we must adopt a more complex strategy.

EXAMPLE

The matrix gives the payoffs to the row player: $\begin{bmatrix} 4 & -3 \\ -4 & 3 \end{bmatrix}$. How should the game be played?

SOLUTION

The row and column summaries are:

$$\begin{bmatrix} 4 & -3 \\ -4 & 3 \end{bmatrix} \quad \begin{matrix} \text{row min.} \\ -3 \\ -4 \end{matrix}$$

col. max.   4 3

The largest row minimum is –3 and the smallest column maximum is 3. Thus the row player will want to choose the largest row minimum and should choose row 1. The column player should choose column two when s/he will lose 3. However, had the row player chosen row 2 instead of row 1, s/he would win 3 instead of losing 3. Unfortunately the column player may guess that the row player will mean to do this and play column 1. In this case the row player loses 4 and the column player gains 4.

This is a more complex situation than those discussed earlier. There is the potential for each player to mix their strategy so that their opponent will not be able to win by reasoning what the other will do. What should each do?

The first possibility is that they could collaborate and fix which move each will make. This does not work as the game is zero sum and one player's gain is the other's loss. The only other possibilities are espionage (cheating by finding out what your opponent intends to do) or choosing a randomly based strategy so that your opponent cannot guess what you intend to do. Whilst espionage is the most common choice of military commanders, it is not considered good form by the players of games! We will assume that there is no possibility of knowing the opponent's intentions and that a random strategy is best. How should each player proceed?

As far as the row player is concerned, suppose s/he plays row 1 with probability p and row 2 with probability $1 - p$, then if the column player chooses column 1 the expectation is:

Expected payoff = $4p + (-4)(1 - p) = 8p - 4$

If, instead, the column player chooses column 2, the row player's expectation is:

Expected payoff = $-3p + 3(1 - p) = 3 - 6p$.

This could now be viewed graphically plotting the row player's expected payoff against p.

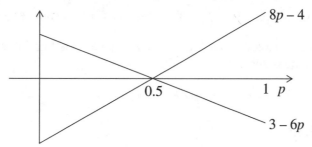

The two lines represent the expected payoffs for the row player if the column player chooses either column 1 or column 2. The intersection point can be found by solving the equation:

$$8p - 4 = 3 - 6p$$
$$14p - 4 = 3$$
$$14p = 7$$
$$p = \frac{1}{2}$$

If the row player uses a p value of less than 0.5 then the column player can choose column 1 all the time and be certain that the payoff will overall be negative (which is good for the column player). If the row player uses a p value of more than 0.5 then the column player can choose column 2 all the time and be certain that the payoff will overall again be negative.

We now need to look at the game as far as the column player is concerned. If s/he chooses column 1 with a probability of q and column 2 with a probability of $1 - q$, the expected outcomes are:

If the row player chooses row 1 the expected outcome is $4q + (-3)(1 - q) = 7q - 3$.

If the row player chooses row 2 the expected outcome is $-4q + 3(1 - q) = -7q + 3$.

The intersection point is: $7q - 3 = -7q + 3$

$$q = \frac{3}{7}$$

Option: Matrices and Graph Theory

Thus if the column player chooses column 1 fewer then 3 times in every 7 then the row player can choose row 2 all the time and expect to win. If the column player chooses column 1 more then 3 times in every 7 then the row player can choose row 1 all the time and again expect to win.

In summary, the row player should choose row 1 at random half the time and the column player should choose column 1 3 times in every 7 (for example by using a random number generator).

If both players do this then the expected payoff to each.

Row player expected payoff $= 8p - 4 = 8 \times \frac{1}{4} - 4 = 0$.

Column player expected payoff $= 7q - 3 = 7 \times \frac{3}{7} - 3 = 0$. Thus if both players play

optimally the expected payoff to each is zero and the game is fair. We sometimes say that the **value** of this game is zero.

EXERCISE 18.12

1. For the following payoff matrices (given as row player payoffs), if the row player plays row 1 with probability p and the column player plays column 1 with probability q, find the values of p & q.

i. $\begin{bmatrix} -3 & 5 \\ 3 & -1 \end{bmatrix}$ ii. $\begin{bmatrix} -3 & 7 \\ 2 & -1 \end{bmatrix}$ iii. $\begin{bmatrix} 5 & -3 \\ -2 & -1 \end{bmatrix}$

iv. $\begin{bmatrix} 1 & -3 \\ -2 & 4 \end{bmatrix}$ v. $\begin{bmatrix} 3 & -4 \\ -2 & 7 \end{bmatrix}$ vi. $\begin{bmatrix} -1 & 3 \\ 5 & -4 \end{bmatrix}$

vii. $\begin{bmatrix} -12 & 15 \\ 17 & -9 \end{bmatrix}$ viii. $\begin{bmatrix} 7 & -12 \\ -9 & 15 \end{bmatrix}$ ix. $\begin{bmatrix} 4 & -44 \\ -37 & 15 \end{bmatrix}$

2. Two companies are companies are competing for the same market. Each has the choice of advertising on two TV stations. Neither can afford to advertise on both. The additional profits for Amco in thosands of crowns are shown and those for Beeco are shown in brackets.

Amco ⇓ Beco ⇒	TV 1	TV 2
TV 1	15 (5)	9 (11)
TV 2	8 (12)	17 (3)

i.   Explain why the game is zero sum.
ii.   Give Amco's payoff matrix.
iii. What strategy should each company adopt?

3. Two general are facing each other. General White is attacking and General Black is defending. The diagram shows the battlefield.

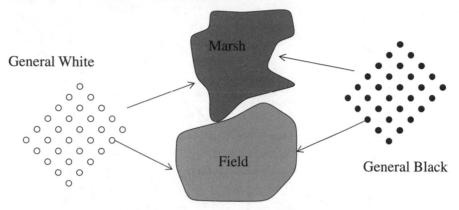

General White can decide to either direct his attack through the marsh or the field. Likewise, General Black can choose to defend either part of the battlefield. Viewing the battle from general White's point of view, he wants to have the biggest positive difference between his casualties and Black's. These figures (in hundreds) are given in the table.

White ⇓ Black ⇒	Marsh	Field
Marsh	−3	5
Field	7	−2

How should each General direct their forces?

FURTHER STATISTICS AND PROBABILITY 1

THE NORMAL DISTRIBUTION

OPTION

1 9

19.1 THE NORMAL DISTRIBUTION

The examples considered earlier in this chapter dealt with data that was **discrete**. Discrete data is generally counted and can be found exactly. Discrete data is often made up of whole numbers. For example, we may have counted the number of occupants in each of the cars passing a particular point over a period of two hours. In this case the data is made up of whole numbers. If we collect information on the European standard shoe sizes of a group of people, we will also be collecting discrete data even though some of the data will be fractional: shoe size nine and a half.

Alternatively, sometimes we collect data using measurement. For example, we might collect the birth weights of all the babies delivered at a maternity hospital over a year. Because weight is a continuous quantity (all weights are possible, not just whole numbers or certain fractions), the data collected is **continuous**. This remains the case even though we usually round continuous data to certain values. In the case of weight, we might round the data to the nearest tenth of a kilogram. In this case, if a baby's weight is given as 3.7kg it means that the weight has been rounded to this figure and lies in the interval [3.65,3.75). If we are looking at data such as these weights it may seem as if the data is discrete even in cases when it is in fact continuous.

When dealing with continuous data, we use different methods. The most important distinction is that we can never give the number of babies that weigh *exactly* 3.7kg as there are *none* of these. All that we can give is the number of babies born that have weights in the range [3.65,3.75).

One of the ways in which we can handle continuous data is to use the **normal distribution**. This distribution is only a model for real data. This means that its predictions are only approximate. The normal distribution generally works best in a situation in which the data clusters about a particular mean and varies from this as a result of **random factors**. The birth weights of babies cluster about a mean with variations from this mean resulting from a range of chance factors such as genetics, nutrition etc. The variation from the mean is measured by the standard deviation of the data. In examples such as this, the normal distribution is often a fairly good model. The basis of all normal distribution studies is the **standard normal curve**.

THE STANDARD NORMAL CURVE

The standard normal curve models data that has a mean of zero and a standard deviation of one. The equation of the standard normal curve is:

$$f(z) = \frac{1}{\sqrt{2\pi}} e^{\left(-\frac{z^2}{2}\right)}, -\infty < z < \infty$$

The equation of this distribution is complex and does not directly give us any information about the distribution. The shape of the curve does, however, indicate the general shape of the distribution.

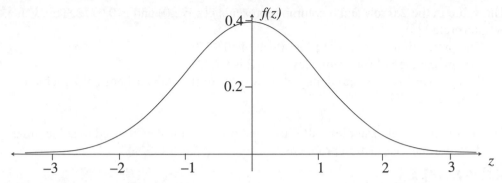

As a result of the fact that the variable z is continuous, it is not the height of the curve but the areas underneath the curve that represent the proportions of the variable that lie between various values. The total area under the curve is 1 (even though the curve extends to infinity in both directions without actually reaching the axis).

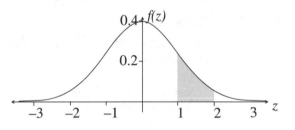

For example, the proportion of the standard normal data that lies between 1 and 2 is represented by the area shown. Areas under curves are usually found using a method covered in Chapter 15. In the case of the normal curve, the complexity of the equation of the graph makes this impossible at least at this level. Instead, we rely on a table of values. The full table can be found at the end of this chapter.

USING THE STANDARD NORMAL TABLE

The table tells us the proportion of values of the standard normal variable that are less than any given value. It is best to view this graphically.

The diagram shows the area that represents the proportion of values for which $z < 2$. This proportion can also be interpreted as the probability that a randomly chosen value of z will have a value of less than 2 or $p(z < 2)$.

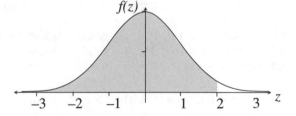

This value can be found from the row beginning with 2.0 in the table:

	0	0.01	0.02	0.03	0.04	0.05	0.06	0.07	0.08	0.09
0.0	0.5000	0.5040	0.5080	0.5120	0.5160	0.5199	0.5239	0.5279	0.5319	0.5359
1.8	0.9641	0.9649	0.9656	0.9664	0.9671	0.9678	0.9686	0.9693	0.9699	0.9706
1.9	0.9713	0.9719	0.9726	0.9732	0.9738	0.9744	0.9750	0.9756	0.9761	0.9767
2.0	0.9772	0.9778	0.9783	0.9788	0.9793	0.9798	0.9803	0.9808	0.9812	0.9817
2.1	0.9821	0.9826	0.9830	0.9834	0.9838	0.9842	0.9846	0.9850	0.9854	0.9857
2.2	0.9861	0.9864	0.9868	0.9871	0.9875	0.9878	0.9881	0.9884	0.9887	0.9890

Option: Normal Distribution

The value in the 2.0 row and 0 column represents $p(z < 2.0)$ and is 0.9772. This value can be interpreted as:

- The proportion of values of z less than 2 is 0.9772
- The percentage of values of z less than 2 is 97.72%
- The probability that a randomly chosen value of the standard normal variable is less than 2 is 0.9772.

The following set of examples will illustrate how the table can be used to solve other standard normal distribution problems.

EXAMPLES

For the standard normal variable z, find:

    (i) $p(z < 1)$ (ii) $p(z < 0.96)$ (iii) $p(z < 0.03)$

SOLUTIONS

(i)   All these examples can be solved by direct use of the tables

        $p(z < 1) = 0.8413$

	0	0.01	0.02	0.03	0.04	0.05	0.06	0.07	0.08	0.09
0.0	0.5000	0.5040	0.5080	0.5120	0.5160	0.5199	0.5239	0.5279	0.5319	0.5359
0.9	0.8159	0.8186	0.8212	0.8238	0.8264	0.8289	0.8315	0.8340	0.8365	0.8389
1.0	0.8413	0.8438	0.8461	0.8485	0.8508	0.8531	0.8554	0.8577	0.8599	0.8621
1.1	0.8643	0.8665	0.8686	0.8708	0.8729	0.8749	0.8770	0.8790	0.8810	0.8830

(ii) $p(z < 0.96)$ $(= 0.8315)$ can be found by using the row for 0.9 and the column for 0.06. The required value can be found at the row and column intersection..

	0	0.01	0.02	0.03	0.04	0.05	0.06	0.07	0.08	0.09
0.0	0.5000	0.5040	0.5080	0.5120	0.5160	0.5199	0.5239	0.5279	0.5319	0.5359
0.8	0.7881	0.7910	0.7939	0.7967	0.7995	0.8023	0.8051	0.8078	0.8106	0.8133
0.9	0.8159	0.8186	0.8212	0.8238	0.8264	0.8289	0.8315	0.8340	0.8365	0.8389
1.0	0.8413	0.8438	0.8461	0.8485	0.8508	0.8531	0.8554	0.8577	0.8599	0.8621

(iii) $p(z < 0.03)$ $(= 0.5120)$ is found similarly

	0	0.01	0.02	0.03	0.04	0.05	0.06	0.07	0.08	0.09
0.0	0.5000	0.5040	0.5080	0.5120	0.5160	0.5199	0.5239	0.5279	0.5319	0.5359
0.1	0.5398	0.5438	0.5478	0.5517	0.5557	0.5596	0.5636	0.5675	0.5714	0.5753

Other problems are best solved using a combination of graphs and the table. The problems arise when we have 'greater than' problems or negative values of z.

EXAMPLES

For the standard normal variable z, find:

(i) $p(z > 1.7)$ (ii) $p(z < -0.88)$ (iii) $p(z > -1.53)$

SOLUTIONS

(i) $p(z > 1.7)$. Graphically this is the
area shaded in the diagram. Since
we can only look up 'less than'
probabilities using the table, we
must use the fact that the total area
under the curve is 1. It follows that:

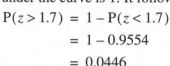

$P(z > 1.7) = 1 - P(z < 1.7)$

$= 1 - 0.9554$

$= 0.0446$

(ii) $p(z < -0.88)$. The table does not
give any negative z values. This
question can be solved by looking
at the diagram on the right. By the
symmetry of the curve, the
required area (shaded) is the same
as the area shown with vertical
stripes. It follows that:

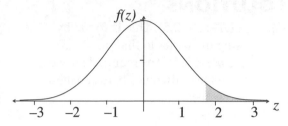

$P(z < -0.88) = P(Z > 0.88)$

$= 1 - P(z < 0.88)$

$= 1 - 0.8106$

$= 0.1894$

(iii) $p(z > -1.53)$. Again, we cannot
look up a negative z value, but we
can use the symmetry of the graph
again.

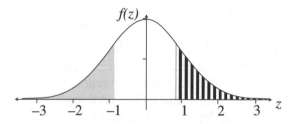

The shaded area in this diagram is
the same as the required area so:

$P(z > -1.53) = P(z < 1.53)$

$= 0.9370$

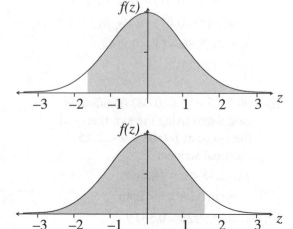

The final set of examples look at some 'between values' type of problems.

EXAMPLES

For the standard normal variable z, find:

   (i) $p(1.7 < z < 2.5)$ (ii) $p(-1.12 < z < 0.67)$ (iii) $p(-2.45 < z < -0.08)$

SOLUTIONS

(i) $p(1.7 < z < 2.5)$. This is found by
      using the tables to find $p(z < 2.5)$
      and $p(z < 1.7)$. The required answer
      is then the difference between these
      two values.

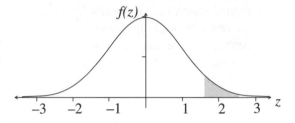

$p(1.7 < z < 2.5)$

$\quad = p(z < 2.5) - p(z < 1.7)$

$\quad = 0.9938 - 0.9554$

$\quad = 0.0384$

(ii) $p(-1.12 < z < 0.67)$. The area is
      shown shaded. The same principal
      is used to solve this problem as the
      previous example. The additional
      difficulty is the negative z value.
      $p(-1.12 < z)$ is calculated as
      $p(z > 1.12) = 1 - p(z < 1.12)$.

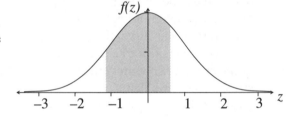

$p(-1.12 < z < 0.67)$

$\quad = p(z < 0.67) - p(z < -1.12)$

$\quad = p(z < 0.67) - p(z > 1.12)$

$\quad = p(z < 0.67) - (1 - p(z < 1.12))$

$\quad = 0.7486 - (1 - 0.8686)$

$\quad = 0.6172$

(iii) $p(-2.45 < z < -0.08)$ (shaded) is
       calculated using the symmetry of
       the curve as $p(0.08 < z < 2.45)$
       (vertical stripes).

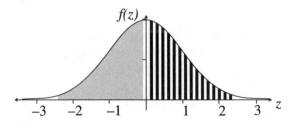

$p(-2.45 < z < -0.08)$

$\quad = p(0.08 < z < 2.45)$

$\quad = 0.9928 - 0.5319$

$\quad = 0.4609$

EXERCISE 19.1

1. For the standard normal variable z, find:

(i) $p(z < 0.5)$ (ii) $p(z < 1.84)$ (iii) $p(z < 1.62)$

(iv) $p(-2.7 < z)$ (v) $p(-1.97 < z)$ (vi) $p(z < -2.55)$

(vii) $p(1.9 < z)$ (viii) $p(z < -1.56)$ (ix) $p(2.44 < z)$

(x) $p(-0.95 < z)$ (xi) $p(z < 0.37)$ (xii) $p(1.39 < z)$

(xiii) $p(-2.05 < z)$ (xiv) $p(z < 2.04)$ (xv) $p(0.39 < z)$

2. For the standard normal variable z, find:

(i) $p(1.75 < z < 2.65)$ (ii) $p(0.3 < z < 2.5)$

(iii) $p(1.35 < z < 1.94)$ (iv) $p(-1.92 < z < -1.38)$

(v) $p(2.23 < z < 2.92)$ (vi) $p(-1.51 < z < -0.37)$

(vii) $p(-2.17 < z < 0.76)$ (viii) $p(1.67 < z < 2.22)$

(ix) $p(-0.89 < z < 0.8)$ (x) $p(-2.64 < z < -1.04)$

(xi) $p(-1.43 < z < 2.74)$ (xii) $p(-1.59 < z < -0.46)$

(xiii) $p(-2.12 < z < 0.58)$ (xiv) $p(-2.61 < z < 1.39)$

(xv) $p(-1.86 < z < 0.13)$ (xvi) $p(-2.56 < z < 0.92)$

(xvii) $p(-1.75 < z < 2.03)$ (xviii) $p(-0.9 < z < 1.34)$

GENERAL NORMAL CURVES

Very few practical applications will have data whose mean is 0 and whose standard deviation is 1. The standard normal curve is, therefore, not directly usable in most cases. We get over this difficulty by relating every problem to the standard normal curve. A general variable, x, is related to the standard normal variable, z, using the relation:

$z = \dfrac{x - \mu}{\sigma}$ where μ = the mean of the data and σ is the standard deviation.

EXAMPLE

A production line produces bags of sugar with a mean weight of 1.01kg and a standard deviation of 0.02kg.

(i)   Find the proportion of the bags that weigh less than 1.03kg

(ii)   Find the proportion of the bags that weigh more than 1.02kg

(iii)   Find the percentage of the bags that weigh between 1.00kg and 1.05kg.

SOLUTION

(i)   The first step is to relate the x value of 1.03 to the z value using the values of the mean and standard deviation.

$$z = \frac{x - \mu}{\sigma} = \frac{1.03 - 1.01}{0.02} = 1$$

Option: Normal Distribution

Graphically, this means that we have related the normal distribution that models the weights of the bags of sugar to the standard normal distribution.

Distribution of weights of sugar bags   Standard normal distribution

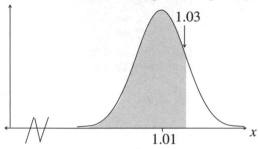

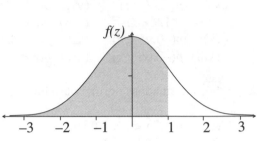

The problem that we are trying to solve: $p(x < 1.03)$ has the same solution as the standard problem $p(z < 1)$. This can be solved directly from the table to get 0.8413.

(ii) Again, transforming this into a standard problem with $x = 1.02$ gives:

$$z = \frac{x - \mu}{\sigma} = \frac{1.02 - 1.01}{0.02} = 0.5$$

Graphically, this is:

Distribution of weights of sugar bags   Standard normal distribution

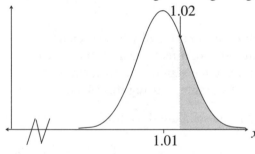

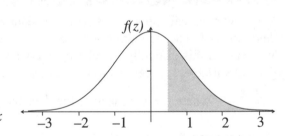

$$
\begin{aligned}
p(x > 1.02) &= p(z > 0.5) \\
&= 1 - p(z < 0.5) \\
&= 1 - 0.6915 \\
&= 0.3085
\end{aligned}
$$

(iii) Again, transforming both the x values to z values, we get:

$$z_1 = \frac{x_1 - \mu}{\sigma} = \frac{1 - 1.01}{0.02} = -0.5$$

$$z_2 = \frac{x_2 - \mu}{\sigma} = \frac{1.05 - 1.01}{0.02} = 2$$

The graphical interpretation of this is:

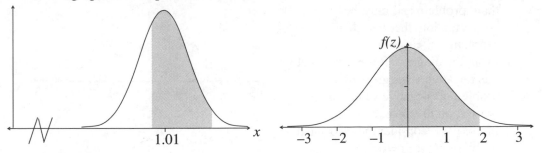

The solution is now found in a similar way to the above examples:

$$\begin{aligned} p(1 < x < 1.05) &= p(-0.5 < z < 2) \\ &= p(z < 2) - p(z < -0.5) \\ &= p(z < 2) - p(z > 0.5) \\ &= p(z < 2) - (1 - p(z < 0.5)) \\ &= 0.9772 - (1 - 0.6915) \\ &= 0.6687 \end{aligned}$$

INVERSE PROBLEMS

There are occasions when we are told the proportion of the data that we are to consider and asked questions about the data conditions that are appropriate to these proportions.

EXAMPLES

Find the values of a in each of these statements that refer to the standard normal variable, z.

(i) $p(z < a) = 0.5478$ (ii) $p(z > a) = 0.6$

(iii) $p(z < a) = 0.05$

SOLUTIONS

(i) $p(z < a) = 0.5478$. In this case, we are given the proportion and asked for the value of z which makes the condition true. Because we know the proportion, we must look for the figure 0.5478 in the body of the table.

	0	0.01	0.02	0.03	0.04	0.05	0.06	0.07	0.08	0.09
0.0	0.5000	0.5040	0.5080	0.5120	0.5160	0.5199	0.5239	0.5279	0.5319	0.5359
0.1	0.5398	0.5438	0.5478	0.5517	0.5557	0.5596	0.5636	0.5675	0.5714	0.5753
0.2	0.5793	0.5832	0.5871	0.5910	0.5948	0.5987	0.6026	0.6064	0.6103	0.6141

Once the figure has been found in the table, it is necessary to infer the value of z that fits the condition. In this case the value is in the row for 0.1 and the column for 0.02 and we can infer that $a = 0.12$. You should check that $p(z < 0.12) = 0.5478$.

(ii) $p(z > a) = 0.6$. This is a 'greater than' problem and must be converted into the 'less than' problem $p(z < a) = 0.4$
From the diagram, it is evident that a is negative. This gives us a problem as negative values are not present on the table.
In this case, consider the associated problem $p(z < b) = 0.6$. By symmetry, if we can find the appropriate value of b, a will follow because $a = -b$.

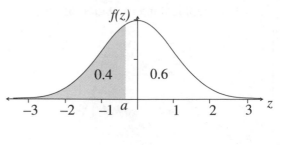

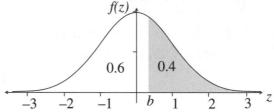

There is a second problem as 0.6 is not present (exactly) in the table. In this case, we find the entries that are as close to 0.6 as possible.

	0	0.01	0.02	0.03	0.04	0.05	0.06	0.07	0.08	0.09
0.0	0.5000	0.5040	0.5080	0.5120	0.5160	0.5199	0.5239	0.5279	0.5319	0.5359
0.1	0.5398	0.5438	0.5478	0.5517	0.5557	0.5596	0.5636	0.5675	0.5714	0.5753
0.2	0.5793	0.5832	0.5871	0.5910	0.5948	0.5987	0.6026	0.6064	0.6103	0.6141
0.3	0.6179	0.6217	0.6255	0.6293	0.6331	0.6368	0.6406	0.6443	0.6480	0.6517

From the table, $p(z < 0.25) = 0.5987$ and $p(z < 0.26) = 0.6026$ and it is clear that the correct value of b is between 0.25 and 0.26 and closer to 0.25 than to 0.26 as 0.5987 is closer to 0.6 than is 0.6026. A reasonable value for b would seem to be about 0.253. There are several ways in which we could do better than this. Some texts provide 'difference values' in the main table and a separate inverse table. At the time of writing, neither of these were provided in IB exams. Also, there is a technique known as linear interpolation that can make the above argument more precise, but this is not strictly necessary in most applications. In the present case, $b \approx 0.253$ so the answer to our problem is that $a \approx -0.253$.

(iii) $p(z < a) = 0.05$. Again, thinking graphically, there is a better associated problem:
$p(z < a) = 0.05$ is the same as $p(z > b) = 0.05$ or $p(z < b) = 0.95$
By symmetry $a = -b$.
Looking for the closest value to 0.95 in the table gives $b \approx 1.645$ and $a \approx -1.645$

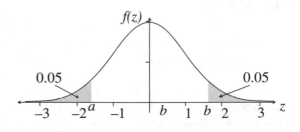

	0	0.01	0.02	0.03	0.04	0.05	0.06	0.07	0.08	0.09
1.6	0.9452	0.9463	0.9474	0.9484	0.9495	0.9505	0.9515	0.9525	0.9535	0.9545

Similar techniques can be applied to non-standard problems.

EXAMPLE

A group of adults have a mean weight of 76kg and a standard deviation of 7kg. If the heaviest 10% of the group are to take a diet and exercise program, what is the weight of the lightest adult that will take the program?

SOLUTION

This is an inverse problem and must be solved by completely reversing the methods for non-standard problems discussed earlier. Also, the data clearly refers to a sample and, whilst we will use the same method as used for populations, we should use the notation for sample statistics rather than population parameters. In the present case,

$\bar{x} = 76, s = 7$.

The first step is to solve the
standard problem $p(z > a) = 0.1$ or
$p(z < a) = 0.9$
As before, the value of a is found
by using the table in reverse to get
an approximate value of a of 1.28

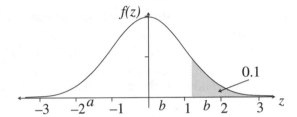

Finally, we must use the transformation formula $z = \dfrac{x - \mu}{\sigma}$ in its sample statistics

version $z = \dfrac{x - \bar{x}}{s}$ to solve for the required value of the non-standard variable.

$1.28 = \dfrac{x - 76}{7}$

$x = 7 \times 1.28 + 76$

$\quad = 84.96$

Any adults who weigh 85kg or more should take the diet and exercise program.

EXAMPLE

A production line produces cans of soft drink. The mean contents of the cans is 332ml. 65% of the cans contain less than 333.5ml. Find the standard deviation of the contents of the cans.

SOLUTION

Firstly, we must find the value of the standard normal variable such that
$p(z < a) = 0.65$ by using the table in reverse. This is about 0.385.

	0	0.01	0.02	0.03	0.04	0.05	0.06	0.07	0.08	0.09
0.3	0.6179	0.6217	0.6255	0.6293	0.6331	0.6368	0.6406	0.6443	0.6480	0.6517

Finally, substitute all the values known into $z = \dfrac{x - \mu}{\sigma}$ and solve for σ.

$$z = \frac{x - \mu}{\sigma}$$

$$0.385 = \frac{333.5 - 332}{\sigma}$$

$$\sigma = \frac{333.5 - 332}{0.385}$$

$$= 3.896$$

EXERCISE 19.2

1. A normally distributed variable, x, has a mean of 99 and a standard deviation of 1.6. Find:
   (i) $p(x < 98.72)$ (ii) $p(x > 99.49)$ (iii) $p(98.72 < x < 99.49)$

2. A normally distributed variable, x, has a mean of 126 and a standard deviation of 3. Find:
   (i) $p(x < 128.56)$ (ii) $p(x > 125.96)$ (iii) $p(125.96 < x < 128.56)$

3. The weights of a sample of a species of small fish are normally distributed with a mean of 37grams and a standard deviation of 3.8grams. Find the percentage of fish that weigh between 34.73 and 38.93grams. Give your answer to the nearest whole number.

4. The weights of the bars of chocolate produced by a machine are normally distributed with a mean of 232grams and a standard deviation of 3.6grams. Find the proportion of the bars that could be expected to weigh less than 233.91grams.

5. For a normal variable, x, $\mu = 196$ and $\sigma = 4.2$. Find:
   (i) $p(x < 193.68)$ (ii) $p(x > 196.44)$ (iii) $p(193.68 < x < 196.44)$

6. The circumferences of a sample of drive belts produced by a machine are normally distributed with a mean of 292cm and a standard deviation of 3.3cm. Find the percentage of the belts that have diameters between 291.69cm and 293.67cm.

7. A normally distributed variable, x, has a mean of 52. $p(x < 51.15) = 0.0446$. Find the standard deviation of x.

8. The lengths of the drive rods produced by a small engineering company are normally distributed with a mean of 118cm and a standard deviation of 0.3cm. Rods that have a length of more than 118.37cm are rejected. Find the percentage of the rods that are rejected. Give your answer to the nearest whole number.

9. After their manufacture, the engines produced for a make of lawn mower are filled with oil by a machine that delivers an average of 270ml of oil with a standard deviation of 0.7ml. Assuming that the amounts of oil delivered are normally distributed, find the percentage of the engines that receive more than 271.12ml of oil. Give your answer to the nearest whole number.

10. A sample of detergent boxes have a mean contents of 234grams with a standard deviation of 4.6grams. Find the percentage of the boxes that could be expected to contain between 232.22 and 233.87grams. Give your answer to the nearest whole number.

11. A normally distributed variable, x, has a mean of 259. $p(x < 261.51) = 0.9184$. Find the standard deviation of x.

12. A normally distributed variable, x, has a standard deviation of 3.9. Also, 71.37% of the data are larger than 249.8. Find the mean of x.

13. The times taken by Maisie on her way to work are normally distributed with a mean of 26 minutes and a standard deviation of 2.3 minutes. Find the proportion of the days on which Maisie's trip takes longer than 28 minutes and 22 seconds.

14. In an experiment to determine the value of a physical constant, 100 measurements of the constant were made. The mean of these results was 138 and the standard deviation was 0.1. What is the probability that a final measurement of the constant will lie in the range 138.03 to 139.05?

15. In an experiment to determine the times that production workers take to assemble an electronic testing unit, the times had a mean of 322 minutes and a standard deviation of 2.6 minutes. Find the proportion of units that will take longer than 324 minutes to assemble. Answer to 2 significant figures.

16. A normally distributed variable, x, has a standard deviation of 2.6. $p(x < 322.68) = 0.6032$. Find the mean of x.

17. The errors in an experiment to determine the temperature at which a chemical catalyst is at its most effective, were normally distributed with a mean of 274°C and a standard deviation of 1.2°C. If the experiment is repeated once more, what is the probability that the result will be between 275°C and 276.°C?

18. The weights of ball bearings produced by an engineering process have a mean of 215gms with a standard deviation of 0.1gms. Any bearing with a weight of 215.32gms or more is rejected. The bearings are shipped in crates of 10000. Find the number of bearings that might be expected to be rejected per crate.

19. A normally distributed variable, x, has a standard deviation of 3.6. $p(85.30 < x < 89.01) = 0.3933$. Find the mean of x.

19.3 USING A GRAPHICS CALCULATOR

Below are a number of symmetry properties that are useful:
If $a \geq 0$, $b \geq 0$ and Z has a **standard normal distribution**, we have the standard results:

1.

$$p(Z < a) = \Phi(a)$$

In this case we simply look up the tables
e.g $p(Z < 2.10) = \Phi(2.01) = 0.9778$

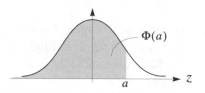

2. $\quad p(Z > a) = 1 - p(Z < a) = 1 - \Phi(a)$

e.g $p(Z > 1.54) = 1 - p(Z < 1.54)$
$\qquad = 1 - \Phi(1.54)$
$\qquad = 1 - 0.9382$
$\qquad = 0.0618$

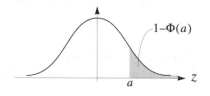

3. $\quad p(Z < -a) = p(Z > a) = 1 - \Phi(a)$

e.g $p(Z < -1.26) = p(Z > 1.26)$
$\qquad = 1 - \Phi(1.26)$
$\qquad = 1 - 0.8962$
$\qquad = 0.1038$

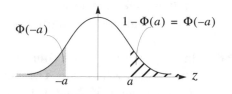

4. $\quad p(Z > -a) = p(Z < a) = \Phi(a)$

e.g $p(Z > -0.1) = p(Z < 0.1) = 0.5398$

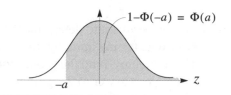

5. $\quad p(a < Z < b) = p(Z < b) - p(Z < a)$
$\qquad\qquad\qquad = \Phi(b) - \Phi(a)$

e.g $p(0.40 < Z < 1.2) = p(Z < 1.2) - p(Z < 0.4)$
$\qquad\qquad\qquad = 0.8849 - 0.6554$
$\qquad\qquad\qquad = 0.2295$

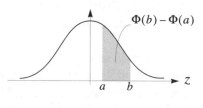

All of this is very good, if we are dealing with the standard normal distribution. However, most of the time (if not practically, all of the time) the data collected will be such that we do not have a mean of zero and a variance of 1. That is, the information gathered from a population (concerning some attribute) will be presented in such a way that the mean and the variance will not comply with those of the standard normal distribution. And so, it will be necessary to first carry out the transformation which we have already discussed, and then work out the required probabilities. That is, we will need to first standardise the statistics obtained from our data, using the Z–transformation, and then use the standard normal distribution table.

STANDARDISING ANY NORMAL DISTRIBUTION

When evaluating probabilities for a random variable X which is **normally distributed** (as opposed to X having a standard normal distribution), the following steps should be carried out:

Step 1: Find the value of z which corresponds to the value of x

That is, transform the given random variable X, which is $X \sim N(\mu, \sigma^2)$ to that of $Z \sim N(1, 0)$, using the transformation $Z = \dfrac{X - \mu}{\sigma}$.

Step 2: Sketch a diagram of the standard normal curve with the required region shaded.

Step 3: Use the standard normal distribution tables to evaluate the required region.
NB: This last step often requires the use of the symmetrical properties of the curve to be able to evaluate the required region.

EXAMPLE

If X is a normal random variable with mean $\mu = 80$ and variance $\sigma^2 = 16$, find
(a) $p(X \le 78)$ (b) $p(76 \le X \le 84)$ (c) $p(X \ge 86)$

SOLUTION

(a) $p(X \le 78) = p\left(Z \le \dfrac{78 - \mu}{\sigma}\right) = p\left(Z \le \dfrac{78 - 80}{4}\right)$ $\Phi(-0.5)$

$= p(Z \le -0.5)$
$= 1 - p(Z \le 0.5)$
$= 1 - 0.6915$
$= 0.3085$

(b) $p(76 \le X \le 84) = p\left(\dfrac{76 - 80}{4} \le Z \le \dfrac{84 - 80}{4}\right)$

$= p(-1 \le Z \le 1)$
$= 0.6826$

Notice that: $p(-1 \le Z \le 1) = \Phi(1) - \Phi(-1)$
$= \Phi(1) - (1 - \Phi(1))$
$= 2\Phi(1) - 1$
$= 2 \times 0.8413 - 1 = 0.6826$

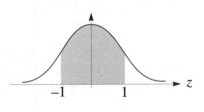

(c) $p(X \ge 86) = p\left(Z \ge \dfrac{86 - 80}{4}\right) = p(Z \ge 1.5)$

$= 1 - p(Z \le 1.5)$
$= 1 - 0.9332$
$= 0.0668$

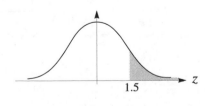

Option: Normal Distribution

We can also use the TI–83 to find these probabilities using the DISTR function:

(a) $p(Z \le -0.5)$

First, set up the window using an appropriate scale:

Next, follow through each of the displays shown:

After using the **ShadeNorm(** function, use the **ENTER** function:

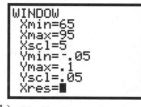

```
WINDOW
 Xmin=-3
 Xmax=3
 Xscl=1
 Ymin=-.25
 Ymax=.5
 Yscl=.25
 Xres=1
```

Using a domain of [–3,3] will be sufficient in most cases.

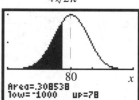

```
Area=.308538
low=-100   lup=-.5
```

Notice that we have used a lower bound of –100, so that in fact, we are finding $p(-100 \le Z \le 0.5)$. Having such a 'large' lower bound (of –100 say), provides an accurate (at least to 4 d.p) value for $p(Z \le 0.5)$. That is, $p(Z \le 0.5) = p(-100 \le Z \le -0.5) = 0.3085$. It should be noted that although we are using values obtained after carrying out the standardization process, the TI–83 also enables us to find the required probability directly:

This time the window has been set to reflect the information based on the data:

Again, we use a 'large' lower bound, the upper limit and then the parameters:

The graph shows the actual curve defined by its parameters:

$$f(x) = \frac{1}{4\sqrt{2\pi}} e^{-\frac{1}{2}\left(\frac{x-80}{4}\right)^2}$$

```
WINDOW
 Xmin=65
 Xmax=95
 Xscl=5
 Ymin=-.05
 Ymax=.1
 Yscl=.05
 Xres=■
```

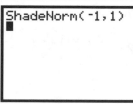

```
ShadeNorm(-1000,
78,80,4)
```

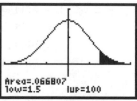

```
       80      x
Area=.308538
low=-1000   up=78
```

(b) Similarly, we have:

```
ShadeNorm(-1,1)
■
```

```
Area=.682689
low=-1   lup=1
```

(c) As before, this time we use a large upper bound:

```
ShadeNorm(1.5,10
0)
```

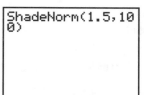

```
Area=.066807
low=1.5   lup=100
```

FINDING QUANTILES

That is, finding the value of a, where $p(X \leq a) = p$, where p is the pth percentile.

The process is very straight forward, it only requires that we read the normal distribution tables in reverse (or use the **Inverse Cumulative Normal Distribution Table**.
Therefore we have,

$$p(X \leq a) = p \Leftrightarrow p\left(Z \leq \frac{a - \mu}{\sigma}\right) = p \text{ where } 0 \leq p \leq 1.$$

$$\therefore \frac{a - \mu}{\sigma} = \Phi^{-1}(p)$$

For which we then solve for a.

To find the value of $\Phi^{-1}(p)$, we look up the Normal tables in reverse (or use a calculator).

EXAMPLE

If $X \sim N(100, 25)$ find the value of k, such that (a) $p(X \leq k) = 0.90$ (b) $p(X \leq k) = 0.20$.

SOLUTION

(a) $p(X \leq k) = 0.90 \Leftrightarrow p\left(Z \leq \dfrac{k - 100}{5}\right) = 0.90$

Therefore, $\dfrac{k - 100}{5} = 1.2816$ (from Inverse CND Table)

$$\Rightarrow k = 106.408$$

ii. $p(X \leq k) = 0.20 \Leftrightarrow p\left(Z \leq \dfrac{k - 100}{5}\right) = 0.20$

Because the probability is less than 0.5, the z–value must be negative.
This is shown below:

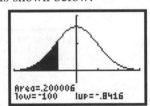

As $p(Z \leq -a) = 1 - p(Z \leq a)$ we can determine the value of a from $p(Z \leq a) = 0.8$. Giving $a = 0.8416$.

Therefore, $\dfrac{k - 100}{5} = -0.8416$

$$k = 100 + 5(-0.8416) = 95.792$$

Note: In the example above, we obtained the upper bound value of –0.8416 by using the **invNorm** function on the TI–83 (otherwise we need to look up the Inverse Normal tables):

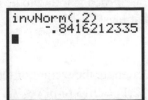

Option: Normal Distribution

EXAMPLE

The Board of Examiners have decided that 85% of all candidates sitting Mathematical Methods will obtain a pass grade in the examination. The actual Examination marks are found to be normally distributed with a mean of 55 and a variance of 16. What is the lowest score a student can get on the exam to be awarded a pass grade?

SOLUTION

Let the random variable X denote the exam score. We then have that $X \sim N(55, 16)$.
We now need to find the score x, such that $p(X \geq x) = 0.85$ (or $p(X \leq x) = 0.15$).

Now, $p(X \leq x) = 0.15 \Leftrightarrow p\left(Z \leq \dfrac{x-55}{4}\right) = 0.15$

$$\Leftrightarrow \dfrac{x-55}{4} = -1.0364$$

$$\Leftrightarrow x = 55 + 4(-1.0363)$$

$$\therefore x = 50.8544$$

```
invNorm(.15)
            -1.03643338
4*Ans+55
            50.85426648
```

Therefore a student needs to score at least 51 marks to pass the exam.

APPLICATIONS OF THE NORMAL DISTRIBUTION

EXAMPLE

The lifetime of a particular make of television tube is normally distributed with a mean of 8 years, and a standard deviation of σ years. The chances that the tube will not last 5 years is 0.05. What is the value of the standard deviation?

SOLUTION

Let X denote the life-time of the television tubes, so that $X \sim N(8, \sigma^2)$.

Given that $p(X < 5) = 0.05 \Rightarrow p\left(Z < \dfrac{5-8}{\sigma}\right) = 0.05$.

That is, we have that $p\left(Z < -\dfrac{3}{\sigma}\right) = 0.05$

```
invNorm(.05)
           -1.644853626
-3/Ans
            1.823870497
```

$$\Leftrightarrow -\dfrac{3}{\sigma} = -1.6449$$

$$\Leftrightarrow \sigma = 1.8238$$

And so, the standard deviation is approximately one year and 10 months.

EXAMPLE

The weight of a population of men is found to be normally distributed with mean 69.5 kg. If 13% of the men weigh at least 72.1 kg, find the standard deviation of their weight.

SOLUTION

Let the random variable X denote the weight of the men, so that $X \sim N(69.5, \sigma^2)$.
We then have that $p(X \geq 72.1) = 0.13$ or $p(X \leq 72.1) = 0.87$.

Therefore, $p\left(Z \le \dfrac{72.1 - 69.5}{\sigma}\right) = 0.87 \Leftrightarrow \dfrac{72.1 - 69.5}{\sigma} = 1.1264$

$$\therefore \sigma = 2.3082$$

```
(72.1-69.5)/invN
orm(.87)
         2.308256818
```

SELF ASSESSMENT TEST (30 MINUTES)

1. For the standard normal variable, z, find $p(z > -1.62)$

[2 marks]

2. The daily maximum temperature in May in a small town is normally distributed with a mean of 21°C and a standard deviation of 3.1°C. Find the percentage of May days which could be expected to have a temperature in the range 18.14°C to 19.43°C.

[3 marks]

3. A random variable X has a normal distribution with a mean 10 and variance of 2.
   (a) Find the standardised value corresponding to 8. Hence, find $p(X > 8)$.
   (b) Find the value of c such that $p(X \le 9 + c) = 0.05$.

[4 marks]

4. The time taken for students aged 11 to run 100 metres can be considered as having a normal distribution with a mean of 15.6 seconds and a standard deviation of 0.24 seconds. Find the probability that the time taken for a student to complete this race is:
   (a) under 15 seconds   (b) at least 16 seconds
   (c) between 15 and 16 seconds

[5 marks]

5. Steel rods are manufactured to be 2.15 cm in diameter, but they are accepted if they lie within the limits of 2.0085 and 2.2715. It is observed that about 5% are rejected as oversize and 5% are rejected as undersize. Assuming that the diameters are normally distributed find the standard deviation of the distribution.

[4 marks]

[3 marks]

CUMULATIVE STANDARD NORMAL DISTRIBUTION TABLE

$$F(x) = \frac{1}{\sqrt{2\pi}}\int_{-\infty}^{x} e^{\left(-\frac{1}{2}t^2\right)}dt$$

	0	0.01	0.02	0.03	0.04	0.05	0.06	0.07	0.08	0.09
0.0	0.5000	0.5040	0.5080	0.5120	0.5160	0.5199	0.5239	0.5279	0.5319	0.5359
0.1	0.5398	0.5438	0.5478	0.5517	0.5557	0.5596	0.5636	0.5675	0.5714	0.5753
0.2	0.5793	0.5832	0.5871	0.5910	0.5948	0.5987	0.6026	0.6064	0.6103	0.6141
0.3	0.6179	0.6217	0.6255	0.6293	0.6331	0.6368	0.6406	0.6443	0.6480	0.6517
0.4	0.6554	0.6591	0.6628	0.6664	0.6700	0.6736	0.6772	0.6808	0.6844	0.6879
0.5	0.6915	0.6950	0.6985	0.7019	0.7054	0.7088	0.7123	0.7157	0.7190	0.7224
0.6	0.7257	0.7291	0.7324	0.7357	0.7389	0.7422	0.7454	0.7486	0.7517	0.7549
0.7	0.7580	0.7611	0.7642	0.7673	0.7704	0.7734	0.7764	0.7794	0.7823	0.7852
0.8	0.7881	0.7910	0.7939	0.7967	0.7995	0.8023	0.8051	0.8078	0.8106	0.8133
0.9	0.8159	0.8186	0.8212	0.8238	0.8264	0.8289	0.8315	0.8340	0.8365	0.8389
1.0	0.8413	0.8438	0.8461	0.8485	0.8508	0.8531	0.8554	0.8577	0.8599	0.8621
1.1	0.8643	0.8665	0.8686	0.8708	0.8729	0.8749	0.8770	0.8790	0.8810	0.8830
1.2	0.8849	0.8869	0.8888	0.8907	0.8925	0.8944	0.8962	0.8980	0.8997	0.9015
1.3	0.9032	0.9049	0.9066	0.9082	0.9099	0.9115	0.9131	0.9147	0.9162	0.9177
1.4	0.9192	0.9207	0.9222	0.9236	0.9251	0.9265	0.9279	0.9292	0.9306	0.9319
1.5	0.9332	0.9345	0.9357	0.9370	0.9382	0.9394	0.9406	0.9418	0.9429	0.9441
1.6	0.9452	0.9463	0.9474	0.9484	0.9495	0.9505	0.9515	0.9525	0.9535	0.9545
1.7	0.9554	0.9564	0.9573	0.9582	0.9591	0.9599	0.9608	0.9616	0.9625	0.9633
1.8	0.9641	0.9649	0.9656	0.9664	0.9671	0.9678	0.9686	0.9693	0.9699	0.9706
1.9	0.9713	0.9719	0.9726	0.9732	0.9738	0.9744	0.9750	0.9756	0.9761	0.9767
2.0	0.9772	0.9778	0.9783	0.9788	0.9793	0.9798	0.9803	0.9808	0.9812	0.9817
2.1	0.9821	0.9826	0.9830	0.9834	0.9838	0.9842	0.9846	0.9850	0.9854	0.9857
2.2	0.9861	0.9864	0.9868	0.9871	0.9875	0.9878	0.9881	0.9884	0.9887	0.9890
2.3	0.9893	0.9896	0.9898	0.9901	0.9904	0.9906	0.9909	0.9911	0.9913	0.9916
2.4	0.9918	0.9920	0.9922	0.9925	0.9927	0.9929	0.9931	0.9932	0.9934	0.9936
2.5	0.9938	0.9940	0.9941	0.9943	0.9945	0.9946	0.9948	0.9949	0.9951	0.9952
2.6	0.9953	0.9955	0.9956	0.9957	0.9959	0.9960	0.9961	0.9962	0.9963	0.9964
2.7	0.9965	0.9966	0.9967	0.9968	0.9969	0.9970	0.9971	0.9972	0.9973	0.9974
2.8	0.9974	0.9975	0.9976	0.9977	0.9977	0.9978	0.9979	0.9979	0.9980	0.9981
2.9	0.9981	0.9982	0.9982	0.9983	0.9984	0.9984	0.9985	0.9985	0.9986	0.9986
3.0	0.9987	0.9987	0.9987	0.9988	0.9988	0.9989	0.9989	0.9989	0.9990	0.9990
3.1	0.9990	0.9991	0.9991	0.9991	0.9992	0.9992	0.9992	0.9992	0.9993	0.9993
3.2	0.9993	0.9993	0.9994	0.9994	0.9994	0.9994	0.9994	0.9995	0.9995	0.9995
3.3	0.9995	0.9995	0.9995	0.9996	0.9996	0.9996	0.9996	0.9996	0.9996	0.9997
3.4	0.9997	0.9997	0.9997	0.9997	0.9997	0.9997	0.9997	0.9997	0.9997	0.9998
3.5	0.9998	0.9998	0.9998	0.9998	0.9998	0.9998	0.9998	0.9998	0.9998	0.9998
3.6	0.9998	0.9998	0.9999	0.9999	0.9999	0.9999	0.9999	0.9999	0.9999	0.9999
3.7	0.9999	0.9999	0.9999	0.9999	0.9999	0.9999	0.9999	0.9999	0.9999	0.9999
3.8	0.9999	0.9999	0.9999	0.9999	0.9999	0.9999	0.9999	0.9999	0.9999	0.9999
3.9	1.0000	1.0000	1.0000	1.0000	1.0000	1.0000	1.0000	1.0000	1.0000	1.0000

FURTHER STATISTICS AND PROBABILITY 2

BIVARIATE ANALYSIS

OPTION

2 0

20.1 CORRELATION

This chapter deals with the study of **bivariate data**. In particular we will be looking at the use of **scatter diagrams** as an initial visual aid in describing any relationship that might exist between the two variables. Next we look at measuring the strength of such a relationship (if one exists) and finally we consider the issue of **regression analysis** using the method of **least squares**. This method will help us obtain an equation that will be enable us to predict (or explain) the value of one variable (the dependent variable) based on the value of a second observation (the independent variable). In particular, we will only be considering **linear relationships**, and hence, when using the method of least squares, we will obtain the least squares regression line, $y = a + bx$.

SCATTER DIAGRAM

A scatter diagram is simply a method by which we can obtain a very quick **visual appreciation** of how two variables are related. Such diagrams are obtained by plotting a set of points that correspond to the bivariate data. Usually the independent variable runs along the horizontal axis, whilst the dependent variable runs along the vertical axis. Once the data has been plotted we are interested in giving some indication about the **correlation** between the two variables. Qualitative descriptors that are useful include: **direction**, **form** and **strength of relationship**.

Direction: If the dependent variable tends to **increase** as the independent variable increases, we say that there is a **positive association** (or relationship) between the variables.

If the dependent variable tends to **decrease** as the independent variable increases, we say that there is a **negative association** (or relationship) between the variables.

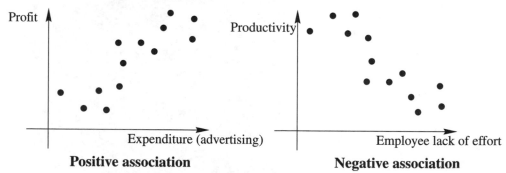

Positive association   **Negative association**

Form: The form depends on the general shape of the scatter plot. The examples below indicate the type of forms that can be observed.
However, we will only consider **linear forms** in this course.

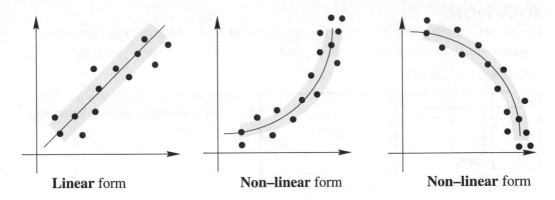

Linear form   **Non–linear** form   **Non–linear** form

Strength of relationship:

The strength of a linear relationship gives an indication of **how closely** the points in the scatter diagram **fit a straight line**. The measure of the **strength of a linear relationship** is determined by the **correlation coefficient, *r*.**

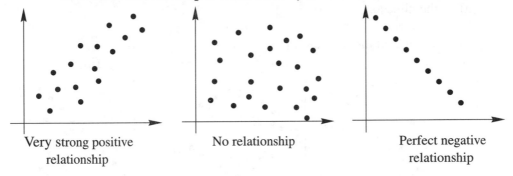

Very strong positive   No relationship   Perfect negative
relationship   relationship

Using the TI–83 to construct a scatter plot

One of the great features of a graphics calculator is its ability to provide a visual display of bivariate data. First we need to make sure that the calculator has been set up correctly.

Press 2nd   Y = (i.e., **STAT PLOT**) and then press ENTER , ENTER and then press 2nd   MODE (to **QUIT**)

We now look at a specific example:

EXAMPLE

Determine if the data has a linear relationship, stating the direction and strength.

x	2	4	5	7	9	10	11	15
y	3	4	6	6	7	9	10	11

SOLUTION

Having set our calculator in the appropriate statistical mode, we now draw the scatter diagram: Enter data as two lists, $x \leftrightarrow L_1$ and $y \leftrightarrow L_2$, set the window [0,16] by [–1,12] and then press GRAPH :

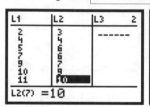 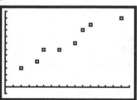

Clearly there is a linear relationship. It is a very strong positive relationship

EXERCISE 20.1

1. For each of the following, give a statment about
 (a)   the direction
 (b)   the form
 (c)   strength of the relationship

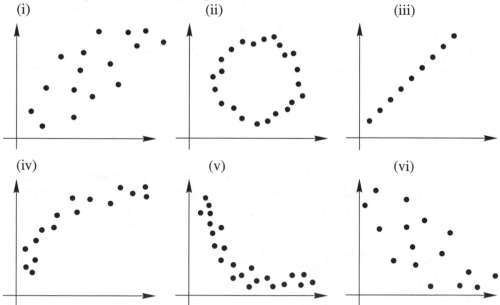

(i) (ii) (iii)

(iv) (v) (vi)

2. A group of students had their Science and Maths results tabulated:

Student	1	2	3	4	5	6	7	8	9	10
Science	55	70	40	67	80	80	55	60	20	84
Maths	60	78	39	65	82	90	50	71	18	79

 (a)   Plot this data on a scatter diagram.
 (b)   Describe the direction, form and strength of the relationship between Science marks and Maths marks.

3. The data in the table below shows students' reading–test scores and their corresponding I.Q scores

Student	1	2	3	4	5	6	7	8	9	10
Reading score	50	73	74	62	70	57	60	62	70	65
I.Q scores	99	118	131	111	113	101	106	113	121	118

(a) Plot this data on a scatter diagram.
(b) Describe the direction, form and strength of the relationship between reading scores and IQ scores.

20.2 CORRELATION COEFFICIENT

STRENGTH OF A LINEAR RELATIONSHIP

The **strength of a linear relationship** is an indication of how closely the points in the scatter diagram fit a straight line. A measure of the strength of a **linear relationship** is given by the **Pearson correlation coefficient** (or simply the **correlation coefficient**) and is denoted by *r*.

The properties of *r* can be summarised as follows:

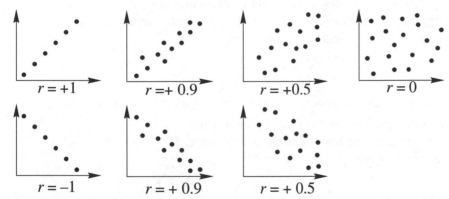

Overall, we have that if

1. $1 < |r| \le 0.75$, there is a **strong linear relationship** (positive or negative)

2. $0.75 < |r| \le 0.5$, there is a **moderate linear relationship** (positive or negative)

3. $0.5 < |r| \le 0.25$, there is a **weak linear relationship** (positive or negative)

At this stage it is important to mention the relationship between the variables and the issue of **causality**. For example, the degree of fatigue you experience during summer may be influenced by the temperature of the day (i.e., your fatigue depends on the temperature level), however, if you happen to reach a certain level of fatigue on some other day, this will not in turn indicate the temperature level of the day! That is, the temperature is independent of your fatigue level, and so, a rise in your fatigue level will not cause the temperature to rise. In particular, for studies in psychology and education the presence of a correlation between two variables can rarely be interpreted as implying a direct causal relation. However, if we have established that a linear relationship exists, if, however, a direct causal relation does exists between the two variables, then these two variables will be correlated. The presence of what may appear to be a cause, could be due to a third 'hidden' variable.

CALCULATING AND INTERPRETING THE PEARSON'S CORRELATION COEFFICIENT

The ratio of the explained variation to the total variation is called the **coefficient of determination** and is denoted by $r^2 = \dfrac{\text{Explained variation}}{\text{Total variation}}$. Notice then, that $|r| \leq 1$.

The **coefficient of correlation**, r, is then simply equal to $\pm \sqrt{\dfrac{\text{Explained variation}}{\text{Total variation}}}$.

This definition can be used to to determine the correlation coefficient for non–linear relationships as well as linear relationships.

However, we will only be dealing with linear relationships and so we can use more specific definitions that can be applied to linear relationships.

As we've already mentioned, **Pearson's correlation coefficient** gives a numerical measure of the degree to which the points in the scatter diagram behave linearly. To compute this value, we can make use the formula

$$r = \frac{1}{n-1} \sum \left(\frac{x - \bar{x}}{s_x} \right) \left(\frac{y - \bar{y}}{s_y} \right)$$

where $\bar{x}$ and $\bar{y}$ represent the mean of the x and y scores respectively and s_x and s_y represent the standard deviation of the x and y scores respectively.
However, other formulae for finding the value of r do exist.
Some common expression are:

$$r = \frac{\sum (x - \bar{x})(y - \bar{y})}{\sqrt{\sum (x - \bar{x})^2 \sum (y - \bar{y})^2}} \quad \text{and} \quad r = \frac{\sum xy - \dfrac{\sum x \sum y}{n}}{\sqrt{\left(\sum x^2 - \dfrac{(\sum x)^2}{n} \right) \left(\sum y^2 - \dfrac{(\sum y)^2}{n} \right)}}$$

The last expression is probably the most useful form for use in calculations. However, most calculators that have the facility to deal with bivariate data will be able to produce a value of r with the push of a few buttons. In particular, the TI–83 is excellent for this.

There also exists other forms of the correlation coefficient which are easily derived and easy to use, one example is $r = \dfrac{s_{xy}}{s_x s_y}$ where $s_{xy} = \dfrac{1}{n} \left(\sum xy - n\bar{x}\bar{y} \right)$.

The terms s_x and s_y can quickly be recognised as the standard deviations of the random variables X and Y, whilst the new quantity, s_{xy}, is called the **covariance of X and Y**.

Before we look a little closer at how to interpret the value of r we proceed with an example on how to calculate the value of r.

EXAMPLE

Assuming that the data has a linear relationship, find the coefficient of correlation for this set of data.

x	2	4	5	7	9	10	11	15
y	3	4	6	6	7	9	10	11

SOLUTION

As we are going to use the formula $r = \dfrac{\sum xy - \dfrac{\sum x \sum y}{n}}{\sqrt{\left(\sum x^2 - \dfrac{(\sum x)^2}{n}\right)\left(\sum y^2 - \dfrac{(\sum y)^2}{n}\right)}}$,

we need:

$$\sum x = 63, \quad \sum y = 56$$

$$\sum xy = 2 \times 3 + 4 \times 4 + 5 \times 6 + \ldots + 15 \times 11 = 522.$$

$$\sum x^2 = 2^2 + 4 + \ldots + 15^2 = 621, \quad \sum y^2 = 3^2 + 4 + \ldots + 11^2 = 448$$

So that $r = \dfrac{522 - \dfrac{63 \times 56}{10}}{\sqrt{\left(621 - \dfrac{(63)^2}{10}\right)\left(448 - \dfrac{(56)^2}{10}\right)}} = 0.9749$.

We now make use of the TI–83:

1. Enter data as two lists, $x \leftrightarrow L_1$ and $y \leftrightarrow L_2$.
2. Check to see if in fact there is a linear relationship.
3. Press, $\boxed{\text{STAT}}$ then **CALC** and then choose **2:2–Var Stats** and enter L_1, L_2.

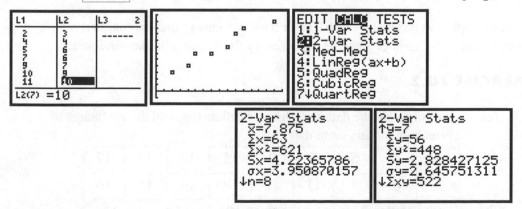

From these results we can now determine the correlation coefficient.

However, we can also obtain the correlation coefficient without the above. First make sure that the TI–83 has **DiagnosticOn**.

That is, Starting from the HOME screen, press $\boxed{\text{2nd}}$ $\boxed{\text{MODE}}$.

Next, press $\boxed{\text{2nd}}$ $\boxed{0}$ (this enables you to access the **CATALOGUE** menu)
Locate the **DiagnosticOn** option (using the down arrow)
Then press $\boxed{\text{ENTER}}$ $\boxed{\text{ENTER}}$.

We can now find the correlation coefficient:

Press $\boxed{\text{STAT}}$ choose the **CALC** option and then select **8:LinReg(a + bx)** and then

enter $\boxed{L_1, L_2}$. Notice that we obtain the values of r, r^2 and the equation of a straight line. This straight line is in fact the line of best fit using the method of least squares (which we shall look at in the next section).

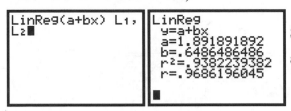

We see that $r = 0.9686 \approx 0.97$.
So, what exactly does r tell us and what
about r^2?

INTERPRETING r AND r^2

Recall that by definition $r^2 = \dfrac{\text{Explained variation}}{\text{Total variation}}$ so that in fact, r^2 is a proportion

whereas r is the square root of a proportion. As such, a coefficient of 0.8 does not represent a degree of relationship that is twice as great as a coefficient of 0.4. Also the difference between coefficients of 0.6 and 0.7 is not equal to the difference between 0.7 and 0.8. In general, when interpreting the magnitude of the relation between two variables, regardless of directionality, r^2, the coefficient of determination, is more informative. So that for two linearly related variables, this values provides the proportion of variation in one variable that can be explained by the variation in the other variable.

In our example, we had that $r^2 = 0.938$ or 93.8%, meaning that approximately 94% of the variation in the variable y can be explained by the variation in the variable x.

EXERCISE 20.2

1. (a) Assuming that the data has a linear relationship, find the coefficient of correlation for this set of data.

x	4	6	7	9	11	12	13	17
y	8	9	11	11	12	14	15	16

(b) Draw a scatter diagram for the given data.

2. (a) Draw a scatter diagram for the given data.

x	1	5	6	6	2	3	4	4
y	2	4	5	3	1	2	5	4

(b) Find the coefficient of correlation for this set of data. What assumption have you made in determining this value.

3. For the set of paired data, find the correlation between x and y. Is this an appropriate use of the correlation cefficient?

x	1	2	3	4	5	6	7
y	4	3	2	1	2	3	4

4. Would it be appropriate to calculate the coefficient of correlation for the data shown below?

x	1	2	3	4	5	6
y	3	2	1	1	2	3

5. Calculate the proportion of the variance of Y which
(a) can be predicted from (or explained by) the variance of X if
i. $r = 0.8$. ii. $r = -0.9$
(b) cannot be predicted from (or explained by) the variance of X if
i. $r = 0.7$. ii. $r = -0.6$.

6. The data shown below represents entrance examination marks (x) and first year average test marks (y) for a group of 10 students.

x	55	59	62	80	92	63	69	84	62	55
y	61	69	52	61	90	85	70	67	72	60

(a) Draw a scatter diagram for the data
(b) Determine the correlation coefficient between x and y.

7. How many times is a difference in predictive capacity between correlations of 0.70 and 0.80 greater than between correlations of 0.20 and 0.30?

8. What correlation between X and Y is required in order to assert that 85% of the variance of X depends on the variance of Y.

9. For the data shown below, calculate the proportion of the variance of y which can be explained by the variance of x

x	3	4	6	7	9	12
y	20	14	12	10	9	7

20.3 LINEAR REGRESSION

Having established that a linear relation exists between two variables x and y (say), we can then search for a line of best fit. That is, a line that will best represent the data on the scatter diagram. This process is known as **simple linear regression**. The question then is, of all the possible straight lines that would appear to reasonably model the data, which one would be the best one?

There are a number of different ways this can be acheived, however, we will consider the method known as '**the method of least squares**'. The least squares regression line is the line which makes the sum of the squares of the vertical deviations of the data from the line as small as possible:

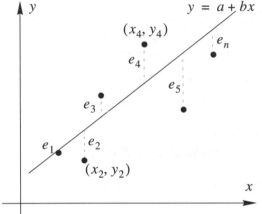

That is, having drawn the scatter diagram, we want to determine the equation $y = a + bx$ for which the sum of the square of the errors between observed values and the predicted values (based on the straight line) is minimal. i.e., we want to minimise the expression

$$\Delta = \sum_{i=1}^{n} e_i^2 = \sum_{i=1}^{n} (y_i - a - bx_i)^2.$$

Although the mathematics is beyond the scope of this course, we can obtain a rather neat expression that will enable us to determine the value of a and b that give the line of best fit. We quote this result now.

The line of best fit using the method of least squares on n pairs (x_i, y_i) is called the **line of regression of y on x** and is given by $y = a + bx$, where a and b are determined by

$$a = \bar{y} - b\bar{x} \qquad \text{and} \qquad b = \frac{\sum xy - \frac{1}{n}(\sum x)(\sum y)}{\sum x^2 - \frac{1}{n}(\sum x)^2}$$

Again, it can be seen from these formulae that manual calculations are very tedious, so, it is highly recommended that graphics calculators are used (or any calculator that handles bivariate data).

Once we obtain the line of regression of y on x it is important that we can not only use it to predict values but also that we can interpret the intercept and the slope of the line in terms of the problem being discussed. When dealing with regression lines, predictions take on the form of **interpolation** and **extrapolation**. Interpolation is the process of using a regression line to make **predictions within the range of data** that was used to derive the equation. Whereas extrapolation is the process of using a regression line to make **predictions outside the range of data** that was used to derive the equation.

We consider one more time the example we have already looked at

EXAMPLE

Assuming that the data has a linear relationship, find the regression line of y on x..

x	2	4	5	7	9	10	11	15
y	3	4	6	6	7	9	10	11

SOLUTION

Using the graphics calculator, we have

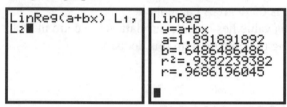

That is, the regression line is given by
$$y = 1.89 + 0.65x.$$

From this equation we can then make predictions about other data points that are not in the table.

We leave it to the student to verify this result by finding the value of a and b 'by hand'.

EXAMPLE

The data shown represents observations made on the rate of cricket sounds by the number y chirps per 15 seconds at different temperatures x in degrees Fahrenheit.

x	62	61	60	59	58	55	53	52	50
y	24	21	19	18	19	15	15	12	11

(a) Plot these points on a scatter diagram.
(b) Determine the line of regression of y on x and draw it on your scatter diagram.
(c) Estimate the cricket's rate when the temperature is 65 degrees fahrenheit.

SOLUTION

(a) We first enter the data into the TI–83 and then proceed to answer the questions..

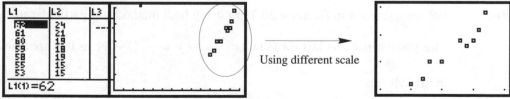

Quite clearly there is a strong positive relationship

(b) The regression equation is given by $y = -36.62 + 0.95x$ (see screen dump over the page)

413

Option: Bivariate Analysis

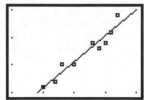

The line of regression of y on x:

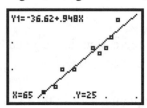

(c)   Again, using the TI–83, we have

To do this we used the **CALC** function (above **TRACE**).
So we estimate that the crickets rate will be 25 when the temperatue is 65 degrees Fahrenheit.
Because this value lies outside our data set, we are in fact extrapolating to come up with this decision.

ANOTHER FORM OF THE REGRESSION LINE

The regression equation can also be obtained by using the expression

$$(y - \bar{y}) = \frac{s_{xy}}{s_x^2}(x - \bar{x}) \qquad \text{where} \qquad \frac{s_{xy}}{s_x^2} = r \times \frac{s_y}{s_x}$$

For example, from our previous example we have that $r = 0.9686$ (using the TI–83 output), $s_x = 3.9508$, $s_y = 2.8284$, $\bar{x} = 7.875$ and $\bar{y} = 7$. Substituting these values into the equation we have that $(y - 7) = \dfrac{0.9686 \times 2.8284}{3.9508}(x - 7.875)$

So that, $(y - 7) = 0.6486(x - 7.875) \Rightarrow y = 0.6486x + 1.8922$.
Giving us the same result (as expected).

Note: For the questions in Exercise 20.3, try using both methods, in particular make

sure you can use this last formula, i.e., $(y - \bar{y}) = \dfrac{s_{xy}}{s_x^2}(x - \bar{x})$ as it is specified

in the syllabus.

EXERCISE 20.3

1. For the sets of data shown below,
 (a) draw a scatter diagram.
 (b) determine the least squares regression line.
 (c) draw the regression line on the scatter diagram.
 (i)

x	3	4	6	7	9	12
y	20	14	12	10	9	7

 (ii)

x	2	1	4	5	3
y	4	2	6	5	3

 (iii)

x	11	5	4	5	2	3
y	52	31	30	34	20	25

 (iv)

x	1	2	3	4	5
y	2	1	3	5	4

2. The following table shows the income (in thousands of dollars) and the annual expenditure, in hundreds of dollars for ten single working people aged 20 – 24 yrs.

Income	22	14	16	18	20	19	16	18	19	18
Expenditure	75	59	67	69	75	73	62	64	70	71

(a) Plot the data on a scatter diagram.
(b) Find the correlation coefficient.
(c) Calculate the proportion of the variance of *Expenditure* which can be explained by the variance of the *Income*.
(d) Find the least squares equation of the regression line.
(e) On the scatter diagram from (a), sketch the regression line.
(f) Estimate the expenditure by a single working person aged 20–24 yrs if their annual income is $17 000.

3. The result of the first two tests given to a group of mathematics students is shown in the table below:

Test 1(x)	60	50	80	80	70	60	100	40	90	70
Test 2 (y)	80	70	70	100	50	80	100	60	80	60

(a) Draw a scatter diagram for this data.
(b) Find the coefficient of correlation.
(c) Find the least squares regression line of (i) y on x (ii) x on y.

4. A cafe owner wishes to improve on the efficiency of his cafe. One aspect that needs to be looked into is that of the rate at which customers are being served by the staff. The table below shows the number of weeks that eight employees have been working at the cafe and the average number of cutomers that each served **per hour**.

Weeks at cafe	8	5	15	3	10	2	13	6
Customers served	18.4	12.2	32.3	10	21.0	8.2	28.1	16.5

(a) Draw a scatter diagram for the given set of data.

Define the variable C to represent the average number of customer an employee served per hour and the variable w to represent the number of weeks that employee has been working at the cafe.

(b) The owner decides to use a straight line to model the the data. Is the owner justified? Give a reason for your answer.

(c) i. Calculate the correlation coefficient for the given data set.
    ii. Use the method of least squares to determine the line of best fit.
    iii. Graph the regression line on the scatter diagram in part a.

(d) Estimate how many customers an employee should be able to serve in one hour if they have been working at the cafe for
    i. 9 weeks.
    ii. 50 weeks.
    iii. What constaints can you see this model having?

5. The table below shows the results of measurements taken for systolic blood pressures (y) of 8 women and their respective ages (x).

Age (x)	60	42	68	72	42	36	55	49
Blood pressure (y)	155	140	152	160	125	118	155	145

(a) Draw a scatter diagram for the given set of data.

(b) Calculate the correlation coefficient for the given data set. Is this an appropriate statistic to calculate for this data set?

(c) i. Use the method of least squares to determine the line of best fit.
    ii. Graph the regression line on the scatter diagram in part a.

(d) Based on your line of best fit, determine the level of systolic blood pressure for a women aged
    i. 45.
    ii. 85.
    iii. What is the difference in using the line of best fit when answering i., and ii.?

(e) A women is found to have a blood pressure level of 135, how old would she be (based on your line of best fit) ?

6. The yield, y kilograms, of a vegetable, obtained by using x kilograms of a new fertiliser produced the following results:

x	1.4	3.3	5.9	8.8	7.3	5.1
y	5.0	7.5	7.7	10	9	8.3

(a)   Draw a scatter diagram for the given set of data.
(b)   Calculate the correlation coefficient for the given data set. Is this an appropriate statistic to calculate for this data set?
(c)   i.   Use the method of least squares to determine the line of best fit.
        ii.   Graph the regression line on the scatter diagram in part a.
(d)   Based on your line of best fit, determine the yield if
        i.   6.5 kg of fertiliser were to be used.
        ii.   10 kg of fertiliser were to be used.
(e)   A yield of 6 kg of this vegetable was produced. How much fertiliser would have been used?

7.   The expected yield, y kilogram per unit area of a crop is related to the amount of fertiliser x kilogram per unit area. The data below give observed yields for various values of x:

x	2	12	3	16	5	6	20	8	13	10
y	20	50	20	57	29	38	67	44	59	39

(a)   Draw a scatter diagram for the given set of data.
(b)   Calculate the correlation coefficient for the given data set. Is this an appropriate statistic to calculate for this data set?
(c)   i.   Use the method of least squares to determine the line of best fit.
        ii.   Graph the regression line on the scatter diagram in part a.
(d)   Based on your line of best fit, determine the yield if
        i.   4 kg of fertiliser were to be used.
        ii.   15 kg of fertiliser were to be used.
(e)   A yield of 70 kg of this vegetable was produced. How much fertiliser would have been used?

8.   A firm which produces fungicides notices that the sales in its region appear to depend on rainfall during the previous month. The following data was collected from six months (that are non–consecutive). Unfortunately, some of the data has been smudged and cannot be read.

Rainfall x mm	11		25	27	48	
Demand y (1000kg)		38	28		51	81

However, the following results were calculated just prior to the data smudging.

$$\sum x = 180, \sum y = 270, \sum(x-\bar{x})^2 = 1240, \sum(y-\bar{y})^2 = 2554, \sum xy = 9592$$

(a)   Find the correlation coefficient for the given data set.
(b)   Calculate the proportion of the variance of y which can be explained by the variance of x.

417

(b)   Find the least square linear regression line, $y = a + bx$.

(c)   Based on your regression line, predict the values that should be placed where the smudges occured.

9.   The relationship between the temperature, $T\,°C$ of water and the mass, M kg of a chemical substance dissolving in the water has been tabulated:

$T\,°C$	10	20	30	40	50	60	70	80	90
M kg	50	53	56	61	66	69	70	71	72

(a)   Draw a scatter diagram for the given data set.

(b)   Find   (i)   the coefficient of correlation.

(ii)   the covariance.

(c)   Find the least squares regression line which best fits the data by evaluating the constants a and b in the equation $T = a + bM$.

10.   The data set shown below, has a least squares regression line $y = a + bx$. Adding a constant, m to each x_i and a constant n, to each y_i in the data set shown, how will

x	x_1	x_2	x_3	x_4	x_5
y	y_1	y_2	y_3	y_4	y_5

this effect   (a)   the coefficient of correlation?

(b)   the least squares regression line $y = a + bx$?

SELF ASSESSMENT TEST (45 MINUTES)

1. Describe the type of relationship that exists between the variables X and Y,
including   i.   the direction
            ii.   the form
            iii.   strength of relationship

x	1	9	7.5	10	2.5	5.0	11	5.5	14	6
y	10	47	45	60	20	35	65	23	68	35

[4 marks]

2. The following summary was based on 7 ordered pairs of data (x, y):

$$\sum x = 144, \sum y = 223, \sum xy = 4960, s_x = 6.08, s_y = 10.59, s_{xy} = 62.10.$$

(a) What is the mean of x and y?
(b) Determine the product–moment correlation coefficient.
(c) Find the least squares regression line of y on x.

[5 marks]

3. The results of a set of 10 paired data (x, y) is summarised as follows:

$$\sum x = 224.4, \sum x^2 = 5099.12, \sum y = 254.3, \sum y^2 = 6706.91, \sum xy = 5595.30$$

(a) Determine the equation of the least squares regression line, $y = a + bx$.
(b) Predict the value of x when $y = 25$.
(b) Determine the covariance, $\text{Cov}(X, Y)$.

[5 marks]

4. The yield, y kilograms, of potato, obtained by using x kilograms of no–name brand fertiliser produced the following results:

x	10	49	54	14	69	77	60
y	500	710	770	500	780	830	740

(a) Draw a scatter diagram for the given set of data.
(b) Calculate the correlation coefficient for the given data set. Is this an appropriate statistic to calculate for this data set?
(c) Calculate the proportion of the variance of y which can be explained by the variance of x.
(d)   i.   Use the method of least squares to determine the line of best fit.
      ii.   Graph the regression line on the scatter diagram in part a.
(e) Based on your line of best fit, determine the yield if 50 kg of fertiliser were used.
(f) A yield of 600 kg of this potatoes were produced. How much fertiliser would have been used?

[10 marks]

Option: Bivariate Analysis

FURTHER STATISTICS AND PROBABILITY 3

CONTINGENCY TABLES & GOODNESS OF FIT

OPTION

2 1

21.1 CONTINGENCY TABLES

In this chapter we will consider the problem of testing for the independence of two factors from the same sample. The testing will not involve any distribution parameters (for example, if we where considering a normal distribution, we might want to see if our sample was selected from a normal population with mean μ – where μ is known as a parameter). Rather we will look at the difference between **observed values** and **expected values** (under some underlying (Null) hypothesis, denoted by H_0) without assuming an underlying distribution. If we reject the null hypothesis H_0, then we accept the alternative hypothesis, denoted by H_1. In particular we will be looking at contingency tables as well as the use of the Chi–square distribution to construct a test that will enable us to determine the independence (or otherwise) of two factors.

The basis for such a statistic, i.e., one that involves a comparison between observed values and expected values, is that if the observed values are in fact very different to their expected values then it would seem reasonable that there was some influencing factor involved to create such a discrepancy.

Consider the situation where we want to decide if hair colour is dependent on eye colour. A sample of 200 randomly selected people had their eye and hair colour noted, the results are shown in the frequency table below:

	Dark hair	Fair Hair	
Brown eyes	54	32	86
Blue eyes	42	72	114
	96	104	200

Tables such as these, in which the number of observations are entered according to two different factors (or classifications) is called a **contingency table**. The question that we wish to answer is "Is the colour of a person's eyes and the colour of a person's hair statistically independent?" The general idea is that if these two factors are independent then we would **expect** the results shown in the following table

	Dark hair	Fair Hair	
Brown eyes	41.28	44.72	86
Blue eyes	54.76	59.28	114
	96	104	200

So, how did we arrive at these figures? Also, why these figures?
We consider the following observed and expected tables:

Observed frequencies

	B1	B2	
A1	a	b	$a+b$
A2	c	d	$c+d$
	$a+c$	$b+d$	N

Expected frequencies

	B1	B2	
A1	$\frac{(a+b)(a+c)}{N}$		
A2			
			N

If the B's and A's are independent, then $p(A1 \cap B1) = p(A1) \times p(B1) = \dfrac{a+b}{N} \times \dfrac{a+c}{N}$

Therefore, under the assumption that the factors are independent, the expected observation

in cell $A1 \cap B1$ is given by $\left(\dfrac{a+b}{N} \times \dfrac{a+c}{N}\right) \times N = \dfrac{(a+b)(a+c)}{N}$. The same can then be

done for the other cells. So, looking back at our example, we have:

	Dark hair	Fair Hair	
Brown eyes	$\frac{86 \times 96}{200} = 41.28$	$\frac{86 \times 104}{200} = 44.72$	86
Blue eyes	$\frac{96 \times 114}{200} = 54.76$	$\frac{114 \times 104}{200} = 59.28$	114
	96	104	200

It turns out that the statistic $U = \sum \dfrac{(Obs - Exp)^2}{Exp}$, where **Obs** stands for the **observed**

value and **Exp** stands for the **expected value**, can be approximated by a distribution
known as the **chi squared distribution**, which depends only on the number of degrees of

freedom, υ and is denoted by χ^2. The notation $\chi^2(\upsilon)$ is used to indicate the number of
degrees of freedom explicitly. For contingency tables made up of $r \times c$ cells, the number
of degrees of freedom is given by $\upsilon = (r-1) \times (c-1)$. So that in our situation, we have
that $r = 2$ and $c = 2$, therefore, $\upsilon = (2-1) \times (2-1) = 1$.

That is, we have that the χ^2–test of independence in an $r \times c$ contingency table is based

on the result that $\qquad U = \sum \dfrac{(Obs - Exp)^2}{Exp} \sim \chi^2(\upsilon)$, where $\upsilon = (r-1) \times (c-1)$.

In our example we have $U = \dfrac{(54 - 41.28)^2}{41.28} + \dfrac{(32 - 44.72)^2}{44.72} + \dfrac{(42 - 54.76)^2}{54.76} + \dfrac{(72 - 59.28)^2}{59.28} = 13.24$.

There now remains the question, what does this value tell us?

As we have already mentioned, if H_0 is true (i.e., factors are independent), then U is inclined to be small, since the observed values should be near the observed values. On the other hand, if H_0 is not true, then U is inclined to be large since the observed values are unlikely to be near the expected values, so that each term $(Obs - Exp)^2$ is large. Therefore, 'extreme' values of U are large values of U, and hence we

$$\text{reject } H_0 \text{ if } U > c_{0.95}\chi^2(\upsilon)$$

using a 5% level of significance.

A list of $c_{0.95}\chi^2(\upsilon)$ values for different values of υ is provided:

υ	1	2	3	4	5	6	7
$c_{0.95}\chi^2(\upsilon)$	3.841	5.991	7.815	9.488	11.07	12.59	14.07

These are the critical values that determine if we reject H_0 at the 5% level of significance. So that if we observe a value of U greater than 9.488 (say) when dealing with 4 degrees of freedom we would reject H_0. For our example, as $U = 13.24 > c_{0.95}\chi^2(1)(= 3.841)$ then we would clearly reject H_0 at the 5% level of significance.

This problem can also be solve using the TI–83:
First we need to set up the observed contingency table using matrices:
Press **MATRX** go to **EDIT** and enter the observed values in the matrix cells. The TI–83 will automatically calculate the expected values in matrix B. Then, press **STAT**, go to **TESTS**, press **ENTER** and then use either the **Calculate** or **Draw** option.

Note that the 'p–value' is very small, 0.000276. If we do not have the critical values that will determine if we reject H_0, we can use the p–value. That is, if $p < 0.05$, then reject H_0.

EXAMPLE

It is decided to test the hypothesis that there is no relationship between smoking and gender. A sample of 30 males and 40 females has been randomly selected from a population. The results are: Male   7 Smokers (S), 23 Non–smokers(N)
                                    Female   13 Smokers (S), 27 Non–smokers(N).
Is there a significant relationship between smoking and gender?

SOLUTION

The first thing to do is set up a 2×2 contingency table.
We use M to denote Male, F for Female and S and N as described in question.

<table>
<tr><td colspan="4" align="center">**Observed** frequencies</td></tr>
</table>

	S	N	
M	7	23	30
F	13	27	40
	20	50	70

	S	N	
M	8.57	21.43	30
F	11.43	28.57	40
	20	50	70

Expected frequencies

Using the test statistic U with $\upsilon = (2-1) \times (2-1) = 1$ degree of freedom, we have

(working it out manually $U = \dfrac{(7-8.57)^2}{8.57} + \dfrac{(23-21.43)^2}{21.43} + \dfrac{(13-11.43)^2}{11.43} + \dfrac{(27-28.57)^2}{28.57} = 0.705$.

We now make use of the TI–83

We can now check the expected values:

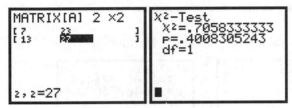

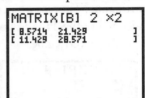

Based on the p–value, we accept H_0. Also, $U = 0.7058 < c_{0.95}\chi^2(1)(=3.841)$, meaning that the value of U is still in the acceptance region and so we accept H_0.

EXAMPLE

A serum is administered to one of two groups of adults who all have a disease. In group A (the group who were given the serum), 76 recover from the disease and in group B (known as the control group) 64 of them recover from the disease. There are 100 people in each group. Does this serum help to cure the disease?

SOLUTION

We set up our test as follows:

Hypothesis: H_0 : Serum has no effect versus H_1 : Serum has an effect

That is, recovery is independent of the use of the serum.

Test statistic: $U = \sum \dfrac{(Obs - Exp)^2}{Exp} \sim \chi^2(1)$

Level: Use 5% level of significance.

Therefore reject H_0 if $U > c_{0.95}\chi^2(1) = 3.841$.

We set up the observed and expected tables:

Observed frequencies

	R	$\bar{R}$	
A	76	24	100
B	64	36	100
	140	60	200

Expected frequencies

	R	$\bar{R}$	
A	70	30	100
B	70	30	100
	140	60	200

Therefore, our test statistic has a value

$$U = \frac{(76-70)^2}{70} + \frac{(24-30)^2}{30} + \frac{(64-70)^2}{70} + \frac{(36-30)^2}{30} = 3.4287$$

Therefore, as our value of U is less than 3.841 we accept H_0 at the 5% level of significance. That is, we accept the hypothesis that the serum has no effect. Again, using the TI–83, we have:

Observed values

Expected values

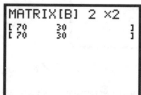

Results:

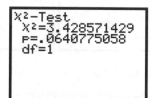

Again seeing as $p > 0.05$, we accept the null hypothesis.

YATE'S CONTINUITY CORRECTION

When results from continuous distributions are applied to discrete data, as is the case for the χ^2 distribution (i.e., χ^2 is continuous, whereas U is discrete), then a continuity correction must be applied so that we may compensate against this. This continuity correction is known as **Yate's continuity correction** and it minimises the error by reducing by 0.5 the absolute value of differences between the observed and expected frequencies. In general the **correction is made** only **when the degrees of freedom are 1**, (for example, in 2×2 contingency tables!).
Therefore, our corrected value of U becomes:

$$U(\text{corrected}) = \sum \frac{(|Obs - Exp| - 0.5)^2}{Exp} \sim \chi^2(1)$$

For small samples (e.g. expected values between 5 and 10) it might be best to compare both U and U(corrected). **However, if we accept H_0 using U, we will certainly accept it using U(corrected).** In the last example we would have

$$U(corrected) = \frac{(|76-70|-0.5)^2}{70} + \frac{(|24-30|-0.5)^2}{30} + \frac{(|64-70|-0.5)^2}{70} + \frac{(|36-30|-0.5)^2}{30} = 2.927$$

So we clearly still accept H_0.

21.2 GOODNESS OF FIT TEST

Although we have mentioned that the chi–square test can be applied to data from which no distribution is assumed, this test can also be used to determine how well a theoretical distribution, for example the normal distribution, will fit empirical distributions, i.e., distributions obtained from sample data. For example, assume that we have take a sample from some population and then we measure a particular attribute that we are interested in e.g., we have taken a sample of 50 fish from a lake and then we have recorded their lengths. The local wildlife authorities believe that the length of fish in their lake follows a normal distribution. Based on our sample can we confirm or reject this claim? For example, if the authorities are correct then the proportion of fish in our sample that are of length less than 20 cm (say) should be close to the proportion that is predicted by the distribution under question. The underlying question to be answered is

how good of a fit is our observed data to the distribution under question

EXAMPLE

The number of accidents per week that have occurred in a small factory have been recorded over a period of 100 weeks. The data is shown below:

No. of accidents per week	0	1	2	3	≥ 4
No. of week	53	32	11	4	0

An insurance company believes that the number of accidents closely follows a particular type of distribution which provides the probability for the number of accidents that can be predicted to occur each week (for a standard factory of this size). The probabilities are shown in the table below:

No. of accidents per week	0	1	2	3	≥ 4
Pr(No. of accidents per week)	0.41	0.37	0.15	0.05	0.02

Is the insurance company correct?

SOLUTION

As we wish to compare the observed values against those predicted by the distribution we can set up a table of observed values and expected values (as in the last section) and then

apply the formula $U = \sum \dfrac{(Obs - Exp)^2}{Exp} \sim \chi^2(\upsilon - 1)$, where υ = the number of classes.

There are 100 weeks, so the expected values (based on the given probability values) are

No. of accidents per week	0	1	2	3	≥ 4
Observed (*Obs*)	53	32	11	4	0
Expected(*Exp*)	41	37	15	5	2

Before we proceed with determining the value of U, we need to make a note about the size of the expected values. If the expected values in a class is less than 5, then we need to combine classes until we have that $Exp \geq 5$. In this case we see that the last class has an expected value of 1, and so we need to combine this with the previous class, so that our table now looks like:

No. of accidents per week	0	1	2	≥ 3
Observed (*Obs*)	53	32	11	4
Expected(*Exp*)	41	37	16	7

Therefore, we have 4 classes, meaning that there are $4 - 1 = 3$ degrees of freedom. Evaluating the value of U, we have

$$U = \sum \frac{(Obs - Exp)^2}{Exp} = \frac{(53 - 41)^2}{41} + \frac{(32 - 37)^2}{37} + \frac{(11 - 16)^2}{16} + \frac{(4 - 7)^2}{7} = 7.036.$$

Then, as $U = 7.036 < 7.81 (= c_{0.95}\chi^2(3))$ we accept (at the 0.05 level) that the observed data follow the probability distribution predicted by the insurance company.

Notice then that if we wish to check if a sample was obtained from a normal distribution with parameters μ (= mean) and σ^2 (= variance) then once we have our observed values, we simply need to find the expected frequencies by finding the probability relevant to each class. Once we have the probabilities for each class, we can determine the expected values for each corresponding class, by multiplying the probability values by the total size of the sample. From these values, we set up a table as in the last example and determine the value of U, from which we can then either accept the null hypothesis, H_0, or reject it (in favour of the alternative hypothesis, H_1).

EXERCISE 21.1

1. For the tables shown below, test (at a 5% level of significance) if Factor A is independent of Factor B.

(a)

FACTOR A

		A1	A2	
FACTOR B	B1	72	418	490
	B2	38	92	130
		110	510	620

(b)

FACTOR A

		A1	A2	
FACTOR B	B1	40	12	52
	B2	11	9	20
		51	21	72

2. The following table shows the results from a random sample carried out so that the question about the relationship between education and job satisfaction could be analysed.

Completed University

Satisfied in job		YES	NO	
	YES	272	618	890
	NO	238	292	530
		510	910	1420

The questions were: "Have you completed University studies?" and "Are you satisfied in your job?" Test the hypothesis, using a 5% level of confidence, that the responses are independent.

3. The issue of capital punishment was raised in a particular country. There was some thought that one of the sexes were prone to agree with the use of capital punishment for some crimes. The responses of 1000 people were recorded as follows:

Gender

Use capital punishment		FEMALE	MALE
	YES	272	303
	NO	188	237

Test, at the 5% level of significance, whether a person's view on capital punishment is independent of their gender.

4. A new therapy is to be tested on patients at a local hospital. The following data relates to patients that attend this local hospital.
In particular, it is desirable to determine if the method of therapy is independent of the patient's level of improvement. The data from this test is as follows:
Therapy 1: 21 registered improvement   33 did not register improvement
Therapy 2: 14 registered improvement   42 did not register improvement
Is the level of improvement independent of the method of therapy?

5. Test for the independence between factor A and factor B in the following tables.

(a) FACTOR A

FACTOR B		A1	A2	A3
	B1	16	30	40
	B2	20	12	12

(b) FACTOR A

FACTOR B		A1	A2
	B1	50	30
	B2	30	60
	B3	10	20

Use a 5% level of significance.

6. Researches say that alcoholism is linked to marital status. A random sample on the people of a particular state had the following results:

Classification of alcoholic

		Type 1	Type 2	Type 3
Marital status	Married	31	47	68
	Not married	69	73	52

A type 1 result stands for a person being diagnosed as an alcoholic. A type 2 result stands for an undiagnosed alcoholic and type 3 stands for a non–alcoholic.
Use a 5% level of significance to determine if there is a relationship between the marital status of a person and their alcoholic classification.

7. A study is carried out to determine the 'relationship' between parent and child obesity level. A random sample of 100 obese and 100 nonobese children was taken and then the obesity status of their parents were recorded. The results are shown below:

Parent

		Obese	Not obese
Child	Obese	68	58
	Not obese	32	42

Using a 5% level of significance, determine if child obesity is dependent on parental obesity.

8. Social researches believe that alcohol consumption amongst teenagers is dependent on family status. The results of a random sample of 230 teenagers produced the following information:

	Frequently	Occasional	None
Lower class	10	21	9
Middle class	24	90	24
Upper class	13	19	7

Use a 5% level of significance to test this hypothesis.

SELF ASSESSMENT TEST (20 MINUTES)

1. We want to decide if hair colour is dependent on eye colour. A sample of 200 randomly selected people had their eye and hair colour noted, the results are shown in the frequency table below:

	Dark hair	Fair Hair	
Brown eyes	54	32	86
Blue eyes	42	72	114
	96	104	200

Based on these figures, what conclusion can you make?

2. (a) In an experiment with a flu injection, the following data, representing the number of patients was obtained:

	Treated	Not treated
Developed flu	20	60
Did not develop flu	80	40

Use an appropriate test for the significance of the effect of the flu injection an describe the conclusions from the analysis .

(b) If on the other hand, the data was

	Treated	Not treated
Developed flu	2	6
Did not develop flu	8	4

How are the values of U (χ^2), and the significance of the results affected by this change? Would the significance test used in (a) have been accurate?

[8 marks]

INTRODUCTION TO DIFFERENTIAL CALCULUS 1

RATES OF CHANGE

OPTION

2 2

22.1 RATES OF CHANGE

FUNCTIONAL DEPENDENCE

We have already discussed the notion of functional dependence of a function $f(x)$ on the variable x. However, apart from an algebraic representation of the dependence on a variable, often it is desirable to be able to describe a given graphical representation from a qualitative rather than quantitative perspective. In doing so, there are a number of key words that are used.

Words to be kept in mind are:

Rate of change (slow, fast, zero)	Increasing, decreasing
Positive, negative	Maximum, minimum
Average	Instantaneous
Stationary	Initial, final
Continuous, discontinuous	Range, domain

Such terms enable us to describe many situations that are presented in graphical form. There is one crucial point to be very careful of when describing a graphical representation of a given situation. Graphs that look identical could very well be describing completely different scenarios. Not only must you consider the behaviour (shape) of the graph itself, but also take into account the variables involved.

Consider the two graphs below. Although identical in shape, they tell two completely different stories. We describe what happens in the first five minutes of motion:

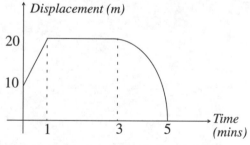
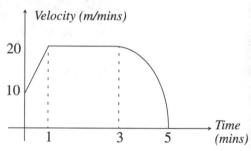

An object is moving in such a way that its displacement is increasing at a constant rate, that is, the object maintains a constant velocity (or zero acceleration) for the first minute. During the next two minutes the object remains stationary, that is, it maintains its displacement of 20 metres (meaning that it doesn't move any further from its starting position). Finally the particle returns to the origin.

An object is moving at 10 m/min and keeps increasing its velocity at a constant rate until it reaches a velocity of 20 m/min, that is, it maintains a constant acceleration for the first minute. During the next two minutes the object is moving at a constant velocity of 20 m/mins (meaning that it is moving further away from its starting position). Finally, the particle slows to rest.

Clearly then, although the shape of the graphs are identical, two completely different situations have been described!

QUANTITATIVE ASPECTS OF CHANGE

In dealing with the issue of rates of change, there are concepts that need to be considered;
1.   that of the **average rate** of change and
2.   that of the **instantaneous rate** of change.

AVERAGE RATE OF CHANGE.

The average rate of change can be best described as an 'overview' of the effect that one variable (the independent variable) has on a second variable (the dependent variable). If we consider the graph below, we can describe the change in the y-values (relative to the change in the x-values) as follows:

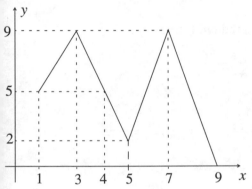

$x \in [1, 3]$:

There is a **constant** increase from $y = 5$ to $y = 9$ as x increases from 1 to 3. So that an increase of 2 units in x has produced an increase of 4 units in y. We say that the **average rate** of change of y with respect to x is $\frac{4}{2} = 2$

$x \in [1, 4]$:

This time, the overall change in y is 0. That is, although y increases from 5 to 9, it then decreases back to 5. So from its initial value of 5, because it is still at 5 as x increases from 1 to 4, the overall change in y is still 0. This time the average rate of change is $\frac{0}{3} = 0$.

$x \in [1, 5]$:

As x now increases from 1 to 5 we observe that there is an overall decrease in the value of y, i.e., there is an overall decrease of 3 units (y: $5 \to 9 \to 5 \to 2$).

In this instance we say that the average rate of change is $-\frac{3}{4} = -0.75$.

Notice that we have included a negative sign to indicate that there was an overall decrease in the y values (as x has increased by 4).

The same could be done for the rest of the graph. It should be noted that we need not start at $x = 1$. We could just as easily have found the change in y for $x \in [3, 5]$.

In this case, the average rate of change would have been $-\frac{7}{2} = -3.5$.

The question then remains, is there a simple way to find these average rates of change and will it work for the case where we have non–linear sections? The answer is yes.

DETERMINING THE AVERAGE RATE OF CHANGE

To find the average rate of change in y it is necessary to have an initial point and an end point, as x increases from x_1 to x_2.

So that at A $x = x_1, y = y_1$

and at B $x = x_2, y = y_2$.

To obtain a numerical value, we find the gradient of the straight line joining these two points.

This is the gradient of a straight line:

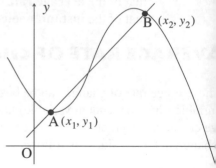

Average rate of change from A to B = gradient from A to B

$$= \frac{y_2 - y_1}{x_2 - x_1}$$

EXAMPLE

For each of the graphs below, find the average rate of change of y with respect to x over the interval specified (i.e., region L).

(a)

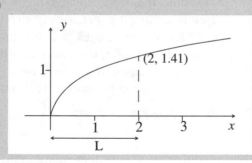

(b)

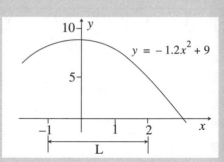

SOLUTION

(a) For this case we have the 'starting point' at the origin (with coordinates (0,0)) and the 'end' point with coordinates (2,1.41).

This means that the average rate of change of y with respect to x, over the region L is given by

$$\frac{y_2 - y_1}{x_2 - x_1} = \frac{1.41 - 0}{2 - 0} = 0.705 .$$

(b) This time we will need to first determine the coordinates of the extreme points:

For $x = -1$, $y = -1.2 \times (-1)^2 + 9 = 7.8$.

For $x = 2$, $y = -1.2 \times (2)^2 + 9 = 4.2$.
Therefore, the average rate of change is equal to

$$\frac{y_2 - y_1}{x_2 - x_1} = \frac{4.2 - 7.8}{2 - (-1)} = -1.2 .$$

is not always necessary to have a graph in order to find the average rate of change. Often we are given information in the form of a table.

EXAMPLE

The table below shows the number of bacteria, N, present in an enclosed environment. Find the average growth rate of the population size over the first 4 hours.

Time (hrs)	0	1	2	3	4	5	6	7	9
N	30	36	43	52	62	75	90	107	129

SOLUTION

This time we need to consider the time interval $t = 0$ to $t = 4$. From the table we observe that the coordinates corresponding to these values are; (0,30) and (4,62). Therefore, the average rate of growth of the number of bacteria over the first 4 hours is equal to

$$\frac{62 - 30}{4 - 0} = \frac{32}{4} = 8.$$

This means that during the first 4 hours, the number of bacteria was increasing (on average) at a rate of 8 every hour.

Notice that in the 1st hour, the average rate was $\frac{36 - 30}{1 - 0} = \frac{6}{1} = 6$ (< 8), whereas in the 4th hour the average rate of increase was $\frac{62 - 52}{4 - 3} = \frac{10}{1} = 10$ (> 8).

VELOCITY AS THE RATE OF CHANGE OF DISPLACEMENT

Consider a marble that is allowed to free fall from a height of 2 metres (see diagram). As the marble is falling, photographs are taken of its fall at regular intervals of 0.2 second.
From its motion, we can tell that the rate at which the marble is falling is increasing (i.e., its velocity is increasing).
What is its average velocity over the first 0.6 second?
What is its velocity after 0.6 second?
Reading from the diagram, we see that the marble has fallen a total distance of 1.75 (approximately), therefore, the average velocity v_{ave} of the marble, given by the rate at which its displacement increases (or decreases), is given by

$$v_{ave} = \frac{1.75 - 0}{0.6 - 0} \approx 2.92 \text{ m/sec}$$

The second question, "its velocity after 0.6 sec", will be answered in the next section. Note also, that we have found the average rate of change of displacement with respect to time.

EXAMPLE

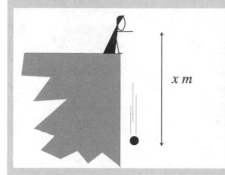

The displacement, x m, of an object, t seconds after it is dropped from the roof of a building is given by

$$x = 4.9t^2 \text{ m.}$$

x m

(a) What is the object's displacement after 4 seconds?

(b) What is the average velocity of the object over the first 4 seconds of its motion?

SOLUTION

(a) After 4 seconds of free fall, the object's displacement will be $4.9(4)^2 = 78.4 \ m$. We obtained this result by substituting the value of $t = 4$ into the equation for the displacement $x = 4.9t^2$.

(b) This time we want the average rate of change of displacement, x m, with respect to the time t seconds.

To do this, use the fact that $\qquad v_{ave} = \dfrac{x_2 - x_1}{t_2 - t_1} = \dfrac{78.4 - 0}{4 - 0} = 19.6$.

That is, the object's average velocity over the first 4 seconds is 19.6 m/s.

EXAMPLE

The concentration of a drug, in milligrams per millilitre, in a patient's bloodstream, t hours after an injection is approximately modelled by the function

$$t \mapsto \frac{2t}{8 + t^3}, t \geq 0.$$

Find the average rate of change in the concentration of the drug present in a patient's bloodstream;　　(a)　during the first hour,

(b)　during the first two hours,

(c)　during the 2nd and 4th hour after the drug was administered.

SOLUTION

To help us visualise the behaviour of this function we will make use of the TI–83. Begin by introducing the variable C, to denote the concentration of the drug in the patient's bloodstream t hours after it is administered. So that $C(t) = \dfrac{2t}{8 + t^3}, t \geq 0$.

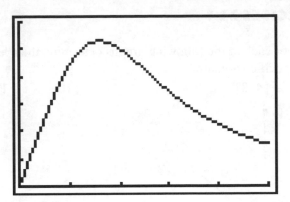

a) Initially the concentration is 0 milligrams per millilitre, the concentration after 1 hr

is given by $C(1) = \dfrac{2 \times 1}{8 + 1^3} = \dfrac{2}{9} \approx 0.22$.

Therefore, the average rate of change in concentration (C_{ave}) during the first hour

is given by $C_{ave} = \dfrac{0.22 - 0}{1 - 0} = 0.22$.

Note that the units would be *mg/ml/hr*.

b) The concentration 2 hours after the drug has been administered is $C(2) = \dfrac{2 \times 2}{8 + 2^3}$.

That is, 0.25 *mg/ml*.
Therefore, the average rate of change in concentration with respect to time is

$$C_{ave} = \frac{0.25 - 0}{2 - 0} = 0.125 . \ (\ \approx 0.13)$$

Notice that although the concentration has increased (compared to the concentration after
hour), the rate of change in the
oncentration has actually decreased!
This should be evident from the graph of
$C(t)$ versus t.
The slope of the straight line from the
origin to A(1, 0.22), m_{OA}, is greater than
he slope from the origin O to the point
B(2, 0.25), m_{OB}.

That is $m_{OA} > m_{OB}$.

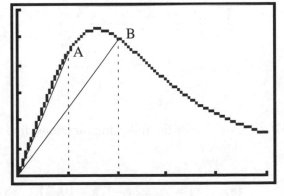

c) The average rate of change in concentration from $t = 2$ to $t = 4$ is given by

$$\frac{C(4) - C(2)}{4 - 2} = \frac{\dfrac{2 \times 4}{8 + 4^3} - 0.250}{4 - 2} \approx \frac{0.111 - 0.250}{2} = -0.0695$$

The average rate of change of concentration is -0.070 *mg/ml/hr*. Meaning that the overall
amount of drug in the patient's bloodstream is decreasing during the time interval $2 \le t \le 4$.

EXERCISES 22.1

1. For each of the following graphs determine the average rate of change over the specified domain.

(a) $x \in [4, 8]$

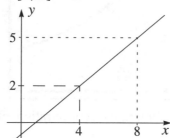

(b) $x \in [-b, 3b]$

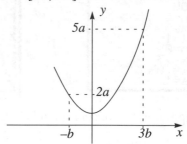

(c) $x \in [-2, 2]$

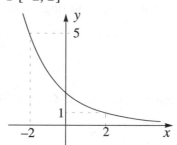

(d) $x \in [-3, 2]$

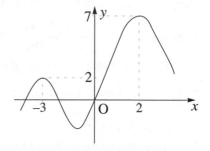

(e) $x \in [-2, 6]$

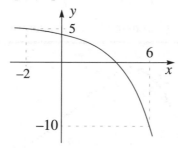

(f) $x \in [-1, 1]$

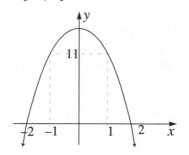

2. For each of the following functions, find the average rate of change over the given domain.

(a) $x \mapsto x^2 + 2x - 1, x \in [0, 2]$

(b) $x \mapsto \sqrt{x + 1}, x \in [3, 8]$

(c) $x \mapsto 10 - \dfrac{1}{\sqrt{x}}, x \in [2, 20]$

(d) $x \mapsto \dfrac{x}{x + 1}, x \in [0.1, 1.1]$

(e) $x \mapsto \dfrac{1}{1 + x^2} - 1, x \in [0, 100]$

(f) $x \mapsto x\sqrt{400 - x}, x \in [100, 300]$

(g) $x \mapsto 2^x, x \in [0, 5]$

(h) $x \mapsto (x - 2)(x + 3), x \in [-3, 2]$

3. The displacement of an object, t seconds into its motion is given by the equation,

$$s(t) = t^3 + 3t^2 + 2t, t \geq 0.$$

Find the average rate of change of displacement during;
(a)   the first second,
(b)   the first 4 seconds.
(c)   the interval when $t = 1$ to $t = 1 + h$.

4. The distance s metres that a particle has moved in t seconds is given by the function

$s = 4t + 2t^2, t \geq 0$. Find the particle's average speed over the first 4 seconds.

5. The distance s metres that a particle has moved in t seconds is given by the function

$s = 4t + 2t^2, t \geq 0$. Find the particle's average speed during the time interval from when $t = 1$ to $t = 1 + h$.

6. The temperature $T\,°C$ of food placed inside cold storage is modelled by the equation

$T = \dfrac{720}{t^2 + 2t + 25}$ where t is measured in hours.

Find the average rate of change of the temperature, $T°C$, with respect to the time, t hours, during the first 2 hours that the food is placed in the cold storage.

7. The volume of water in a hemispherical bowl of radius r is given by

$V = \frac{1}{3}\pi h^2(3r - h)$, where h is the height of the water surface inside the bowl. For the

case where r is 20 cm,
(a)   find the average rate of increase in the amount of water inside the bowl with respect to its height, h cm, as the water level rises from 2 cm to 5 cm.
(b)   Find the average rate of increase in the amount of water inside the bowl with respect to its height, h cm, as the water level rises by
   i.   1 cm   ii.   0.1 cm   iii.   0.01 cm

8. An amount of money is placed in a bank and is accumulating interest on a daily basis. The table below shows the amount of money in the savings account over a period of 600 days.

t(days)	100	200	300	400	500	600	700
D/day	1600	1709	1823	1942	2065	2194	2328

(a)   Plot the graph of D versus t (days).
(b)   Find the average rate of change in the amount in the account during the periodof 100 days to 300 days.

9. The temperature of coffee since it was poured into a cup was recorded and tabulated below.

t min	0	2	4	6	9
T °C	60	50	30	10	5

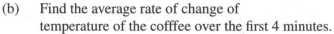

(a) Plot these points on a set of axes that show the relationship between the temperature of coffee and the time it has been left in the cup.

(b) Find the average rate of change of temperature of the cofffee over the first 4 minutes.

(c) Over what period of time is the coffee cooling the most rapidly?

10. The displacement, d metres, of an object, t seconds after it was set is motion is described by the equation

$$d = 4t + 5t^2, \text{ where } t \geq 0.$$

(a) Find the distance that the object travels in the first 2 seconds of its motion.

(b) Find the average rate of change of distance with respect to time undergone by the object over the first 2 seconds of its motion.

(c) What quantity is being measured when determining the average rate of change of distance with repect to time?

(d) How far does the object travel during the 5th second of motion?

(e) Find the object's average speed during the 5th second.

11. A person invested $1000 and estimates that on average, the investment will increase each year by 16% of its value at the beginning of the year.

(a) Calculate the value of the investment at the end of each of the first 5 years.

(b) Find the average rate at which the investment has grown over the first 5 years.

22.2 QUALITATIVE ASPECTS OF CHANGE

Apart from quantitative measures (i.e., providing numerical values), it is also important to be able to provide qualitative descriptions of the behaviour of graphs. In doing so, many of the key words mentioned at the start of this chapter should be referred to.

DESCRIBING THE BEHAVIOUR OF A GRAPH

Consider the graph shown:

We can see that in both Section A and Section B, the gradients of the lines are both positive. However, the gradient of the straight line in section B is steeper than that of the line in Section A. We can then say that over Section B the graph is increasing at a faster rate than it is over Section A. In fact, if we were able to walk along this curve, from left to right, we could describe our 'journey' as follows:

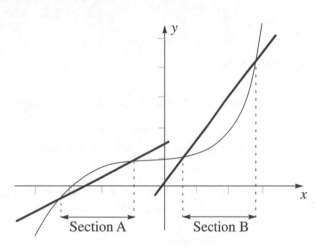

As we walk from the left hand side and towards that part of the graph that lies above Section A, the function is increasing, i.e., as the values of x increase, so too do the values of y. As the values of x approach 0 (from the left side of the y–axis) the rate at which the function is increasing is slowing down. That is, I do not need to make as much effort to move as I keep getting closer to the y–axis. We have then, even though the function itself is still increasing (as we are getting closer to the y–axis), that the rate of change of the function is in fact decreasing! Actually, by the stage where we have reached the y–axis we could almost say that the function remains stationary, i.e., it has stopped increasing. In this instance, we would say that the rate of change of the function is zero. As we pass the y–axis and keep moving along the curve we find it more difficult to walk along the curve. That is, the effort that we need to make to keep walking is increasing. In this instance the function is increasing but so too is the rate at which it is increasing.

PRODUCING A GRAPH FROM A PHYSICAL SITUATION

In the next section we will concentrate on producing a graph to describe the behaviour of the flow of liquid into a container. The importance of such problems is that they enable us to describe how changing one variable will effect a second (related) variable. That is, the effect the independent variable has on the dependent variable. One way to do this is by increasing the independent variable (usually x) and observing the change in the dependent variable (usually y).

EXAMPLE

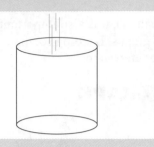

A cylindrical vase is placed under a tap and water is allowed to flow into it at a constant rate. Provide a graphical representation of the relationship between the volume of water in the vase and,

(a) the time for which water flows into the vase.
(b) the level of water.

SOLUTION

(a) The independent variable in this case is time, t seconds. Consider how much water, $V\ cm^3$, flows into the vase in equal time intervals (of 2 seconds). In this case we have that equal amounts of water will flow into the vase during each (equal) time interval.

For example, if $10\ cm^3$ of water flows into the vase every 2 seconds, we could produce the following table of values:

t seconds	0	2	4	6	...
$V\ cm^3$	0	10	20	30	...

Based on the results of this table we can produce a graph of $V\ cm^3$ versus t seconds:

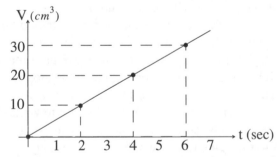

(b) To see how the volume changes with respect to the level of water, we use a different approach— this time we consider a 'frame–by–frame' sequence of the vase as it is filled.

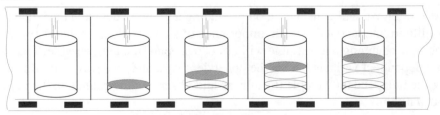

From our 'snap–shots', we see that for equal heights, equal amounts of water flow into the vase. So that every time the water level increases by 1cm, the volume increases by

8 cm^3.

This would imply that the relationship

between the volume, $V \ cm^3$ of water

in the vase and the level of water, h

cm, is linear:

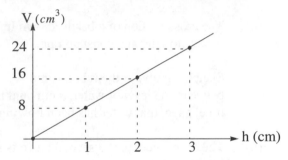

EXAMPLE

Sketch a graph showing the relationship between the level of water in a flask and the time for which water has been flowing into the flask.

SOLUTION

Let the level of water in the flask be denoted by h cm and the time for which water has been flowing be denoted by t seconds. This time we use our 'frame–by frame' approach:

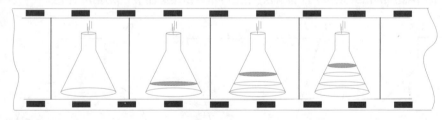

As we consider equal time intervals we see that the same amount of water will flow into the flask during each of these time intervals. However, because the flask becomes narrower as the level rises, then (because we still have the same volume of water flowing into the flask), the height

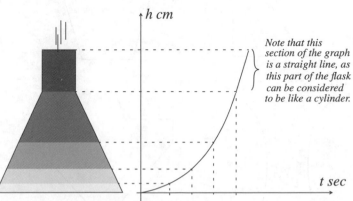

Note that this section of the graph is a straight line, as this part of the flask can be considered to be like a cylinder.

of the space occupied by these equal volumes of water must increase at a faster rate than it had for the cylindrical section. A cross sectional view of the flask (shown above) shows this more clearly.

EXERCISES 22.2

1. (a) The cross section of a basin, shown in Figure A, is being filled by water flowing at a constant rate.

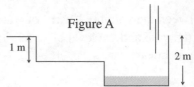
Figure A

Sketch a graph of the relationship between the level of water, h cm, and the time, t sec, that water has been flowing.

(b) The cross section of a second basin is shown in Figure B. Water is flowing into this basin at the same rate as in (a).

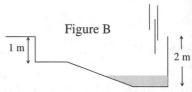
Figure B

Sketch a graph of the relationship between the level of water, h cm, and the time, t sec, that water has been flowing for this basin.

2. For each of the following bottles, sketch the graph that would show the relationship between the level of water, h cm, and the volume of water, V cm^3 in the bottle. That is, sketch a graph of h versus V.
You may assume that water is flowing into each bottle at a constant rate.

(a)

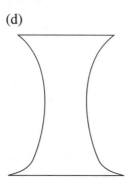

(b)

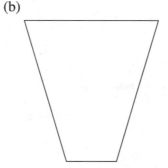

(c)

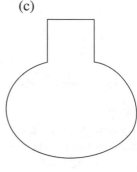

(d)

(e)

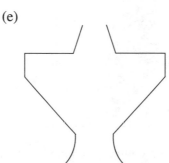

(f)

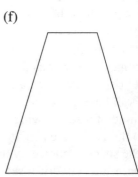

22.3 FROM AVERAGE RATE OF CHANGE TO AN INSTANTANEOUS RATE OF CHANGE

As already discussed, the average rate of change between two points on a curve is determined by finding the gradient of the straight line joining these two points. However we often need to find the rate of change at a particular instant, and so the method used for finding the average rate of change is no longer appropriate. However, it does provide the foundation that leads to obtaining the instantaneous rate of change. Following, we see how we refine our definition of the average rate of change to incorporate the notion of the instantaneous rate of change. The basic argument revolves around the notion of magnifying near the point where we wish to find the instantaneous rate of change, that is, by repeatedly 'closing in' on a section of a curve. This will give the impression that over a very small section, the curve can be approximated by a straight line. Finding the gradient of that straight line will provide us with a very good approximation to the rate of change of the curve (over the small region under investigation). To obtain the exact rate of change at a particular point on the curve we will then need to use a **limiting** approach.

The process used to determine the rate of change at P is carried out as follows;

1.   start by drawing a secant from A to B. This will provide an approximate value for the rate of change at P (i.e., average rate of change over a region from point A to point B will provide a reasonable first approximation).
2.   then zoom–in towards point P, whereby a better measure for the rate of change at point P is obtained because we can now place the secant closer to the point P,
3.   finally, the zooming–in process has reached the stage whereby the secant is now virtually the same as the curve at P. (In fact the secant is now the tangent to the curve at the point P.

As we magnify, we move the secant closer to the point P

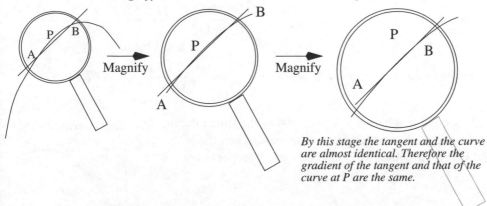

Magnify   Magnify

By this stage the tangent and the curve are almost identical. Therefore the gradient of the tangent and that of the curve at P are the same.

We are now in a position where we can put in place some form of mathematical argument to describe this limiting process more formally. The key in obtaining a mathematical result requires the use of limits, this will be the subject of the next chapter.

EXAMPLE

An object moves along a straight line. Its position, x metres (from a fixed point O), at time t seconds is given by $x(t) = t - \frac{1}{4}t^2, t \geq 0$.

Determine
i.   its average velocity over the interval from $t = 1$ to $t = 2$
ii.   its average velocity over the interval $t = 1$ to $t = 1.5$
iii.   its average velocity over the interval $t = 1$ to $t = 1.1$
iv.   its average velocity over the interval $t = 1$ to $t = 1 + h$, where h is small.

SOLUTION

i.   The average velocity over the required second (from $t = 1$ to $t = 2$) is found by finding the slope of the secant joining those two points on the graph of $x(t)$.

At $t = 2$, we have $x(2) = 2 - \frac{1}{4}(2)^2 = 1$, and at $t = 1$, $x(1) = 1 - \frac{1}{4}(1)^2 = \frac{3}{4}$.

Therefore, we have that

$$v_{ave} = \frac{x(2) - x(1)}{2 - 1}$$

$$= \frac{1 - 0.75}{1}$$

$$= 0.25$$

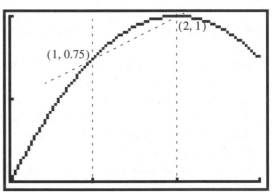

Therefore, the average velocity over the second is 0.75m/s.
Note that we could have used the DRAW LINE function from the TI–82.

ii.   For $t = 1$ to $t = 1.5$ we have, $v_{ave} = \frac{x(1.5) - x(1)}{1.5 - 1} = \frac{(1.5 - 0.25 \times 1.5^2) - 0.75}{0.5}$

$$= 0.375$$

iii.   Similarly, for $t = 1$ to $t = 1.1$, we have $v_{ave} = \frac{x(1.1) - x(1)}{1.1 - 1} = 0.475$

From the second graph shown we see that as the time interval decreases, the gradient of the secant increases (i.e., the straight line joining the two points becomes steeper):

Gradient increases

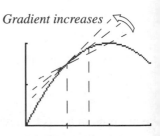

iv.   We are now in a position to determine the average rate over the interval $t = 1$ to

$t = 1 + h$, the average velocity is given by $v_{ave} = \dfrac{x(1 + h) - x(1)}{1 + h - 1}$

Now, $x(1 + h) = (1 + h) - 0.25(1 + h)^2 = 1 + h - 0.25(1 + 2h + h^2)$

$$= 0.75 + 0.5h - 0.25h^2$$

Therefore, $v_{ave} = \dfrac{0.75 + 0.5h - 0.25h^2 - 0.75}{1 + h - 1} = \dfrac{0.5h - 0.25h^2}{h}$

$$= \dfrac{h(0.5 - 0.25h)}{h}$$

$$= 0.5 - 0.25h, \ h \neq 0$$

Notice that for ii. (i.e., $t = 1$ to $t = 1.5$) $h = 0.5$, so that substituting $h = 0.5$ into this equation we have, $v_{ave} = 0.5 - 0.25(0.5) = 0.375$. Providing the same result as before.

We can set up a table of values, and from it determine what happens as we decrease the time difference.

We notice that as h becomes very small, the average rate of change from $t = 1$ to $t = 1 + h$ becomes the instantaneous rate of change at $t = 1$! This is because we are zooming in onto the point where $t = 1$.

This means that the rate of change at $t = 1$ ($h = 0$) would therefore be 5 m/s. So that the particle would have a velocity of 5 m/s after 1 second of motion.

h	v_{ave}
0.1	0.475
0.01	0.4975
0.001	0.4999

EXAMPLE

For the graph with equation $f : x \mapsto (x + 2)(x - 1)(x - 4)$,

a.   Find the average rate of change of f over the interval $[-1, 2]$.

b.   Find the rate of change of f, where $x = 4$.

SOLUTION

a.   We first find the coordinates of the end points for the interval $[-1, 2]$:
       At $x = -1$, we have
       $y = f(-1) = (-1 + 2)(-1 - 1)(-1 - 4) = 10$.
       At $x = 2$, we have
       $y = f(2) = (2 + 2)(2 - 1)(2 - 4) = -8$.
       Therefore, the average rate of change in y with respect to x over the interval $[-1, 2]$ is given by
       $$\dfrac{f(2) - f(-1)}{2 - (-1)} = \dfrac{-8 - 10}{3} = -6$$

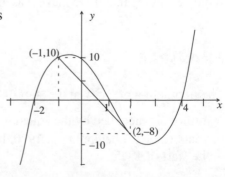

449

b. To determine the rate of change at $x = 4$, we choose a second point close to $x = 4$, in this case, we use the point $x = 4 + h$, where h can be considered to be a very small number, i.e., we will look at what happens to the gradient of the secant joining the points $(4, 0)$ and $(4 + h, f(4 + h))$ as h approaches zero. The gradient of the secant is given by

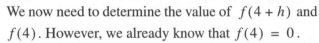

$$\frac{f(4 + h) - f(4)}{(4 + h) - 4} = \frac{f(4 + h) - f(4)}{h}$$

We now need to determine the value of $f(4 + h)$ and $f(4)$. However, we already know that $f(4) = 0$.

We can now find values for $f(4 + h)$ as h approaches zero.

For $h = 0.1$ we have,

$$f(4 + 0.1) = f(4.1) = (4.1 + 2)(4.1 - 1)(4.1 - 4) = 6.1 \times 3.1 \times 0.1 = 1.891.$$

Therefore, $\dfrac{f(4 + h) - f(4)}{h} = \dfrac{1.891 - 0}{0.1} = 18.91$.

We can then continue in this same manner by making the value of h smaller still. We do this by setting up a table of values:

h	$\dfrac{f(4 + h) - f(4)}{h}$
0.01	18.09010000
0.001	18.00900100
0.0001	18.00090001

From the table, it appears that as h approaches zero, the gradient of the secant (which becomes the gradient of the tangent at $(4,0)$) approaches a value of 18.

Therefore, we have that the rate of change of f at $(4,0)$ is 18.

More formally we write this result as $\displaystyle\lim_{h \to 0} \frac{f(4 + h) - f(4)}{h} = 18$, which is read as

"The limit as h tends to zero of $\dfrac{f(4 + h) - f(4)}{h}$ is equal to 18."

Which is saying that if we make h as small as we please, then $\dfrac{f(4 + h) - f(4)}{h}$ equals 18.

EXAMPLE

The population of a city at the start of 1990 was 2.3 million, and its projected population, N million, is modelled by the equation $N(t) = 2.3e^{0.0142t}$, where $t \geq 0$ and is measured in years since the beginning of 1990. Find the rate of growth of the population in this city at the start of 1995.

SOLUTION

Finding the rate of growth of the population at the start of 1995 as opposed to finding the rate over a period of time means that we are finding the instantaneous rate of change. To do this, we proceed as in the previous example, i.e., we use a limiting approach.

Consider the two points, $P(5, N(5))$ (start of 1995) and $A(5 + h, N(5 + h))$ on the curve representing the population size:

The gradient of the secant passing through P and A is given by

$$\frac{N(5 + h) - N(5)}{(5 + h) - 5} = \frac{N(5 + h) - N(5)}{h}$$

Now, $N(5) = 2.3e^{0.0142 \times 5} = 2.3e^{0.071}$

and $N(5 + h) = 2.3e^{0.0142(5 + h)}$

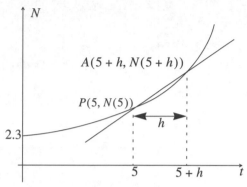

Therefore, the gradient of the secant is given by

$$\frac{2.3e^{0.0142(5 + h)} - 2.3e^{0.071}}{h} = \frac{2.3e^{0.071 + 0.0142h} - 2.3e^{0.071}}{h}$$

$$= \frac{2.3e^{0.071}(e^{0.0142h} - 1)}{h}$$

Again we set up a table of values:

h	$\dfrac{2.3e^{0.071}(e^{0.0142h} - 1)}{h}$
0.1	$\dfrac{2.3e^{0.071}(e^{0.0142 \times 0.1} - 1)}{0.1} = 0.035088$
0.01	$\dfrac{2.3e^{0.071}(e^{0.0142 \times 0.01} - 1)}{0.01} = 0.035066$
0.001	$\dfrac{2.3e^{0.071}(e^{0.0142 \times 0.001} - 1)}{0.001} = 0.035063$
0.0001	$\dfrac{2.3e^{0.071}(e^{0.0142 \times 0.0001} - 1)}{0.0001} = 0.035063$

Using limiting notation we have, $\displaystyle\lim_{h \to 0} \frac{N(5 + h) - N(5)}{h} = 0.035063$.

That is, the growth rate at the start of 1995 is 35,063 people per year.

EXERCISES 22.3

1. For each of the graphs shown below, find the gradient of the secant joining the points P and Q.

(a)

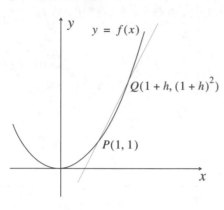

(b)

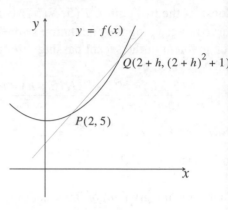

(c)

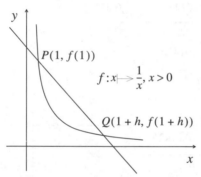

(d)

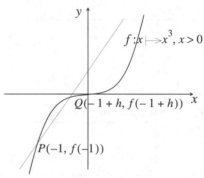

2. For each of the graphs in Q.1., use a limiting argument to deduce the instantaneous rate of change of the given function at the point P.

3. For each of the functions, f, given below, find the gradient of the secant joining the points $P(a, f(a))$ & $Q(a + h, f(a + h))$.

(a) $f(x) = 3 + x^2$ (b) $f(x) = 1 - x^2$ (c) $f(x) = (x + 1)^2 - 2$

(d) $f(x) = x^3 + x$ (e) $f(x) = 2 - x^3$ (f) $f(x) = x^3 - x^2$

(g) $f(x) = \dfrac{2}{x}$ (h) $f(x) = \dfrac{1}{x - 1}$ (i) $f(x) = \sqrt{x}$

4. For each of the functions, f, given below, find the gradient of the secant joining the points $P(a, f(a))$ & $Q(a + h, f(a + h))$ and hence deduce the gradient of the tangent drawn at the point P.

(a) $f(x) = x$ (b) $f(x) = x^2$ (c) $f(x) = x^3$ (d) $f(x) = x^4$.

Hence deduce the gradient of the tangent drawn at the point $P(a, f(a))$ for the function $f(x) = x^n, n \in N$.

22.4 THE PROCESS OF DIFFERENTIATION

THE DERIVATIVE AND THE GRADIENT FUNCTION

In the previous sections we concentrated on determining the average rate of change of a function and then proceeded to find the instantaneous rate of change at a particular point (on the curve). We now consider the same process, with the exception that we will discuss the instantaneous rate at any point $P(x, f(x))$. The result will be an expression that will enable us to determine the instantaneous rate of change of the function at any point on the curve. Because the instantaneous rate of change at a point on a curve is simply a measure of the gradient of the curve at that point, our newly found result will be known as the gradient function (otherwise known as the derivative of the function).

For a continuous function, $y = f(x)$, we deduced that the instantaneous rate of change at the point $P(a, f(a))$ is given by $\dfrac{f(a+h) - f(a)}{h}$, where h is taken to be very small (in fact we say that h approaches or tends to zero). In other words, to determine the rate at which a graph changes (i.e., rises or falls) at a single point, all that you need to find is the slope of the tangent line at

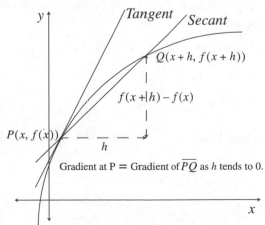

$P(a, f(a))$

$P(a, f(a))$

At the point P, the tangent and the line are one and the same.
So that, finding the gradient of the tangent at P is the same as finding the rate of change of the function at P.

the point. This becomes obvious if we look back at our 'zooming in process—where the tangent line to the function at the point $P(a, f(a))$ is the line that best approximates the graph at that point.

Rather than a fixed point $P(a, f(a))$, we now consider any point $P(x, f(x))$ on the curve with equation $y = f(x)$:

The rate of change of the function f at $P(x, f(x))$ is therefore given by the gradient of the tangent to the curve at P. However, the gradient of the tangent at P is given by the gradient of the secant joining the points $P(x, f(x))$ and $Q(x + h, f(x + h))$ and allowing the point Q to come as close as possible to the point P. In other words, we make h approach zero. In symbols we have:

$$\text{Rate at P} = \lim_{h \to 0} \frac{f(x + h) - f(x)}{h}$$

Tangent / Secant

$Q(x + h, f(x + h))$

$f(x + h) - f(x)$

$P(x, f(x))$

h

Gradient at P = Gradient of $\overline{PQ}$ as h tends to 0.

NOTATION AND LANGUAGE

We now introduce the term **derivative of a function**:

$$
\begin{aligned}
\text{The } \textbf{rate of change} \text{ of } f(x) \text{ at } P(x, f(x)) \;\; &= \textbf{Gradient function} \text{ of } f(x) \text{ at } P(x, f(x)) \\
&= \textbf{The derivative} \text{ of } f(x) \\
&= \lim_{h \to 0} \frac{f(x+h) - f(x)}{h}
\end{aligned}
$$

The derivative of a function $f(x)$ is denoted by $f'(x)$ and is read as "f dash of x".
That is,

$$
f'(x) = \lim_{h \to 0} \frac{f(x+h) - f(x)}{h}
$$

Finding the derivative of a function using this approach is referred to as *finding the derivative of f from first principles*.

It is important to realise that in finding $f'(x)$ we have a new function—called the gradient function, because the expression $f'(x)$ will give the gradient anywhere on the curve of $f(x)$. So that if we want the gradient of the function $f(x)$ at $x = 5$, we first determine $f'(x)$ and then substitute the value of $x = 5$ into the equation of $f'(x)$.

EXAMPLE

Find the derivative (*or the gradient function*) of the function $f(x) = 3x^2 + 4$ using the first principles method.
Hence, find the gradient of the function at $x = 3$.

SOLUTION

By definition we have that $f'(x) = \lim_{h \to 0} \dfrac{f(x+h) - f(x)}{h}$, therefore, we can first evaluate

the expression $f(x+h) - f(x)$ and then substitute the result into the equation for $f'(x)$.
So that:

$$
\begin{aligned}
f(x+h) - f(x) &= 3(x+h)^2 + 4 - [3x^2 + 4] = 3(x^2 + 2xh + h^2) + 4 - 3x^2 - 4 \\
&= 3x^2 + 6xh + 3h^2 - 3x^2 \\
&= 6xh + 3h^2
\end{aligned}
$$

$$
\begin{aligned}
\text{We then have:} \quad \lim_{h \to 0} \frac{f(x+h) - f(x)}{h} &= \lim_{h \to 0} \frac{6xh + 3h^2}{h} \\
&= \lim_{h \to 0} \frac{h(6x + 3h)}{h} \\
&= \lim_{h \to 0} (6x + 3h), \, h \neq 0 \\
&= 6x
\end{aligned}
$$

That is, we now have the gradient function $f'(x) = 6x$.

To determine the gradient of the function at $x = 3$, we need to substitute the value $x = 3$ into the gradient function. That is, $f'(3) = 6 \times 3 = 18$.

Using the TI–82 we can determine the derivative at $x = 3$ by using the 'nDeriv(' command from the MATH menu:

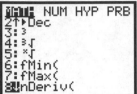 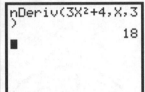

EXERCISES 22.4

1. Use a limiting process to find the gradients of these curves at the points indicated:

(a) $x \mapsto x^3$ at $x = 1$

(b) $v = 2t^2 - 1$ at $t = 2$

(c) $f(x) = \dfrac{1}{x}$ at $x = 3$

(d) $x \mapsto 2^x$ at $x = 1$

(e) $f = t^2 - 2t + 3$ at $t = 0.5$

(f) $t \mapsto \dfrac{t^2 - 1}{t}$ at $t = 4$

2. An object is dropped from a high building. The distance, d metres, that the object has fallen, t seconds after it is released, is given by the formula

$$d = 4.9t^2, 0 \le t \le 3.$$

(a) Find the distance fallen during the first second.
(b) Find the distance fallen between $t = 1$ and $t = h + 1$ seconds.
(c) **Hence**, find the speed of the object 1 second after it is released.

3. Find, from first principles, the gradient function, f', of the following

(a) $f : x \mapsto 4x^2$

(b) $f : x \mapsto 5x^2$

(c) $f : x \mapsto 4x^3$

(d) $f : x \mapsto 5x^3$

(e) $f : x \mapsto 4x^4$

(f) $f : x \mapsto 5x^4$

Can you see a pattern in your results?

4. Find, from first principles, the derivative of the following functions

(a) $f(x) = 2x^2 - 5$

(b) $g(x) = 2 - x$

(c) $g(x) = 2 - x + x^3$

(d) $f(x) = \dfrac{1}{x}$

(e) $f(x) = \dfrac{2}{x + 1}$

(f) $f(x) = \sqrt{x}$

SELF ASSESSMENT TEST (30 MINUTES)

1. A ride at an amusement park has a track and cars that move along it. The cars start at rest at the top of the track and roll down under the pull of gravity. They are not braked until they reach the end of the track.

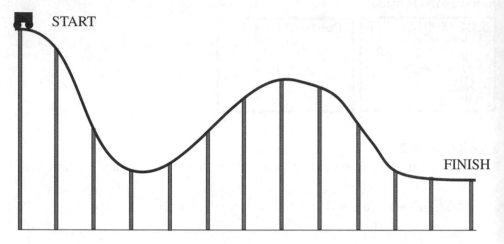

Sketch a graph of the velocity of the car against time.

2. The daily profits ($ thousands) made by a company n years after its formation is modelled by the equation:

$$P = 7 - \frac{5}{n+1}, n > 0$$

(a) Find the daily profit that the company makes 1 year after its formation.
(b) Find the average rate of change in daily profit between $n = 1$ and $n = 2$.
(c) Find the average rate of change in daily profit between $n = 1$ and $n = 1 + h$.
(d) Hence find the rate at which the daily profit is changing when $n = 1$.

3. Use a limiting argument to find the slope of the curve with equation $y = x + \dfrac{x}{2x+1}$ at the point where $x = 2$.

INTRODUCTION TO DIFFERENTIAL CALCULUS

2

DIFFERENTIATION AND APPLICATIONS

OPTION

2 3

23.1 DIFFERENTIATION

RECALL:
1. RATE OF CHANGE, GRADIENT AND THE DERIVATIVE

The **rate of change** of a curve at a point gives a **measure of the gradient** of the curve at that point. When finding the **derivative** of the equation of a curve we obtain the **gradient function**. As the name suggests, the gradient function enables us to find the gradient at any point on the curve.

2. DIFFERENTIATION

Differentiation is the process of finding the derivative of a function. The derivative of a function is often called its **derived function**.

3. LANGUAGE AND NOTATION

The **derivative of** $f(x)$ **with respect to** x is usually written as $f'(x)$ (read as "f dash of x") or $\frac{d}{dx}(f(x))$ (read as "dee–dee–x of $f(x)$").

The **derivative of** y **with respect to** x is usually written as $\frac{dy}{dx}$ (read as "dee–y–dee–x") or y' (read as "y–dash of x").

4. AVERAGE RATE → INSTANTANEOUS RATE

The **average rate** of change of the function $f(x)$ over the interval $x = x_1$ to $x = x_2$ is graphically represented by the **gradient of the secant** passing through the two points $(x_1, f(x_1))$ and $(x_2, f(x_2))$ on the curve $y = f(x)$. Whereas the **instantaneous rate** of change of $f(x)$ at the point $x = x_1$ is graphically represented by the **gradient of the tangent** at the point $(x_1, f(x_1))$ on the curve $y = f(x)$.

Average rate of change

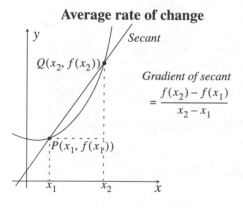

Instantaneous rate of change

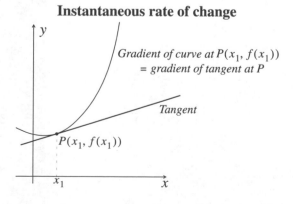

There are two forms of notation that can be used; (a) functional notation and (b) delta notation.

The basic difference between the two can be seen in the diagram below:

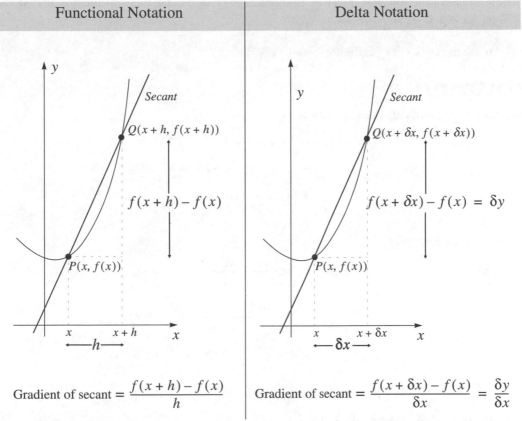

Functional Notation	Delta Notation

Gradient of secant $= \dfrac{f(x+h)-f(x)}{h}$ $\qquad$ Gradient of secant $= \dfrac{f(x+\delta x)-f(x)}{\delta x} = \dfrac{\delta y}{\delta x}$

To find the gradient at some point P, that is, to find the derivative of the function at any point P on the curve defined by the equation $y = f(x)$, we use the method of first principles:

$$f'(x) = \lim_{h \to 0} \frac{f(x+h)-f(x)}{h}, h \neq 0 \qquad\qquad \frac{dy}{dx} = \lim_{\delta x \to 0} \frac{\delta y}{\delta x}, \delta x \neq 0$$

Using the delta notation, we read $\dfrac{dy}{dx} = \lim\limits_{\delta x \to 0} \dfrac{\delta y}{\delta x}, \delta x \neq 0$ as "dee–y–dee–x is equal to the limit as delta x (δx) tends to zero of delta y (δy) on delta x (δx)". This is in part where the expression "The derivative of y with respect to x" stems from.

The notation $f'(x)$ is due to one of the greatest eighteenth century mathematicians, Joseph Louis Lagrange (1736–1813), whereas the notation $\dfrac{dy}{dx}$ is attributed to that other great mathematician, Gottfried Wilhelm Leibniz (1646–1716).

As we have already seen, the definition of the derivative is given by the expression

$$f'(x) = \lim_{h \to 0} \frac{f(x+h)-f(x)}{h}, h \neq 0 \text{ or } \frac{dy}{dx} = \lim_{\delta x \to 0} \frac{\delta y}{\delta x}, \delta x \neq 0. \text{ Meaning that, to}$$

differentiate a function $y = f(x)$ all that needs to be done is use one of these expressions.

EXAMPLE

Find the derivative (the gradient function) of $f(x) = x^3 + 1$

SOLUTION

We start by simplifying the expression $f(x+h) - f(x)$:

$$f(x+h) - f(x) = (x+h)^3 + 1 - (x^3 + 1)$$

$$= x^3 + 3x^2h + 3xh^2 + h^3 + 1 - x^3 - 1$$

$$= 3x^2h + 3xh^2 + h^3$$

$$= h(3x^2 + 3xh + h^2)$$

Therefore we have that

$$f'(x) = \lim_{h \to 0} \frac{f(x+h)-f(x)}{h}, h \neq 0$$

$$= \lim_{h \to 0} \frac{h(3x^2 + 3xh + h^2)}{h}, h \neq 0$$

$$= \lim_{h \to 0} (3x^2 + 3xh + h^2), h \neq 0$$

$$= 3x^2$$

That is, $f(x) = x^3 + 1 \Rightarrow f'(x) = 3x^2$

EXAMPLE

Differentiate the function $f(x) = \sqrt{x}$.

SOLUTION

As in the previous example, we first simplify the expression $f(x+h) - f(x)$:

$$f(x+h) - f(x) = \sqrt{x+h} - \sqrt{x}.$$

However, in this case it appears that we can go no further. However;

$$f'(x) = \lim_{h \to 0} \frac{\sqrt{x+h} - \sqrt{x}}{h} = \lim_{h \to 0} \frac{\sqrt{x+h} - \sqrt{x}}{h} \times \frac{\sqrt{x+h} + \sqrt{x}}{\sqrt{x+h} + \sqrt{x}}$$

Multiplying by $\dfrac{\sqrt{x+h} + \sqrt{x}}{\sqrt{x+h} + \sqrt{x}}$ is tricky! We are rationalising the numerator. This will

hopefully lead to an expression which will be more manageable.

Carrying out the multiplication:

$$f'(x) = \lim_{h \to 0} \frac{(\sqrt{x+h} - \sqrt{x})(\sqrt{x+h} + \sqrt{x})}{h(\sqrt{x+h} + \sqrt{x})}, h \neq 0$$

$$= \lim_{h \to 0} \frac{((x+h) - x)}{h(\sqrt{x+h} + \sqrt{x})}, h \neq 0$$

$$= \lim_{h \to 0} \frac{h}{h(\sqrt{x+h} + \sqrt{x})}, h \neq 0$$

$$= \lim_{h \to 0} \frac{1}{\sqrt{x+h} + \sqrt{x}}, h \neq 0$$

$$= \frac{1}{\sqrt{x} + \sqrt{x}}$$

$$= \frac{1}{2\sqrt{x}}$$

Notice that although $f(x) = \sqrt{x}, x \geq 0$, $f'(x) = \frac{1}{2\sqrt{x}}, x > 0$, i.e., the domain of the

function and that of its derivative are not the same!

Finding the derivative from first principles can be tedious. The previous two examples clearly show this. However, using the first principles approach, produces the results shown in the table below:

Function	Derivative
$y = f(x)$	$\frac{dy}{dx} = f'(x)$
x^4	$4x^3$
x^3	$3x^2$
x^2	$2x^1$
x	$1(= x^0)$
x^{-1}	$-1x^{-2}$
x^{-2}	$-2x^{-3}$

Based on these results it is reasonable to assume the general result that

if $y = x^n, n \in Z$, then $\frac{dy}{dx} = nx^{n-1}$.

In fact this rule is true for any exponent $n \in \mathbb{R}$.

For example, suppose that $n = \frac{1}{2}$, we then have that

$$y = \sqrt{x} = x^{\frac{1}{2}} \Rightarrow \frac{dy}{dx} = \frac{1}{2}x^{\frac{1}{2}-1} = \frac{1}{2}x^{-\frac{1}{2}}$$

$$= \frac{1}{2\sqrt{x}}$$

Which is the result already obtained by making use of the first principle method. This result is known as the **power rule for differentiation**.

Notice that for the case where $y = k$ (a real constant) $y = kx^0 \Rightarrow \frac{dy}{dx} = k \times 0x^{0-1} = 0$.

Note: The function $y = k$ is a horizontal straight line and so its gradient will always be 0.

We therefore have the power rule:

> For the function $f : x \mapsto x^n$, we have its derivative given by $f' : x \mapsto n x^{n-1}$.
>
> This can also be written as: If $y = x^n$ then $\dfrac{dy}{dx} = n x^{n-1}$
>
> or
>
>   If $f(x) = x^n$ then $f'(x) = n x^{n-1}$

EXAMPLE

Use the power rule to differentiate the following functions

(a) x^6 (b) $\dfrac{1}{\sqrt{x}}$ (c) $\sqrt[3]{x}$ (d) $\dfrac{1}{x^2}$

SOLUTION

Before we differentiate each of these functions, note that each function must be rewritten in the form x^n before we can use the power rule.

(a)   Let $f(x) = x^6 \Rightarrow f'(x) = 6x^{6-1} = 6x^5$

(b)   Let $y = \dfrac{1}{\sqrt{x}}$. To differentiate this expression we need to rewrite it in the form x^n:

Function	Step 1 Rewrite:	Step 2 Use power rule:	Step 3 Simplify:
$y = \dfrac{1}{\sqrt{x}}$	$y = x^{-\frac{1}{2}}$	$\dfrac{dy}{dx} = -\dfrac{1}{2} x^{-\frac{1}{2}-1}$	$\dfrac{dy}{dx} = -\dfrac{1}{2} x^{-\frac{3}{2}} = -\dfrac{1}{2\sqrt{x^3}}$

(c)   Let $y = \sqrt[3]{x}$. As in the previous example, we need to rewrite this function in the form x^n before we can use the power rule:

Function	Step 1 Rewrite:	Step 2 Use power rule:	Step 3 Simplify:
$y = \sqrt[3]{x}$	$y = x^{\frac{1}{3}}$	$\dfrac{dy}{dx} = \dfrac{1}{3} x^{\frac{1}{3}-1}$	$\dfrac{dy}{dx} = \dfrac{1}{3} x^{-\frac{2}{3}} = \dfrac{1}{3\sqrt[3]{x^2}}$

(d)   Let $f(x) = \dfrac{1}{x^2}$ so that $f(x) = x^{-2}$.

Using the power rule we have, $f'(x) = -2x^{-2-1} = -2x^{-3}$. That is, $f'(x) = -\dfrac{2}{x^3}$.

An extension of the power rule is the derivative of $f:x \mapsto ax^n$, where a is a real constant. In this case we have the general result that;

$$\text{If } f:x \mapsto ax^n \text{ then } f':x \mapsto anx^{n-1}$$

EXAMPLE

Differentiate the following functions:

(a) $12x^3$ (b) $-\dfrac{4}{x}$ (c) $\dfrac{x^2}{7}$

SOLUTION

(a) Let $y = 12x^3 \Rightarrow \dfrac{dy}{dx} = 12 \times 3x^{3-1} = 36x^2$.

(b) Let $f(x) = -\dfrac{4}{x}$, that is, $f(x) = -4x^{-1} \Rightarrow f'(x) = -4 \times -1x^{-1-1} = 4x^{-2} = \dfrac{4}{x^2}$.

(c) Let $f(x) = \dfrac{x^2}{7}$, that is, $f(x) = \dfrac{1}{7}x^2 \Rightarrow f'(x) = \dfrac{1}{7} \times 2x^{2-1} = \dfrac{2}{7}x$.

DERIVATIVE OF A SUM OR DIFFERENCE

This rule states that the derivative of a sum (or a difference) is equal to the sum (or the difference) of the derivatives. That is,

$$\text{If } y = f(x) + g(x) \text{, then } \dfrac{dy}{dx} = f'(x) + g'(x)$$

Similarly,

$$\text{If } y = f(x) - g(x) \text{, then } \dfrac{dy}{dx} = f'(x) - g'(x)$$

EXAMPLE

Differentiate the following functions;

(a) $2x^3 + 5x - 9$ (b) $\sqrt{x} - \dfrac{5}{x^3} + x$

SOLUTION

(a) Let $y = 2x^3 + 5x - 9 \Rightarrow \dfrac{dy}{dx} = \dfrac{d}{dx}(2x^3 + 5x - 9) = \dfrac{d}{dx}(2x^3) + \dfrac{d}{dx}(5x) - \dfrac{d}{dx}(9)$

$$= 6x^2 + 5$$

Notice we have used a slightly different notation, namely that $f'(x) = \dfrac{d}{dx}(f(x))$.

(b)   Let $f(x) = \sqrt{x} - \dfrac{5}{x^3} + x \Rightarrow f'(x) = \dfrac{d}{dx}\left(\sqrt{x} - \dfrac{5}{x^3} + x\right) = \dfrac{d}{dx}\left(x^{\frac{1}{2}} - 5x^{-3} + x\right)$

$$= \frac{1}{2}x^{-\frac{1}{2}} - 5 \times -3x^{-3-1} + 1$$

$$= \frac{1}{2\sqrt{x}} + \frac{15}{x^4} + 1$$

MISCELLANEOUS EXAMPLES

Differentiate the following

(a) $5\sqrt{x} - 9,\ x \geq 0$

(b) $(x^3 + 2)^2$

(c) $\left(\sqrt{x} - \dfrac{2}{\sqrt{x}}\right)^2$

(d) $\dfrac{5x^2 + 4x - 3}{x}$

(e) $\sqrt{x}(7x^2 - 3x + 2)$

SOLUTION

(a) $\dfrac{d}{dx}(5\sqrt{x} - 9) = \dfrac{d}{dx}\left(5x^{\frac{1}{2}} - 9\right) = 5 \times \dfrac{1}{2}x^{\frac{1}{2}-1} - 0 = \dfrac{5}{2}x^{-\frac{1}{2}} = \dfrac{5}{2\sqrt{x}}.$

(b)   The first step is to expand the bracket so that each term is in the form of ax^n.

$\dfrac{d}{dx}((x^3 + 2)^2) = \dfrac{d}{dx}(x^6 + 4x^3 + 4) = 6x^5 + 12x^2$

(c)   Again we expand first, and then differentiate:

$\dfrac{d}{dx}\left(\left(\sqrt{x} - \dfrac{2}{\sqrt{x}}\right)^2\right) = \dfrac{d}{dx}\left((\sqrt{x})^2 - 2\sqrt{x} \times \dfrac{2}{\sqrt{x}} + \left(\dfrac{2}{\sqrt{x}}\right)^2\right) = \dfrac{d}{dx}\left(x - 4 + \dfrac{4}{x}\right)$

$$= \frac{d}{dx}(x - 4 + 4x^{-1})$$

$$= 1 - \frac{4}{x^2}$$

(d) $\dfrac{d}{dx}\left(\dfrac{5x^2 + 4x - 3}{x}\right) = \dfrac{d}{dx}\left(\dfrac{5x^2}{x} + \dfrac{4x}{x} - \dfrac{3}{x}\right) = \dfrac{d}{dx}(5x + 4 - 3x^{-1}) = 5 + \dfrac{3}{x^2}$

(e) $\dfrac{d}{dx}(\sqrt{x}(7x^2 - 3x + 2)) = \dfrac{d}{dx}\left(x^{\frac{1}{2}}(7x^2 - 3x + 2)\right) = \dfrac{d}{dx}\left(7x^{\frac{5}{2}} - 3x^{\frac{3}{2}} + 2x^{\frac{1}{2}}\right)$

$$= \frac{35}{2}x^{\frac{3}{2}} - \frac{9}{2}x^{\frac{1}{2}} + x^{-\frac{1}{2}}$$

$$= \frac{35}{2}\sqrt{x^3} - \frac{9}{2}\sqrt{x} + \frac{1}{\sqrt{x}}$$

EXERCISE 23.1

1. Find the derivative of each of the following:

(a) x^5

(b) x^9

(c) x^{25}

(d) $9x^3$

(e) $-4x^7$

(f) $\frac{1}{4}x^8$

(g) $x^2 + 8$

(h) $5x^4 + 2x - 1$

(i) $-3x^5 + 6x^3 - x$

(j) $20 - \frac{1}{3}x^4 + 10x$

(k) $3x^3 - 6x^2 + 8$

(l) $3x - 1 + \frac{x^2}{5} + x^4$

2. Find the derivative of each of the following:

(a) $\dfrac{1}{x^3}$

(b) $\sqrt{x^3}$

(c) $\sqrt{x^5}$

(d) $\sqrt[3]{x}$

(e) $4\sqrt{x}$

(f) $6\sqrt{x^3}$

(g) $2\sqrt{x} - \dfrac{3}{x} + 12$

(h) $x\sqrt{x} + \dfrac{1}{\sqrt{x}} + 2$

(i) $5\sqrt[3]{x^2} - 9x$

(j) $5x - \dfrac{x}{\sqrt{x}} + \dfrac{4}{5x^2}$

(k) $8\sqrt{x} + 3x^{-5} + \dfrac{x}{2}$

(j) $\dfrac{x}{\sqrt{x^3}} - \dfrac{2}{x}\sqrt{x^3} + \dfrac{1}{3}x^3$

3. Find the derivative of each of the following:

(a) $\sqrt{x}(x + 2)$

(b) $(x + 1)(x^3 - 1)$

(c) $x\left(x^2 + 1 - \dfrac{1}{x}\right), x \neq 0$

(d) $\dfrac{2x - 1}{x}, x \neq 0$

(e) $\dfrac{\sqrt{x} - 2}{\sqrt{x}}, x > 0$

(f) $\dfrac{x^2 - x + \sqrt{x}}{2x}, x \neq 0$

(g) $\dfrac{3x^2 - 7x^3}{x^2}, x \neq 0$

(h) $\left(x - \dfrac{2}{x}\right)^2, x \neq 0$

(i) $\left(x + \dfrac{1}{x^2}\right)^2, x \neq 0$

(j) $\sqrt{3x} - \dfrac{1}{3\sqrt{x}}, x > 0$

(k) $(x - \sqrt[5]{x})^2, x \geq 0$

(l) $\left(\dfrac{1}{\sqrt{x}} - \sqrt{x}\right)^3, x > 0$

4. (a) Show that if $f(x) = x^2 - x$, then $f'(x) = 1 + \dfrac{2f(x)}{x}$.

(b) Show that if $f(x) = \sqrt{2x} - 2\sqrt{x}, x \geq 0$, then $\sqrt{2x}f'(x) = 1 - \sqrt{2}, x > 0$.

(c) Show that if $y = ax^n$, where a is real and $n \in N$, then $\dfrac{dy}{dx} = \dfrac{ny}{x}, x \neq 0$.

(d) Show that if $y = \dfrac{1}{\sqrt{x}}, x > 0$, then $\dfrac{dy}{dx} + \dfrac{y}{2x} = 0$.

EXAMPLE

Find the gradient of the curve with equation $y = 9x - x^3$ at the point (2, 11).

SOLUTION

We first determine the equation that will give the gradient at any point on the curve, that is, we find $\dfrac{dy}{dx}$:

Using the power rule we have, $y = 9x - x^3 \Rightarrow \dfrac{dy}{dx} = 9 - 3x^2$.

Therefore, for $x = 2$ we have that $\dfrac{dy}{dx} = 9 - 3(2)^2 = -3$.

The gradient of the curve with equation $y = 9x - x^3$ at the point (2, 11) is -3.

EXAMPLE

(a)   Determine the coordinate(s) on the curve $x \mapsto x^3 - x + 2$ where the gradient is 11.
(b)   Find the value(s) of x such that a tangent drawn on this curve would be horizontal.

SOLUTION

(a)   Let $f(x) = x^3 - x + 2$, we need to find values of x for which $f'(x) = 11$:

We have that $f'(x) = 3x^2 - 1$, so that $3x^2 - 1 = 11 \Leftrightarrow 3x^2 - 12 = 0$

$$\Leftrightarrow 3(x^2 - 4) = 0$$
$$\Leftrightarrow 3(x - 2)(x + 2) = 0$$
$$x = 2 \text{ or } x = -2$$

So for $x = 2$, $f(2) = 8$. Similarly, for $x = -2$, $f(-2) = -4$.
Therefore, the required coordinates are (2, 8) and (−2,−4).

(b)   When a horizontal tangent is drawn to a curve, the gradient of that tangent must be zero. Therefore the gradient of the curve will also be zero at that point. We need to find x, such that $f'(x) = 0$:

Now, $f'(x) = 3x^2 - 1 = 0 \Leftrightarrow x^2 = \dfrac{1}{3}$

$$x = \pm\dfrac{1}{\sqrt{3}}$$

EXERCISE 23.2

1. Find the gradient of the function at the indicated point.

(a) $f(x) = x^3 - 2$ at $(1, -1)$ (b) $f(x) = \dfrac{1}{x}$ at $(2, 0.5)$

(c) $f(x) = (2x - 1)^2$ at $(2, 9)$ (d) $y = (2x + 1)^2$ at $(0, 1)$

(e) $y = x^2 - \dfrac{1}{x^2} + 2$ at $(1, 2)$ (f) $y = \sqrt[3]{x^2} - \sqrt{x} + x$ at $(1, 1)$

(g) $f(x) = 1 - \sqrt[3]{x}$ at $(8, -1)$ (h) $y = x\sqrt{x} + \dfrac{x}{\sqrt{x}} - \dfrac{\sqrt{x}}{x}$ at $(4, \dfrac{19}{2})$

2. Find the value(s) of x, so that $f'(x) = 0$ given that $f(x) = x^3 - 8x$.

3. For the curve with equation $y = x^2 - 12x$, find:

(a) $\dfrac{dy}{dx}$

(b) the gradient where $x = -3$

(c) the coordinates of the point where the gradient is 4.

4. For the curve with equation $y = -x^3 + 3x$, find:

(a) $\dfrac{dy}{dx}$

(b) the gradient where $x = 1$

(c) the coordinates of the point where the gradient is -3.

5. For the curve with equation $f(x) = \dfrac{1}{4}x^2(x^2 - 1)$,

(a) find the coordinates where its gradient is zero,

(b) the set of values of x for which its gradient is positive.

6. Determine those values of x for which the curve with equation $y = 8 - x^2$ will have the same gradient as the curve with equation $y = x^3 - x$.

7. Find the gradient of the function $x: \mapsto x^3 + x^2 - 2x$ at the point(s) where

(a) it crosses the x–axis,

(b) it cuts the y–axis.

8. The curve with equation $y = ax + \dfrac{b}{x^2}$ passes through the point $(2, 0)$, where its gradient is found to be 3. Determine the values of a and b.

DIFFERENTIATING WITH VARIABLES OTHER THAN x AND y

Although it was convenient to establish the underlying theory of differentiation based on the use of the variables x and y, it must be pointed out that not all expressions are written in terms of x and y. In fact, many of the formulae that we use are often written in terms of variables other than y and x, e.g., volume of a sphere is given by $V = \frac{4}{3}\pi r^3$, the

displacement of a particle moving with constant acceleration is given by $s = ut + \frac{1}{2}at^2$.

However, it is reassuring to know that the rules are still the same regardless of the variables involved. Thus, if we have that y is a function of x, we can differentiate y *with respect to*

(w.r.t) x to find $\frac{dy}{dx}$. On the other hand, if we have that y is a function of t, we would

differentiate y w.r.t. t and write $\frac{dy}{dt}$. Similarly, if W was a function of θ, we would

differentiate W w.r.t. θ and write $\frac{dW}{d\theta}$.

EXAMPLE

Differentiate the following functions with respect to the appropriate variable

(a) $V = \frac{4}{3}\pi r^3$ (b) $p = 3w^3 - 2w + 20$ (c) $s = 10t + 4t^2$

SOLUTION

(a)   For this expression we have that V is a function of r, so that we would need to

differentiate V with respect to r: $V = \frac{4}{3}\pi r^3 \Rightarrow \frac{dV}{dr} = \frac{4}{3}\pi(3r^2) = 4\pi r^2$.

(b)   This time we have that p is a function of w, and so we would differentiate p with

respect to w: $p = 3w^3 - 2w + 20 \Rightarrow \frac{dp}{dw} = 9w^2 - 2$.

(c)   In this expression we have that s is a function of t and so we differentiate s w.r.t t:

$s = 10t + 4t^2 \Rightarrow \frac{ds}{dt} = 10 + 8t$

EXERCISE 23.3

1.   Differentiate the following functions with respect to the appropriate variable.

(a) $s = 12t^4 - \sqrt{t}$ (b) $Q = \left(n + \frac{1}{n^2}\right)^2$ (c) $P = \sqrt{r}(r + \sqrt[3]{r} - 2)$

(d) $T = \frac{(\theta - \sqrt{\theta})^3}{\theta}$ (e) $A = 40L - L^3$ (f) $F = \frac{50}{v^2} - v$

(g) $V = 2l^3 + 5l$ (h) $A = 2\pi h + 4h^2$ (i) $N = n^4 - \sqrt[3]{n} + \pi n$

23. 2 RATES OF CHANGE

As we have already seen, $\dfrac{dy}{dx}$ measures **the rate of change of y with respect to x**. In the same way, we have that

$$\dfrac{dA}{dr} \text{ measures the rate of change of } A \text{ with respect to } r,$$

$$\dfrac{dV}{dt} \text{ measures the rate of change of } V \text{ with respect to } t \text{ and}$$

$$\dfrac{dP}{dV} \text{ measures the rate of change of } P \text{ with respect to } V.$$

For example, if Am^2 is a measure of the area of a circle of radius r, then $\dfrac{dA}{dr}$ measures the rate of change of the area A with respect to its radius r. Given that $A = \pi r^2$, we, then have that $\dfrac{dA}{dr} = 2\pi r$. We note that a rate of change needs to have two quantities specified: what quantity is changing, and what it is changing in respect to. However, often we simply use the term 'the rate of change of ...'. If no reference is made to a second quantity, then it can be assumed that we are referring to the rate of change with respect to time. So that the rate of change of N, where N measures the population size of a herd of elephants, would be given by $\dfrac{dN}{dt}$.

THE SIGN OF RATES OF CHANGE

If we have a positive rate over some interval $[a, b]$, then the **function increases** over the interval $[a, b]$.

e.g., If $\dfrac{dy}{dx}$ is positive on the interval $[a, b]$, then the values of y increase as the values of x increase (on $[a, b]$).

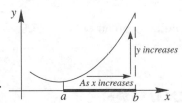

If we have a negative rate over some interval $[a, b]$, then the **function decreases** over the interval $[a, b]$.

e.g., If $\dfrac{dy}{dx}$ is negative on the interval $[a, b]$, then the values of y decrease as the values of x increase (on $[a, b]$).

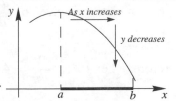

If we have a zero rate over some interval $[a, b]$, then the **function is constant** over the interval $[a, b]$.

e.g., If $\dfrac{dy}{dx}$ is zero on the interval $[a, b]$, then the values of y are constant for all values of x (on $[a, b]$).

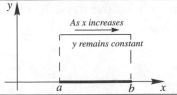

EXAMPLE

The number, $N(t)$, of bacteria in a colony is given by the function

$$t \mapsto 1.25t^2 + 20t + 980, \, t \geq 0$$

where t is measured in hours.
(a)   Find the rate of growth of the bacteria when $t = 4$.
(b)   Show that $N(t)$ is an increasing function.

SOLUTION

(a)   Let $N(t) = 1.25t^2 + 20t + 980, t \geq 0$. The rate of growth is given by $\dfrac{dN}{dt}$ or $N'(t)$,

therefore, we have $N'(t) = 2.5t + 20$.
So that when $t = 4$, $N'(4) = 2.5 \times 4 + 20 = 30$.
That is, the colony is growing at a rate of 30 bacteria per hour (when $t = 4$).

(b)   To show that $N(t)$ is an increasing function, we need to show that its derivative is
positive over its given domain. That is, we need to show that $N'(t) > 0$ (for $t \geq 0$).

Now, $N'(t) = 2.5t + 20$,
so that for $t \geq 0$, $N'(t) \geq 20$.
Therefore we have that
$$N'(t) > 0 \text{ for } t \geq 0,$$
$\therefore N(t)$ is an increasing function.

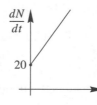

Graphical approach:
The graph of $N'(t)$ clearly
shows that $N'(t) > 0$ for $t \geq 0$,
and so, $N(t)$ is an increasing
function (for $t \geq 0$).

EXAMPLE

The radius of a sphere is increasing in such a way that its volume , V cm^3, at time t

minutes is given by $V = 5000 + 4500t - 300t^2 + 12t^3$, for $0 \leq t \leq 10$.
Find the rate at which the volume iis increasing when $t = 5$.

SOLUTION

The rate of change is given by $\dfrac{dV}{dt} = 4500 - 600t + 36t^2$

Therefore, when $t = 5$, $\dfrac{dV}{dt} = 4500 - 600 \times 5 + 36 \times 5^2 = 2400$.

That is, after five days, the volume of the balloon is **increasing** at a rate of 2400 cm^3 per
minute..

APPLICATION TO ECONOMICS

There are three important functions used in the area of manufacturing a commodity:

1. The **Cost** function, $C(x)$

2. The **Revenue** function, $R(x)$

3. The **Profit** function. $P(x)$,

where x is the number of items produced.

The rate of change with respect to x for each of these functions, $\dfrac{dC}{dx}, \dfrac{dR}{dx}$ and $\dfrac{dP}{dx}$ are referred to as the **Marginal Cost**, the **Marginal Revenue** and the **Marginal Profit** respectively.

EXAMPLE

The cost in dollars of manufacturing x units of a product is given by the equation
$$C(x) = x^3 - 20x^2 + 300x + 1000, x \geq 0.$$
If each item sells for $300, find the marginal profit when 100 units are being manufactured.

SOLUTION

First we need the profit equation:
By definition, we have that **Profit = Revenue – Cost**,
$$P(x) = R(x) - C(x)$$
where the revenue, $R(x) = 300x$ (as each item sells for $300).

Therefore we have
$$P(x) = 300x - (x^3 - 20x^2 + 300x + 1000)$$
$$= -x^3 + 20x^2 - 1000$$

So that the marginal profit, $\dfrac{dP}{dx} = -3x^2 + 40x$.

Therefore, for $x = 100$, we have that $\dfrac{dP}{dx} = -3(100)^2 + 40(100)$
$$= -26,000$$

EXERCISE 23.4

1. The number of deer, N, involved in a breeding program set up in a reserve has been modelled by the function $N = \dfrac{1}{10}t^2 + 4t + 50$, where t is measured in years since the program started. Find the rate at which the deer population is increasing 2 years after the program started.

2. The volume, $V\ cm^3$, of an object is given by the relation

$$V(t) = 0.5t^3 - 18t^2 + 216t + 200,\ t \ge 0\ ,$$

where t is measured in days.
(a) Find the initial volume of the object.
(b) Find the rate of change of the volume when $t = 5$.

3. The number of organisms, N, present in a culture of bacteria, t hours from when

observations were first made, is given by $N(t) = 3t^2 + 15t + 800\ ,\ t \ge 0$.
(a) Find the rate of change of the number of organisms after 10 hours.
(b) Show that the number of organisms will always increase. Is this a realistic
   model?

4. The number of sales, N thousand, made by a company is related to its advertising

cost, x thousand dollars, by the function $N = \dfrac{x^2}{9000}(300 - x),\ 0 \le x \le 200$.

(a) Find the rate of change of the number of sales (*with respect to the advertising
   cost*) for   (i) $x = 50$ (ii) $x = 100$ (iii) $x = 150$

5. The profit P made by an entertainment centre when selling x bags of lollies was

modelled by the equation $P = 2.5x - \dfrac{1}{20000}x^2 - 3000,\ 0 \le x \le 50000$.

(a) For what values of x is the centre making a positive profit?
(b) For what values of x is the profit   (i)   increasing   (ii)   decreasing?

6. The production strategy of a company manufacturing electrical components is based
on the following models;
Demand equation: $x = 12000 - 30p$
Where x is the number of components retailers are likely to buy per month at $\$p$ per
component.
Cost equation: $C(x) = 50000 + 20x$

(a) Show that the revenue equation , $R(x)$, is given by $x \mapsto x\left(400 - \dfrac{x}{30}\right)$.

(b) Find the marginal revenue for a production level of 4000 units.

(c) Show that the profit, $P(x)$, is given by $x \mapsto 380x - \dfrac{1}{30}x^2 - 50000$.

(d) Determine the marginal profit when 5000 units are produced.
(e) For what values of x is the profit increasing?

23.3 CURVE SKETCHING

INCREASING AND DECREASING FUNCTIONS

We have already come across the following definitions:

A function f is said to be **increasing** if its **graph rises** as it is sketched from left to right.

That is, $\qquad x_2 > x_1 \Rightarrow f(x_2) > f(x_1)$

(i.e., the y–values increase as the x–values increase).

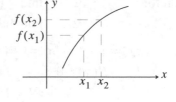

Similarly,

A function f is said to be **decreasing** if its **graph falls** as it is sketched from left to right.

That is, $\qquad x_2 > x_1 \Rightarrow f(x_2) < f(x_1)$

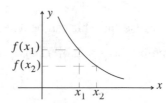

(i.e., the y–values decrease as the x–values increase).

... A CALCULUS POINT OF VIEW

The derivative can be used to determine whether a function is increasing or decreasing. It can also be used to help us find the values of x for which the function is increasing or decreasing.

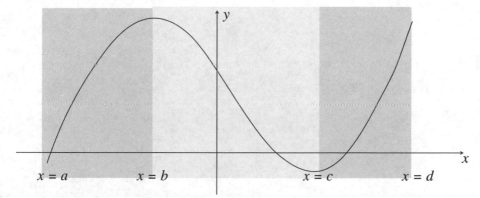

We see that any tangent line drawn in the interval $a < x < b$ will always have a positive gradient. This means that $\dfrac{dy}{dx} = f'(x) > 0$ in this region.

We see that any tangent line drawn in the interval $b < x < c$ will always have a negative gradient. This means that $\dfrac{dy}{dx} = f'(x) < 0$ in this region.

We see that any tangent line drawn in the interval $c < x < d$ will always have a positive gradient. This means that $\dfrac{dy}{dx} = f'(x) > 0$ in this region.

This means that to determine where a function is increasing or decreasing, find those values of x for which $f'(x) > 0$ or $f'(x) < 0$ respectively.

EXAMPLE

Find the values of x for which the function with equation $f(x) = 1 + 4x - x^2$ is increasing.

SOLUTION

By definition, a function is increasing for those values of x for which $f'(x) > 0$.

Therefore: 1.   find $f'(x)$

                2.   find the values of x such that $f'(x) > 0$

Now, $f(x) = 1 + 4x - x^2 \Rightarrow f'(x) = 4 - 2x$

Therefore, $f'(x) > 0 \Leftrightarrow 4 - 2x > 0$

$$\Leftrightarrow 4 > 2x$$

$$\Leftrightarrow x < 2$$

Notice also that this can be determined by

sketching the graph of $f(x) = 1 + 4x - x^2$:

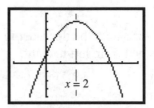

STATIONARY POINTS

So far we have discussed the conditions for a function to be increasing $(f'(x) > 0)$ and for a function to be decreasing $(f'(x) < 0)$.

But what happens at the point where a function changes from an increasing state to a decreasing state (or vice–versa)?

Points where this happens are known as **turning points** or **stationary points**. Stationary points seem to be better descriptors, as the function is in a state where it is neither increasing nor decreasing. Whereas (as we shall find) turning points have an association with aspects of graphs that are also referred to as **local maximum** and **local minimum** points. In any case, the following conditions will hold true:

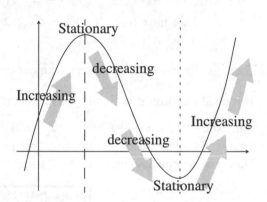

At the point(s) where $\dfrac{dy}{dx} = f'(x) = 0$

we have a **stationary point** (or turning point).

There are three types of stationary points, namely;   **local maximum** point,
                      local minimum point,
                      point of inflection.

1. LOCAL MAXIMUM

When sketching a curve, if the point $P(x_1, y_1)$ is a local maximum point then the following properties hold:

i. $y_1 = f(x_1)$ is the (local) maximum value of $y = f(x)$.

ii.   At $P(x_1, y_1)$, $\dfrac{dy}{dx} = f'(x) = 0$ that is $f'(x_1) = 0$.

iii.   For $x < x_1$ then $\dfrac{dy}{dx} > 0$

               $x > x_1$ then $\dfrac{dy}{dx} < 0$

Where the chosen value of x is just slightly greater than or less than x_1.

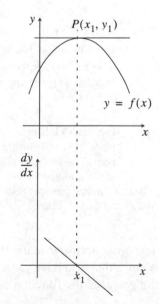

iv.   **Graph of the gradient function**:

        Notice that the values of $\dfrac{dy}{dx}$ are decreasing from

        positive values to **negative** values. Sometimes this is referred to as the sign of the first derivative.

EXAMPLE

Find the local maximum value of the function whose equation is $f(x) = -3 + 4x - x^2$.

SOLUTION

First we differentiate: $\quad f(x) = -3 + 4x - x^2 \Rightarrow f'(x) = 4 - 2x$

Next, equate $f'(x)$ to 0 and solve for x: $\qquad\qquad 0 = 4 - 2x$

$$\Leftrightarrow x = 2$$

To ensure that we actually have obtained a local maximum we now choose values of x slightly greater than 2 and slightly less than 2, for example, choose $x = 1.9$ and $x = 2.1$.

For $x = 1.9$, we have that $f'(1.9) = 4 - 2(1.9) = 0.2$.

For $x = 2.1$ we have that $f'(2.1) = 4 - 2(2.1) = -0.2$.

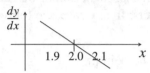

The sign diagram for $\dfrac{dy}{dx}$ agrees with our conditions for a local maximum point to occur.

The local maximum value of $f(x)$, is then found by substituting $x = 2$ into the given

equation: $\quad f(2) = -3 + 4(2) - (2)^2 = 1$.

That is, the local maximum occurs at the point (2,1).

This process can also be carried out using the TI–83:

1. Enter equation

2. Use the **CALC**
   function, and then
   select **4:maximum**

3. Press ENTER.
   This will prompt you to
   choose a lower (left)
   bound and then an upper
   (right) bound.

4. Press ENTER once
   more. This will provide
   both x– and y– values
   of the stationary point.
   The last window provides both
   the x– and the y–ordinate.

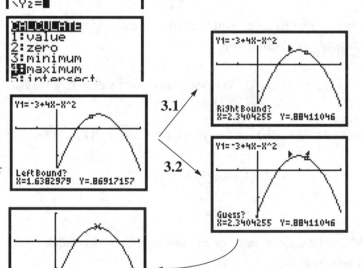

Move the cursor and press ENTER
twice to obtain last window.

The other option is to use the fMax command from the MATH function. However, this will require that you have some idea of the left and right bounds (which can be estimated from the graph of the function). We illustrate this in the next example.

EXAMPLE

Determine the coordinates of the local maximum for the function $f(x) = \frac{1}{3}x^3(4-x)$

SOLUTION

This time we start by sketching a graph of the function, setting the WINDOW parameters with some appropriate range of values :

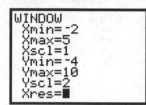

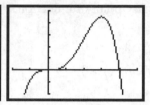

We can now use the **fMax** command from the **MATH** function to determine maximum value of our function. We can also locate the x–value for where the maximum occurs by using the TRACE function:

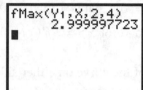

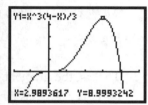

Therefore, the coordinates to 2 d.p are given by (3.0, 9.0).

Using an algebraic approach to this question, we have:

$$f(x) = \frac{1}{3}x^3(4-x) = \frac{1}{3}(4x^3 - x^4) \Rightarrow f'(x) = \frac{1}{3}(12x^2 - 4x^3)$$

Equating to zero, we have, $\frac{1}{3}(12x^2 - 4x^3) = 0 \Leftrightarrow \frac{4}{3}x^2(3-x) = 0 \Leftrightarrow x = 3$ or $x = 0$

From the graph it is clear that the maximum occurs at $x = 3$, so that $f(3) = 9$.

2   LOCAL MINIMUM

When sketching a curve, if the point $P(x_1, y_1)$ is a local minimum point then the following properties hold:

i. $y_1 = f(x_1)$ is the (local) minimum value of $y = f(x)$.

ii.   At $P(x_1, y_1)$, $\frac{dy}{dx} = f'(x) = 0$ that is $f'(x_1) = 0$.

iii.   For $x > x_1$ then $\frac{dy}{dx} > 0$

        $x < x_1$ then $\frac{dy}{dx} < 0$

Where the chosen value of x is just slightly greater than or less than x_1 .

iv.   **Graph of the gradient function**:

      Notice that the values of $\frac{dy}{dx}$ are increasing from

      negative values to **positive** values. Sometimes this is referred to as the sign of the first derivative.

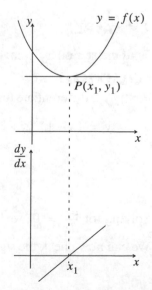

3 POINTS OF INFLECTION

There are two types:

A. **Stationary points of inflection**
B. **Non–stationary points of inflection**.

A. STATIONARY POINT OF INFLECTION

The following properties hold at a stationary point of inflection.

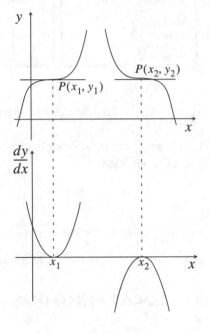

i. At $P(x_1, y_1)$, $f'(x) = 0$. That is $f'(x_1) = 0$.

ii. For $x < x_1$, $f'(x) > 0$ and for $x > x_1$, $f'(x) > 0$

Similarly,

At $P(x_2, y_2)$, $f'(x) = 0$. That is $f'(x_2) = 0$.

For $x < x_2$, $f'(x) < 0$ and for $x > x_2$, $f'(x) < 0$

That is, the gradient of the curve on either side of x_1 (or x_2) has the same sign.

iii. Graph of the **gradient function**, $y = f'(x)$:

Notice that the values of $f'(x)$ have the same sign on either side of $x = x_1$.

Notice that at $x = x_1$, the gradient of $f'(x)$ is also equal to zero. That is, the derivative of the derivative is equal to zero. We write this as $f''(x)$.

Therefore **if we have** a stationary point of inflection at $x = x_1$ then $f''(x_1) = 0$.

EXAMPLE

Find the stationary point of inflection for the graph with equation $y = (x-1)^3(x+2)$.

SOLUTION

Firstly we differentiate (using the product rule):

$$y = (x-1)^3(x+2) \Rightarrow \frac{dy}{dx} = 3(x-1)^2(x+2) + (x-1)^3(1)$$

$$= (x-1)^2[3(x+2) + (x-1)]$$

$$= (x-1)^2(4x+5)$$

Solving for $\frac{dy}{dx} = 0$, we have, $(x-1)^2(4x+5) = 0 \Leftrightarrow x = 1$ or $x = -\frac{5}{4}(= -1.25)$.

We can now check the sign of the derivative on either side of $x = 1$ and $x = -1.25$

At $x = 1$:

For $x = 0.9$, $\dfrac{dy}{dx} = (-0.1)^2(8.6) = 0.086 > 0$

For $x = 1.1$, $\dfrac{dy}{dx} = (0.1)^2(9.4) = 0.094 > 0$

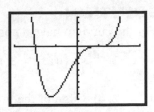

Therefore we have a stationary point of inflection at $x = 1$ and $y = 0$, i.e., at $(1,0)$. This can also be seen from the graph of $y = (x-1)^3(x+2)$.

For $x = -1.25$, the graph shows a local minimum occurring at this point.

B. NON-STATIONARY POINT OF INFLECTION

The following properties hold at a non-stationary point of inflection:

i.   At $P(x_1, y_1)$, $f''(x) = 0$. That is $f''(x_1) = 0$.

ii.   For $x < x_1$, $f'(x) > 0$ and for $x > x_1$, $f'(x) > 0$

Similarly,

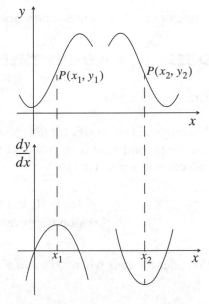

At $P(x_2, y_2)$, $f''(x) = 0$. That is $f''(x_2) = 0$.

For $x < x_2$, $f'(x) < 0$ and for $x > x_2$, $f'(x) < 0$.

That is, the gradient of the curve on either side of x_1 (or x_2) has the same sign.

iii.   Graph of the **gradient function**, $y = f'(x)$:

Notice that the values of $f'(x)$ have the same sign on either side of $x = x_1$.

Notice that at $x = x_1$, the gradient of $f'(x)$ is also equal to zero. That is, the derivative of the derivative is equal to zero. We write this as $f''(x)$.

Therefore if we have a non-stationary point of inflection at $x = x_1$ then $f''(x_1) = 0$.

EXAMPLE

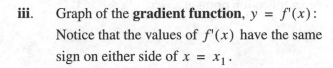

Show that the curve with equation $y = x^4 - 4x^3$ has a non-stationary point of inflection at $x = 2$.

SOLUTION

For the curve to have a non–stationary point of inflection at $x = 2$ we need to show that:

1. $\dfrac{d^2y}{dx^2} = 0$ at $x = 2$ **and**

2. the sign of the gradient, $\dfrac{dy}{dx}$, is the same on both sides of $x = 2$ **and**

3. that $\dfrac{dy}{dx} \neq 0$ when $x = 2$.

A quick sketch of the function indicates that a point of inflection occurs at $x = 2$:

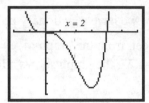

Now, $\dfrac{dy}{dx} = 4x^3 - 12x^2 \Rightarrow \dfrac{d^2y}{dx^2} = 12x^2 - 24x$.

For $x = 2$, $\dfrac{d^2y}{dx^2} = 12(2)^2 - 24(2) = 0$ and $\dfrac{dy}{dx} = -16(\ \neq 0)$.

For $x = 2.1$, $\dfrac{dy}{dx} = -15.876$ and for $x = 1.9$, $\dfrac{dy}{dx} = -15.88$,

Therefore we have a non–stationary point of inflection at $x = 2$.

DOES $f''(a) = 0$ IMPLY THERE IS A POINT OF INFLECTION AT $x = a$?

The answer is **NO**!

Although it is necessary for the second derivative to be zero at a point of inflection, the fact that the second derivative is zero at $x = a$ does not mean that you must have a point of inflection at $x = a$. That is:

$f''(a) = 0$ **is a necessary but not a sufficient**
reason for there to be an inflection point at $x = a$.

Consider the case where $f(x) = x^4$.

Now, $f''(x) = 12x^2$, therefore solving for $f''(x) = 0$,

we have $\qquad\qquad\qquad 12x^2 = 0 \Leftrightarrow x = 0$.

A sketch of f shows that although $f''(x) = 0$ at $x = 0$, there is a local minimum and not a point of inflection at $x = 0$.

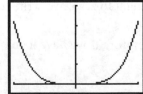

In other words, finding where $f''(x) = 0$ is not enough to indicate that there is an inflection point. To determine if there is a point of inflection you need to check the concavity on either side of the x-value in question. Or, check the sign of the first derivative on either side of the x-value in question.

EXAMPLE

Find and classify all stationary points (and inflection points) of $f(x) = x^3 - 3x^2 - 9x + 1$

SOLUTION

Now, $f(x) = x^3 - 3x^2 - 9x + 1 \Rightarrow f'(x) = 3x^2 - 6x - 9$

Solving for stationary points we have, $3x^2 - 6x - 9 = 0 \Leftrightarrow 3(x-3)(x+1) = 0$

$$\Leftrightarrow x = 3 \text{ or } x = -1$$

Using the sign of the first derivative, we have:

For $x < 3$ $(x = 2.9)$ $f'(2.9) < 0$ and for $x > 3$ $(x = 3.1)$ $f'(3.1) > 0$.

Therefore, there is a local minimum at $(3, -26)$.

For $x < -1$ $(x = -1.1)$ $f'(-1.1) > 0$ and for $x > -1$ $(x = -0.9)$ $f'(-0.9) < 0$

Therefore, there is a local maximum at $(-1, 6)$.

Checking for inflection points, we have: $f''(x) = 0 \Leftrightarrow 6x - 6 = 0 \Leftrightarrow x = 1$.

Now, for $x < 1$ (0.9) $f'(0.9) < 0$ and for $x > 1$ $(x = 1.1)$ $f'(1.1) < 0$.

Therefore, there is a point of inflection at $(1, -10)$.

EXAMPLE

Sketch the graph of the function $f(x) = x^4 - 2x^2$, clearly marking any stationary points and points of inflection.

SOLUTION

We first find the **stationary points** (if any).

This means that we must solve for $f'(x) = 0$:

Now, $\qquad f'(x) = 4x^3 - 4x = 4x(x^2 - 1)$

$\qquad \therefore 4x(x^2 - 1) = 0 \Leftrightarrow 4x(x+1)(x-1) = 0$

$\qquad\qquad\qquad \Leftrightarrow x = -1 \text{ or } x = 1 \text{ or } x = 0$

We now check for the nature of each point

At $x = 0$: $\quad x = -0.1, \ f'(-0.1) = 0.396 > 0$

$\qquad\qquad\quad x = 0.1, \ \ f'(0.1) = -0.396 < 0$

Therefore, we have a local maximum point at $(0,0)$.

At $x = 1$:

$\qquad\qquad x = 0.9, \ f'(0.9) = -0.684 < 0$

$\qquad\qquad x = 1.1, \ \ f'(1.1) = 0.924 > 0$

Therefore, we have a local minimum point at $(1,-1)$.

At $x = -1$:

$\qquad\qquad x = -0.9, \ f'(-0.9) = 0.684 > 0$

$\qquad\qquad x = -1.1, \ f'(-1.1) = -0.924 < 0$

Hence, we have a local minimum point at $(-1, -1)$.

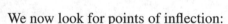

We now look for points of inflection:

We need to solve for $f''(x) = 0$:

Now, $f''(x) = 0 \Rightarrow 12x^2 - 4 = 0$

$\qquad\qquad \Leftrightarrow 4(3x^2 - 1) = 0$

$\qquad\qquad \Leftrightarrow x = \dfrac{1}{\sqrt{3}}(\ \approx 0.58) \text{ or } x = -\dfrac{1}{\sqrt{3}}(\ \approx -0.58)$

At $x = \dfrac{1}{\sqrt{3}}, f\left(\dfrac{1}{\sqrt{3}}\right) = \left(\dfrac{1}{\sqrt{3}}\right)^4 - 2\left(\dfrac{1}{\sqrt{3}}\right)^2 = -\dfrac{5}{9}$ similarly $f\left(-\dfrac{1}{\sqrt{3}}\right) = -\dfrac{5}{9}$

Next, we check to see if these are indeed points of inflection.

At $x = \dfrac{1}{\sqrt{3}}$ we have: $\qquad\qquad\qquad$ At $x = -\dfrac{1}{\sqrt{3}}$ we have:

$\quad x = 0.5, \ f'(0.5) \approx -1.5 < 0 \qquad\qquad\qquad x = -0.5, \ f'(0.5) \approx 1.5 > 0$

$\quad x = 0.6, \ f'(0.6) \approx -1.54 < 0 \qquad\qquad\qquad x = -0.6, \ f'(0.6) \approx 1.54 > 0$

Therefore, there are non–stationary points of inflection at $\left(\dfrac{1}{\sqrt{3}}, -\dfrac{5}{9}\right)$ and $\left(-\dfrac{1}{\sqrt{3}}, -\dfrac{5}{9}\right)$.

EXERCISE 23.5

1. Find the coordinates and nature of the stationary points for the following functions:

(a) $y = 3 + 2x - x^2$ (b) $y = x^2 + 9x$

(c) $y = x^3 - 27x + 9$ (d) $f(x) = x^3 - 6x^2 + 8$

(e) $f(x) = 3 + 9x - 3x^2 - x^3$ (f) $y = (x - 1)(x^2 - 4)$

(g) $f(x) = x - 2\sqrt{x}, x \geq 0$ (h) $g(x) = x^4 - 8x^2 + 16$

(i) $y = (x - 1)^2(x + 1)$ (j) $y = x\sqrt{x} - x, x \geq 0$

(k) $g(x) = x + \dfrac{4}{x}, x \neq 0$ (l) $f(x) = x^2 + \dfrac{1}{x^2}, x \neq 0$

2. Sketch the following functions:

(a) $y = 5 - 3x - x^2$ (b) $f(x) = x^2 + \dfrac{1}{2}x + \dfrac{3}{4}$

(c) $f(x) = x^3 + 6x^2 + 9x + 4$ (d) $f(x) = x^3 - 4x$

(e) $f(x) = \dfrac{1}{3}x^3 - x^2 + 4$ (f) $y = 4x^3 - x^4$

(g) $y = x^3 - 8$ (h) $y = x^4 - 16$

(i) $y = x - 4x\sqrt{x}, x \geq 0$ (j) $f(x) = x - 2\sqrt{x}, x \geq 0$

3. Find and describe the nature of all stationary points and points of inflection for the function $f(x) = x^3 + 3x^2 - 9x + 2$.

4. Sketch the graph of $x \mapsto x^4 - 4x^2$.

5. (a) Find the maximum value of the function $y = 6x - x^2, 4 \leq x \leq 7$

(b) Find the minimum value of the function $y = 6x - x^2, 2 \leq x \leq 6$

(c) Find the maximum value of the function $y = 2x - x^3, -2 \leq x \leq 6$

(d) Find the maximum value of the function $y = 36x - x^4, 2 \leq x \leq 3$

6. For the function $f(x) = \dfrac{1}{3}x^3 - x^2 - 3x + 8, -6 \leq x \leq 6$ find;

i.   the minimum value,   ii.   the maximum value.

23.4 APPLIED MAXIMUM AND MINIMUM PROBLEMS

The techniques and theory that have been developed in previous sections can be applied to practical problems in which the maximum or minimum value of a quantity is required. Problems that require the use of this theory can be found in many real life situations: manufacturers wanting to minimize their costs, designers wanting to maximize the available space to be used (under specific constraints), farmers wanting to maximize the area of a paddock at a minimum cost, etc. These types of problems often require the construction of an appropriate function that models a particular situation, from which we can then derive some optimum quantity or a critical value for which this optimum quantity exists. We proceed with a number of examples:

EXAMPLE

The points PQR form the corner of a house, where angle PQR is a right angle. Running parallel to these walls is a garden patch.
20 metres of fencing is available to create an enclosure PUTSRQ, in such a way that
$PU = RS = x$. Assume that $PQ = QR = y$.

a. Express ST in terms of x and y.
b. Find an expression for y in terms of x.
c. What area does this garden patch cover (give your answer in terms of x).
d. Find the maximum area enclosed by this fence and the walls. Justify your answer.

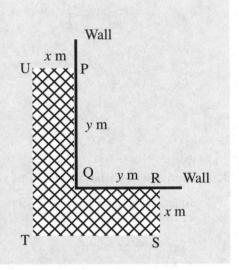

SOLUTION

a. $ST = UP + QR = x + y$.

b. There is 20 m of fencing available, therefore, $PU + UT + TS + SR = 20$
Therefore we have, $x + x + 2(x + y) = 20$ and so $y = 10 - 2x$.
Note: As $y \geq 0 \Rightarrow 10 - 2x \geq 0$
$$\Leftrightarrow x \leq 5, \text{ we must have that } x \geq 0.$$
That is, there is a restriction on x: $0 \leq x \leq 5$.

c.   The required area, Am^2, is found by breaking
     the shape into three sections:
     So that

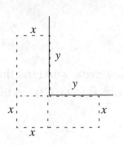

$$A = xy + xy + x^2$$
$$= 2xy + x^2$$
$$= 2x(10 - 2x) + x^2 \text{ Given that } y = 10 - 2x$$
$$= 20x - 3x^2$$

     Therefore, we have that $A = 20x - 3x^2, 0 \leq x \leq 5$

d.   Finding stationary points: $\dfrac{dA}{dx} = 20 - 6x$

     Now, $\dfrac{dA}{dx} = 0 \Leftrightarrow 20 - 6x = 0 \Leftrightarrow x = \dfrac{10}{3}$.

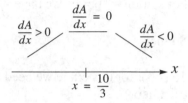

     Using the sign test we see that a local maximum

     does occur at $x = \dfrac{10}{3}$:

     (Note: For $x = 0$, $A = 0$ and for $x = 5$, $A = 25$.)

     Substituting $x = \dfrac{10}{3}$ into the area equation, we have that the maximum area in

     square metres is $A = 20\left(\dfrac{10}{3}\right) - 3\left(\dfrac{10}{3}\right)^2 = \dfrac{100}{3}$.

EXAMPLE

Find the point on the curve $y = x^2$ so that the square of the distance to the point (10,0) is
a minimum.

SOLUTION

We start by drawing a diagram:

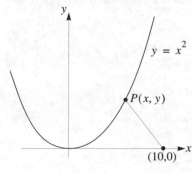

Consider some point $P(x, y)$ on the curve $y = x^2$.
By closest, we mean the shortest distance from the point
P to the point (10,0).
In this case we use the formula for the distance between

two points: $L = \sqrt{(x_2 - x_1)^2 + (y_2 - y_1)^2}$,

where L is the distance from (x_1, y_1) to (x_2, y_2).
Using the points $P(x, y)$ and (10,0) we have:

$$L = \sqrt{(x-10)^2 + (y-0)^2}$$
$$= \sqrt{(x-10)^2 + y^2}$$

However, we know that $y = x^2$ (seeing as P lies on the curve). Therefore the distance from P to $(10,0)$ (in terms of x) is given by

$$L = \sqrt{(x-10)^2 + (x^2)^2} = \sqrt{(x-10)^2 + x^4}$$

But we want the square of the distance, i.e., we let $S = L^2 = (x-10)^2 + x^4$
$$= x^2 - 20x + 100 + x^4$$

Differentiating S, we have:
$$\frac{dS}{dx} = 2x - 20 + 4x^3 = 2(x - 10 + 2x^3)$$

For stationary points we have $\dfrac{dS}{dx} = 0$:

So that
$$2(x - 10 + 2x^3) = 0 \Leftrightarrow x - 10 + 2x^3 = 0$$

To solve for this cubic we need to use a numerical method (or simply use a graphics calculator)

In this instance we sketch (plot) the graph

of $y = x - 10 + 2x^3$ and then we can concentrate on where it crosses the x-axis:

Using the TRACE function on the TI–83, we see that the intercept occurs where $x \approx 1.6$.

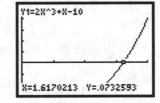

Notice:
Using the CALC function and Zero subcommand we obtain the value $x = 1.612$.

Now, use the sign of the first derivative to check the nature of the stationary point:

$$\left.\begin{array}{ll} x = 1.8 & \dfrac{dL}{dx} > 0 \\[2ex] x = 1.4 & \dfrac{dL}{dx} < 0 \end{array}\right\} \therefore \text{ we have a local maximum at } x = 1.6$$

Therefore, the point on the curve $y = x^2$ so that the square of the distance to the point $(10,0)$ is a minimum occurs at $x = 1.6$, i.e., at $(1.6, 2.56)$.

EXAMPLE

A box needs to be constructed with the condition that it has a volume of $800 \ cm^3$ and a square base. If the box is to be open ended (at one end), find the dimensions of the box that will require the least amount of material.

SOLUTION

Let the square base have side of lengths x cm and the let the height be h cm.

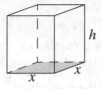

Therefore the volume of the box is $x^2h \ cm^3$.

As the volume is $800 \ cm^3$, we have

$$x^2h = 800 \qquad ..... \text{Eq. 1.}$$

Next we denote the surface area of the box by $S \ cm^2$.

Therefore $\qquad S = x^2 + 4xh \qquad ..... \text{Eq. 2.}$

We wish to minimize S, therefore we need to find the stationary point(s) of S. However, we must first obtain an expression for S (exclusively) in terms of x.

From Eq. 1., we have that $\qquad h = \dfrac{800}{x^2} \qquad ..... \text{Eq. 3.}$

Substituting Eq. 3. into Eq. 2. we have

$$S(x) = x^2 + 4x \times \frac{800}{x^2}$$

$$= x^2 + \frac{3200}{x}$$

Differentiating, we have, $\qquad S'(x) = 2x - \dfrac{3200}{x^2}$

For stationary points we need to solve $S'(x) = 0$

$$2x - \frac{3200}{x^2} = 0 \Leftrightarrow 2x = \frac{3200}{x^2}$$

$$\Leftrightarrow x^3 = 1600$$

$$\Leftrightarrow x = \sqrt[3]{1600} (\ \approx 11.70)$$

Next, we check the nature of the stationary point.

For $x = 12$, $S'(12) > 0$ and for $x = 11$, $S'(11) < 0$.

Therefore there is a local minimum at $x = 11.70$ and the amount of material required is least when $x = 11.70$ and $h = 5.85$.

EXERCISE 23.6

1. (a) Find the greatest value of the function $2 + x - 3x^2$.

2. (a) Find the least value of the function $8 - 3x + 2x^2$.

3. Two real numbers x and y are such that $x + y = 21$. Find the value of x for which
   (a) the product, xy, is a maximum.
   (b) the product xy^3 is a maximum.

4. If $x + y = 12$, find the minimum value that $x^2 + y^2$ can have.

5. A farmer wishes to fence off a rectangular paddock using an existing stretch of a river as one side. The total length of wiring available is $100\ m$.
Let $x\ m$ and $y\ m$ denote the length and width of this rectangular paddock respectively, and let $A m^2$ denote its area.
   (a) Obtain an expression for y in terms of x.
   (b) Find an expression for A in terms of x, stating any restrictions on x.
   (c) Determine the dimensions which will maximize the area enclosed by this rectangle.

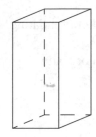

6. A closed rectangular box with square ends is to be constructed in such a way that its total surface area is $400\ cm^2$. Let x cm be the side length of the ends and y cm its height.
   (a) Obtain an expression for y in terms of x, stating any restrictions on x.
   (b) Find the largest possible volume of all such boxes.

7. A barrel is being filled with water in such a way that the volume of water, V ml, in the barrel after time t seconds is given by

$$V(t) = \frac{2}{3}\left(20t^2 - \frac{1}{6}t^3\right),\ 0 \le t \le 120$$

   (a) Find the rate of flow into the barrel after 20 seconds.
   (b) When will the rate of flow be greatest?
   (c) Sketch the graph of $V(t), 0 \le t \le 120$.

8. The total cost, $C, for the production of x items of a particular product is given by the linear relation $C = 600 + 20x$, $0 \le x \le 100$, whilst its total revenue, $R, is given by $R = x(100 - x)$, $0 \le x \le 100$.

(a) Sketch the graph of the cost function and revenue function on the same set of axes.

(b) Determine the break–even points on your graph.

(c) For what values of x will the company be making a positive profit?

(d) Find an expression that gives the profit made in producing x items of the product, and hence determine the maximum profit.

9. A rectangle is bounded by the positive x-axis the positive y-axis and the line with equation

$$y = \frac{2}{3}(8 - x).$$

Find the dimensions of the rectangle having the largest area.

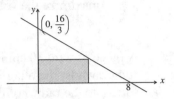

10. A certificate is to be printed on a page having an area of 340 cm^2. The margins at the top and bottom of the page are to be 2cm and, on the sides, 1cm.

(a) If the width of the page is x cm, show that the area, $A \text{ cm}^2$ where printed material is to appear is given by

$$A = 348 - \frac{680}{x} - 4x.$$

(b) Hence, determine the maximum area of print.

11. Find the minimum value of the sum of a positive integer and its reciprocal.

12. A cylinder is to have a surface area of $20\pi \text{ cm}^2$. Determine the dimensions of the cylinder which will have the largest volume.

13. A right circular cylinder of radius r cm and height h cm is to have a fixed volume of 30 cm^3.

(a) Show that the surface area, $A \text{ cm}^2$ of such a cylinder is given by $A = 2\pi r\left(r + \frac{30}{\pi r^2}\right)$.

(b) Determine the value of r that will yield the minimum surface area.

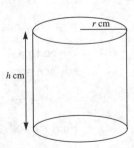

14. A rectangular container is made by cutting out squares from the corners of a 25cm by 40cm rectangular sheet of metal and folding the remaining sheet to form the container.

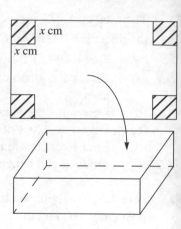

(a) If the squares that are cut out are x cm in length, show that the volume, V cm^3 of the container is given by

$$V = x(25 - 2x)(40 - 2x), 0 \le x \le \tfrac{25}{2}$$

(b) What size squares must be cut out in order to maximize the volume of the container?

15. A piece of wire 30 cm long is cut into 2 pieces. One of the pieces is bent into a square whilst the other is bent into a circle. Find the ratio of the side length of the square to the radius of the circle which provides the smallest area sum.

16. A cylindrical biscuit tin having a lid 1cm deep is to have a capacity of 144π cm^3.

If the cylinder is of radius r cm and height h cm, find the ratio $r{:}h$ which will give the smallest surface area.

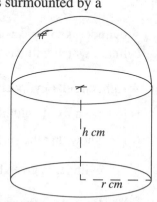

17. A closed tin is to be constructed as shown in the diagram below. It is made up of a cylinder of height h cm and radius base r cm which is surmounted by a hemispherical cap.

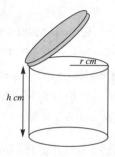

(a) Find an expression in terms of r and h for

i. its volume, $V\ cm^3$

ii. its surface area, $A\ cm^2$.

(b) Given that $V = \pi k^3, k > 0$, show that its surface area is given by

$$A = 2\pi k^3 \frac{1}{r} + \frac{5\pi}{3} r^2.$$

(c) Find $r{:}h$ for A to be a minimum.

23.5 KINEMATICS & CALCULUS

In Chapter 16 we saw how rates where used to define certain quantities, for example, we saw that the average rate of change of displacement provided a measure for the average velocity. In this section we provide a summary of the relationship between three aspects of kinematics, namely, displacement, velocity and acceleration.

Velocity: **Velocity measures the rate of change of displacement.**

So that if an object has a velocity v m/s and a displacement of s metres, then the relationship between v and s is given by

$$\frac{ds}{dt} = v.$$

Acceleration: **Acceleration measures the rate of change of velocity.**

So that if an object has an acceleration a m/s^2 and a velocity of v m/s, then the relationship between a and v is given by

$$\frac{dv}{dt} = a.$$

Notice then that two other relationships can be derived:

1.   From $a = \frac{dv}{dt}$, we have $a = \frac{dv}{dt} = \frac{d}{dt}(v) = \frac{d}{dt}\left(\frac{ds}{dt}\right) = \frac{d^2s}{dt^2}.$

2.   From $a = \frac{dv}{dt}$, we have $a = \frac{dv}{dt} = \frac{dv}{ds}\frac{ds}{dt} = v\frac{dv}{ds}.$

EXAMPLE

A particle is moving along a straight line has its displacement, x m, from a fixed point O given by the equation $x = t^3 - 12t^2 + 45t + 10, t \geq 0$.

(a)   Find the time when the particle first comes to rest/
(b)   The particle's acceleration at this instant.

SOLUTION

(a)   When the particle first comes to rest, its speed will be zero. That is $\frac{dx}{dt} = 0$.

Now, $x = t^3 - 12t^2 + 45t + 10 \Rightarrow \frac{dx}{dt} = 3t^2 - 24t + 45$.

So that $\frac{dx}{dt} = 0 \Leftrightarrow 3t^2 - 24t + 45 = 0 \Leftrightarrow t^2 - 8t + 15 = 0$

That is, $\frac{ds}{dt} = 0 \Rightarrow (t-5)(t-3) = 0 \Leftrightarrow t = 3$ or $t = 5$.

So that the first time the particle comes to rest is $t = 3$.

(b) To determine the acceleration, we first need to differentiate the particle's velocity:

Let $\dfrac{dx}{dt} = v$ so that the acceleration $a = \dfrac{dv}{dt} = 6t - 24$

Therefore when $t = 3$ the particle's acceleration is $\dfrac{dv}{dt} = 6 \times 3 - 24 = -6$.

When discussing velocity, acceleration and displacement as functions of t, it is also important to understand the relationship between their signs and their relative position to some origin O (say). This can easily be summarised in the diagram below:

Displacement:

If $s > 0$, then P is to the right of O.
If $s < 0$, then P is to the left of O.
If $s = 0$, then P is at O.

$v = \dfrac{ds}{dt}$

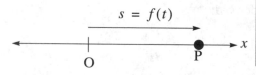

Velocity:

If $v > 0$, then P is moving to the right of O.
If $v < 0$, then P is moving to the left of O.
If $v = 0$, then P is stationary.

Acceleration:

If $a > 0$, then velocity of P is increasing.
If $a < 0$, then velocity of P is decreasing.
If $a = 0$, then velocity of P is a max or min.

$a = \dfrac{dv}{dt}$

Note also that if both $v > 0$ and $a > 0$ (or $v < 0$ and $a < 0$) i.e., they have the **same sign**, then the **speed** of the particle **is increasing**. Whereas, if they have **opposite signs**, then the **speed** of the particle **is decreasing**.

EXAMPLE

A particle moving in a straight line relative to some origin O, has its displacement, s metres, after being in motion for t seconds, governed by the equation $s = t^3 - 4t + 2$.
(a) Find the particle's velocity and acceleartion at any time t seconds.
(b) Describe the particle's motion for $t \geq 0$.

SOLUTION

(a) Given that $s = t^3 - 4t + 2$, then the velocity $v = \dfrac{ds}{dt} = 3t^2 - 4$.

Similarly, its acceleration $a = \dfrac{dv}{dt} = 6t$.

(b) We make use of the TI–83 to help us describe the motion of the particle.

We first make use of the displacement–time graph:

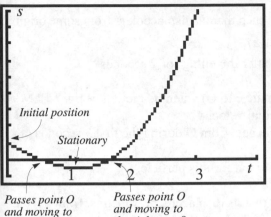

S

Initial position

Stationary

1   2   3   *t*

Passes point O and moving to the left, v < 0.

Passes point O and moving to the right, v > 0.

From the graph we see that the particle started 2 metres to the right of O and then started to move to the left, i.e., $v < 0$. After passing O, the particle kept moving left until it was stationary, at which point it turned around and started to move to the right. It passed the point O again and kept going.

Although this is a basic descriptive account of the particle's motion, more details can be easily included:

. Solving for $s = 0$, will tell us when the particle reached the origin.
. Solving for $v = 0$ will tell when the particle was stationary as well as how far away from the origin it reached before returning towards O.

. Solving for $s = 0 \Rightarrow t^3 - 4t + 2 = 0$ & making use of the **CALC** function on the TI–83, we have that $s = 0$ when $t = 0.54$ and $t = 1.68$.
That is, press **2nd CALC** then use the arrow keys to provide two suitable intervals over which a good guess can be made.

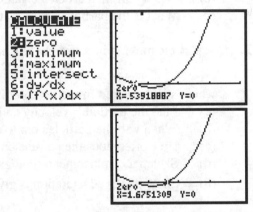

We could also use the **Solve** option under the **MATH** menu:

Either way, we can quote the result accurately to 2 decimal places.

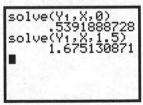

2. Solving for $v = 0$, is slightly easier for this example as we end up with solving a

quadratic. That is, $v = 0 \Rightarrow 3t^2 - 4 = 0$, so that $t = \pm\sqrt{\dfrac{4}{3}} \approx \pm 1.15$.

However, $t \geq 0$, therefore we have that the particle becomes stationary after 1.15 seconds (at which point it turns back and moves to the right).

Note: For $0 \leq t < 1,15$, $v < 0$ but $a > 0$. Meaning that the particle is slowing down. However, for $t > 1.15$, $v > 0$ and $a > 0$. Meaning that the particle is speeding up.

EXERCISE 23.7

1. A particle moving in a straight line is such that its displacement from some origin O at time t seconds is given by $s = t^2 + 4t - 5$.
   (a) What is the particle's velocity after travelling for 2 seconds?
   (b) When is the particle at rest?
   (c) i. Where is the particle (relative to O) when its motion begins?
       ii. What is the particle's initial velocity?
   (d) What is the furthest this particle gets from O during the first 5 seconds of motion?
   (e) Sketch the displacement–time graph for this particle.

2. A particle moves in a straight line so that its displacement, s metres, from a fixed origin after t seconds, is given by the formula
   $$s = t^3 - 2t^2 + t.$$
   (a) What is the particle initial velocity?
   (b) How many times will the particle pass through the origin?
   (c) When will the particle be stationary?
   (d) What is the particle's acceleration after 4 seconds?

3. A particle moving in a straight line has its displacement governed by the equation
   $$s = -2t^3 + 12t - 1,$$
   where s is measured in metres and t in seconds.
   (a) Find the particle's velocity and acceleration at time t.
   (b) When will the particle com to rest?
   (c) How often does the particle change its direction of motion?
   (d) Sketch a displacement–time graph for this particle.
   (b) Show that is acceleration is given by $g - kv$.

ELF ASSESSMENT TEST (60 MINUTES)

. If $y = -\dfrac{2}{\sqrt{x}}$ find the derivative, $\dfrac{dy}{dx}$.

[2 marks]

.. Find the local maximum point on the curve $f(x) = 2x^3 + 3x^2 - 12x + 1,\ x \in \mathbb{R}$.

[5 marks]

. The total cost, C dollars, of running a large boat is given by $C(v) = 200v + \dfrac{800}{v}$

where v is the average speed of the boat. At what seed will the cost be a minimum?

[3 marks]

.. Find the average rate of change of $y = 2x^2 - 3x$ between the points for which $x = -1$ and $x = 1$.

[3 marks]

. Sketch the graph of the function $y = 5x^3 - x^2$, clearly showing all intercepts with the axes as well as stationary points.

[5 marks]

. A particle is projected vertically upwards from ground level, so that its displacement

s metres after t seconds in motion is given by $s = 28t - 4.9t^2$.
(a)   How long will it be before the particle returns to the ground?
(b)   What is the maximum height reached by the particle?
(c)   What is the particle's
      (i)   initial velocity?
      (ii)   velocity after 3 seconds?
(d)   Show that the particle is travelling with a constant acceleration.

[6 marks]

INTRODUCTION TO DIFFERENTIAL CALCULUS 3

INTEGRATION

OPTION

2 4

24.1 INTEGRATION
ANTIDIFFERENTIATION AND THE INDEFINITE INTEGRAL

As the name suggests— *Anti* differentiation is the reverse process to that of differentiation. We are then in search of the answer to the following:

Given an expression $f'(x)$ (i.e., the derivative of the function $f(x)$), what must the original function $f(x)$ been?

For example, if $f'(x) = 2x$ then clearly $f(x) = x^2$ is a *possible expression* for the original function.

Why do we say ' ... *is a possible expression for the original function* ' ?

Consider the following results:

$$f(x) = x^2 + 3 \Rightarrow f'(x) = 2x$$
$$f(x) = x^2 - 5 \Rightarrow f'(x) = 2x$$

We see that given an expression for $f'(x)$, there are a number of possible different original functions, $f(x)$. This is due to the fact that the derivative of a constant is zero and so when we are given an expression for $f'(x)$, there is no real way of knowing if there was a constant in the original function or even what that constant might be (without being given some extra information).

The best that we can do at this stage is to write the following:

Given that $f'(x) = 2x$, then $f(x) = x^2 + c$.

Where c is some real number (it could very well be that $c = 0$).

The antidifferentiation process described above can be summarised as follows:

Given that $\dfrac{dy}{dx} = f'(x)$, then (after antidifferentiating) $y = f(x) + c$, where $c \in \mathbb{R}$

We say that $y = f(x) + c$, where $c \in \mathbb{R}$ is the **antiderivative** of $f'(x)$.

LANGUAGE AND NOTATION

The set of all antiderivatives of a function $h(x)$ is called the **indefinite integral** of $h(x)$, and is denoted by $\int h(x)dx$.

The symbol $\int$ is called the **integral sign**,

the function $h(x)$ is the **integrand** of the integral

and x is the **variable of integration**.

Once we have found an antiderivative (or indefinite integral) of $h(x)$, $H(x)$ (say) we can then write

$$\int h(x)dx = H(x) + c, \text{ where } c \in \mathbb{R},$$

The constant c is called the **constant of integration**. The above result is read as:

  'The **antiderivative** of $h(x)$ with respect to x is $H(x) + c$, where c is a real constant'

or

'The **indefinite integral** of $h(x)$ with respect to x is $H(x) + c$, where c is a real number'

OBTAINING THE INDEFINITE INTEGRAL

So — how do we find the indefinite integral of $h(x)$?

We approach this problem by searching for a pattern (pretty much as we did when dealing with the derivative of a function). Consider the following results, where we have a list of functions and their derivatives:

$h(x)$	$h'(x)$
x	1
x^2	$2x$
x^3	$3x^2$
x^4	$4x^3$
x^5	$5x^4$
x^n	nx^{n-1}

As we had already seen, the differentiation process was easily described using the following flow diagram:

Differentiating process

$$x^n \longrightarrow nx^{n-1}$$

Step 1	Step 2
Multiply by the power	Decrease the power by one.

Finding the indefinite integral requires that we 'reverse the process' (i.e., carry out the inverse operation). Again this can be illustrated using a flow diagram:

Antidifferentiating process

$$x^n \longrightarrow \frac{x^{n+1}}{n+1}$$

Step 1	Step 2
Increase the power by one	Divide by the new power.

However, as we discussed previously, we must add a real constant to complete the process of antidifferentiation.

We then have the general result:

$$\int x^n dx = \frac{x^{n+1}}{n+1} + c \quad \text{or} \quad \frac{1}{n+1}x^{n+1} + c \text{ as long as } n \neq -1.$$

A slightly more general result is one where we have ax^n rather than simply x^n. In this case we have that

$$\int ax^n dx = \frac{ax^{n+1}}{n+1} + c \quad \text{or} \quad \frac{a}{n+1}x^{n+1} + c \text{ as long as } n \neq -1.$$

EXAMPLE

Find the indefinite integral of the following

(a) $4x^2$ (b) x^{-3} (c) $5\sqrt{x}$ (d) $\sqrt[5]{x^3}$

SOLUTION

(a) $\int 4x^2 dx = \frac{4}{2+1}x^{2+1} + c, c \in \mathbb{R} = \frac{4}{3}x^3 + c, c \in \mathbb{R}$

(b) $\int x^{-3} dx = \frac{1}{-3+1}x^{-3+1} + c, c \in \mathbb{R} = -\frac{1}{2}x^{-2} + c, c \in \mathbb{R}$

$$= -\frac{1}{2x^2} + c, c \in \mathbb{R}$$

(c) $\int 5\sqrt{x} dx = \int 5x^{\frac{1}{2}} dx = \frac{5}{\frac{1}{2}+1}x^{\frac{1}{2}+1} + c, c \in \mathbb{R}$

$$= \frac{5}{\frac{3}{2}}x^{\frac{3}{2}} + c, c \in \mathbb{R}$$

$$= \frac{10}{3}\sqrt{x^3} + c, c \in \mathbb{R}$$

Notice that before we can start the antidifferentiation process we must express the integrand in the form ax^n, i.e., in power form.

(d) $\int \sqrt[5]{x^3} dx = \int x^{\frac{3}{5}} dx = \frac{1}{\frac{3}{5}+1}x^{\frac{3}{5}+1} + c, c \in \mathbb{R}$

$$= \frac{1}{\frac{8}{5}}x^{\frac{8}{5}} + c, c \in \mathbb{R}$$

$$= \frac{5}{8}\sqrt[5]{x^8} + c, c \in \mathbb{R}$$

Although we have been working through examples that are made up of only one integrand, we can determine the indefinite integral of expressions that are made up of several terms.

EXAMPLE

Find the integral of

(a) $\int (2x^2 + x^3 - 4)dx$ (b) $\int (x-1)(x^4 + 3x)dx$ (c) $\int \frac{z^4 - 2z^2 + 3}{z^2}dz$

SOLUTION

(a) $\int (2x^2 + x^3 - 4)dx = \int 2x^2 dx + \int x^3 dx - \int 4dx = \frac{2}{2+1}x^{2+1} + \frac{1}{3+1}x^{3+1} - 4x + c$

$= \frac{2}{3}x^3 + \frac{1}{4}x^4 - 4x + c, c \in \mathbb{R}$

Notice that when determining the indefinite integral of 4, we have actually thought of '4'

as '$4x^0$'. So that $\int 4dx = \int 4x^0 dx = \frac{4}{0+1}x^{0+1} = 4x$.

(b) $\int (x-1)(x^4 + 3x)dx = \int (x^5 - x^4 + 3x^2 - 3x)dx = \frac{1}{6}x^6 - \frac{1}{5}x^5 + \frac{3}{3}x^3 - \frac{3}{2}x^2 + c$

$= \frac{1}{6}x^6 - \frac{1}{5}x^5 + x^3 - \frac{3}{2}x^2 + c, c \in \mathbb{R}$

(c) $\int \frac{z^4 - 2z^2 + 3}{z^2}dz = \int \left(\frac{z^4}{z^2} - \frac{2z^2}{z^2} + \frac{3}{z^2} \right)dz = \int (z^2 - 2 + 3z^{-2})dz$

$= \frac{1}{3}z^3 - 2z + \frac{3}{-1}z^{-1} + c$

$= \frac{1}{3}z^3 - 2z - \frac{3}{z} + c, c \in \mathbb{R}$

Notice that in part (b) it was necessary to first multiply out the brackets **before** we could integrate. Similarly, for part (c) we had to first carry out the division **before** integrating.

PROPERTIES OF THE INDEFINITE INTEGRAL

In many of the above examples we made use of the following properties

Properties	Examples
1. $\int h'(x)dx = h(x) + c$	$\int \frac{d}{dx}(x^2)dx = \int (2x)dx = x^2 + c$
2. $\frac{d}{dx}(\int h(x)dx) = h(x)$	$\frac{d}{dx}(\int (x^3)dx) = \frac{d}{dx}\left(\frac{1}{4}x^4 + c\right) = x^3$
3. $\int kh(x)dx = k\int h(x)dx$	$\int 12x^3 dx = 12\int x^3 dx = 12 \times \frac{1}{4}x^4 + c = 3x^4 + c$
4. $\int (h(x) \pm f(x))dx = \int h(x)dx \pm \int f(x)dx$	$\int (2x - 3x^2)dx = x^2 - x^3 + c$

EXERCISE 24.1

1. Find the indefinite integral of the following:

(a) x^3 (b) x^7 (c) x^5 (d) x^8

(e) $4x^2$ (f) $7x^5$ (g) $9x^8$ (h) $\frac{1}{2}x^3$

2. Find:

(a) $\int 5\,dx$ (b) $\int 3\,dx$ (c) $\int 10\,dx$ (d) $\int \frac{2}{3}\,dx$

(e) $\int -4\,dx$ (f) $\int -6\,dx$ (g) $\int -\frac{3}{2}\,dx$ (h) $\int -dx$

3. Find:

(a) $\int (1-x)\,dx$ (b) $\int (2+x^2)\,dx$ (c) $\int (x^3-9)\,dx$

(d) $\int \left(\frac{2}{5}+\frac{1}{3}x^2\right)dx$ (e) $\int \left(\frac{2}{4}\sqrt{x}-\frac{1}{x^2}\right)dx$ (f) $\int \left(\frac{5}{2}\sqrt{x^3}+8x\right)dx$

(g) $\int x(x+2)\,dx$ (h) $\int x^2\left(3-\frac{2}{x}\right)dx$ (i) $\int (x+1)(1-x)\,dx$

4. Find the antiderivative of the following:

(a) $(x+2)(x-3)$ (b) $(x^2-3x)(x+1)$ (c) $(x-3)^3$

(d) $(x+2x^3)(x+1)$ (e) $(1-\sqrt{x})(1+x)$ (f) $\sqrt{x}(x+1)^2-2$

5. Find:

(a) $\int \frac{x^2-3x}{x}\,dx$ (b) $\int \frac{4u^3+5u^2-1}{u^2}\,du$ (c) $\int \frac{(x+2)^2}{x^4}\,dx$

(d) $\int \frac{x^2+5x+6}{x+2}\,dx$ (e) $\int \frac{x^2-6x+8}{x-2}\,dx$ (f) $\int \left(\frac{t^2+1}{t}\right)^2 dt$

6. Find the indefinite integral of the following:

(a) $\sqrt[4]{x^3}+\frac{1}{\sqrt{x}}-5$ (b) $\sqrt{x}(\sqrt{x}-2x)(x+1)$

(c) $\frac{1}{z^3}-\frac{2}{z^2}+4z+1$ (d) $\left(2t+\frac{3}{t^2}\right)\left(t^2-\frac{1}{t}\right)+\frac{3}{t^3}$

(e) $\frac{(t-2)(t-1)}{\sqrt{t}}-\frac{2}{\sqrt{t}}$ (f) $\frac{u^3+6u^2+12u+8}{u+2}$

24.2 SOLVING FOR "C"

Although we have already discussed the reason for 'adding' a constant, c, when finding the indefinite integral, it is important that we can also determine the value of c.

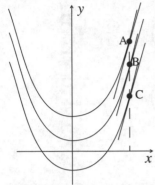

Given that $\dfrac{dy}{dx} = 2x$, upon antidifferentiating, we have that

$y = x^2 + c$. This result is known as the **general solution**.

Sketching some of the possible curves, $y = x^2 + c$, we observe that at A, B and C, the gradients are equal.
To determine which of these curves is the one that we actually require, we must be provided with some extra information. In this case we would need to be given the coordinates of the points on the curve.

EXAMPLE
Find $f(x)$ given that $f'(x) = 2x$ and that the curve passes through the point (2,9).

SOLUTION
Now, $f'(x) = 2x \Rightarrow f(x) = x^2 + c$.

Using the fact that at $x = 2$, $y = 9$, or that $f(2) = 9$, we have $9 = 2^2 + c \Leftrightarrow c = 5$.

Therefore, of all possible solutions of the form $y = x^2 + c$, the function satisfying the

given information is $f(x) = x^2 + 5$.

Sometimes, information need not be given in the form of a set of coordinates. Information can also be given in terms of the context in which the problem is set.

EXAMPLE
The rate of change in pressure, p units, at a depth x cm from the surface of a liquid is given by $p'(x) = 0.03x^2$.
If the pressure at the surface is 10 units, find the pressure at a depth of 5 cm.

SOLUTION
Antidifferentiating both sides with respect to x, we have

$$\int p'(x)dx = \int 0.03x^2 dx.$$

$$\therefore p(x) = 0.01x^3 + c.$$

Now, at $x = 0$, $p = 10$. Substituting into the equation we have

$$10 = 0.01(0)^3 + c \Leftrightarrow c = 10$$

Therefore, the equation for the pressure at a depth of x cm is $p(x) = 0.01x^3 + 10$.

At $x = 5$, we have $p(5) = 0.01(5)^3 + 10 = 11.25$. That is, the pressure is 11.25 units.

Option: Integration

We have already considered the relationship between displacement, velocity and acceleration in terms of their rates of change (Chapter 18). We can now consider their relationships via the use of integration:

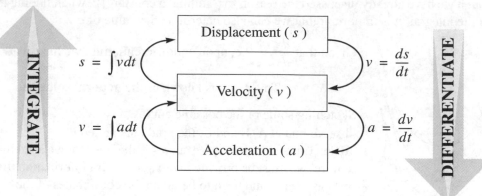

EXAMPLE

Given that an object has a velocity in m/s is defined by the equation $v = 3t^2 + t$ and is such that it is initially 8 metres from its origin. Find its displacement at any time $t, t \geq 0$.

SOLUTION

We have that $v = 3t^2 + t$, meaning that $\dfrac{ds}{dt} = 3t^2 + t$.

Integrating both sides of the equation with respect to t, we have:

$$\int \frac{ds}{dt} dt = \int (3t^2 + t) dt \Rightarrow s = t^3 + \frac{1}{2}t^2 + C.$$

However, when $t = 0$, we have that $s = 8$. So, substituting these values into the last equation we have that:

$$8 = 0^3 + \frac{1}{2} \times 0^2 + C \Rightarrow C = 8.$$

Therefore, the displacement equation at any time t is given by $s = t^3 + \dfrac{1}{2}t^2 + 8$.

EXERCISE 24.2

1. Find the equation of the function in each of the following:

    (a) $f'(x) = 2x + 1$, given that the curve passes through (1,5).

    (b) $f'(x) = 2 - x^2$ and $f(2) = \dfrac{7}{3}$.

    (c) $\dfrac{dy}{dx} = 4\sqrt{x} - x$, given that the curve passes through (4,0).

    (d) $f'(x) = x - \dfrac{1}{x^2} + 2$, and $f(1) = 2$

    (e) $\dfrac{dy}{dx} = 3(x + 2)^2$, given that the curve passes through (0,8).

(f) $\dfrac{dy}{dx} = \sqrt[3]{x} + x^3 + 1$, given that the curve passes through (1,2).

(g) $f'(x) = (x+1)(x-1) + 1$, and $f(0) = 1$

(h) $f'(x) = 4x^3 - 3x^2 + 2$, and $f(-1) = 3$

2.   Find the equation of the function $f(x)$ given that it passes through the point $(-1,2)$ and is such that $f'(x) = ax + \dfrac{b}{x^2}$, where $f(1) = 4$ and $f'(1) = 0$.

3.   The marginal cost for producing x units of a product is modelled by the equation $C'(x) = 30 - 0.06x$. The cost per unit is \$40. How much will it cost to produce 150 units?

4.   If $\dfrac{dA}{dr} = 6 - \dfrac{1}{r^2}$, and $A = 4$ when $r = 1$, find A when $r = 2$.

5.   The rate, in $cm^3/\sec$, at which the volume of a sphere is increasing is given by the relation $\dfrac{dV}{dt} = 4\pi(2t + 1)^2, 0 \le t \le 10$. If initially the volume is $\pi\ cm^3$, find the volume of the sphere when $t = 2$.

6.   The rate of change of the number of deer, N, in a controlled experiment, is modelled by the equation $\dfrac{dN}{dt} = 3\sqrt{t^3} + 2t, 0 \le t \le 5$. There are initially 200 deer in the experiment. How many deer will there be at the end of the experiment.

7.   If $\dfrac{dy}{dx} \propto \sqrt{x}$, find an expression for y, given that $y = 4$ when $x = 1$ and $y = 9$ when $x = 4$.

8.   (a)   If $\dfrac{ds}{dt} = 1 - 2t$, find s interms of t given that $s = 1$ when $t = 1$.

(b)   Given that $v(t) = 9t^2 - 2t + 3$, find $s(t)$ if $s = 10$ when $t = 0$.

(c)   If $a(t) = t^2 - 2t$ and the initial $v(0) = 4$ and $s(0) = 2$, find $s(1)$.

9.   A particle moving in a straight line passes a fixed point O with a velocity of 4 m/s. It has an acceleration, $a\ m/s^2$, given by $a = 4 - 12t^2$, where t seconds is the time after the particle passes the origin, O.

(a)   Determine its velocity at time t seconds after passing O.

(b)   Find its displacement equation.

(c)   Find the particle's position 5 seconds after passing point O.

SELF ASSESSMENT TEST (30 MINUTES)

1. Find the antiderivative of the following

    (a) $x^3 - 4x + 1$

    (b) $\dfrac{1}{\sqrt{x}} - \sqrt{x}$

    (c) $(3 - x)^2$

                             [5 marks]

2. Find the equation of the curve with slope $6x + m$ that passes through the point with coordinates (2,15).

                             [3 marks]

3.   A particle moving along a straight line has its velocity given by the equation $t^2 + 5 - \dfrac{2}{t^2}$. If the particle is 3 m away from some fixed origin after travelling for one second, find the particle's displacement after a further 2 seconds.

                             [4 marks]

4. The marginal revenue for the production of the xth unit of a particular commodity is given by the equation

$$\frac{dR}{dx} = \frac{2500 - x}{10}.$$

    (a)   Find the total revenue function, $R(x)$.

    (b)   Find $R(1000)$

                             [3 marks]

ANSWERS

EXERCISE 2.1

1. (a) 4 (b) 5 (c) 2   (d) 4 (e) 3 (f) 3 (g) 5 (h) 3 (i) 6 (j) 3 (k) 6 (l) 5
2. (a) 2.5 (b) 24700 (c) 0.35 (d) 45630 (e) 0.45 (f) 4 (g) 57000 (h) 0.0454 (i) 0.0045
(j) 346000 (k) 0.045 (l) 90000
3. 8.2 cm   4. 11cm   5. 44m 6. 1040mm 7. 30 terms 8. 3 S.F. 9. 19

EXERCISE 2.2

1. (i) 2.2×10^1 (ii) 1.2×10^{-12} (iii) 4.8×10^9 2. $r = 4.72 \times 10^9 m$ $C = 2.97 \times 10^{10} m$
SA $= 7.00 \times 10^{19} m^2$, Vol $= 4.40 \times 10^{29} m^3$ 3. $7.48 \times 10^{-6} m^3$ 4. 280km
5. $4.49 \times 10^{15} \, kgm^2 s^{-2}$ 6. 3.4×10^9 7. 74 generations, 1.9×10^{22} relations. 8. 10^8
9. 3.1×10^{-24} gms 10. 4.3×10^6

EXERCISE 2.3

1. 0.0033333 (etc.), 0.01, 1% 2. 0.0144, 0.0053 0.53% 3. The absolute errors are all
0.2kg. The relative and percentage errors are: (i) 0.027 (2.7%) (ii) 0.0102 (1.02%)
(iii) 0.00893 (0.893%) (iv) 0.00352 (0.352%) (v) 0.00202 (0.202%). 4. (i) 0.1 (10%)
(ii) .05 (5%) (iii) .00417 (0.417%) (iv) 0.002 (0.2%) 5. (i) 0.018% (ii) 0.0014%(iii)
0.27% (iv) 0.0030% 6. (i) 0.45% (ii) 0.073% (iii) 0.020% (iv) 0.0022% 7. 7×10^{-4} %
which is plainly far more accuracy than can be justified in the times quoted for this flight.

EXERCISE 2.4

1. (a) 0.209 [0.204, 0.215] (b) 3384 [1726, 64752] (c) -194.9 [-206.3, -184.1]
2. 516577mm^2 [513978, 519175] 0.47% 3. 164553cm^2 [150456, 179503] 9.1%
4. 17961 [17936, 17986] 5. 28.24m [27.39, 29.11] 3% accuracy.
6. 105.6m [104.9, 106.2] 0.66% 7. $a{\approx}b$ 8. 0.25kg 9. 15.42cm [14.90, 15.97] 3.6%
10. 12096 [10646, 13672] 13% 11. 2208 [2076, 2344] 6.2% 12. 0.00069%

EXAMINATION STYLE QUESTIONS

1.(a) 0.380568 (b) 0.381 (c) 0.38 (d) 3.80568×10^{-1} 2. (a) 24548.616 (b) 24500
(c) 24548.62 (d) 24549 (e) 2.4548616×10^4 3. (a) (i) 74.9 (ii) 74.97 (iii) 75
(b) 7.5×10^1 4. (a) 790 (b) 790.02 (c) 790

SELF ASSESSMENT TEST

1. $\frac{1}{7} = 0.14286$ to 5 SF [1], absolute error $= 2.86 \times 10^{-6}$ [1] % error $= 0.0020$ [1]

2. $\frac{\sqrt{12} - \sqrt{5}}{6} \approx 0.20467227$ [1] or 0.205 to 3SF [1]

3. (a) 3 [1] (b) 3 [1] (c) 2 [1]
4. (a) 4.51×10^{21} [1] (b) 6.01×10^{-17} [1] (c) 2.12×10^{-1} [1]
5. 34000 [1] (b) 0.000705 [1]
6. (a) 19.9 ± 0.8 [1] (b) 45.44 or 41.54 to 49.5 [1] (c) ≈ 1.429 [1] 0.769 to 10 [1]
7. Series gives 2.96339 [1] error (-)0.1782 [1] (5.7%) [1]

EXERCISE 3.1

1. (a) Need to show that they have a common difference (b) (i) 4 (ii) 3 (iii) –5 (iv) 0.5 (v) 2 (vi) –2 (c) (i) $4n - 2$ (ii) $3n + 17$ (iii) $6 - 5n$ (iv) $0.5n$ (v) $2n + y - 1$ (vi) $x - 2n$ 2. –28
3. $x = 9, y = 17$ 4. –43 5. 7 6. 7 7. –5 8. 0 9. (a) 41 (b) 31 10. $x = 2, y = \sqrt{3}$.

EXERCISE 3.2

1. (a) $a = 1, d = 3, 145$ (b) 3, 6, 300 (c) 10, –6, –220 2. (a) –18 (b) 690 (c) 70.4
3. (a) 315 (b) 507 (c) 224 4. 123 5. -3, -0.5, 2, 4.5, 7, 9.5, 12 6. 3.25 7. a=3 d=-0.05 8.
10000 9. 330 10. -20 11. 328 12. \$725 37weeks 13. \$55 2750 cards 14. (a)(i) 8m (ii)
40m (b) 84m (c) Dist $= 2n^2 - 2n = 2n(n - 1)$ (d) 8 (e) 26 players, 1300m

EXERCISE 3.3

1. (a) 3 (b) $\dfrac{1}{3}$ (c) -1 (d) $-\dfrac{1}{3}$ (e) 1.25 (f) $-\dfrac{2}{3}$ 2. (a) 216513 (b) 1.6384×10^{-10}

(c) $\dfrac{256}{729}$ (d) $\dfrac{729}{2401}$ (e) $-\dfrac{81}{1024}$ 2. (a) 216513 (b) 1.6384×10^{-10} (c) $\dfrac{256}{729}$

(d) $\dfrac{729}{2401}$ (e) $-\dfrac{81}{1024}$ 3. (a) 11; 354292 (b) 7; 473 (c) 8; 90.90909 (d) 8; 172.778

(e) 5; 2.256 (f) 13; 111.1111111111 4. 4; 118096 5. \$2109.50 6. 9.28cm

7. $V_n = V_0 \times 0.7^{n-1}$ 7 years 8. 54 9. 54gms; 51 weeks. 10. 7 11. 9 12. -0.5

13. $r = 5$, 1.8×10^{10} 14. \$8407.35 15. 1.8×10^{19} or about 200 billion tonnes.

EXERCISE 3.4

1. Term 9 AP = 180, GP = 256. Sum to 11 terms AP = 1650, GP = 2047. 2. 18. 3. 12
4. 4,4 5. 8 weeks (Ken \$220 & Bo-Youn \$255) 6. (a) week 8 (b) week 12 7. (a) 1.618
(b) 121389, answer depends on rounding errors (the true answer is 121392)

EXAMINATION STYLE QUESTIONS

1. (a) (i) 5 (ii) 3 (b) 5, 8, 11, 14, 15 (c) 62 (d) 100 2. 29 3. (b) (i) 10, 22, 34, 46 (ii) 238
(c) d = 12, a = 10, sum = 640 4. (a) 3 (b) 98415 (c) 147620 5 (a) \$3026 (b) 5526.70

6. (a) 0.85 (b) \$6264.10 (c) (i) $u_n = 12000 \times (0.85)^n$ (ii) 8.53 years

7. (a) 5.78 (b) 13 (c) 51.34

SELF ASSESSMENT TEST

1. The series is arithmetic [1] there are 12 terms [1] and the sum is 288 [1].
2. The series is geometric [1] the common ratio is -2 [1] and x is -96 [1].
3. The series is geometric [1] the common ratio is -1/3 [1] and there are 7 terms [1].
4. The series is arithmetic [1]. Making an equation [1]. 1000 numbers.
5. (a) $1250 \times 1.12^5 \approx \$2203$ [1] (b) Making the equation $1250 \times 1.12^x = 10000$ [1] Use of logs to solve [1] Solution 18.35, 19 years [1].
6. $A_n = 12000 + 200n$ [1] $B_n = 8000 \times 1.05^n$ [1] Working with

$8000 \times 1.05^n > 12000 + 200n$, probably by tabulation or trial and error [1]. n = 13.

Answers

EXERCISE 4.1

1. (a)   (b)   (c)   (d)   (e)

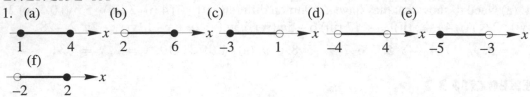

(f)
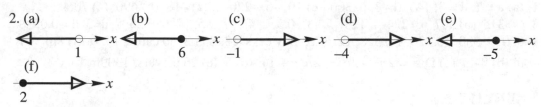

2. (a)   (b)   (c)   (d)   (e)

(f)

EXERCISE 4.2

1. (a) 5 (b) 5 (c) –3 (d) 21 (e) $\frac{28}{3}$ (f) $-\frac{19}{3}$ (g) 11 (h) 11 3. (a) 9 (b) 20 (c) 10 (d) $\frac{4}{3}$

(e) –9 (f) 15 5. (a) –1 (b) 2 (c) –5 (d) –1 (e) 1 (f) $\frac{11}{13}$ 7. (a) $-\frac{13}{7}$ (b) $-\frac{7}{4}$ (c) 22 (d) $\frac{1}{31}$

(e) –19 (f) $\frac{16}{7}$ (g) $-\frac{9}{2}$ (h) –24.5 9. (a) $\frac{5}{6}$ (b) $-\frac{4}{3}$ (c) $-\frac{2}{3}$ (d) $\frac{11}{4}$ (e) $-\frac{1}{2}$ (f) $\frac{1}{4}$ (g) $\frac{11}{7}$ (h) $\frac{6}{5}$

(i) $\frac{4}{3}$ (j) $\frac{1}{2}$ (k) $\frac{5}{2}$ (l) $\frac{7}{6}$

EXERCISE 4.3

1. (a) $12 - y = 5$ (b) 7 2. (a) $4x + 2 = 30$ (b) 7 3. $2x - 5 = 19, x = 12$ 4. 12 5. 31
6. $x + 3x + 2x = 84$, 14, 28, 42 7. 20 8. 28 9. 200 10. $2409.10

EXERCISE 4.4

1. (a) $x > 4$ (b) $x \le 9$ (c) $x < 4$ (d) $x < -1$ (e) $x \le 6$ (f) $x \le -1$ (g) $x \ge 5$ (h) $x < 5$ (i) $x \le -3$
(j) $x > 21$ (k) $x \ge \frac{28}{3}$ (l) $x > -\frac{19}{3}$ (m) $x \le 11$ (n) $x < 11$ (o) $x < -\frac{3}{2}$

2. (a)   (b)   (c)   (d)   (e)

(f)   (g)   (h)   (i)   (j)

(k)   (l)   (m)   (n)   (o)

3. (a) $x < 9$ (b) $x \ge 20$ (c) $x > -10$ (d) $x \le \frac{4}{3}$ (e) $x > -9$ (f) $x \ge 15$

4. (a)   (b)   (c)   (d)   (e)   (f)

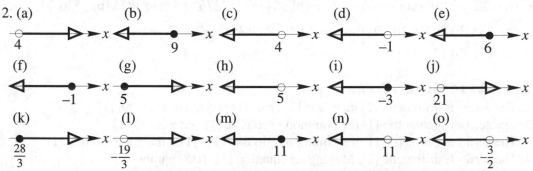

510

5. (a) $x > -1$ (b) $y < 2$ (c) $x \leq -5$ (d) $x \geq -1$ (e) $x \leq 1$ (f) $x < \frac{11}{13}$

6. (a)   (b)   (c)   (d)   (e)   (f)

7. (a) $x < -\frac{13}{7}$ (b) $x \leq -\frac{7}{4}$ (c) $x \geq 22$ (d) $y \geq \frac{1}{31}$ (e) $x \leq -19$ (f) $w < \frac{16}{7}$

8. (a)   (b)   (c)   (d)   (e)   (f)

EXAMINATION STYLE QUESTIONS

1. $x = \frac{5}{3}$ 2. (a) $x = -3$ (b) $x < \frac{5}{4}$ 3. (a) $x \leq -\frac{9}{2}$ (b) $x < 1$

4. (a) $\frac{27}{2}$ (b) 1 5. (a) $x > -5$ 6.

(a) $-\frac{5}{2}$ (b) $\frac{19}{5}$ 7. 23 8. 26 five cent coins.

SELF ASSESSMENT TEST

1. (a) $2a = 14$ [1] $a = 7$ [1] (b) $-12 = 5y$ [1] $y = -2.4$ [1] (c) $3x = 5$ [1] $x = \frac{5}{3}$ [1]

2. (a) $7x - 21 = 6x - 15$ [1] $x = 6$ [1] [1] (b) $3 - 5x > 16$ [1] $-5x > 13$ [1] $x < -\frac{13}{5}$.

3. (a) $2x - 1 \leq 4 - 3 + 3x$ [1] $-2 \leq x$ [1]   (b) $4y - 4 - 60 > 5y - 10$ [1] [1] $-54 > y$ [1]

4. (a) $ax = ba + a$ [1] $ax = a(b + 1)$ [1] $x = b + 1$

(b) $\frac{x}{a} - \frac{x}{b} = b - a$ [1] $\frac{(b - a)}{ab} = b - a$ [1] $x = ab$ [1] [1]

5. $x + 0.9 \times 3 = 0.95(x + 3)$ [1] [1] [1] $x = 3$ [1][1]

EXERCISE 5.1

1. (a) $2(ax + 2)$ (b) $y(9 - a)$ (c) $t(4 + s)$ (d) $x^2(1 + x)$ (e) $xy(3 - y)$ (f) $rs(r^2 + s^2)$
(g) $z(2z - 3y)$ (h) $ab^2(1 - a^3b)$ (i) $xy(3xy - 8)$ (j) $3y^2(xy + 3)$ (k) $2wt(1 + 4w)$
(l) $3ps(1 - 4ps)$ 2. (a) $(2 + z)(x + y)$ (b) $(3 - r)(t - s)$ (c) $(x - y)(x + 2)$ (d) $(st + 2)(a - b)$
(e) $(r^2 + 4)(xy + 1)$ (f) $(y^3 + 5)(2 + z)$ 3. (a) $(4 + x)(s + 1)$ (b) $(a + b)(2 - c)$
(c) $(2 + t)(5x + y)$ (d) $(3 - 5k)(x + 2)$ (e) $(b + 4)(ab - 1)$ (f) $(y - z)(a + b)$

4. (a) $(a^2 + 4)(a - 1)$ (b) $(1 - yz)(x + 1)$ (c) $(m - 1)(n - 1)$ (d) $(y^2 + 3)(y - 1)$

EXERCISE 5.2

1. (a) $(x + 1)(x + 2)$ (b) $(x + 6)(x + 1)$ (c) $(x + 4)(x + 2)$ (d) $(x + 4)(x + 5)$
(e) $(z + 6)(z + 3)$ (f) $(x + 2)(x + 5)$ 2. (a) $(x - 2)(x - 1)$ (b) $(x - 6)(x - 1)$ (c) $(x - 4)(x - 2)$
(d) $(x - 4)(x - 5)$ (e) $(z - 5)(z - 3)$ (f) $(x - 2)(x - 5)$ 3. (a) $(x - 3)(x + 1)$

(b) $(y + 5)(y - 2)$ (c) $(s - 5)(s + 2)$ (d) $(x - 4)(x + 3)$ (e) $(y - 7)(y + 2)$ (f) $(r - 9)(r + 5)$
4. (a) $2(x - 2)(x - 1)$ (b) $3(x + 2)(x + 5)$ (c) $4(s - 5)(s + 2)$ (d) $3(y + 5)(y - 2)$
(e) $5(x + 4)(x + 2)$ (f) $6(x + 1)(x - 3)$ 5. (a) $(y - 15x)(y - x)$ (b) $(z + 7w)(z - 6w)$
(c) $(a + 7b)(a - 5b)$ (d) $2(y + 6x)(y + 3x)$ (e) $3(x - 4y)(x + 3y)$
(f) $5(a - 2b)(a - 3b)$ 6. (a) $(2x + 1)(x + 2)$ (b) $(3x + 2)(x + 1)$ (c) $(3x + 1)(x + 2)$
(d) $(2x - 1)(x - 2)$ (e) $(2x - 1)(x + 2)$ (f) $(7s - 5)(s + 1)$ (g) $(5x - 3)(x + 1)$
(h) $(7x - 1)(x - 5)$ (i) $(3y + 1)(y - 2)$ (j) $(3z - 4)(z - 2)$ (k) $(5w + 4)(w - 1)$
(l) $(2x + 3)(x - 5)$ (m) $(2y + 3)(y + 2)$ (n) $(5x + 4)(x + 1)$ (o) $(3z + 2)(z + 2)$
(p) $2(1 - 4x)(1 + x)$ (q) $(3 - 5x)(1 + x)$ (r) $(4 + 5x)(1 - x)$ 7. (a) $(x + 4)^2$ (b) $(y + 5)^2$
(c) $(z + 3)^2$ (d) $(x - 5)^2$ (e) $(b - 6)^2$ (f) $(x - 7)^2$ (g) $(y - 5)(y + 5)$ (h) $(x - 6)(x + 6)$
(i) $(z - 4)(z + 4)$ (j) $4x(x - 3)(x + 3)$ (k) $3(s - 4)(s + 4)$ (l) $(2x - 3y)(2x + 3y)$
(m) $(2x + 1)^2$ (n) $(3z + 2)^2$ (o) $(3z + 1)^2$ 8. (a) $(x + 1 - \sqrt{5})(x + 1 + \sqrt{5})$
(b) $(x - 1 - \sqrt{3})(x - 1 + \sqrt{3})$ (c) $(x + 2 - \sqrt{2})(x + 2 + \sqrt{2})$
(d) $(x - 3 - \sqrt{6})(x - 3 + \sqrt{6})$ (e) $(x + 3 - \sqrt{7})(x + 3 + \sqrt{7})$ (f) $(x + 4 - \sqrt{3})(x + 4 + \sqrt{3})$
(g) $(x - 4 - \sqrt{2})(x - 4 + \sqrt{2})$ (h) $(z + 5 - \sqrt{5})(z + 5 + \sqrt{5})$ (i) $(x - 5 - \sqrt{5})(x - 5 + \sqrt{5})$
(j) $(z - 2 - \sqrt{3})(z - 2 + \sqrt{3})$ (k) $(a + 7 - \sqrt{19})(a + 7 + \sqrt{19})$

EXERCISE 5.3

1. (a) 0,7 (b) $\pm\sqrt{7}$ (c) 0,-3 (d) no real solutions. (e) -4,3 (f) 0,2 (g) -4,2 (h) -2,5
(i) -2,5 (j) -6,5 (k) -6,1 (l) -4,7 (m) -4, 3.5 (n) 4,7 (o) 3,9 (p) -3,9 (q) -4,-3
(r) -3,-4/3 (s) -7,-2 (t) -0.5,4 (u) -1/3,4 (v) 0.5,5 (w) 0.5, 5/3 (x) 1/4,5/3 (y) 1/3,2/5
(z) 1/4,2 2. $x = -p, 2p$.

EXERCISE 5.4

(a) $\dfrac{-5 \pm \sqrt{17}}{2}$ (b) $-2 \pm \sqrt{7}$ (c) $1 \pm \sqrt{6}$ (d) N.R.S (e) $\dfrac{-5 \pm \sqrt{53}}{2}$ (f) $\dfrac{-7 \pm \sqrt{85}}{2}$ (g) $\dfrac{-11 \pm \sqrt{157}}{2}$

(h) $\dfrac{-3 \pm \sqrt{57}}{2}$ (i) $\dfrac{-5 \pm \sqrt{73}}{2}$ (j) N.R.S (k) $2 \pm \sqrt{11}$ (l) $3 \pm 2\sqrt{5}$ (m) $-2 \pm 2\sqrt{6}$ (n) N.R.S

(o) $1 \pm \dfrac{\sqrt{22}}{2}$ (p) $-\dfrac{1}{2}, 3$ (q) $-\dfrac{1}{2}, 4$ (r) $\dfrac{3 \pm \sqrt{41}}{4}$ (s) $\dfrac{3 \pm \sqrt{57}}{6}$ (t) $\dfrac{5 \pm \sqrt{73}}{6}$

EXERCISE 5.5

1. (a) $\dfrac{3 \pm \sqrt{37}}{2}$ (b) $\dfrac{5 \pm \sqrt{33}}{2}$ (c) $\dfrac{3 \pm \sqrt{33}}{2}$ (d) $\dfrac{7 \pm \sqrt{57}}{2}$ (e) $\dfrac{-7 \pm \sqrt{65}}{2}$ (f) -4,2 (g) $-1 \pm 2\sqrt{2}$

(h) $\dfrac{-5 \pm \sqrt{53}}{2}$ (i) $\dfrac{3 \pm \sqrt{37}}{2}$ (j) no real solutions (k) $4 \pm \sqrt{7}$ (l) no real solutions (m) $\dfrac{2 \pm \sqrt{13}}{2}$

(n) $\dfrac{3 \pm 2\sqrt{11}}{5}$ (o) $\dfrac{6 \pm \sqrt{31}}{5}$ (p) $\dfrac{6 \pm \sqrt{29}}{7}$

EXERCISE 5.6

1. Graphs are shown using the ZOOM4 viewing window:

(a)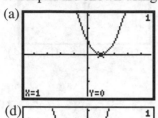
X=1   Y=0

(b)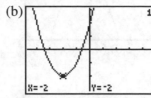
X=-2   Y=-2

(c)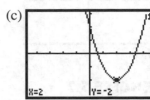
X=2   Y=-2

(d)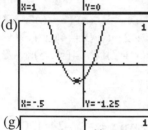
X=-.5   Y=-1.25

(e)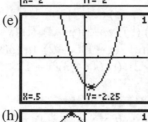
X=.5   Y=-2.25

(f)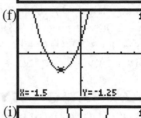
X=-1.5   Y=-1.25

(g)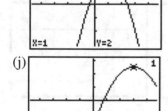
X=1   Y=2

(h)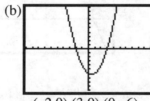
X=-1   Y=3

(i)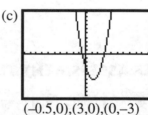
X=.5   Y=-1.5

(j)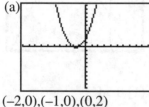
X=3   Y=2.5

(k)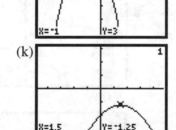
X=1.5   Y=-1.25

(l)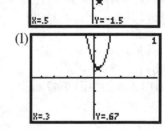
X=.3   Y=.67

1. Graphs are shown using the ZOOM6 viewing window:

(a)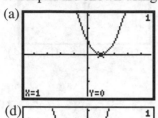
(−2,0),(−1,0),(0,2)

(b)
(−2,0),(3,0),(0,−6)

(c)
(−0.5,0),(3,0),(0,−3)

(d)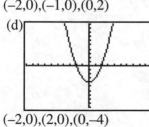
(−2,0),(2,0),(0,−4)

(e)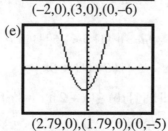
(2.79,0),(1.79,0),(0,−5)

(f)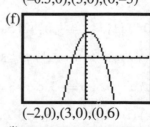
(−2,0),(3,0),(0,6)

(g)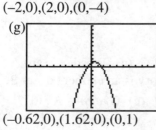
(−0.62,0),(1.62,0),(0,1)

(h)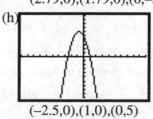
(−2.5,0),(1,0),(0,5)

(i)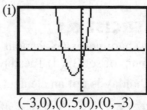
(−3,0),(0.5,0),(0,−3)

(j)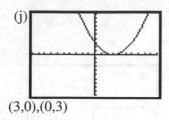

(3,0),(0,3)

(k)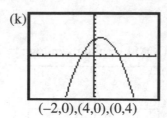

(−2,0),(4,0),(0,4)

(l)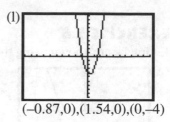

(−0.87,0),(1.54,0),(0,−4)

EXERCISE 5.7

1. (a) $(x-2)(x-1)$ (b) $(x-6)(x-1)$ (c) $(x-4)(x-2)$ (d) $(x-4)(x-5)$ (e) $(x-6)(x-3)$
(f) $(x-2)(x-5)$ (g) $(x-3)(x+1)$ (h) $(y+5)(y-2)$ (i) $(s-5)(s+2)$ (j) $(x-4)(x+3)$
(k) $(y-7)(y+2)$ (l) $(r-9)(r+5)$ (m) $2(x-1)(x-2)$ (n) $3(x+5)(x+2)$ (o) $4(s-5)(s+2)$
(p) $3(y+5)(y-2)$ (q) $5(x+4)(x+2)$ (r) $6(x-3)(x+1)$

EXAMINATION STYLE QUESTIONS

1. (a) $(x+4)(x-2)$ (b) Using the graph of $y = (x+4)(x-2)$ we have $x = -3, -2, -1, 0, 1$.
2. (a) (i) $(x+5)(x+1)$ (ii) $(x-6)(x+1)$ (b) (i)   (ii)

3. (a) $(x-4)(x+3)$ (b) $(3x-2)(2x-3)$
   (e) $(x-1-y)(x-1+y)$
4. $x = 5$
5. (a) $b = 16, a = 10$
   (b) $(x-8)(x-2)$
6. (i) 12 units (ii) 4.47 units

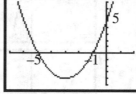

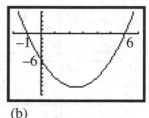

7. (a)   (b)

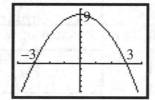

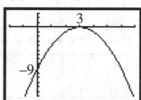

SELF ASSESSMENT TEST

1. $y = \left(x-\dfrac{3}{2}\right)^2 + 4\dfrac{3}{4}$ [2] $\left(\dfrac{3}{2}, 4\dfrac{3}{4}\right)$ [1]   2. $a = -1$ [1] $b = -3$ [1] 3. -3 [1] 0.5 [1]

4. $(0,7)$ [1] $\left(\dfrac{2 \pm \sqrt{32}}{2}, 0\right)$ [2] 5. $b^2 - 4ac > 0$ [1] $b < -6$ [1] or $b > 6$ [1]

6. $x(x+7) = 8918 \Rightarrow x^2 + 7x - 8918 = 0$ [1] 91 [1] & 98 [1]

7. (a) $a = 0.5, b = -3, c = -8$ [1][1][1] (b) $\dfrac{1}{2}(x+2)(x-8)$ [1] [1]

   (c) (i) $-1, 0, 1, 2, 3, 4, 5, 6, 7$ (ii) -12.5

EXERCISE 6.1

1. (a) hammer is an element of set A. (b) axe is an element of set C. (c) Tuesday is an element of set B. (d) Tuesday is not an element of set A. (e) January is an element of set B. (f) Sunday is not an element of set C. 2. (a) $32 \in C$ (b) $45 \in N$ (c) $Green \notin K$ (d) $Mary \notin P$ (e) $Horse \notin M$ (f) $Banana \in H$

EXERCISE 6.2
(a) F (b) T (c) T (d) F (e) F (f) T (g) T (h) F (i) F (j) F (k) F

EXERCISE 6.3
1. (a) T (b) F (c) F (d) T (e) T (f) F (g) T (h) T (i) T 2.(a) 4 (b) 12 (c) 7 (d) 11
3. (a) Finite (b) Infinite (c) Finite (d) Finite (e) Infinite (f) Finite

EXERCISE 6.4

1. (a) { } (b) {a , e} (c) {Monday, Tuesday, Wednesday, Thursday, Friday, Saturday, Sunday} (d) {4, 5} (e) {–4, –3, –2, –1, 0, 1, 2, 3, 4, 5} (f) {–4, –3, –2, –1, 0, 1, 2, 3, 4, 5}
(g) Not possible (h) Not possible 2. (a) 0 (b) 2 (c) 7 (d) 2 (e)10 (f) 10 (g) Infinite
(h) Infinite 3. G and H 4. (a) $\{x|x \in \mathbb{N}, 3 < x < 18\}$ (b) $\{x|x \in \mathbb{R}, x < 12\}$
(c) $\{x|x \in \mathbb{Z}, -56 \le x \le 45\}$ (d) $\{x|x \in \mathbb{Q}, -5 \le x \le 5\}$

EXERCISE 6.5
1. (a) T (b) T (c) T (d) T (e) T (f) T (g) T (h) T (i) F 2. (a) T (b) F (c) T (d) T
(e) T (f) T (g) F (h) T (i) F
3. { }, { α }, { β }, { μ }, { σ }, { α, β }, { α, μ }, { α, σ }, { β, μ }, { β, σ }, { μ, σ },
{ α, β, μ }, { α, β, σ }, { β, μ, σ }, { α, μ, σ }, { α, β, μ, σ }

EXERCISE 6.6

1. (a) {6, 12, 18} (b) {4, 16} (c) {9} (d) {} (e) {2, 3, 4, 6, 8, 9, 10, 12, 14, 16, 18} (f) {1, 3, 4, 6, 9, 12, 15, 16, 18} (g) {1, 2, 4, 6, 8, 10, 12, 14, 16, 18}
(h) {1, 2, 3, 4, 6, 8, 9, 10, 12, 14, 15 16, 18} (i) {4, 9, 16} (j) {3, 4, 6, 9, 12, 15, 18} (k) {2, 4, 6, 8, 9, 10, 12, 14, 16, 18} 2. (a) 3 (b) 2 (c) 1 (d) 0 (e) 12 (f) 9 (g) 11 (h) 13
3. (a) {-3, -2} (b) {-3, -2} (c) {-3, -2, -1, 0, 1, 2, 3} (d) {-3, -2} (e) {-5, -4, -3, -2, -1, 0, 1, 2, 3} (f) {-3, -2, -1, 0, 1, 2, 3, 4, 5}(g) {-5, -4, -3, -2, -1, 0, 1, 2, 3, 4, 5} (h) {-5, -4, -3, -2, -1, 0, 1, 2, 3, 4, 5} (i) {-3, -2, -1, 0, 1, 2, 3} (j) {-3, -2, -1, 0, 1, 2, 3} (k) {-5, -4, -3, -2, -1, 0, 1, 2, 3} 4. (a) 2 (b) 2 (c) 7 (d) 2 (e) 9 (f) 9 (g) 11(h) 11
5. (a) {x | x ∈ R , –3 ≤ x ≤ –2 } (b) {x | x ∈ R , –3 < x ≤ –2 }
(c) {x | x ∈ R , –3 < x < 4 } (d) {x | x ∈ R , –3 < x ≤ –2 }(e) {x | x ∈ R , –5 ≤ x < 4 }
(f) {x | x ∈ R , –3 ≤ x ≤ 5 }(g) x | x ∈ R , –5 ≤ x ≤ 5 } (h) {x | x ∈ R , –5 ≤ x ≤ 5 }
(i) {x | x ∈ R , –3 < x < 4 } (j) {x | x ∈ R , –3 ≤ x < 4 } (k) {x | x ∈ R , –5 ≤ x < 4 }

EXERCISE 6.7
1. (a) { b, d, f, g, j, k, l, n, o, p, q, r, u, v, w, x, y, z } (b) { a, e, i, o, u }
(c) { c, e, f, g, h, i, k, q, r, s, t, u, v, w, x, y } (d) { o, u } (e) { u } (f) { o, u } (g) { u }
(h) { b, d, e, f, g, i, j, k, l, n, o, p, q, r, u, v, w, x, y, z }
2. (a) { -10, -9, -8, -7, -6, 3, 4, 5, 6, 7, 8, 9, 10 }
(b) { -10, -9,-8, -7, -6, -5, -4, -3, -2, 7, 8, 9, 10 }
(c) { -10, -9, -8, -7, -6, -5, -4, -3, -2, -1, 0, 3, 4, 5, 6,7,8, 9, 10 }

(d) { -10, -9, -8, -7, -6, 7, 8, 9, 10 (e) { -10, -9, -8, -7, -6, 7, 8, 9, 10 }
(f) {-10, -9, -8, -7, -6, 7, 8, 9, 10 } (g) { -10, -9, -8, -7, -6, 7, 8, 9, 10 }
(h) { -10, -9, -8, -7, -6, -5, -4, -3, -2, 3, 4, 5, 6, 7, 8, 9, 10 }
3. (a) {x | x ∈ R , x ≤ −5 or x > −3 } (b){x | x ∈ R , x ≤ 3 }

(c) {x | x ∈ R , x ≤ −3 , x ≥ 4 } (d) {x | x ∈ R , x ≤ −5 } (e) {x | x ∈ R , x ≤ −5 }
4. (a) 28 (b) 19 (c) 25

EXERCISE 6.8

1. (a) A = {3, 6, 9, 12, 15, 18, 21, 24, 27, 30, 33, 36, 39}
   B = {4, 8, 12, 16, 20, 24, 28, 32, 36}
(b)   Multiples of both 3 and 4, less than 40
(c) (i) 13 (ii) 9 (iii) 3 (iv) 19

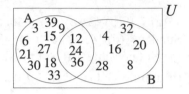

2.   (a)   A = { 1, 2, 3, 4, 6, 9, 12, 36 }
             B = { 1, 2, 3, 4, 5, 6, 10, 12, 15, 20, 30, 60 }
(b) Numbers that are both factors of 36 and 60
(c) (i) 9 ii) 12 (iii) 6 (iv) 15

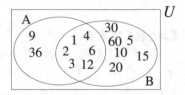

3.(a) A = {2, 3, 5, 7, 11, 13, 17, 19, 23, 29}
       B = {1, 3, 5, 7, 9, 11, 13, 15, 17, 19, 21, 23, 25, 27, 29}
(b)   Odd numbers less than 30 that are prime numbers
(c) (i) 0 (ii) 15 (iii) 9 (iv) 16

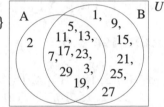

4. (a)

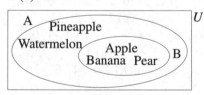

(b) The fruits that are common to both sets
(c) (i) 5 (ii) 3 (iii) 3 (iv) 5

5. (b) Capital cities that are in both Europe and South America. (Obviously impossible)
6. (a) A = {1, 2, 3, 4, 6, 9, 12, 18, 36}
B = {6, 12, 18, 24, 30, 36, 42, 48, 54, 60}
C = {2, 4, 6, 8, 10, 12, 14, 16, 18, 20}
(b) Nunbers that are factors of 36, multiples of 6 and even.
(c) (i) 9 (ii) 10 (iii) 10 (iv) 3 (v) 19

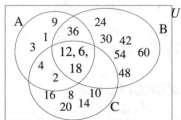

EXCERCISE 6.9

1.(a) (i)   (ii)   (iii)   (iv)

(v)   (vi)   (vii)

2. (a) (i)   (ii)   (iii)   (iv)

(v)   (vi)   (vii)

3.(a) (i)   (ii)   (iii)

(v)   (vi)   (vii)

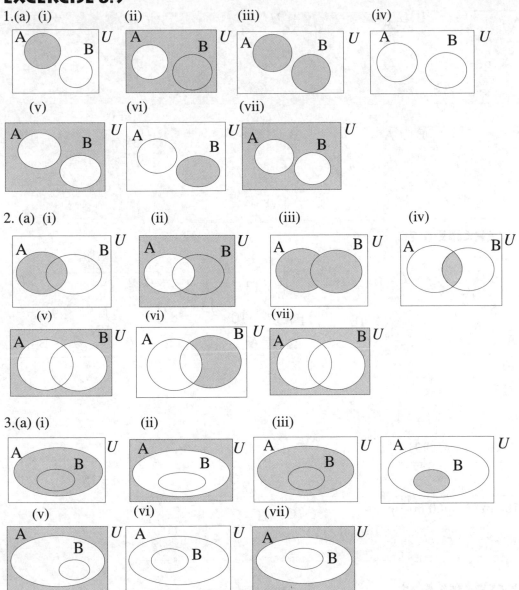

Answers

4. (a) (i)   (ii)   (iii)   (iv)

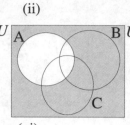 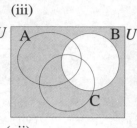 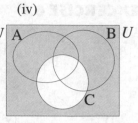

(v)   (vi)   (vii)   (viii)

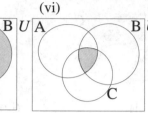 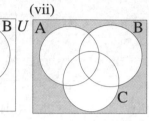 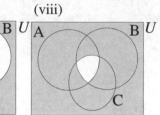

EXCERCISE 6.10

1. (a)   (b)   (c)   (d)

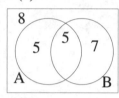 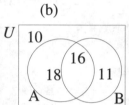 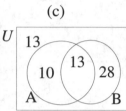 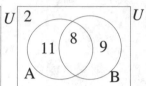

(e)

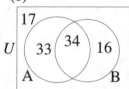

2.   3.   4.   5. $p = 15$

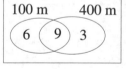 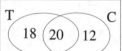 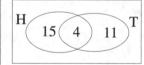

EXCERCISE 6.11

1.   2.   3.

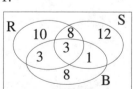 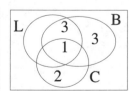 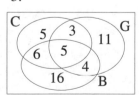

EXERCISE 6.12

(a) (b) (c) (d) (f) (h) (i) (k) (l)

EXERCISE 6.13

(a) Brutus is not sick (b) The cup is not empty (c) Monday is not a holiday
(d) There are not twelve months in a year (e) 4 is not less than 6 (f) Ismael does not study
Geography (g) Yoshi does not play football (h) All roses are not red (i) March does not
have 31 days (j) Not all quadrilaterals are rectangles (k) Carlos does not live in Japan

EXERCISE 6.14

1. (a) All trees are green and all mammals are warm blooded (b) Josh and Anne study
French (c) Abdul plays both football and squash (d) The moon orbits the earth and the
earth orbits the sun (e) It is raining and today is Saturday
2.
(a) p: Jennifer studies Physics q: Jennifer studies Chemistry
(b) p: All mammals are warm blooded q: All roses are red
(c) p: Ruth is 16 years old q: Janet is 17 years old
(d) p: Today is Sunday q: It is fine
(e) p: Ronnie plays football q: Renee plays tennis

EXERCISE 6.15

(a) (i) P = {4, 8, 12, 16}, Q = {6, 12, 18} (iii) $p \wedge q$ truth set = {12} (ii)

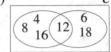

(b) (i) P = { 1, 4, 9, 16, 25, 36, 49, 64, 81 } Q = { 6, 16, 26, 36 }
(iii) $p \wedge q$ truth set = {16, 36}   (ii)

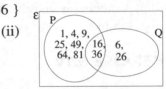

(c) (i) P = { 2, 3, 5, 7, 11, 13, 17, 19 } Q = { 3, 6, 9, 12, 15, 18 } $p \wedge q$ truth set = { 3 }
(ii)

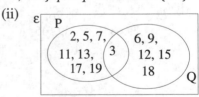

EXERCISE 6.16

1. (a) All trees are green or all mammals are warm blooded (b) Josh or Anne study French
(c) Abdul plays football or squash (d) The moon orbits the earth or the earth orbits the sun
(e) It is raining or today is Saturday
2.(a) p: Josh will buy a TV   q: Josh will buy a stereo
  (b) p: Yoshi plays tennis   q: Mohammed plays squash
  (c) p: The moon the earth   q: The moon orbits the sun
  (d) p: Emus are birds   q: Goats are horses
  (e) p: Ruth likes watching the theatre   q: Ruth likes watching sports

EXERCISE 6.17

(a) (i) P = { 4, 8, 12, 16 } Q = { 6, 12, 18 }

(iii) p ∨ q   truth set = { 4, 6, 8, 12, 16, 18 }

(ii)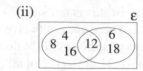

(b) (i) P = {1, 4, 9, 16 25, 36, 49, 64, 81} Q = { 6, 16, 26, 36} (ii)

(iii) *p* ∨ *q*   truth set = { 1, 4, 6, 9, 16, 25, 26, 36, 49, 64, 81}

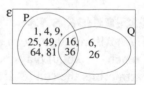

(c) (i) P = {2, 3, 5, 7, 11, 13, 17, 19}Q = { 3, 6, 9, 12, 15, 18 }(ii)

(iii) *p* ∨ *q*   truth set = {2, 3, 5, 6, 7, 9, 11, 12, 13, 15, 17, 18, 19}

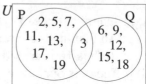

EXERCISE 6.18

1.(a) If x is a multiple of 9 then x is divisible by 3 (b) If Yoshi is sick then Yoshi is not at work (c) If Paris is in France then the sky is blue (d) If this is the right time for an argument then it is the right place for an argument (e) If John works hard then John earns money

2.(a) p: A number is divisible by 10   q: A number ends in zero

 (b) p: I will earn more money   q: I work hard

 (c) p: The flowers will grow   q: There is enough rain

 (d) p: A number is divisible by 4   q: A number is even

 (e) p: I think   q: I am

EXERCISE 6.19

(a) (i) P = { 16, 25, 49 } Q = { 15, 16, 19, 25, 26, 29, 35, 36, 39, 45, 46, 49 }

(ii)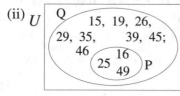

(b)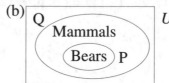

EXERCISE 6.20

(a) Converse : If a number ends in zero then it is divisible by 10

    Inverse : If a number is not divisible by then it does not end in zero

    Contrapositive: If a number does not end in zero then it is not divisible by 10

(b) Converse : I work hard only if I will earn more money

    Inverse : If I will not earn more money then I will not work hard

    Contrapositive : If I do not work hard then I will not earn more money

(c) Converse : There is enough rain only if the flowers will grow

    Inverse : The flowers will not grow only if there is not enough rain

    Contrapositive : If there is not enough rain then the flowers will not grow

(d) Converse : If a number is even then it is divisible by four

Inverse : If a number is not divisible by four then it is not even

Contrapositive : If a number is not even then it is not divisible by four

(e) Converse : If I am then I think

Inverse : If I do not think then I am not

Contrapositive : If I am not then I do not think

EXERCISE 6.21

(a) I will paint the house if and only if it is fine

(b) We will go to Disneyland if and only if there are exciting rides

(c) I will take my umbrella if it is raining

(d) John will hit a home run if the pitcher is useless

EXERCISE 6.22

(a)

p	q	$\neg p$	$\neg p \vee q$
T	T	F	T
T	F	F	F
F	T	T	T
F	F	T	T

(b)

p	q	$\neg p$	$\neg q$	$\neg p \vee \neg q$
T	T	F	F	F
T	F	F	T	T
F	T	T	F	T
F	F	T	T	T

(c)

p	q	$\neg p$	$\neg q$	$\neg p \wedge \neg q$
T	T	F	F	F
T	F	F	T	F
F	T	T	F	F
F	F	T	T	T

(d)

p	q	$\neg p$	q	$\neg p \Rightarrow q$
T	T	F	T	T
T	F	F	F	T
F	T	T	T	T
F	F	T	F	F

(e)

p	q	¬q	p ∨ ¬q	q	(p ∨ ¬q) ⇒ q
T	T	F	T	T	T
T	F	T	T	F	F
F	T	F	F	T	T
F	F	T	T	F	F

(f)

p	q	¬p	¬p ⇔ q
T	T	F	F
T	F	F	T
F	T	T	T
F	F	T	F

(g)

p	q	¬q	p ∨ ¬q	p ∧ ¬q	(p ∨ ¬q) ⇒ (p ∧ ¬q)
T	T	F	T	F	F
T	F	T	T	T	T
F	T	F	F	F	T
F	F	T	T	F	F

(h)

p	q	¬p	¬p ∧ q	q ∧ p	(¬p ∧ q) ∨ (q ∧ p)
T	T	F	F	T	T
T	F	F	F	F	F
F	T	T	T	F	T
F	F	T	F	F	F

(i)

p	q	¬q	p ⇒ ¬q	¬(p ⇒ ¬q)
T	T	F	F	T
T	F	T	T	F
F	T	F	T	F
F	F	T	T	F
T	T	F	F	T
T	F	T	T	F
F	T	F	T	F
F	F	T	T	F

(j)

p	q	p ∧ q	p ∨ q	(p ∧ q) ⇒ (p ∨ q)
T	T	T	T	T
T	F	F	T	T
F	T	F	T	T
F	F	F	F	T

(k)

p	q	p ∧ q	¬(p ∧ q)	q ⇔ p	¬(q ⇔ p)	¬(p ∧ q) ∨ ¬(q ⇔ p)
T	T	T	F	T	F	F
T	F	F	T	F	T	T
F	T	F	T	F	T	T
F	F	F	T	T	F	T

EXERCISE 6.23

(a)

p	q	r	p ∨ q	r	(p ∨ q) ⇒ r
T	T	T	T	T	T
T	T	F	T	F	F
T	F	T	T	T	T
T	F	F	T	F	F
F	T	T	T	T	T
F	T	F	T	F	F
F	F	T	F	T	T
F	F	F	F	F	T

(b)

p	q	r	¬p	¬q	¬p ∨ ¬q	(¬p ∨ ¬q) ∧ r
T	T	T	F	F	F	F
T	T	F	F	F	F	F
T	F	T	F	T	T	T
T	F	F	F	T	T	F
F	T	T	T	F	T	T
F	T	F	T	F	T	F
F	F	T	T	T	T	T
F	F	F	T	T	T	F

(c)

p	q	r	¬p	¬q	¬r	¬p ∧ ¬q ∧ ¬r
T	T	T	F	F	F	F
T	T	F	F	F	T	F
T	F	T	F	T	F	F
T	F	F	F	T	T	F
F	T	T	T	F	F	F
F	T	F	T	F	T	F
F	F	T	T	T	F	F
F	F	F	T	T	T	T

(d)

p	q	r	¬p	q ∨ r	¬p ⇒ (q ∨ r)
T	T	T	F	T	T
T	T	F	F	T	T
T	F	T	F	T	T
T	F	F	F	F	T
F	T	T	T	T	T
F	T	F	T	T	T
F	F	T	T	T	T
F	F	F	T	F	F

(e)

p	q	r	¬q	p ∨ ¬q	r	(p ∨ ¬q) ⇒ r
T	T	T	F	T	T	T
T	T	F	F	T	F	F
T	F	T	T	T	T	T
T	F	F	T	T	F	F
F	T	T	F	F	T	T
F	T	F	F	F	F	T
F	F	T	T	T	T	T
F	F	F	T	T	F	F

(f)

p	q	r	¬p	¬p ⇔ q	(¬p ⇔ q) ∨ r
T	T	T	F	F	T
T	T	F	F	F	F
T	F	T	F	T	T
T	F	F	F	T	F
F	T	T	T	T	T
F	F	T	T	F	T
F	F	F	T	F	T

(g)

p	q	r	¬r	p ∨ ¬r	¬q	r ∧ ¬q	(p ∨ ¬r) ⇒ (r ∧ ¬q)
T	T	T	F	T	F	F	F
T	T	F	T	T	F	F	F
T	F	T	F	T	T	T	T
T	F	F	T	T	T	F	F
F	T	T	F	F	F	F	T
F	T	F	T	T	F	F	F
F	F	T	F	F	T	T	T
F	F	F	T	T	T	F	F

(h)

p	q	r	¬p	¬p ∧ q	q ∧ r	(¬p ∧ q) ∨ (q ∧ r)
T	T	T	F	F	T	T
T	T	F	F	F	F	F
T	F	T	F	F	F	F
T	F	F	F	F	F	F
F	T	T	T	T	T	T
F	T	F	T	T	F	T
F	F	T	T	F	F	F
F	F	F	T	F	F	F

(i)

p	q	r	p ∧ r	r ∨ q	(p ∧ r) ⇒ (r ∨ q)
T	T	T	T	T	T
T	T	F	F	T	T
T	F	T	T	T	T
T	F	F	F	F	T
F	T	T	F	T	T
F	T	F	F	T	T
F	F	T	F	T	T
F	F	F	F	F	T

(j)

p	q	r	p ∧ q	¬(p ∧ q)	q ⇔ r	¬(q ⇔ r)	¬(p ∧ q) ∨ ¬(q ⇔ r)
T	T	T	T	F	T	F	F
T	T	F	T	F	F	T	T
T	F	T	F	T	F	T	T
T	F	F	F	T	T	F	T
F	T	T	F	T	T	F	T
F	T	F	F	T	F	T	T
F	F	T	F	T	F	T	T
F	F	F	F	T	T	F	T

EXERCISE 6.24

(a) Invalid
(b) Invalid
(c) Invalid

EXAMINATION STYLE QUESTIONS

1. (a) p : Today is Tuesday $\neg p$ (b) p : x is a even number q : x is a prime number $p \lor q$

(c) p : Mary studies French q : John studies French $p \land q$

(d) p : It is raining q : The concert will be cancelled $p \Rightarrow q$

(e) p : Yoshi will go to the concert q : It is raining $p \Leftrightarrow \neg q$

(f) p : Birgit likes ice cream q : Birgit likes cake $p \land q$

(g) p : Jessica will go to the concert q : Mary goes to the concent r : It is raining

$p \Leftrightarrow (q \land \neg r)$

(h) p : It is fine q : Temperature is between $20°$ C and $30°$ C

r : Paul will play tennis $(p \land q) \Rightarrow r$

(i) p : I work hard q : I will pass my exams $p \Rightarrow q$

(j) p : Bill wins his race q : Bill will make the final $p \Rightarrow q$

(k) p : Bill wins his race q : Bill will make the final $\neg p \Rightarrow \neg q$

2. (a) He does not eat too much (b) He does not eat too much and he is healthy

(c) He is healthy or happy (d) If he eats too much then he is not happy

(e) If he does not eat too much and he is healthy than he is happy

(f) He eats too much if and only if he is not happy (g) He eats too much or he is happy (h)
If he does not eat too much or he is healthy than he is happy

(i) If he does not eat too much then he is healthy and happy

(j) He is happy if and only if he does not eat too much and he is healthy

3. (a) P = { 3, 6, 9, 12, 15, 18, 21, 24, 27, 30, 33, 36, 39 }

Q = { 2, 4, 6, 8, 10, 12, 14, 16, 18, 20, 22, 24, 26, 28, 30 32, 34, 36, 38 }

R = { 1, 2, 3, 4, 6, 9, 12, 18, 36 }

(i) x is not a multiple of 3 between 0 and 40

(ii)

p	$\neg p$
T	F
F	T

(iii)

(b) (i) x is a multiple of 3 and an even number between 0 and 40

(ii)

p	q	$p \wedge q$
T	T	T
T	F	F
F	T	F
F	F	F

(iii)

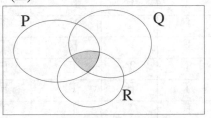

(c) (i) x is a multiple of 3 and an even number and a factor of 36 between 0 and 40

(ii)

p	q	r	$p \wedge q \wedge r$
T	T	T	T
T	T	F	F
T	F	T	F
T	F	F	F
F	T	T	F
F	T	F	F
F	F	T	F
F	F	F	F

(iii)

(iv) $p \cap q \cap r$ = { 6, 12, 18, 36 }

(d) (i) x is either a multiple of 3 between 0 and 40 or an even number between 0 and 40 or a factor of 36

(ii)

p	q	r	p ∨ q ∨ r
T	T	T	T
T	T	F	T
T	F	T	T
T	F	F	T
F	T	T	T
F	T	F	T
F	F	T	T
F	F	F	F

(iii)

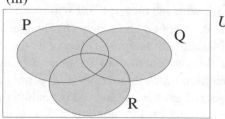

(iv) $P \cup Q \cup R$

(e) (i) x is not a multiple of 3 between 0 and 40 and x is not an even number between 0 and 40

(ii)

p	q	¬p	¬q	¬p ∧ ¬q
T	T	F	F	F
T	F	F	T	F
F	T	T	F	F
F	F	T	T	T

(iii)

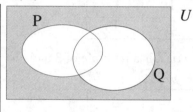

(iv) $P' \cap Q' = \{1, 5, 7, 11, 13, 17, 19, 23, 25, 29, 31, 35, 37\}$

(f) (i) x is not a multiple of 3 between 0 and 40 and x is not an even number between 0 and 40 and x is not a factor of 36 (ii)

p	q	r	¬p	¬q	¬r	¬p ∧ ¬q ∧ ¬r
T	T	T	F	F	F	F
T	T	F	F	F	T	F
T	F	T	F	T	F	F
T	F	F	F	T	T	F
F	T	T	T	F	F	F
F	T	F	T	F	T	F
F	F	T	T	T	F	F
F	F	F	T	T	T	T

(iii)

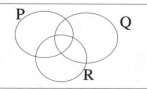

(iv) $P' \cap Q' \cap R'$
= { 5, 7, 11, 13, 17, 19, 23, 25, 29, 31, 35, 37}

(g) (i) x is not an even factor of 36 that is a multiple of 3

(ii)

p	q	r	p ∧ q ∧ r	¬(p ∧ q ∧ r)
T	T	T	T	F
T	T	F	F	T
T	F	T	F	T
T	F	F	F	T
F	T	T	F	T
F	T	F	F	T
F	F	T	F	T
F	F	F	F	T

(iii)

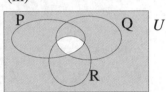

(iv) $(P \cap Q \cap R)'$

(h) (i) x is an even number or a factor of 36 but is not a multiple of 3

(ii)

p	q	r	¬p	q ∨ r	¬p ∧ (q ∨ r)
T	T	T	F	T	F
T	T	F	F	T	F
T	F	T	F	T	F
T	F	F	F	F	F
F	T	T	T	T	T
F	T	F	T	T	T
F	F	T	T	T	T
F	F	F	T	F	F

(iii)

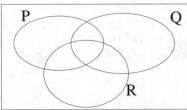

(iv) $P' \cap (Q \cup R)$
$= \{1, 2, 4, 8, 10, 14, 16, 20, 22, 26, 28, 32, 34, 38\}$

4. (a) Neither (b) Neither (c) Neither (d) Contradiction (e) Tautology (f) Tautology
(g) Contradiction (h) Neither
5. (a) Invalid (b) Invalid (c) Invalid (d) Valid (f) Invalid

SELF ASSESSMENT TEST

1. { 2 } [1] 2 (a) Yes [1](b) No [1](c) No [1](d) No [1](e) Yes [1](f)Yes [1]

3.

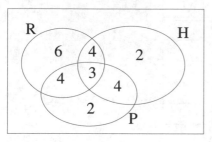

Each set [1] [1] [1]
Intersections [1] [1] [1]

4. [Two marks each]

(a) Implication :   If Fuzzy is a bear then Fuzzy is cute
   Converse :   If Fuzzy is cute then Fuzzy is a bear
   Inverse :   If Fuzzy is not a bear then Fuzzy is not cute
   Contrapositive :   If Fuzzy is not cute then Fuzzy is not a bear

(b) Implication :   If Mary lives in Spain then Mary loves fish
   Converse :   If Mary loves fish then Mary lives in Spain
   Inverse :   If Mary does not live in Spain then Mary does not love fish
   Contrapositive :   If Mary does not love fish then Mary does not live in Spain

(c) Implication :   If it is fine then we will go to the concert
   Converse :   We will go to the concert only if it is fine
   Inverse :   If it is not fine then we will not go to the concert
   Contrapositive :   We will not go to the concert only if it is not fine

(d) Implication :   If I work hard then I will pay taxes
   Converse :   I will pay taxes only if I work hard
   Inverse :   If I do not work hard then I will not pay taxes
   Contrapositive :   I will not pay taxes only if I do not work hard

(e) Implication :   If John loves fishing then John lives by the sea
   Converse :   If John lives by the sea then John loves fishing
   Inverse :   If John does not love fishing then he does not live by the sea
   Contrapositive :   If John does not live by the sea then John does not love fishing

EXERCISE 7.1

	a cm	b cm	c cm	A	B	C
1	3.8	4.1	1.6	67°	90°	23°
2	81.5	98.3	55.0	56°	90°	34°
3	32.7	47.1	33.9	44°	90°	46°
4	1.61	30.7	30.7	3°	90°	87°

	a cm	b cm	c cm	A	B	C
5	2.3	2.74	1.49	57°	90°	33°
6	48.5	77	59.8	39°	90°	51°
7	44.4	81.6	68.4	33°	90°	57°
8	2.93	13.0	12.7	13°	90°	77°
9	74.4	94.4	58.1	52°	90°	38°
10	71.8	96.5	64.6	48°	90°	42°
11	23.3	34.1	24.9	43°	90°	47°
12	43.1	43.2	2.3	87°	90°	3°
13	71.5	80.2	36.4	63°	90°	27°
14	33.5	34.1	6.5	79°	90°	11°
15	6.1	7.2	3.82	58°	90°	32°
16	29.1	30	7.3	76°	90°	14°
17	29.0	29.1	2.0	86°	90°	4°
18	34.5	88.2	81.2	23°	90°	67°
19	24.0	29.7	17.5	54°	90°	36°
20	41.2	46.2	21.0	63°	90°	27°
21	59.6	72.9	41.8	55°	90°	35°
22	5.43	6.8	4.09	53°	90°	37°
23	13.0	19.8	14.9	41°	90°	49°
24	14.0	21.3	16.1	41°	90°	49°
25	82.4	88.9	33.3	68°	40°	22°

2. (i) 3.01km N, 3.99km E (ii) 2.87km E 0.88km S (iii) 6.86km E 2.13km N
(iv) 7.19km 253° true. 3. 524m

EXERCISE 7.2

	a cm	b cm	c cm	A	B	C
1	13.3	37.1	48.2	10°	29°	141°
2	2.7	1.2	2.8	74°	25°	81°
3	11.0	0.7	11.3	60°	3°	117°
4	31.9	39.1	51.7	38°	49°	93°
5	18.5	11.4	19.5	68°	35°	77°
6	14.6	15.0	5.3	75°	84°	21°
7	26.0	7.3	26.4	79°	16°	85°
8	21.6	10.1	28.5	39°	17°	124°
9	0.8	0.2	0.8	82°	16°	82°
10	27.7	7.4	33.3	36°	9°	135°
11	16.4	20.7	14.5	52°	84°	44°
12	21.4	45.6	64.3	11°	24°	145°
13	30.9	27.7	22.6	75°	60°	45°

14	29.3	45.6	59.1	29°	49°	102°
15	9.7	9.8	7.9	65°	67°	48°
16	21.5	36.6	54.2	16°	28°	136°
17	14.8	29.3	27.2	30°	83°	67°
18	10.5	0.7	10.9	52°	3°	125°
19	11.2	6.9	17.0	25°	15°	140°
20	25.8	18.5	40.1	30°	21°	129°

EXERCISE 7.3

	a	b	c	$A°$	$B°$	$C°$	$c*$	$B*°$	$C*°$
1	7.40	18.10	21.06	20.00	56.78	103.22	12.95	123.22	36.78
2	13.30	19.50	31.36	14.00	20.77	145.23	6.49	159.23	6.77
3	13.50	17.00	25.90	28.00	36.24	115.76	4.12	143.76	8.24
4	10.20	17.00	25.62	15.00	25.55	139.45	7.22	154.45	10.55
5	7.40	15.20	19.55	20.00	44.63	115.37	9.02	135.37	24.63
6	10.70	14.10	21.41	26.00	35.29	118.71	3.94	144.71	9.29
7	11.50	12.60	22.94	17.00	18.68	144.32	1.16	161.32	1.68
8	8.30	13.70	18.67	24.00	42.17	113.83	6.36	137.83	18.17
9	13.70	17.80	30.28	14.00	18.32	147.68	4.27	161.68	4.32
10	13.40	17.80	26.19	28.00	38.58	113.42	5.24	141.42	10.58
11	12.10	16.80	25.63	23.00	32.85	124.15	5.30	147.15	9.85
12	12.00	14.50	24.35	21.00	25.66	133.34	2.72	154.34	4.66
13	12.10	19.20	29.34	16.00	25.94	138.06	7.57	154.06	9.94
14	7.20	13.10	19.01	15.00	28.09	136.91	6.30	151.91	13.09
15	12.20	17.70	23.73	30.00	46.50	103.50	6.93	133.50	16.50
16	9.20	20.90	27.97	14.00	33.34	132.66	12.59	146.66	19.34
17	10.50	13.30	21.96	20.00	25.67	134.33	3.03	154.33	5.67
18	9.20	19.20	26.29	15.00	32.69	132.31	10.80	147.31	17.69
19	7.20	13.30	18.33	19.00	36.97	124.03	6.82	143.03	17.97
20	13.50	20.40	25.96	31.00	51.10	97.90	9.01	128.90	20.10
21	10.80	20.80	24.48	26.00	57.59	96.41	12.91	122.41	31.59
22	13.00	12.20	23.91	19.00	17.79	143.21	0.84	162.21	1.21
23	13.60	20.40	22.92	36.00	61.85	82.15	10.09	118.15	25.85
24	11.40	12.50	22.88	16.00	17.59	146.41	1.15	162.41	1.59
25	8.00	16.80	23.99	10.00	21.39	148.61	9.10	158.61	11.39

EXERCISE 7.4

	a cm	b cm	c cm	A	B	C
1	13.5	9.8	16.7	54°	36°	90°
2	8.9	10.8	15.2	35°	44°	101°
3	22.8	25.6	12.8	63°	87°	30°
4	21.1	4.4	21.0	85°	12°	83°
5	15.9	10.6	15.1	74°	40°	66°
6	8.8	13.6	20.3	20°	32°	128°
7	9.2	9.5	13.2	44°	46°	90°
8	23.4	62.5	58.4	22°	89°	69°
9	10.5	9.6	15.7	41°	37°	102°
10	21.7	36.0	36.2	35°	72°	73°

	a cm	b cm	c cm	A	B	C
11	7.6	3.4	9.4	49°	20°	111°
12	7.2	15.2	14.3	28°	83°	69°
13	9.1	12.5	15.8	35°	52°	93°
14	14.9	11.2	16.2	63°	42°	75°
15	2.0	0.7	2.5	38°	13°	129°
16	7.6	3.7	9.0	56°	24°	100°
17	18.5	9.8	24.1	45°	22°	113°
18	20.7	16.3	13.6	87°	52°	41°
19	14.6	22.4	29.9	28°	46°	106°
20	7.0	6.6	9.9	45°	42°	93°
21	21.8	20.8	23.8	58°	54°	68°
22	1.1	1.7	1.3	41°	89°	50°
23	1.2	1.2	0.4	85°	76°	19°
24	23.7	27.2	29.7	49°	60°	71°
25	3.4	4.6	5.2	40°	60°	80°

EXERCISE 7.5

1. 39.60m 52.84m, 2. 30.2m 3. 54°, 42° & 84° 4. 37° 5. 028° true. 6. 108.1cm 7. (i) 135° (ii) 136cm 8. 41°, 56°, 83° 9. (i) 158° left (ii) 43.22km 10. 264m 11. 53.33cm 12. 186m 13. 50.12cm 14. 5.17cm 15. (i) 5950m (ii) 13340m (iii) 160° (iv) 243°

EXAMINATION STYLE QUESTIONS

1. (a) 87.3 m (b) 2.92° 2. (b) 1701 m (c) 17187 (d) 185.8 km/hr 3. (a) 3.4 m (b) 3.12 m 4. (b) 1.0 m (c) 1.71 m 5. (b) 67°28', 112°32' (c) 68.76, 11.26

SELF ASSESSMENT TEST

1. Use of cosine [1] 19.48 [1] 2. Use of the sine rule [1] $C = 50.06°$ & $A = 92.94°$ [1] $a = 12.11$cm [1] $C' = 129.94°$ & $A' = 13.05°$ [1] $a = 2.741$cm [1] 3. Use of the cosine rule [1] 46° [1] 55° [1] 79° [1] 4. There a six unit equilateral triangles [1] Each has area

$\frac{1}{2} \times 1 \times 1 \times \sin 60° = \frac{\sqrt{3}}{4} u^2$ [1] Total area $= \frac{3\sqrt{3}}{2} u^2$ [1]

5. Diagram [1] [1]

$\tan \alpha = \frac{h}{x}$ [1], $\tan \beta = \frac{h}{x+d}$ [1], $\tan \beta = \frac{x \tan \alpha}{x+d}$ [1]

Transposing last equation to correct expression [1] [1]

6. Diagram [1] [1]

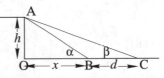

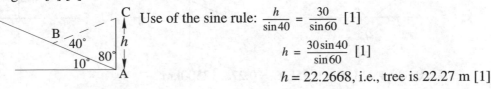

Use of the sine rule: $\frac{h}{\sin 40} = \frac{30}{\sin 60}$ [1]

$h = \frac{30 \sin 40}{\sin 60}$ [1]

$h = 22.2668$, i.e., tree is 22.27 m [1]

EXERCISE 8.1

1. (i) $\sqrt{41}$ (ii) $\sqrt{72}$ (iii) $\sqrt{225}=15$ (iv) $\sqrt{250}$ (v) $\sqrt{85}$ (vi) $\sqrt{173}$ (vii) $\sqrt{41}$ (viii) $\sqrt{89}$
(ix) $\sqrt{226}$ (x) $\sqrt{106}$ (xi) $\sqrt{205}$ (xii) $\sqrt{180}$ (xiii) $\sqrt{400} = 20$ (xiv) $\sqrt{145}$ (xv) 4
2. (i) (-5,0) (ii) (0,6.5) (iii) (-1,-1) (iv) (-2.5,-5.5) (v) (-5.5,0.5) (vi) (2.5,1) (vii) (-2.5,-3.5
(viii) (4,2.5) (ix) (-1.5,4) (x) (2,4.5) (xi) (8.5,5) (xii) (-1,3.5)(xiii) (-0.5,1.5) (xiv) (-6,0)
(xv) (0.5,0.5)

EXERCISE 8.2

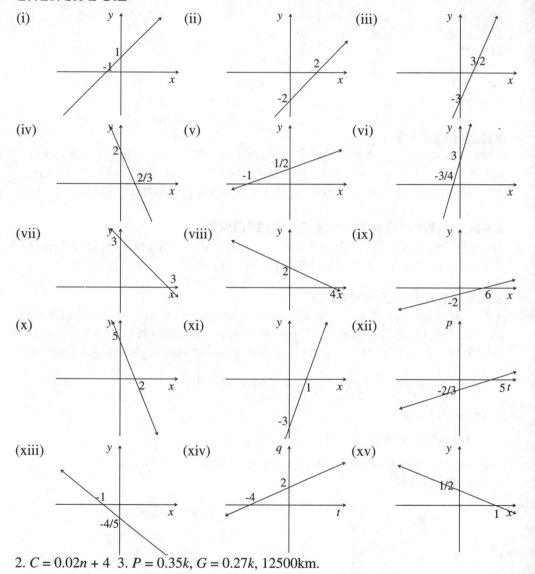

2. $C = 0.02n + 4$ 3. $P = 0.35k$, $G = 0.27k$, 12500km.

EXERCISE 8.3

1. (i) 2 (ii) 3 (iii) $\frac{5}{3}$ (iv) 8 (v) 0 (vi) 2 (ii) –2 (viii) undefined.
2. (i) 45° (ii) 63°26' (iii) 75°58' (iv) 26°34' (v) 135° (vi) 143°7' (vii) 108°26' (viii) 30°58

. (a) $y = 2x - 1$ (b) $y = 3x + 9$ (c) $y = -x - 1$ 4. (a) $-\frac{1}{2}$ (b) $\frac{1}{3}$ (c) $\frac{3}{2}$ (d) $-\frac{4}{5}$ 5. $y = 2x$

. $y = -x + 1$ 7. $2y - x - 2 = 0$ 8. ± 12 9. 2. 10. Parallelogram.

1. (a) $y = \frac{5}{2}x$ (b) $y = -\frac{3}{2}x + 3$ (c) $y = \frac{5}{6}x - \frac{1}{2}$ (d) $y = -2x + 1$

EXERCISE 8.4

. (i) $x = 1, y = 2$ (ii) $x = 3, y = 5$ (iii) $x = -1, y = 2$ (iv) $x = 0, y = 1$ (v) $x = -2, y = -3$

vi) $x = -5, y = 1$ 2. (i) $x = \frac{13}{11}, y = \frac{17}{11}$ (ii) $x = \frac{9}{14}, y = \frac{3}{14}$ (iii) $x = 0, y = 0$ (iv) $x = \frac{4}{17}, y = -\frac{22}{17}$

v) $x = -\frac{16}{7}, y = \frac{78}{7}$ (vi) $x = \frac{5}{42}, y = -\frac{3}{28}$ 3. (i) -3 (ii) -5 (iii) -1.5 4. (i) $m = 2, a = 8$ (ii) $m =$

0, $a = 24$ (iii) $m = -6, a = 9$. 5. 157 & 158. 6. $26 (the tapes cost $18). 7. Adults $17,

hildren $9. 8. (i) $x = 48, y = -70$ (ii) $x = 94.67, y = -140$ (iii) Graphically, the lines are

lmost parallel so small changes in the coefficients produce big changes in the solutions.

EXERCISE 8.5

. (a) (0,1), (2,5) & (6,3) (b) a proof could involve finding the lengths of the sides of the 2

riangles 3.(a) $y = 3x + c$ (b) $y = 3x - 8$ (c) (3,1) (d) $\sqrt{40}$ 4. (36.67,89.5) to (110,265.5)

EXERCISE 8.6

. (a) (i) $\sqrt{8}$ (ii) (2, 2, 2) (b) (i) $\sqrt{27}$ (ii) $\left(\frac{1}{2}, -\frac{3}{2}, \frac{1}{2}\right)$ (b) (i) $\sqrt{61}$ (ii) $\left(-\frac{3}{2}, 3, 3\right)$ (b) (i) $\sqrt{126}$

ii) $\left(\frac{1}{2}, 1, \frac{3}{2}\right)$ (b) (i) $\sqrt{37}$ (ii) $\left(-\frac{1}{2}, 1, 5\right)$ (b) (i) $\sqrt{83}$ (ii) $\left(\frac{5}{2}, \frac{7}{2}, \frac{1}{2}\right)$ (b) (i) $\sqrt{3}$ (ii) $\left(-\frac{1}{2}, -\frac{1}{2}, -\frac{1}{2}\right)$

b) (i) 6 (ii) (0, 0, 0)

EXAMINATION STYLE QUESTIONS

. (a) –3 (b) (2,0), (6, 0) (c) $\frac{1}{3}$ (d) $3y - x - 3 = 0$ 2. (c) $\sqrt{34}$ (d) $\left(5, \frac{1}{2}, 0\right)$ 3. (a) –2

b) $y = -2x + 8$ (c) $a = 4, b = 3$ 4. $7y - 6x - 10 = 0, 6y + 7x - 24 = 0$ 5. (a) $y = 4x - 9$

b) $y = -x + 1$ (c) $2y - x + 4 = 0$ (d) $2y - x + 4 = 0$ 6. (a) $y + 2x - 5 = 0$ (b) $2y - x + 5 = 0$

. $\left(\frac{7}{6}, \frac{5}{6}\right)$ 8. $b = -1.5, a = 0.5$

SELF ASSESSMENT TEST

. $2y - 4x + 3 = 0$ has gradient 2 [1], The required line is $y = 2x + c$. Substitution of

he coordinates (-1,2) [1], to get $c = 4$ and the equation $y = 2x + 4$ [1] 2. Gradient of

$y = -\frac{2}{3}x + \frac{3}{7}$ is $-\frac{2}{3}$ [1] so the gradient of the required line is $\frac{3}{2}$ [1].The equation of the

equired line is $3x - 2y + 2 = 0$ [1]. 3. (1,4) [1] 4. $d = \sqrt{(-5)^2 + (8)^2}$ [1] (i) = $\sqrt{89}$ [1]

ii) 9.43 [1] 5. The gradient of the line segment is -0.5 [1] and so,required line has slope 2

1]. The line also passes throught the mid-point (2,1.5) [1] and has equation $y = 2x - 2.5$

1]. 6. $5x = 20$ [1] $x = 4$ [1] $y = -2$ [1] 7. (a) [1] [1] (b) [1] (c) $\sqrt{2}$ [1][1] (d) (0, 1, 2)[1][1]

EXERCISE 9.1

1. (a) 39°48' (b) 64°45' 2. (a) 12.81 cm (b) 61.35 cm (c) 77°57' (d) 60.38 cm (e) 80° 32
3. (a) 21°48' (b) 42°2' (c) 26°34' 4. (a) 2274 (b) 12.7° 5. 251.29 m 6. (a) 103.5 m

(b) 35.3° 7. (b) 53.43 (c) 155.16 m (d) 196.15 m 8. (b) 48.45 m 9. (a) $\sqrt{(b-c)^2 + h^2}$

(b) $\tan^{-1}\left(\dfrac{h}{a}\right)$ (c) $\tan^{-1}\left(\dfrac{h}{b-c}\right)$ (d) $2(b+c)\sqrt{h^2+a^2} + 2a\sqrt{(b-c)^2+h^2}$ 10. (a) 54.7°

(b) 70.6°

EXAMINATION STYLE QUESTIONS

1. (a) 28.28 cm (b) 34.64 cm (c) 35°16' (d) 45° 2. (a) 9.33cm (Approx) (b) 77°54'
(c) 68°52' 3. (b) 182.07 m

SELF ASSESSMENT TEST

1. (a) $\sqrt{4^2 + 3^2} = 5$ [1] [1] (b) $\sqrt{4^2 + 3^2} = 5$ [1] [1] (c) Diagram [1][1]

$$32 = 25 + 25 - 50\cos\theta \ [1]$$

$$\theta = 68°54' \ [1]$$

2. (a) Diagram [1] [1] (b) $2x^2 = 24^2$ [1] $x = \sqrt{288} \approx 16.97$ [1] (c) 62°[1]

3. (a) $XB = \sqrt{30^2 + 20^2}$ [1] $\tan\theta = \dfrac{15}{XB}$ [1] $\theta = 22°35'$ [1] (b) Use of cosine rule [1]

39°48' [1] 4. (a) Diagram [1] [1] (b) $\tan 25° = \dfrac{10000}{x}$ [1] $x = 21445$ [1]

(c) $\tan 20° = \dfrac{10000}{y}$ [1] $y = 27474.77$ [1] $x^2 + z^2 = y^2$ [1] $z = 17174.78$ [1]

EXERCISE 10.1

1. v 2. s 3. s 4. v 5. v 6. v 7. s 8. s. 9. s 10. s

EXERCISE 10.2

1. (i) $4\vec{i} + 28\vec{j} - 4\vec{k}$ (ii) $12\vec{i} + 21\vec{j} + 15\vec{k}$ (iii) $-2\vec{i} + 7\vec{j} - 7\vec{k}$ (iv) $-6\vec{i} - 12\vec{k}$

2. (i) $3\vec{i} - 4\vec{j} + 2\vec{k}$ (ii) $-8\vec{i} + 24\vec{j} + 13\vec{k}$ (iii) $18\vec{i} - 32\vec{j} + \vec{k}$ (iv) $-15\vec{i} + 36\vec{j} + 12\vec{k}$

3. (i) $\begin{pmatrix} 11 \\ 0 \\ 8 \end{pmatrix}$ (ii) $\begin{pmatrix} -27 \\ 1 \\ -22 \end{pmatrix}$ (iii) $\begin{pmatrix} -3 \\ -6 \\ 12 \end{pmatrix}$ (iv) $\begin{pmatrix} 16 \\ -1 \\ 14 \end{pmatrix}$ 4. $\begin{pmatrix} 2 \\ -1 \end{pmatrix} \begin{pmatrix} -3 \\ 2 \end{pmatrix} \begin{pmatrix} -5 \\ 3 \end{pmatrix}$

5. $\begin{pmatrix} 4 \\ 0 \end{pmatrix} + \begin{pmatrix} 0 \\ 5 \end{pmatrix} + \begin{pmatrix} -6 \\ 0 \end{pmatrix} + \begin{pmatrix} 0 \\ -2 \end{pmatrix} = \begin{pmatrix} -2 \\ 3 \end{pmatrix}$ 6. (i) $8\vec{i} - 4\vec{j} - 28\vec{k}$ (ii) $-19\vec{i} - 7\vec{j} - 16\vec{k}$

(iii) $-17\vec{i} + \vec{j} + 22\vec{k}$ (iv) $40\vec{i} + 4\vec{j} - 20\vec{k}$ 7. (i) $\begin{pmatrix} 20 \\ 1 \\ 25 \end{pmatrix}$ (ii) $\begin{pmatrix} 12 \\ 2 \\ 16 \end{pmatrix}$ (iii) $\begin{pmatrix} -4 \\ -38 \\ -32 \end{pmatrix}$ (iv) $\begin{pmatrix} -20 \\ -22 \\ -40 \end{pmatrix}$

Answers

8. A = –4 B = –7 9. (i) 2, –5 (ii) –4, 3 (iii) –6, –5 10. (i) If the basis is 1 metre east, 1 metre north and 1 metre upwards (not the only correct definition), then

(ii) $\overrightarrow{OD} = 600\vec{i} - 800\vec{j} + 60\vec{k}$, $\overrightarrow{OA} = -1200\vec{i} - 300\vec{j} + 60\vec{k}$ (iii) $\overrightarrow{AD} = 1800\vec{i} - 500\vec{j}$

EXERCISE 10.3

1. (i) $\sqrt{10}$ (ii) $\sqrt{50}$ (iii) $\sqrt{30}$ (iv) 3 (v) $\sqrt{53}$ (vi) $\sqrt{41}$ (vii) $\sqrt{14}$ (viii) $\sqrt{17}$ (ix) 7
(x) $\sqrt{70}$ (xi) $\sqrt{50}$ (xii) $\sqrt{63}$

2. (i) $\frac{1}{\sqrt{32}}(4\vec{i} + 4\vec{j})$ (ii) $\frac{1}{\sqrt{41}}(4\vec{i} + 5\vec{j})$ (iii) $\frac{1}{\sqrt{5}}(-\vec{i} - 2\vec{j})$ (iv) $\frac{1}{\sqrt{46}}(\vec{i} + 6\vec{j} - 3\vec{k})$

(v) $\frac{1}{\sqrt{20}}(2\vec{j} + 4\vec{k})$ (vi) $\frac{1}{\sqrt{17}}(2\vec{i} - 2\vec{j} - 3\vec{k})$ (vii) $\frac{1}{\sqrt{42}}\begin{pmatrix} 6 \\ -1 \\ -2 \\ 1 \end{pmatrix}$ (viii) $\frac{1}{3}\begin{pmatrix} 2 \\ 1 \\ 2 \end{pmatrix}$ (ix) $\frac{1}{\sqrt{27}}\begin{pmatrix} -1 \\ 5 \\ 1 \end{pmatrix}$

(x) $\frac{1}{\sqrt{89}}\begin{pmatrix} 6 \\ 4 \\ 6 \\ -1 \end{pmatrix}$ (xi) $\frac{1}{\sqrt{50}}\begin{pmatrix} 6 \\ -1 \\ 3 \\ 2 \end{pmatrix}$ (xii) $\frac{1}{\sqrt{15}}\begin{pmatrix} -1 \\ 1 \\ -3 \\ 2 \end{pmatrix}$ 3. (i) $3\vec{i} + 4\vec{j} + \vec{k}$ (ii) $\sqrt{26}$ Newtons

EXAMINATION STYLE QUESTIONS

1. (b) $\begin{pmatrix} -5 \\ 0 \end{pmatrix}$ 2. (a) $\begin{pmatrix} 6 \\ -2 \end{pmatrix}$ (b) $\begin{pmatrix} -2 \\ -4 \end{pmatrix}$ (c) (i) $\begin{pmatrix} -4 \\ 6 \end{pmatrix}$ (ii) $\sqrt{52}$ 3. (b) (2, –4) (c) $\sqrt{20}$

4. (a) (i) $5a + 3b$ (ii) $2a - 4b$

SELF ASSESSMENT TEST

1. (i) $6\vec{i} - 4\vec{j}$ [1] (ii) $5\vec{i} - 2\vec{j}$ [1] (iii) $4.5\vec{i} - 7\vec{j}$ [1] 2. (i) $\sqrt{5}$ [1] (ii) $\sqrt{14}$ [1]

3. $|a| = \sqrt{34}$ [1] $\hat{a} = \frac{1}{\sqrt{34}}(-3\vec{i} + 4\vec{j} + 3\vec{k})$ [1] 4. $-5\vec{i} + 2\vec{j} - \vec{k}$ [1] 5. $y = 0.5x + 6$, so that

$\overrightarrow{OP} = \overrightarrow{OR} + \overrightarrow{RP} = \begin{pmatrix} 0 \\ 6 \end{pmatrix} + t\begin{pmatrix} 2 \\ 1 \end{pmatrix}$ [1] [1] 6. $3\vec{i} - 2\vec{j} + 5\vec{k}$ [1]

EXERCISE 11.1
1. (i)

218-220	221-223	224-226	227-229	230-232	233-235	236-238	239-241	242-244	245-247
1	4	4	3	6	8	9	5	7	1

537

(ii)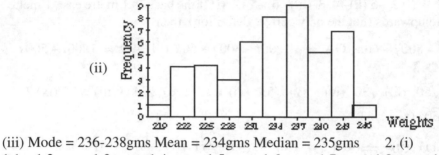

(iii) Mode = 236-238gms Mean = 234gms Median = 235gms   2. (i)

1.1-1.2	1.2-1.3	1.3-1.4	1.4-1.5	1.5-1.6	1.6-1.7	1.7-1.8	1.8-1.9	1.9-2	2-2.1
5	1	2	2	7	6	1	12	7	5

(ii)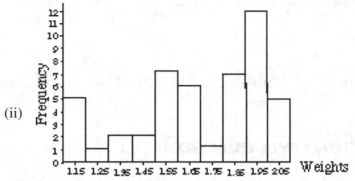

(iii) Mode = 1.8-1.9gms Mean = 1.69gms Median = 1.80gms

3. SetA Mode = 26 Mean = 27.2 Median = 28

Set B Mode = 9 Mean = 26.6 Median = 9. Set B is much more spread out than set A and although the two sets have a similar mean, they have very different mode and median.

4.(i) $27522 (ii) $21015 (iii) Median 5. (i) $233300 (ii) $169000 (iii) Median

6. Mean = 14.25 (i) 14.3125 (ii) 14.354

EXERCISE 11.2

1. (i) Sample A Mean = 1.99kg Sample B Mean = 2.00kg

(ii) Sample A Sample std = 0.0552kg Sample B Sample std = 0.1877kg

(ii) Sample A Population std = 0.0547kg Sample B Population std = 0.1858kg

2. (i) 16.4 (ii) 6.83 3. Mean = 49.97 Std = 1.365

EXERCISE 11.3

1. (i) Med = 5, Q1 = 2, Q3 = 7, IQR = 5 (ii) Med = 3.3, Q1 = 2.8, Q3 = 5.1, IQR = 2.3

(iii) Med = 163.5, Q1 = 143, Q3 = 182, IQR = 39 (iv) Med = 1.055, Q1 = 0.46, Q3 = 1.67, IQR = 1.21 (v) Med = 5143.5, Q1 = 2046, Q3 = 6252, IQR = 4206

2. (i) Med = 3, Q1 = 2, Q3 = 4, IQR = 2 (ii) Med = 13, Q1 = 12, Q3 = 13, IQR = 1

IQR = 2.3 (iii) Med = 2, Q1 = 2, Q3 = 2.5, IQR = 0.5 (iv) Med = 40, Q1 = 30, Q3 = 50, IQR = 20 (v) Med = 20, Q1 = 15, Q3 = 22.5, IQR = 7.5 3. (i) $84.67 (ii) $148

(iii) $11 (iv) Q1 = $4.50, Q3 = $65 IQR = $60.50 (v) Median & IQR. 4. (i) 2.35

(ii) 1.25 (iii) 2 (iv) Q1 = 1, Q3 = 3, IQR = 2 5. (i) $232 (ii) $83

Answers

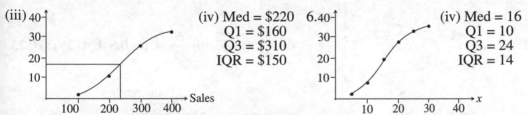

(iii)

(iv) Med = $220
Q1 = $160
Q3 = $310
IQR = $150

(iv) Med = 16
Q1 = 10
Q3 = 24
IQR = 14

EXAMINATION STYLE QUESTIONS

1. (a) 67 (b) 2.39 (c) 2 2. (a) 11, 19, 28, 35, 48, 50 (b) 27.3 (c) 15.96 (d) [41–50]

SELF ASSESSMENT TEST

1. (i) Use of formula [1] Mean ≈ 6.48 [1] (ii) Use of formula [1] s ≈ 1.31 [1]
2. Arranging data in order [1], Med = 5 [1] Q1 = 2.5, Q3 = 6.5 [1] IQR = 4 [1]
3. Med = 63 [1] Q1 = 41, Q3 = 84 [1] IQR = 43 (approx., read from graph) [1]

EXERCISE 12.1

1. (a) $\frac{2}{5}$ (b) $\frac{3}{5}$ (c) $\frac{2}{5}$ 2. (a) $\frac{2}{7}$ (b) $\frac{5}{7}$ 3. (a) $\frac{5}{26}$ (b) $\frac{21}{26}$ 4. {HH, HT, TH, TT} (a) $\frac{1}{4}$ (b) $\frac{3}{4}$

5. {HHH, HHT, HTH, THH, TTT, TTH, THT, HTT} (a) $\frac{3}{8}$ (b) $\frac{1}{2}$ (c) $\frac{1}{4}$ 6. (a) $\frac{2}{9}$ (b) $\frac{2}{9}$ (c) $\frac{2}{3}$

(d) $\frac{1}{3}$ 7.(a) $\frac{1}{2}$ (b) $\frac{3}{10}$ (c) $\frac{3}{10}$ 8.(a) $\frac{11}{36}$ (b) $\frac{1}{18}$ (c) $\frac{1}{6}$ (d) $\frac{5}{36}$ 9.{GGG, GGB. GBG, BGG,

BBB, BBG, BGB, GBB} (a) $\frac{1}{8}$ (b) $\frac{3}{8}$ (c) $\frac{1}{2}$ 10. a) $\frac{1}{2}$ (b) $\frac{1}{4}$ (c) $\frac{1}{4}$ 11.(a) $\frac{3}{8}$ (b) $\frac{1}{4}$ (c) $\frac{3}{8}$ (d) $\frac{3}{4}$

12. (a) {(1, H), (2, H), (3, H), (4, H), (5, H), (6, H),(1,T), (2, T), (3, T), (4, T), (5, T), (6, T)} (b) $\frac{1}{4}$

13. (a) $\frac{1}{216}$ (b) $\frac{1}{8}$ (c) $\frac{3}{8}$

EXERCISE 12.2

1. (a) $\frac{1}{4}$ (b) $\frac{5}{8}$ (c) $\frac{3}{4}$ 2. (a) $\frac{1}{13}$ (b) $\frac{1}{2}$ (c) $\frac{1}{26}$ (d) $\frac{7}{13}$ 3. $\frac{9}{26}$ 4. (a) 1.0 (b) 0.3 (c) 0.5

5. (a) 0.65 (b) 0.70 (c) 0.65 6. (a) 0.95 (b) 0.05 (c) 0.80

7. (a) {TTT, TTH, THT, HTT HHH, HHT, HTH, THH} (b) $\frac{3}{8}$ (c) $\frac{1}{2}$ (d) $\frac{1}{4}$ (e) $\frac{3}{8}$ 8. (a) $\frac{6}{25}$

(b) $\frac{6}{25}$ (c) $\frac{13}{25}$ 9. (b) $\frac{3}{4}$ (c) $\frac{1}{2}$ (d) $\frac{1}{6}$ (e) $\frac{7}{12}$ 10. (a) $\frac{1}{4}$ (b) $\frac{1}{2}$ (c) $\frac{8}{13}$ (d) $\frac{7}{13}$ 11. (a) 0.1399

(b) 0.8797 (c) 0.6 12. (b) $\frac{4}{15}$ (c) $\frac{4}{15}$ (d) $\frac{11}{15}$

EXERCISE 12.3

1. (a) 0.7 (b) 0.75 (c) 0.50 (d) 0.5 2. (a) 0.5 (b) 0.83 (c) 0.10 (d) 0.90

3. (a) 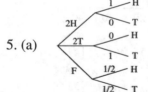 (b) $\dfrac{8}{45}$ (c) $\dfrac{22}{45}$ (d) $\dfrac{6}{11}$ 4. (a) 0.5 (b) 0.30 (c) 0.25

5. (a) 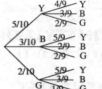 (b) $\dfrac{1}{2}$ (c) $\dfrac{2}{3}$ 6. $\dfrac{1}{3}$ 7. (a) 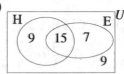 (b) $\dfrac{31}{45}$ (c) $\dfrac{2}{9}$ 8. $\dfrac{2}{3}$

9. (a) 0.88 (b) 0.42 (c) 0.6 (d) 0.28 10. (a) 0.33 (b) 0.27 (c) 0.82 (d) 0.551 11. (a) 0.22
(b) 0.985 (c) 0.8629 12. (a) 0.44 (b) 0.733 14. (a) 0.512 (b) 0.128 (c) 0.6886

EXAMINATION STYLE QUESTIONS

1. (a) 0.16 (b) 0.70 (c) 0.58 2. (a) 0.5 (b) 0.7 (c) 0.4 (d) 0.1 3. (a)
(b) (i) 0.375 (ii) 0.225 (iii) 0.4 (iv) 0.225
4. (a) 0.343 (b) 0.147 (c) 0.8125

SELF ASSESSMENT TEST

1. (i) Use of diagram (e.g. Venn) [1], 19 [1] (ii) $\dfrac{11}{70}$ [1] (iii) Use of conditional formula or

of restricted domain [1] $\dfrac{19}{36}$ [1] (iv) Attempting to check whether probability of

intersection is the same as the product of probabilities. [1]

$$p(F) \times p(B) = \dfrac{36}{70} \times \dfrac{42}{70} = \dfrac{54}{175} \text{[1]} \ p(B \cap F) = \dfrac{19}{70} \text{[1] Dependent. [1]}$$

2. Use of independence [1] (i) $\dfrac{1}{9}$ [1] (ii) $\dfrac{4}{9}$ [1] (iii) $\dfrac{2}{3}$ [1]

3. Events exclusive $p(A \cap B) = 0$ [1] $p(A), p(B) > 0 \Rightarrow p(A) \times p(B) > 0$ [1]
so events are dependent [1]
4. (a) 0.2625 (b) 0.75 (c) 0.4875 (d) 0.7123 5. (a) 0.027 (b) 0.441 (c) 0.453

EXERCISE 13.1

1. (a) dom = {2, 3, -2}, ran = {4, -9, 9} (b) dom = {1, 2, 3, 5, 7, 9},
ran = {2, 3, 4, 6, 8, 10} (c) dom = {0, 1}, ran = {1, 2} 2. (a) $(1, \infty)$ (b) $[0, \infty)$ (c) $(0, \infty)$
(d) $(-\infty, 1]$ (e) $[-3, 3]$ (f) $(-\infty, \infty)$ (g) $(-1, 0]$ (h) $[0, 4]$ (i) $[0, \infty)$ (j) $[1, 5]$ (k) $(0, 4)$
(l) $(-\infty, -1] \cup [1, \infty)$ 3. (a) $r = [-1, \infty)$, $d = [0, 2)$ (b) $r = \{y : y \geq 0\} \backslash \{4\}$, $\mathbb{R}$
(c) $r = \{y : y \geq 0\} \backslash \{3\}$, $d = \{x : x \geq -4\} \backslash \{0\}$ (d) r = [-2, 0), d = [-1, 2) (e) r = $(-\infty, \infty)$
d=$(-\infty, -3] \cup [3, \infty)$ (f) $r = [-4,4]$, $d = [0,8]$

EXERCISE 13.2

Graphs shown as graphics calculator output with standard viewing window unless
otherwise stated.

1. (a) 3, 5, -1 (b) i. $2(x+a) + 3$ ii. $2a$ (c) 3 2. (a) 0, $\dfrac{10}{11}$ (b) no solution (c) $\left[0, \dfrac{10}{11}\right]$

Answers

3. (a) $-\frac{1}{2}x^2 - x + \frac{3}{2}$, $-\frac{1}{2}x^2 + x + \frac{3}{2}$ (b) $\pm\sqrt{2}$ (c) no solution 4. (a) $x = 0, 1$

(b)

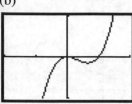

Window [-2,2],
[-1,1]
Range: [-12, 4]

5. (a) i.

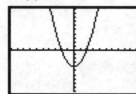

ii.

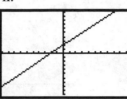

(b) i. $\{2\sqrt{2}, -2\sqrt{2}\}$ ii. $\{3, -2\}$

6. (b), (c), (d), (e) 8. (a), (d), (e), (f) 9. (a)

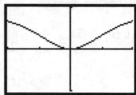

Window [-2,2], [-1,1]

(b) [0, 1) 10. (a) $\{y : y > 1\} \cup \left\{y : y \le -\frac{5}{4}\right\}$ (b) 10

EXERCISE 13.3

1. (a)

(b)

(c)
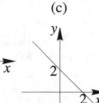

(d)

(e)
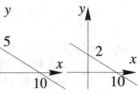

(f)

2. (a)
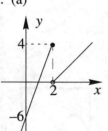

(b)
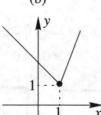

(c)
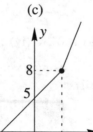

(d)
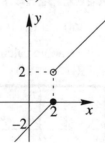

(e)
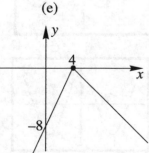

(f)
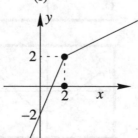

4. $a = -2$

EXAMINATION STYLE QUESTIONS

1. (a) Yes (b)   2. (a) 2 m (b) 66 m (c

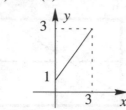

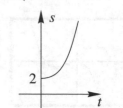

(c) (i) $0 \leq x \leq 3$ (ii) [1, 3] (or $1 \leq y \leq 3$)
(d) None, $x = 12$ lies outside the domain.

3. (a) $y \geq -2$ (b) (i) (0, 4) (ii) 1, 5   4.

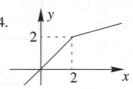

5. (a) 60, 44, 36, 32, 30

(c) $b = 2$, $d = \frac{2}{3}$

(c) 28 (d) $\frac{16}{3}$ minutes

SELF ASSESSMENT TEST

1. (a) 3 [1] $a^2 - a + 1 = -1$ [1] $(a - 2)(a + 1) = 0$ [1] $a = 2, -1$[1]
2. (a) $6 = 1 + b + c$ [1], $0 = 1 - b + c$ [1], [1] (b) $2c = 3$ [1] $c = 1.5$ [1] $b = 3.5$ [1]
3. Range $(-\infty, 7]$ [1] Many:one [1]   4.

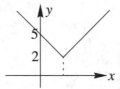

domain [1]
Range   [1]
Graph   [1]

5. $2(2x) + 1 = 2(x + 1) + 1$ [1] [1]
   $x = 1$ [1]
6. (a) $x(12 - 2x)(8 - 2x)$ [1] [1]
   $= 4x(6 - x)(4 - x)$ [1]
   (b) 0 60 64 36 0 [1] (c) 67.6 [1][1]

EXERCISE 14.1

1. (i) 360°, 2 (ii) 1080°, 3 (iii) 180°, 4 (iv) 180°, 3 (v) 120°, 0.25 (vi) 480°, $\frac{2}{3}$

2.   Graphic calculator outputs using a window [-360,360] and [-4,4].

(i)   (ii)   (iii)

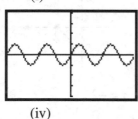

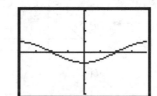

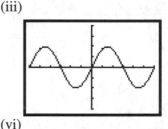

(iv)   (v)   (vi)

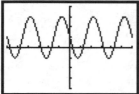

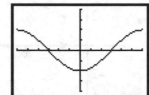

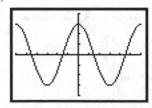

Answers

(vii)   (viii)   (ix)

(x)   (xi)   (xii)

3. (i)   (ii)   (iii)

(iv)   (v)   (vi)

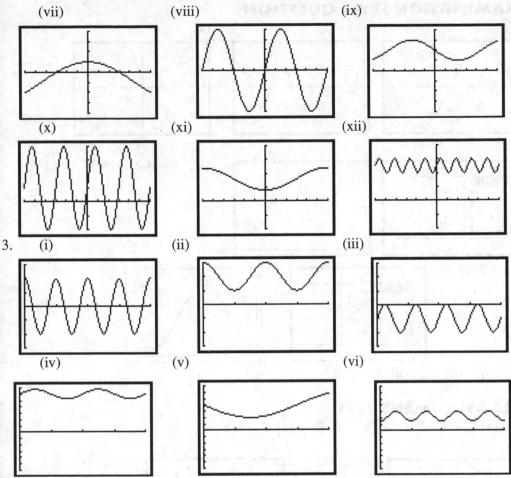

EXERCISE 14.2

1. (i) 5, 24, 3, 19 (ii) $T = 5\sin\left(\dfrac{180t}{12}\right) + 19$ (iii) 23.6° 2. (i) 3. 4.2, 3, 7

(ii) $L = 3\sin\left(\dfrac{180t}{2.1}\right) + 7$ 3. (i) 5, 11, 0, 7 (ii) $V = 5\sin\left(\dfrac{360t}{11}\right) + 7$ 4. (i) 1, 11, 1, 12

(ii) $P = \sin\left(\dfrac{360t}{11}\right) + 12$ 5. (i) 2.7, 7, 2, 6 (ii) $S = 2.7\sin\left(\dfrac{360t}{7}\right) + 6$

6. (i) 0.6, 3.5, 0, 11 (ii) $P = 0.6\sin\left(\dfrac{720t}{7}\right) + 11$

EXERCISE 14.3

1. (i) 30°, 0.524 (ii) 90°, 1.57 (iii) 120°, 2.09 (iv) 60°, 1.05 (v) 53°, 0.927 (vi) 109°, 1.91
(vii) 114°, 1.98 (xiii) no real solutions (ix) 117°, 2.05
2. (i) -300°, -60°, 60, 300° (ii) 60°, 120° (iii) 9°, 81°, 189°, 261° (iv) 10°, 80° (v) 55°, 125°
5. (i) 3 (ii) 1 & 5 (iii) 0.44 6. (i) 6.5, 7.5 (ii) 1.58s & 3.42s

EXAMINATION STYLE QUESTION

1. (a) 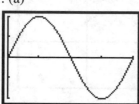 (b) 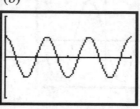 2. (a) 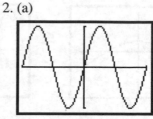 (b) 15°, 75°

3. (a) 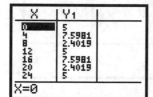 (b) 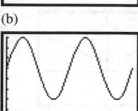 (c) (i) 7 (ii) 5.52
(d) 7.39, 10.61, 19.39, 22.61

4. (a) 60 sec (b) 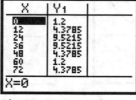 (c)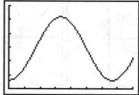

(d) 19.78

5. (a) (i) 5 (ii) 120° (iii) 7 (b) 20°

SELF ASSESSMENT TEST

1. (i) (a) 120° (b) 2 [1] (ii) (a) 720° (b) 4 [1] 2. 6 [1]
3. (i) 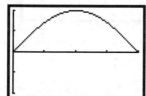 (ii)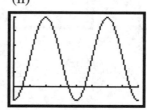

Domain [1]
Shape [1]
Amplitude [1]
Range [1]

Domain [1]
Shape [1]
Amplitude [1]
Range [1]
Number of cycles [1]

4. (a) Amp = 20 mmHg [1], period = 1.2 sec [1] (b) 120 mmHg [1]
(c) Invert cos function [1], starts at (0, 80) [1] range [80, 120] [1] shape [1] (d) 0.4, 0.8 [2]

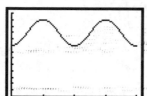

(e) $\dfrac{0.4}{1.2} = 0.333\ldots$, i.e., 33.33% [1]

EXERCISE 15.1

1. (a) 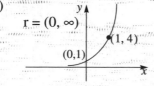 (b) 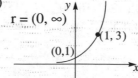 (c)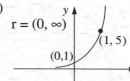

r = (0, ∞) (1, 4) (0,1)

r = (0, ∞) (1, 3) (0,1)

r = (0, ∞) (1, 5) (0,1)

Answers

(d)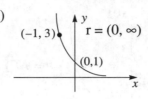
r = (0, ∞)
(0,1) (1, 2.5)

(e)
r = (0, ∞)
(1, 3.2)
(0,1)

(f)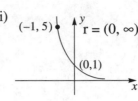
r = (0, ∞)
(0,1) (1, 1.8)

(g)
r = (0, ∞)
(−1, 2)
(0,1)

(h)
(−1, 3)
r = (0, ∞)
(0,1)

(i)
(−1, 5)
r = (0, ∞)
(0,1)

(j)
y
r = (0, ∞)
$\left(-1, \frac{4}{3}\right)$ (0,1)

(k)
y
r = (0, ∞)
$\left(-1, \frac{8}{5}\right)$ (0,1)

(l)
y
r = (0, ∞)
$\left(-1, \frac{10}{7}\right)$ (0,1)

2. '+c' translates the graph of f(x) = a^x by c units parallel to the y-axis

3. 'b' has a dilation effect on f(x) = a^x (along the y axis).

4. 'k' has a dilation effect on f(x) = a^x (along the x axis).

5. (a)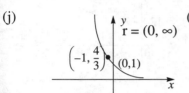
(−1, 3) (1, 3)
(0,1)

(b)
(−1, 5) (1, 5)
(0,1)

(c)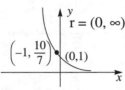
(−1, 10) (1, 10)
(0,1)

 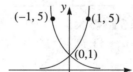
(−1, 3) (1, 3)
(0,1)

a^{-x} is a reflection of a^x about the y-axis

6. b - dilation factor parallel to y-axis, k - dilation factor parallel to x-axis, c - translation parallel to y-axis. 7. (a) [1, 16] (b) [3, 27] (c) $\left[\frac{1}{4}, 16\right]$ (d) $\left[\frac{1}{2}, 4\right]$ (e) $\left[\frac{1}{3}, 27\right]$

(f) $\left[-\frac{1}{16}, 16\right]$ (g) $\left[\frac{1}{16}, 4\right]$ (h) [1, 9] (i) $\left[\frac{1}{8}, \frac{1}{4}\right]$ (j) $\left[\frac{1}{10}, 10\right]$

EXERCISE 15.2

1. (i) 3 (ii) 3 (iii) 2 (iv) 3.91 (v) 2.93 (vi) 1.66 (vii) 2.4 (viii) 1.76 (ix) 4.17 (x) −3 (xi) −3 (xii) −2 (xiii) −3.32 (xiv) 0 (xv) −2.32 2. (i) 1.63 (ii) 1.74 (iii) 2.32 (iv) 1.89

EXERCISE 15.3

1. (a) 444.5
   (b) 31.62%
   (c) 6.02 sec
   (d)

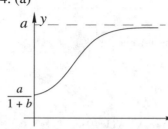

4. (a)

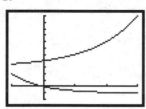

2. (a) 1200
   (b) (i) 2400
       (ii) 4800
   (c) 10.3 yrs (approx)
   (d)

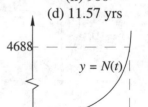

3. (a) 120
   (b) 0.1833
   (c) (i) 750
       (ii) 900
   (d) 11.57 yrs

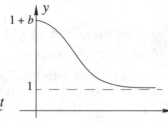

EXAMINATION STYLE QUESTIONS

1.(a)   (b) – 0.6

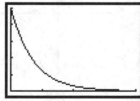

2. (a) c = 1 (b) 3   3. (a) 8 16 32 64 128 256 (b) (i) 45 (ii) 3.6
4. (a) 400   5. (a)
   (b) (i) 705 (ii) 1242   (b) 0.5 sec
   (d) 14.2

SELF ASSESSMENT TEST

1.

$f(x)$: [1] Shape [1] domain [1] Range
$g(x)$: [1] Shape [1] domain [1] Range

2. (a) $3^x = 9$ [1] $x = 2$ [1] (b) $(0.5)^x = 2$ [1] $x = -1$ [1]
3. $c = -2$ [1][1] $0 = 8k - 2$ [1] $k = 0.25$ [1]
4. (a) 10 20 40 80 160 320 640 (b) Graph [1] [1] [1]

   (c) (i) 56 (or 57) [1] [1] (ii) $2^t = 50$ [1] $t = 5.64$ [1][1]

EXERCISE 16.1

1. a. 839 b. 565 c. 516 d.409 e. 749 f. 389
2. a. 1271 b. 573 c. 1111 d. 1646 e. 500 f. 486
3. a. 1745 b. 395 c. 1791 d. 1721 e. 1303 f. 1838
4. a. 31.22 b. 28.48 c. 0.57 d. 20.06 e. 27.21 f. 34.41
5. a. 89 b. 21 c. 38 d. 120 e. 167 f. 73

EXERCISE 16.2

1. a.i. 3514 ii. 977 iii. 23 b.i. 4501 ii. 1252 iii. 29 c.i. 5316 ii. 1478 iii. 35
d. i. 4765 ii. 1325 iii. 31 e.i. 4508 ii. 1254 iii. 29 f. i. 5605 ii. 1559 iii. 36
2. a.i. 1019000 ii. 986 iii. 14 b.i. 1638552 ii. 1586 iii. 22 c.i. 1384821 ii. 1341 iii. 18
d.i. 1495892 ii. 1448 iii. 20 e.i. 1636514 ii. 1584 iii. 22 f.i. 1240123 ii. 1201 iii. 16
3. a.i. 28710 ii. 852 iii. 48 b.i. 45713 ii. 1356 iii. 77 c.i. 44788 ii. 1329 iii. 75
d.i. 44341 ii. 1316 iii. 74 e.i. 42555 ii. 1263 iii. 71 f.i. 47467 ii. 1409 iii. 79
4. a.i. 40358 ii. 6447 iii. 180 b.i. 45620 ii. 7288 iii. 203
c.i. 44810 ii. 7158 iii. 200 d.i. 45504 ii. 7269 iii. 203
e.i. 37764 ii. 6033 iii. 168 f.i. 42813 ii. 6839 iii. 191

EXERCISE 16.3

1. a.$804.00 b. $562.32 c. $218.40 d. $279.00 e. $6,528.00 f. $812.50
2. a. $321.60 b. $515.46 c. $46.80 d. $96.88 e. $191.25 f. $187.50
3. a. 7% b. 3% c. 8% d. 12% e. 11.8% f. 9.3%
4. a. 300 b. 790 c. 2000 d. 365 e. 1362 f. 9035 (all marks)
5. a. 5 b. 7 c. 2 d. 8 e. 11 f. 3.6 (all years)
6. a. 12 b. 7 c. 2 d. 8 e. 11 f. 3.6 (months)

7. Option 1 gives $I = \dfrac{6000 \times 7.3 \times 5}{100} = 2190$ francs. The total is 8190 francs.

Option 2 gives: $6000 \times 153.1 = 918600$ yen.

The interest is $\dfrac{918600 \times 7.4 \times 5}{100} = 339882$ and the total = 1258482 yen.

Conversion back to Swiss francs gives $\dfrac{1258482}{155.7} = 8082.736$ or 8083. Option 1 is better.

EXERCISE 16.4

1. a. 3682 b. 8246 c. 19576 d. 1521 e. 5903 f. 3117
2. a. 12087 b. 112108 c. 128192 d. 151518 e. 194298 f. 48698
3. a. 15821 b. 33469 c. 34835 d. 54444 e. 41405 f. 40993
4. a. 27335 b. 28700 c. 30564 d. 48478 e. 45248 f. 1804
5. A gives $2415.77 B gives $2431.52 & C gives $2411.87 so B is best.

EXERCISE 16.5

1. 1034 2. 21076 3. $159.26 4. 125100 5. 252298

EXERCISE 16.6

a. 56.61 b. 576.65 c. 36.06 d. 152.22 e. 79.08 f. 287.35 g. 43.07 h. 144.84

EXERCISE 16.7

1. $825.95 2. $178.04 3. $72.05 4. $146.74 5. $219.84 6. $402.15 7. $58.93
8. $96.24 9. $713.31 10. $97.16 11. $12.88 12. $359.75 13. $193.42 14. $94.41
15. $5.65 16. $298.74 17. $109.30 18. $39.48 19. $43.77 20. $55.84

EXERCISE 16.8

1. $837.71 2. $1,894.10 3. $1,022.91 4. $602.80 5. $339.67 6. $680.10 7. $1,467.17
8. $150.94 9. $560.68 10. $3,833.22 11. $485.57 12. $557.67 13. $349.06 14. $703.12
15. $3,171.66

EXAMINATION STYLE QUESTIONS
Question No. 1

a. Current account

Date	Detail	Debit	Credit	Balance
1/5/97	Carried			$1263.65
5/5/97	Cheques		$647.45	$1911.10
12/5/97	162345	$56.70		$1854.40
17/5/97	162344	$126.30		$1728.10
25/5/97	Transfer		$2300.00	$4028.10
26/5/97	162347	$534.55		$3493.55
31/5/97	Charges	$3.20		$3490.35

There are 3 debits costing $2.10 and 2 credits costing $1.10, total charges $3.20.[1]
Balances. [1]

b. Deposit account

Date	Detail	Debit	Credit	Balance
1/5/97	Carried			$6500.45
10/5/97	Cheques		$1245.50	$7745.95
31/5/97	Interest	31.36		$7777.31

The interest is 5% annually or $\frac{5}{365}$ % daily. The balances are:$6500.45 for 9 days (simple interest as the interest is not credited until the end of the month). Interest =

$\dfrac{6500.45 \times \frac{5}{365} \times 9}{100} = 8.014$ [1] $7745.95 for 22 days Interest = $\dfrac{7745.95 \times \frac{5}{365} \times 22}{100} = 23.343$

Using full calculator accuracy before finally rounding gives $31.36[1]
Final Balance $7777.31[1]

c. Equity = their assets – their liabilities [1]
Assets = Deposit ($7777.31) + Computer ($4500) + Current a/c ($3490.35) + Car ($18000)
Total Assets = $33767.66
Liabilities = Car Loan ($15000) + Debt ($1500) = $16500
Equity = $33767.66 – $16500 = $17267.66 [1]

Question No. 2

a.

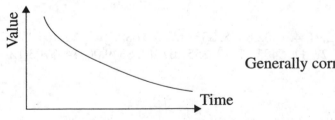

Generally correct shape. [1]

Answers

b. Three years have passed. 22% depreciation per year. [1]

Value $= 4500 \times 0.78^3 = 2135.484$ or \$2135.48 [1]

c. Solving $2250 = 4500 \times 0.78^n$ or $0.78^n = \frac{1}{2}$ by a method that will give an answer

to at least one decimal place (nearest month required). [1] $0.78^n = \frac{1}{2} \Rightarrow n = 2.79$ [1]

Their value converted to months correctly: 2 years, 9.5 months i.e. Mid-February 2000 [1]

SELF ASSESSMENT TEST

1. i. 150 marks $= 23.261 \times 150 = 3489$ rupees [1]

ii. 1250 rupees $= \dfrac{1250}{23.261}$ [1] $= 53.738016$ or about 54 marks [1]

2. The fee is 3% of \$500 = \$15 NZ. This leaves \$485 NZ to convert [1] giving \$291 US [1]
3. Use of formula [1] 20160 lire [1] 4. Use of formula [1] 4863 francs [1]
5. Use of formula [1] with 84 months [1] 2341 crowns [1]

EXERCISE 17.1

1. (i)

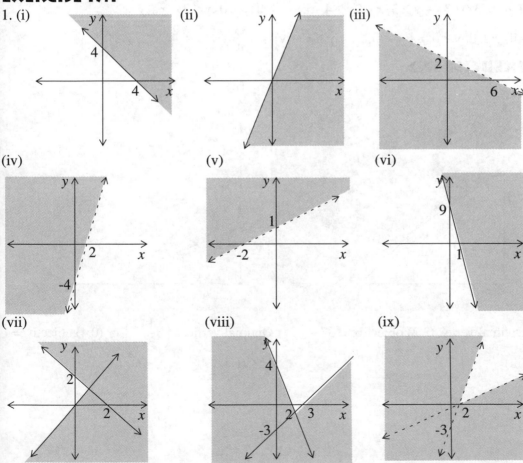

(x)   (xi)   (xii)

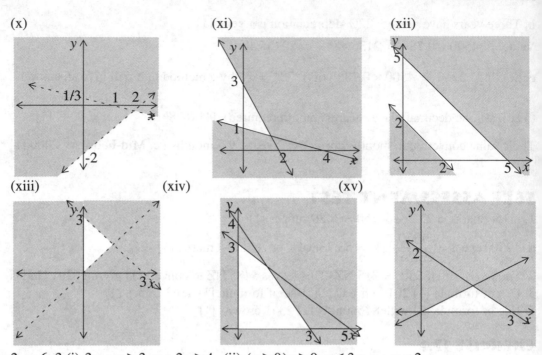

(xiii)   (xiv)   (xv)

2. $p > 6$ 3.(i) $3x + y \geq 3$, $x + 2y \geq 4$ (ii) $(x \geq 0) y \geq 0$, $y \leq 3x$, $x + y < 2$

(iii) $x \geq 0$, $y \geq 0$, $x + y < p$, $2x + y \geq p$ (iv) $y < \dfrac{kx}{4} + k$, $x + \dfrac{2y}{k} < 2$, $y \geq 0$

EXERCISE 17.2

(i)   (ii)

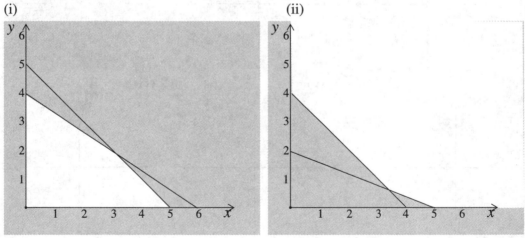

Optimal vertex (3,2) objective = 37   Optimal vertices $\left(3\dfrac{1}{3}, \dfrac{2}{3}\right)$ or (0,4), objective = 4

(iii)   (iv)

Answers

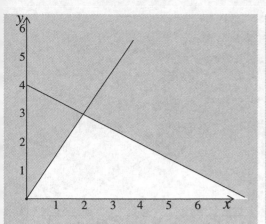

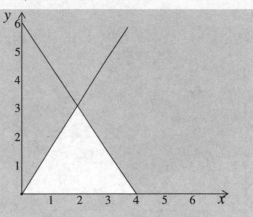

Optimal vertex (2,3) objective = 32   Optimal vertex (4,0), objective = 8

(v)

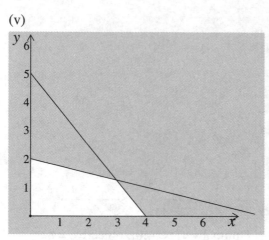

Optimal vertex (3,1.25) objective = 14

(vi)

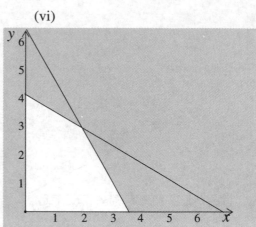

Optimal vertex $\left(\dfrac{41}{23}, \dfrac{72}{23}\right)$ objective = $\dfrac{411}{23}$

(vii)

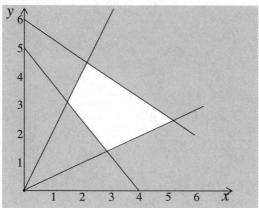

Optimal vertex $\left(\dfrac{36}{7}, \dfrac{18}{7}\right)$ objective = $\dfrac{216}{7}$

(viii)

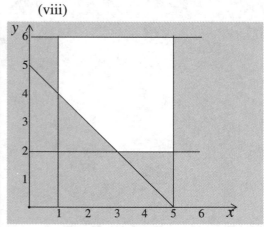

Optimal vertex (5,6) objective = 11

2.

Let p = the number of paperbacks bought and h = the number of hardcovers bought.

The constraints are:

$p \geq 0$

$h \geq 0$

$12p + 18h \leq 108$

Objective: maximise $p + h$

Optimum is $p = 9$, $h = 0$.

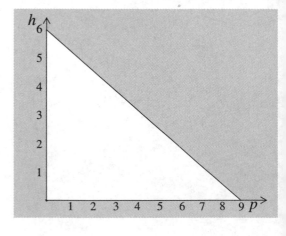

Answers

3. Let x = the number of grams of Xylol used and y = the number of grams of Ylang used. The constraints are:

$x \geq 0$

$y \geq 0$

$6x + 5y \geq 30$

$4x + 8y \geq 32$

Objective: minimise $2x + 3y$

Optimum is $\left(\dfrac{20}{7}, \dfrac{18}{7}\right)$. Cost is $13.43.

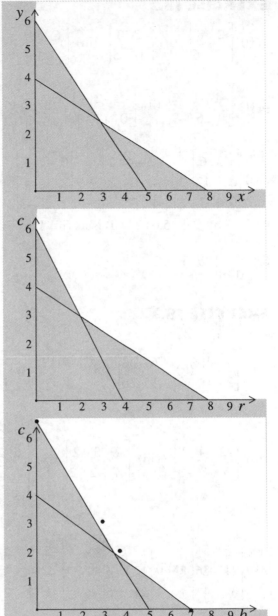

4. Let r = the number of cu. cm. of Rose oil used and c = the number of cu. cm. of Cedar oil used.

The constraints are:

$r \geq 0$

$c \geq 0$

$6r + 4c \geq 24$

$4r + 8c \geq 32$

Objective: minimise $15r + 12c$
Optimum is (2.5,3).
Cost is $73.50.

5.
Let b = the number of trips by 'Belinda' and c = the number of trips by 'Chloe'. The constraints are:

$b \geq 0$

$c \geq 0$ Objective: minimise $120b + 150c$
             Note that this is an integer
$4b + 7c \geq 28$ problem
$7b + 5c \geq 35$ Optimum is (4,2). Cost is $780.

SELF ASSESSMENT TEST

1. Method of solving the simultaneous equations [1]. $x = 4$, [1] $y = -2$. [1]
2. Method [1]. $x = 2.6$, [1] $y = -1.4$. [1]
3. Setting up equations [1] adult $18 [1] child $12 [1]
4. Method [1] $-1.5 < x < 5.5$ [1]

5.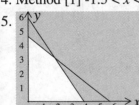

Constraints [1], Feasible region [1] Vertex (2,3) [1] opt = 38 [1]
6. Variables: j = number of 'Jumbos', t = number of 'Titans'
[1]. $7j + 12t \leq 84$ [1]

$3j + 3t \leq 27$ [1].Solving simultaneous equations [1]Vertex is
(4.8,4.2)[1] Profit=$1332[1]

EXERCISE 18.2

1. (i) $\begin{bmatrix} 2 & 8 \\ -2 & 16 \end{bmatrix}$ (ii) $\begin{bmatrix} -2 & 3 \\ 1 & -5 \end{bmatrix}$ (iii) $\begin{bmatrix} 6 & -9 \\ -3 & 15 \end{bmatrix}$ (iv) $\begin{bmatrix} 4 & 5 \\ -3 & 21 \end{bmatrix}$ (v) $\begin{bmatrix} 7 & 6 \\ -5 & 34 \end{bmatrix}$ (vi) $\begin{bmatrix} -2 & -19 \\ 3 & -27 \end{bmatrix}$

2. (i) $\begin{bmatrix} -1 & -1 & -2 \\ 0 & 6 & -9 \end{bmatrix}$ (ii) $\begin{bmatrix} -2 & -2 & -4 \\ 0 & 12 & -18 \end{bmatrix}$ (iii) $\begin{bmatrix} -2 & -5 \\ 2 & 2 \\ 3 & 1 \end{bmatrix}$ (iv) $\begin{bmatrix} 2 & 0 \\ 4 & 2 \\ 0 & -2 \end{bmatrix}$ (v) $\begin{bmatrix} 5 & 5 \\ 4 & 1 \\ -3 & -4 \end{bmatrix}$ (vi) $\begin{bmatrix} -6 & -15 \\ 6 & 6 \\ 9 & 3 \end{bmatrix}$

3. (i) $\begin{bmatrix} 3 & 3 & 6 \\ 0 & 3 & 12 \\ 0 & 6 & 3 \end{bmatrix}$ (ii) $\begin{bmatrix} -2 & -4 & 6 \\ 4 & 0 & 2 \\ 4 & 0 & -8 \end{bmatrix}$ (iii) $\begin{bmatrix} 0 & -1 & 5 \\ 2 & 1 & 5 \\ 2 & 2 & -3 \end{bmatrix}$ (iv) $\begin{bmatrix} 2 & 3 & -1 \\ -2 & 1 & 3 \\ -2 & 2 & 5 \end{bmatrix}$ (v) $\begin{bmatrix} 1 & -1 & 12 \\ 4 & 3 & 14 \\ 4 & 6 & -5 \end{bmatrix}$ (vi) $\begin{bmatrix} -3 & -5 & 4 \\ 4 & -1 & -2 \\ 4 & -2 & -9 \end{bmatrix}$

4. 7 by 5 5. 5. (i) 23 (ii) Nuts (iii) Taps (iv) Week 2 Wednesday - =B3+I3, =B4+I4

6. $\begin{bmatrix} 3a & 3 \\ 0 & 0 \end{bmatrix}$ 7. 3 8. 2

EXERCISE 18.3

1. (i) $\begin{bmatrix} 5 & -4 \\ 2 & -1 \end{bmatrix}$ (ii) $\begin{bmatrix} 6 & -8 \\ -15 & 26 \end{bmatrix}$ (iii) $\begin{bmatrix} -7 & 17 \\ 3 & 3 \end{bmatrix}$ (iv) $\begin{bmatrix} -15 & -10 \\ -10 & -36 \end{bmatrix}$ (v) $\begin{bmatrix} \frac{19}{6} & \frac{89}{3} \\ -\frac{1}{8} & \frac{11}{2} \end{bmatrix}$ (vi) $\begin{bmatrix} 2.6 & 5.5 \\ -8.55 & 0 \end{bmatrix}$

(vii) $\begin{bmatrix} 12 & -4 & 2 \\ 6 & -0 & -3 \end{bmatrix}$ (viii) $\begin{bmatrix} -9 & 3 & 2 \\ 4 & -2 & -2 \end{bmatrix}$ (ix) $\begin{bmatrix} \frac{7}{6} & \frac{3}{2} & \frac{7}{3} \\ \frac{13}{3} & 5 & \frac{29}{3} \end{bmatrix}$ (x) $\begin{bmatrix} 1.6 & -0.7 & 3.8 \\ -3.9 & -4.2 & -5.7 \end{bmatrix}$ (xi) $\begin{bmatrix} 11 & -2 \\ 11 & 3 \\ 1 & -7 \end{bmatrix}$

(xii) $\begin{bmatrix} 7 & 5 \\ 21 & -26 \\ 6 & 4 \end{bmatrix}$ (xiii) $\begin{bmatrix} 12 & 6 & 2 \\ 12 & 1 & 4 \\ 21 & 3 & 6 \end{bmatrix}$ (xiv) $\begin{bmatrix} -5 & 6 & 1 \\ 4 & -4 & -12 \\ -1 & 4 & 2 \end{bmatrix}$ (xv) $\begin{bmatrix} -7 & 2 & 13 \\ 8 & -8 & -17 \\ -4 & -11 & 4 \end{bmatrix}$ (xvi) $\begin{bmatrix} -\frac{25}{2} & -\frac{50}{3} & 4 \\ -\frac{79}{4} & -\frac{83}{6} & \frac{27}{4} \\ -2 & \frac{11}{6} & \frac{3}{4} \end{bmatrix}$

(xvii) $\begin{bmatrix} x + 3x^2 & -x^2 + 1 \\ 2x + 5x^2 & -x^2 + 2 \\ -x^2 + 5x & -2x \end{bmatrix}$ (xviii) $\begin{bmatrix} a + 2x^2 - a^2 & 2a + 4x - 2x^2 + 2a \\ a - 2ax & -2a & 3a + 2ax \\ -0 & 2a & -ax - x \end{bmatrix}$ 2. (i) $\begin{bmatrix} 1 & 0 \\ 0 & 1 \end{bmatrix}$

(ii) $\begin{bmatrix} -1 & 0 \\ 0 & -1 \end{bmatrix}, \begin{bmatrix} 1 & 0 \\ 0 & 1 \end{bmatrix}, \begin{bmatrix} -1 & 0 \\ 0 & -1 \end{bmatrix}$ (iii) $\begin{bmatrix} -1 & 0 \\ 0 & -1 \end{bmatrix}$ if n is odd and $\begin{bmatrix} 1 & 0 \\ 0 & 1 \end{bmatrix}$ if n is even.

Answers

3. (i) $\begin{bmatrix} 0 & 3 & 4 & 2 \\ 1 & 0 & 0 & 6 \\ 1 & 2 & 0 & 2 \\ 4 & 3 & 0 & 0 \end{bmatrix} \begin{bmatrix} 120 \\ 105 \\ 110 \\ 100 \end{bmatrix}$ (ii) $\begin{bmatrix} 955 \\ 720 \\ 530 \\ 795 \end{bmatrix}$ (iii) Loading costs for each depot. 4. $\begin{bmatrix} 0 & -1 \\ 1 & 0 \end{bmatrix}$ $n = 4$.

EXERCISE 18.4

1. (i) −4 (ii) 9 (iii) 12 (iv) 2 (v) 15 (vi) $\dfrac{4}{9}$ (vii) 0.5 (viii) 4 (ix) 1 (x) $x^2 - 2$ (xi) 0

(xii) 1 2. (i) $\begin{bmatrix} 0 & 1 \\ 1 & 1 \\ \frac{1}{4} & 2 \end{bmatrix}$ (ii) $\begin{bmatrix} -1 & -1 \\ 2 & \frac{3}{2} \end{bmatrix}$ (iii) $\begin{bmatrix} -\frac{3}{14} & \frac{1}{7} \\ -\frac{2}{7} & -\frac{1}{7} \end{bmatrix}$ (iv) $\begin{bmatrix} 1 & 0 \\ -\frac{1}{2} & -\frac{1}{4} \end{bmatrix}$ (v) $\begin{bmatrix} 0 & 1 \\ -1 & -4 \end{bmatrix}$ (vi) no inverse

(vii) $\begin{bmatrix} -\frac{1}{5} & \frac{1}{5} \\ \frac{4}{15} & -\frac{1}{15} \end{bmatrix}$ (viii) $\begin{bmatrix} 1 & -\frac{1}{2} \\ 1 & -\frac{3}{4} \end{bmatrix}$ (ix) $\begin{bmatrix} -4 & -1 \\ 1 & -1 \end{bmatrix}$ (x) $\begin{bmatrix} 1 & 3 \\ 1 & 0 \end{bmatrix}$ (xi) $\begin{bmatrix} 2 & 3 \\ 2 & -3 \end{bmatrix}$ (xii) $\begin{bmatrix} 3 & 3 \\ 1 & -2 \end{bmatrix}$

(xiii) $\begin{bmatrix} 3 & -4 \\ -2 & 3 \end{bmatrix}$ (xiv) $\begin{bmatrix} \frac{3}{x} & -\frac{1}{x} \\ -2 & 1 \end{bmatrix}$ (xv) $\begin{bmatrix} -1 & 1 \\ \frac{3}{x} & -\frac{2}{x} \end{bmatrix}$ 3. −2, 2 4. −24 5. $-\dfrac{1}{2}$

EXERCISE 18.5

1. House 1 • — • Gas   At least one pair of lines must cross.
   House 2 • — • Electricity
   House 3 • — • Telephone

2. [triangle graph] 3. A• — C (2) — D (3), D — E (2)   7 hours. 4. All except iv. & v.
   B•   E•

5. No 6. 3 7. 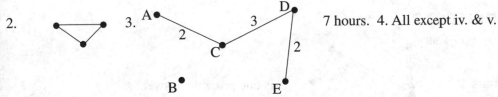   4 edges. 8. i. 4 hours. ii. A tree 9. 1, joining the odd

vertices. 10. i. [graph] ii. 30 iii. 15 iv. $\dfrac{n(n-1)}{2}$. 11. even. 12. Tree. 14. No

EXERCISE 18.6

1. i. $\begin{bmatrix} 0 & 1 & 1 \\ 1 & 0 & 1 \\ 1 & 1 & 0 \end{bmatrix}$ ii. $\begin{bmatrix} 0 & 2 & 0 \\ 2 & 0 & 1 \\ 0 & 1 & 2 \end{bmatrix}$ iii. $\begin{bmatrix} 0 & 1 & 1 & 0 \\ 1 & 0 & 1 & 1 \\ 1 & 1 & 0 & 1 \\ 0 & 1 & 1 & 0 \end{bmatrix}$ iv. $\begin{bmatrix} 0 & 1 & 0 & 0 \\ 1 & 0 & 1 & 1 \\ 0 & 1 & 0 & 1 \\ 0 & 1 & 1 & 0 \end{bmatrix}$ v. $\begin{bmatrix} 0 & 1 & 0 & 0 & 0 \\ 1 & 0 & 1 & 0 & 0 \\ 0 & 1 & 0 & 1 & 1 \\ 0 & 0 & 1 & 0 & 1 \\ 0 & 0 & 1 & 1 & 0 \end{bmatrix}$ vi. $\begin{bmatrix} 0 & 1 & 0 & 0 & 1 \\ 1 & 0 & 1 & 0 & 1 \\ 0 & 1 & 0 & 1 & 0 \\ 0 & 0 & 1 & 0 & 1 \\ 1 & 1 & 0 & 1 & 0 \end{bmatrix}$

2.   i.   ii.   iii.   iv.

3. i. $\begin{bmatrix} 1 & 0 & 1 \\ 1 & 1 & 0 \\ 0 & 1 & 1 \end{bmatrix}$ ii. $\begin{bmatrix} 1 & 1 & 0 \\ 0 & 1 & 1 \end{bmatrix}$ iii. $\begin{bmatrix} 1 & 1 & 0 & 0 \\ 0 & 1 & 0 & 1 \\ 1 & 0 & 1 & 0 \\ 0 & 0 & 1 & 1 \end{bmatrix}$ iv. $\begin{bmatrix} 1 & 1 & 0 & 0 \\ 0 & 1 & 0 & 1 \\ 0 & 0 & 1 & 1 \\ 0 & 1 & 1 & 0 \end{bmatrix}$

4. $A = \begin{bmatrix} 0 & 2 & 2 & 1 \\ 2 & 0 & 0 & 1 \\ 2 & 0 & 0 & 1 \\ 1 & 1 & 1 & 0 \end{bmatrix}$ $A^2 = \begin{bmatrix} 0 & 2 & 2 & 1 \\ 2 & 0 & 0 & 1 \\ 2 & 0 & 0 & 1 \\ 1 & 1 & 1 & 0 \end{bmatrix}^2 = \begin{bmatrix} 9 & 1 & 1 & 4 \\ 1 & 5 & 5 & 2 \\ 1 & 5 & 5 & 2 \\ 4 & 2 & 2 & 3 \end{bmatrix}$ 4 two stage ways from A to D.

5. $A = \begin{bmatrix} 0 & 1 & 1 & 1 & 1 \\ 1 & 0 & 1 & 1 & 1 \\ 1 & 1 & 0 & 1 & 1 \\ 1 & 1 & 1 & 0 & 1 \\ 1 & 1 & 1 & 1 & 0 \end{bmatrix}$ $A^2 = \begin{bmatrix} 4 & 3 & 3 & 3 & 3 \\ 3 & 4 & 3 & 3 & 3 \\ 3 & 3 & 4 & 3 & 3 \\ 3 & 3 & 3 & 4 & 3 \\ 3 & 3 & 3 & 3 & 4 \end{bmatrix}$ 3 two stage routes between adjacent vertices.

6. 2

EXERCISE 18.7

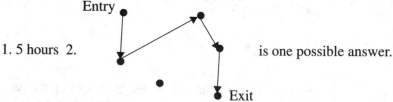

1. 5 hours   2.   is one possible answer.

EXERCISE 18.8

1. Chai, Dennis & Evelyn. 2. Wendy & Xanthos 3. Olive 4. 5 from A to Z (10), 5 from A to Y (20), 15 from B to Y (15), total cost 45 marks. 5. Melanie visits Archer & Denyon, Omar visits Barrington & Psyche visits Custer & Ellings (Nigel has a problem but may, in reality, be the best person for all the jobs. The cheapest solution is not necessarily the best!). The daily cost is $50. 6. Reporting, Croesus, Editing, Earlham & Presenting, Earlham.

EXERCISE 18.9

1. i.  time = 7.

ii. time = 16.

iii. time = 23.

iv. time = 26.

v. time = 30.

2.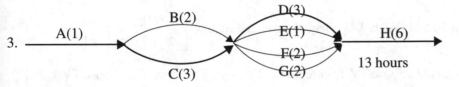

25 hours

3.

13 hours

4.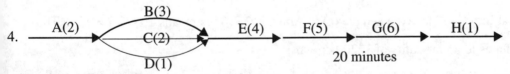

20 minutes

EXERCISE 18.10

1. $M = \begin{bmatrix} 0.7 & 0.3 \\ 0.4 & 0.6 \end{bmatrix}$ $M^{10} = \begin{bmatrix} 0.571 & 0.429 \\ 0.571 & 0.429 \end{bmatrix}$ Pr(rain) = 0.571

2. $M = \begin{bmatrix} 0.8 & 0.2 \\ 0.3 & 0.7 \end{bmatrix}$ $M^5 = \begin{bmatrix} 0.613 & 0.308 \\ 0.581 & 0.410 \end{bmatrix}$ Pr(win) = 0.6 approx.

3. $M = \begin{bmatrix} 0.1 & 0.9 \\ 0.2 & 0.8 \end{bmatrix}$ $M^4 = \begin{bmatrix} 0.1819 & 0.8181 \\ 0.1818 & 0.8182 \end{bmatrix}$ Pr(late Friday) = 0.18 approx.

4. i. o.6 ii. 0.64 iii. 0.6364, 64%
5. Pr(2 hours) = 0.8, Pr(1hour) = 0.2 Expected value = 1.6 + 0.2 = 1.8 hours.

EXERCISE 18.11

1. $\begin{bmatrix} 0 & -3 & -1 \\ -3 & -3 & 0 \\ 1 & 2 & -4 \end{bmatrix}$ No stable solution. 2. i. Row 2 Col. 1. ii. Row 1 Col. 2.

iii. Row 1 Col. 1 or 2. iv. Row 1 or 3 Col. 1 v. Row 1 Col. 3. vi. Row 1 or 3 Col. 2.

3. i. The losses add to 800 whatever happens. The defenders should defend the gate and the attackers should attack the moat. The defenders will lose 300 men and the attackers 500.

EXERCISE 18.12

1. i. $p = \dfrac{1}{3}, q = \dfrac{1}{2}$, Value $= 1$ ii. $p = \dfrac{3}{13}, q = \dfrac{8}{13}$, Value $= \dfrac{11}{13}$

iii. $p = \dfrac{1}{9}, q = \dfrac{2}{9}$, Value $= -\dfrac{11}{9}$ iv. $p = 0.6, q = 0.7$, Value $= -0.2$

v. $p = \dfrac{9}{16}, q = \dfrac{11}{16}$, Value $= -\dfrac{13}{16}$ vi. $p = \dfrac{9}{13}, q = \dfrac{7}{13}$, Value $= \dfrac{11}{13}$

vii. $p = \dfrac{26}{53}, q = \dfrac{24}{53}$, Value $= \dfrac{147}{53}$ viii. $p = \dfrac{24}{43}, q = \dfrac{27}{43}$, Value $= -\dfrac{3}{43}$

ix. $p = 0.52, q = -59$, Value $= -15.68$

2. i. The game is zero sum because each pair of payoffs sum to 20.

ii. Subtracting 10 from each Amco payoff gives the matrix $\begin{bmatrix} 5 & -1 \\ -2 & 7 \end{bmatrix}$.

iii. Amco should choose TV 1 with probability $\dfrac{9}{15}$. Beeco should choose TV 1 with probability $\dfrac{8}{15}$. The expected payoff to Amco is 2.2. This means $10 + 2.2 = 12.2$. This translates to an in profits of 12200 crowns.

3. General White should attack the marsh with probability $\dfrac{9}{17}$ and General Black should defend the marsh with probability $\dfrac{7}{17}$. General White should eliminate about 171 more of Black's troops than he will lose.

EXERCISE 19.1

1. (i) 0.6915 (ii) 0.9671 (iii) 0.9474 (iv) 0.9965 (v) 0.9756 (vi) 0.0054 (vii) 0.0287 (viii) 0.0594 (ix) 0.0073 (x) 0.8289 (xi) 0.6443 (xii) 0.0823 (xiii) 0.9798 (xiv) 0.9793 (xv) 0.3483 2. (i) 0.0361 (ii) 0.3759 (iii) 0.0623 (iv) 0.0564 (v) 0.0111 (vi) 0.2902 (vii) 0.7614 (viii) 0.0343 (ix) 0.6014 (x) 0.1451 (xi) 0.9205 (xii) 0.2669 (xiii) 0.7020 (xiv) 0.9132 (xv) 0.5203 (xvi) 0.8160 (xvii) 0.9387 (xviii) 0.7258

Answers

EXERCISE 19.2

1. (i) 0.4305 (ii) 0.3797 (iii) 0.1898 2. (i) 0.8033 (ii) 0.5053 (iii) 0.3066 3. 42%
4. 0.7021 5. (i) 0.2903 (ii) 0.4583 (iii) 0.2514 6. 0.2310 7. 0.5 8. 11% 9. 5%
10. 14% 11. 1.8 12. 252 13. 0.1518 14. 0.3821 15. 0.22 16. 322 17. 0.2023
18. 7 19. 87

SELF ASSESSMENT TEST

1. $p(z > -1.62) = p(z < 1.62)$ [1] $= 0.9474$ [1] 2. Convert to standard distribution [1] Use of

tables [1] 12.8% [1] 3.(a) $z = -0.5773$ [1] $p(X > 8) = 0.7181$ [1] (b) $\dfrac{c - 1}{\sqrt{12}} = -1.6449$ [1]

$c = -4.6979$ [1] 4.(a) 0.0062 [1] (b) 0.0479 [1] (c) 0.9459 [1] (d) 0.6409 [1] (e) 0.0587 [1]

5. $p(-2.0085 < X < 2.2715) = 0.90$ [1] $p(X < 2.2715) = 0.95$ [1] $p\left(z < \dfrac{0.1215}{\sigma}\right) = 0.95$ [1]

$\sigma \approx 0.0739$ [1]

EXERCISE 20.1

1.(i) (a) Increasing (b) approx. linear (c) mild (ii) (a) No association (b) – (c) 0
 (iii) (a) Increasing (b) linear (c) very strong (iv) (a) Increasing (b) square root
 (c) mild (strength not appropriate as it is a non–linear relationship!) (v) (a) Decreasing (b)
exponential (c) mild (stength not appropriate as it is a non–linear relationship!)
(vi) (a) Decreasing (b) approx. linear (c) mild.

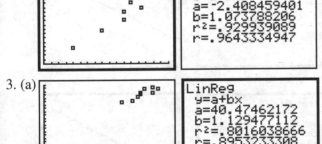

2. (a)   (b) Positive association, linear,
         strength: very strong

LinReg
y=a+bx
a=-2.408459401
b=1.073788206
r²=.929939089
r=.9643334947

3. (a)   (b) Positive association, linear,
         strength: very strong

LinReg
y=a+bx
a=40.47462172
b=1.129477112
r²=.8016038666
r=.8953233308

EXERCISE 20.2

1. (a) r = 0.96   2. (b) r = 0.70 (assumed linear) 3. r = 0. No, not linear!
 (b)   (a)

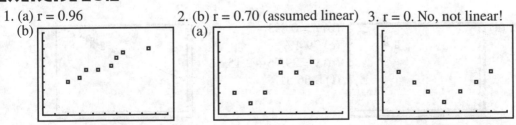

4. No. The relationship is not linear. 5. (a) (i) 64% (ii) 81% (b) (i) 51% (ii) 64%

6. (a) 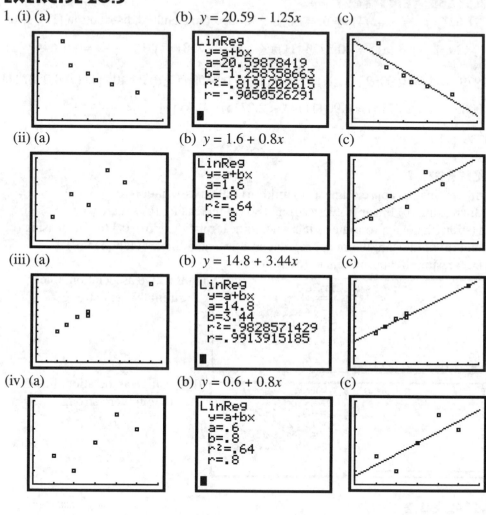 (b) r = 0.45   7. 3 8. 0.922   9. 82%

EXERCISE 20.3

1. (i) (a)   (b) $y = 20.59 - 1.25x$ (c)

(ii) (a)   (b) $y = 1.6 + 0.8x$ (c)

(iii) (a)   (b) $y = 14.8 + 3.44x$ (c)

(iv) (a)   (b) $y = 0.6 + 0.8x$ (c)

2. (a) 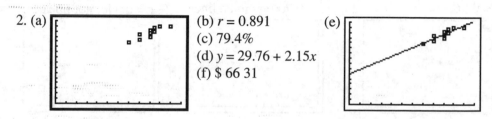   (b) $r = 0.891$
(c) 79.4%
(d) $y = 29.76 + 2.15x$
(f) $ 66 31

(e)

Answers

3. (a)

(b) $r = 0.553$
(c) (i) $y = 40 + 0.5x$
    (ii) $y = 24.1 + 0.61x$

4. (a)

(b) Based on the scatter diagram, there is a definite linear relationship. Therefore, owner is justified.

(c) (i) $r = 0.99$ (ii) $y = 4.19 + 1.82x$ (iii)

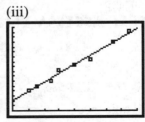

(d) (i) 20.57 i.e., 21
    (ii) 95.19 i.e., 95
    (iii) From (ii), serving 95 people per hr is unrealistic.

5. (a)

(b) Scatter diagram shows a linear relationship. Therefore statistic is appropriate, $r = 0.877$

(c) (i) $y = 89.50 + 1.02x$
    (ii)

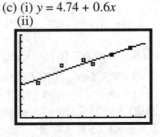

(d) (i) 135.4 (ii) 176.2
    (iii) $x = 85$ is a fair way out from the set of values used to obtain the regression line

(e) 44.61 yrs, i.e., 44 yrs and 7 months (approx).

6. (a)

(b) Scatter diagram shows a linear relationship. Therefore statistic is appropriate, $r = 0.945$

(c) (i) $y = 4.74 + 0.6x$
    (ii)

(d) (i) 8.64 (ii) 10.74
(e) $x = 2.1$

EXERCISE 21.1

Note: *The results in this section were calculated without using Yates continuity correction (unless otherwise stated). It is worthwhile comparing the decision for those results where its use is appropriate (i.e., df = 1) to the ones given here.*
For example. in 1. (b) $U = 3.33603$ whereas U(corrected) $= 2.3832$ (but in both instances we accept H_0). 1. (a) Reject independence (i.e., reject H_0) (b) Accept independence (i.e., accept H_0). 2. Reject H_0 3. Accept H_0 4. Accept H_0 (i.e., independent) 5. (a) Reject H_0 (b) Reject H_0 6. Reject H_0 7. Accept H_0 8. Accept H_0

SELF ASSESSMENT TEST

1. $U = \dfrac{(54-41.28)^2}{41.28} + \dfrac{(32-44.72)^2}{44.72} + \dfrac{(42-54.76)^2}{54.76} + \dfrac{(72-59.28)^2}{59.28} = 13.24$.

As $U = 13.24 > c_{0.95}\chi^2(1)(= 3.841)$ then we would clearly reject H_0 at the 5% level of significance.

4. (a) $U = 33.33$ [1] $> 6.635 = c_{0.99}\chi^2(1)$ [1]. The treatment has a significant effect [1], that is, of those treated, a significantly smaller proportion developed the flu than those that were not treated. [1]

(b) $U = 3.33$ [1] $< 3.84 = c_{0.95}\chi^2(1)$ [1]. Therefore the results are not significant. [1]. The significance test used in (a) is accurate because the sample size is large, but in (b) it is inaccurate because the sample size is too small.[1]

EXERCISE 22.1

1. (a) $\dfrac{3}{4}$ (b) $\dfrac{3a}{4b}$ (c) -1 (d) 1 (e) $-\dfrac{15}{8}$ (f) 0 2. (a) 4 (b) 0.2 (c) 0.027 (d) 0.433 (e) -0.01

(f) 6.34 (g) 6.2 (h) 0 3. (a) 6 m/s (b) 30 m/s (c) $11 + 6h + h^2$ m/s 4. 12 m/s 5. $8 + 2h$

6. -3.49 °C/sec 7. 127π cm³/cm 8. 1.115 9. (a) -7.5 °C/min (b) $t = 2$ to $t = 6$ 10. (a) 28 m
(b) 14 m/s (c) speed (d) 209 m (e) 209 m/s 11. (a) 1160, 1345.6, 1560.89, 1810.64, 2100.34 (b) $220.17 per year

EXERCISE 22.2

1. (a)   (b)   2. (a)   (b)

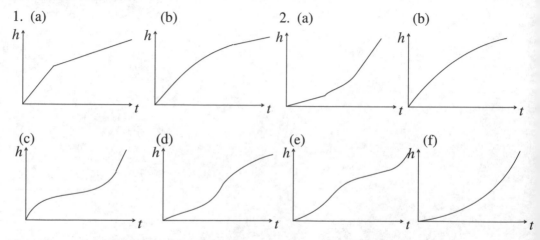

(c)   (d)   (e)   (f)

Answers

EXERCISE 22.3

1. (a) $h + 2$ (b) $4 + 2h$ (c) $\dfrac{-1}{1+h}$ (d) $3 - 3h + h^2$ 2. (a) 2 (b) 4 (c) -1 (d) 3

3. (a) $2a + h$ (b) $-(2a + h)$ (c) $(2a + 2) + h$ (d) $3a^2 + 1 + 3ah + h^2$ (e) $-(3a^2 + 3ah + h^2)$

(f) $3a^2 - 2a + (3a - 1)h + h^2$ (g) $\dfrac{-2}{a(a+h)}$ (h) $-\dfrac{1}{(a-1)(a-1+h)}$ (i) $\dfrac{1}{\sqrt{a+h} + \sqrt{a}}$

4. (a) 1 ; 1 (b) $2a + h$; $2a$ (c) $3a^2 + 3ah + h^2$; $3a^2$ (d) $4a^3 + 6a^2h + 4ah^2 + h^3$; $4a^3$

EXERCISE 22.4

1. (a) 3 (b) 8 (c) $-\dfrac{1}{9}$ (d) 1.39 (e) -1 (f) $\dfrac{17}{16}$ 2. $4.9\ m$ (b) $4.9(h^2 + 2h)$ m (c) 9.8 m/s

3. (a) $8x$ (b) $10x$ (c) $12x^2$ (d) $15x^2$ (e) $16x^3$ (f) $20x^3$ 4. (a) $4x$ (b) -1 (c) $-1 + 3x$ (d) $-\dfrac{1}{x^2}$

(e) $-\dfrac{2}{(x+1)^2}$ (f) $\dfrac{1}{2\sqrt{x}}$

EXERCISE 23.1

1. (a) $5x^4$ (b) $9x^8$ (c) $25x^{24}$ (d) $27x^2$ (e) $-28x^6$ (f) $2x^7$ (g) $2x$ (h) $20x^3 + 2$ (i) $-15x^4 + 18x^2 - 1$

(j) $-\dfrac{4}{3}x^3 + 10$ (k) $9x^2 - 12x$ (l) $3 + \dfrac{2}{5}x + 4x^3$ 2. (a) $-\dfrac{3}{x^4}$ (b) $\dfrac{3}{2}\sqrt{x}$ (c) $\dfrac{5}{2}\sqrt{x^3}$ (d) $\dfrac{1}{3\sqrt[3]{x^2}}$

(e) $\dfrac{2}{\sqrt{x}}$ (f) $9\sqrt{x}$ (g) $\dfrac{1}{\sqrt{x}} + \dfrac{3}{x^2}$ (h) $\dfrac{3}{2}\sqrt{x} - \dfrac{1}{2\sqrt{x^3}}$ (i) $\dfrac{10}{3\sqrt[3]{x}} - 9$ (j) $5 - \dfrac{1}{2\sqrt{x}} - \dfrac{8}{5x^3}$ (k) $\dfrac{4}{\sqrt{x}} - \dfrac{15}{x^6} + \dfrac{1}{2}$ (l)

$-\dfrac{1}{2\sqrt{x^3}} - \dfrac{1}{\sqrt{x}} + x^2$ 3. (a) $\dfrac{3}{2}\sqrt{x} - \dfrac{1}{\sqrt{x}}$ (b) $4x^3 + 3x^2 - 1$ (c) $3x^2 + 1$ (d) $\dfrac{1}{x^2}$ (e) $\dfrac{1}{\sqrt{x^3}}$ (f) $\dfrac{1}{2} - \dfrac{1}{4\sqrt{x^3}}$ (g) -7

(h) $2x - \dfrac{8}{x^3}$ (i) $2x - \dfrac{2}{x^2} - \dfrac{4}{x^5}$ (j) $\dfrac{1}{2}\sqrt{\dfrac{3}{x}} + \dfrac{1}{6\sqrt{x^3}}$ (k) $2x - \dfrac{12}{5}\sqrt[5]{x} + \dfrac{2}{5\sqrt[5]{x^3}}$ (l) $-\dfrac{3}{2\sqrt{x}}\left(\dfrac{1}{x} + 1\right)\left(\dfrac{1}{\sqrt{x}} - \sqrt{x}\right)^2$

EXERCISE 23.2

1. (a) 3 (b) $-\dfrac{1}{4}$ (c) 12 (d) 4 (e) 4 (f) $\dfrac{7}{6}$ (g) $-\dfrac{1}{12}$ (h) $\dfrac{53}{16}$ 2. $\pm\sqrt{\dfrac{8}{3}}$ 3. (a) $2x - 12$ (b) -18

(c) $x = 8$ 4. (a) $-3x^2 + 3$ (b) 0 (c) $\pm\sqrt{2}$ 5. (a) $\left(\pm\dfrac{\sqrt{2}}{2}, -\dfrac{1}{16}\right), (0,0)$ (b) $\left\{x : \dfrac{-1}{\sqrt{2}} < x < 0\right\} \cup \left\{x : x > \dfrac{1}{\sqrt{2}}\right\}$

6. $x = \dfrac{1}{3}, -1$ 7. (a) $-2, 6, 3$ (b) -2 8. $a = 1$ $b = -8$

EXERCISE 23.3

1. (a) $48t^3 - \dfrac{1}{2\sqrt{t}}$ (b) $2n - \dfrac{2}{n^2} - \dfrac{4}{n^5}$ (c) $\dfrac{3}{2}\sqrt{r} + \dfrac{5}{6\sqrt[6]{r}} - \dfrac{1}{\sqrt{r}}$ (d) $2\theta - \dfrac{9}{2}\sqrt{\theta} + 3 - \dfrac{1}{2\sqrt{\theta}}$

(e) $40 - 3L^2$ (f) $-\dfrac{100}{v^3} - 1$ (g) $6l^2 + 5$ (h) $2\pi + 8h$ (i) $4n^3 - \dfrac{1}{3\sqrt[3]{n^2}} + \pi$

EXERCISE 23.4

1. 4.4 2. (a) 200 (b) 73.5 3. (a) 75 (b) No 4. i. 2.50 ii. 3.33 iii 2.50 5. (a)

$x > 1000(25 - \sqrt{565})$

(b) i. $0 < x < 25000$ ii. $25,000 < x < 50000$ 6. (b) 133.33 (d) 46.67 (e) $0 < x < 5700$

EXERCISE 23.5

1. (a) max at (1, 4) (b) min at $\left(-\frac{9}{2}, -\frac{81}{4}\right)$ (c) min at (3, -45) (d) max at (0, 8), min at (4, -24)

(e) max at (1, 8), min at (-3, -24) (f) min at $\left(\frac{1 + \sqrt{13}}{3}, \frac{70 - 26\sqrt{13}}{27}\right)$,

max at $\left(\frac{1 - \sqrt{13}}{3}, \frac{70 + 26\sqrt{13}}{27}\right)$ (g) min at (1, -1) (h) max at (0, 16), min at (2, 0), min at (-2, 0)

(i) min at (1, 0) max at $\left(-\frac{1}{3}, \frac{32}{27}\right)$ (j) min at $\left(\frac{4}{9}, -\frac{4}{27}\right)$ (k) min at (2, 4), max at (-2, -4) (l)

min at (1, 2), min at (-1, 2)

2. (a) (b) (c) (d)

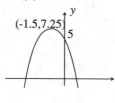
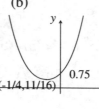
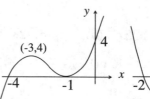
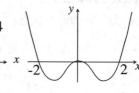

(e) (f) (g) (h)

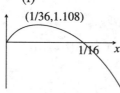
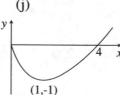
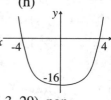
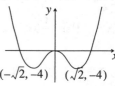

(i) (j) 3. min at (1, -3), max at (-3, 29), non-stationary infl (-1, 13) 4.

5.(a) 8 (b) 0 (c) 4 (d) $27\sqrt[3]{9} \approx 56.16$ 6. max value 26, min value -82.

EXERCISE 23.6

1. (a) $\frac{25}{12}$ 2. (a) $\frac{55}{8}$ 3. 5.25 4. 72 5. (a) $y = 100 - 2x$ (b) $A = x(100 - 2x), 0 < x < 50$

(c) $x = 25, y = 50$ 6. (a) $\frac{100}{x} - \frac{1}{2}x, 0 < x < 10\sqrt{2}$ (b) $\left(\frac{200}{3}\right)^{\frac{3}{2}}$

Answers

7. (a) 400 (b) 40 sec (c)

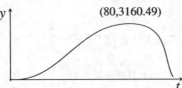

8. (a)

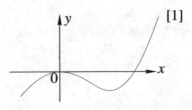

(b) 8.38, 71.62 (c) 8.38 < x < 71.62 (d) $80x - x^2 - 600$, \$1000 9. 4 by $\frac{8}{3}$

10. $348 - 8\sqrt{170}$ cm^2 11. 2 12. radius = $\frac{\sqrt{10}}{3}$ cm,

height = $2\sqrt{\frac{10}{3}}$ cm 13. $\sqrt[3]{\frac{60}{4\pi}}$ 14. 5cm 15. $\frac{2\pi}{3 + \pi}$ 16. 4:9 17. (a) i. $\pi r^2 h + \frac{2}{3}\pi r^3$

ii. $3\pi r^2 + 2\pi rh$ (c) r:h = 1:1

EXERCISE 23.7

1. (a) 8 m/s (b) Never (c) (i) 5 m to the left of O (ii) 4 m/s (d) 40 m (e)

2. (a) 1 m/s (b) Twice, at t = 0, 1 (c) 1, 1/3 (d) 16 m/s^2

3. (a) $v = -6t^2 + 12$, $a = -12t$ (b) $2\sqrt{2}$ sec (c) Once   (d)

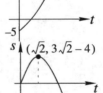

SELF ASSESSMENT TEST

1. $y = -2x^{-1/2} \therefore \frac{dy}{dx} = -2 \times -\frac{1}{2}x^{-3/2}$ [1] $\frac{1}{\sqrt{x^3}}$ [1]

2. $f(x) = 2x^3 + 3x^2 - 12x + 1 \Rightarrow f'(x) = 6x^2 + 6x - 12$ [1] Solving derivative = 0 [1]
x = -2, 1. [1] Test [1] Local Max at (-2,21) [1]

3. $C'(v) = 200 - \frac{800}{v^2} = 0$ [1], $v = \pm 4$ [1], $C(4) = 1000$ [1]

4. $f(-1) = 5$, $f(1) = -1$ [1] Rate = $\frac{(5 - (-1))}{-1 - 1} = -3$ [1] [1]

5. (a) $y = x^2(5x - 1) = 0 \Leftrightarrow x = 0, \frac{1}{5}$ [1],

$\frac{dy}{dx} = 15x^2 - 2x = 0 \Leftrightarrow x = 0, \frac{2}{15}$ [1] [1],

Turning point at $(0, 0)$ & $\left(\frac{2}{15}, -\frac{4}{675}\right)$ [1].

[1]

6. (a) $t = \frac{40}{7}$ sec [1] (b) 40 m [1] (c) (i) 28 m/s [1] (ii) –1.4 m/s [1] (d) showing a = –9.8 [1]

EXERCISE 24.1

1. (a) $\frac{1}{4}x^4 + c$ (b) $\frac{1}{8}x^8 + c$ (c) $\frac{1}{6}x^6 + c$ (d) $\frac{1}{9}x^9 + c$ (e) $\frac{4}{3}x^3 + c$ (f) $\frac{7}{6}x^6 + c$ (g) $x^9 + c$

(h) $\frac{1}{8}x^4 + c$ 2. (a) $5x + c$ (b) $3x + c$ (c) $10x + c$ (d) $\frac{2}{3}x + c$ (e) $-4x + c$ (f) $-6x + c$

(g) $-\frac{3}{2}x + c$ (h) $-x + c$ 3. (a) $x - \frac{1}{2}x^2 + c$ (b) $2x + \frac{1}{3}x^3 + c$ (c) $\frac{1}{4}x^4 - 9x + c$

(d) $\frac{2}{5}x + \frac{1}{9}x^3 + c$ (e) $\frac{1}{3}x^{\frac{3}{2}} + \frac{1}{x} + c$ (f) $x^{\frac{5}{2}} + 4x^2 + c$ (g) $\frac{1}{3}x^3 + x^2 + c$ (h) $x^3 - x^2 + c$

(i) $x - \frac{1}{3}x^3 + c$ 4. (a) $\frac{1}{3}x^3 - \frac{1}{2}x^2 - 6x + c$ (b) $\frac{1}{4}x^4 - \frac{2}{3}x^3 - \frac{3}{2}x^2 + c$ (c) $\frac{1}{4}(x-3)^4$

(d) $\frac{2}{5}x^5 + \frac{1}{2}x^4 + \frac{1}{3}x^3 + \frac{1}{2}x^2 + c$ (e) $x + \frac{1}{2}x^2 - \frac{2}{3}x^{\frac{3}{2}} - \frac{2}{5}x^{\frac{5}{2}} + c$ (f) $\frac{2}{7}x^{7/2} + \frac{4}{5}x^{\frac{5}{2}} + \frac{2}{3}x^{\frac{3}{2}} - 2x + c$

5. (a) $\frac{1}{2}x^2 - 3x + c$ (b) $2u^2 + 5u + \frac{1}{u} + c$ (c) $-\frac{1}{x} - \frac{2}{x^2} - \frac{4}{3x^3} + c$ (d) $\frac{1}{2}x^2 + 3x + c$

(e) $\frac{1}{2}x^2 - 4x + c$ (f) $\frac{1}{3}t^3 + 2t - \frac{1}{t} + c$ 6. (a) $\frac{4}{7}\sqrt[4]{x^7} + 2\sqrt{x} - 5x + c$

(b) $\frac{1}{3}x^3 + \frac{1}{2}x^2 - \frac{4}{7}x^{\frac{7}{2}} - \frac{2}{5}x^{\frac{5}{2}} + c$ (c) $-\frac{1}{2z^2} + \frac{2}{z} + 2z^2 + z + c$ (d) $\frac{1}{2}t^4 + t + c$

(e) $\frac{2}{5}\sqrt{t^5} - 2\sqrt{t^3} + c$ (f) $\frac{1}{3}u^3 + 2u^2 + 4u + c$

EXERCISE 24.2

1. (a) $x^2 + x + 3$ (b) $2x - \frac{1}{3}x^3 + 1$ (c) $\frac{8}{3}\sqrt{x^3} - \frac{1}{2}x^2 - \frac{40}{3}$ (d) $\frac{1}{2}x^2 + \frac{1}{x} + 2x - \frac{3}{2}$ (e) $(x+2)^3$

(f) $\frac{3}{4}\sqrt[3]{x^4} + \frac{1}{4}x^4 + x - 1$ (g) $\frac{1}{3}x^3 + 1$ (h) $x^4 - x^3 + 2x + 3$ 2. $\frac{1}{2}x^2 + \frac{1}{x} + \frac{5}{2}$ 3. $3835.03

4. 9.5 5. 84π cm^3 6. 292 7. $\frac{5}{7}\sqrt{x^3} + \frac{23}{7}$ 8. (a) $s = t - t^2 + 1$ (b) $s = 3t^3 - t^2 + 3t + 10$

(c) 5.75 m 9. (a) $v = 4t - 4t^3 + 4$ (b) $s = 2t^2 - t^4 + 4t$ (c) –555 m

SELF ASSESSMENT TEST

1. (a) $\frac{1}{4}x^4 - 2x^2 + x + c$ (b) $2\sqrt{x} - \frac{2}{3}\sqrt{x^3} + c$ [1] [1] (c) $9x - 3x^2 + \frac{1}{3}x^3 + c$ [1] [1]

2. $\frac{dy}{dx} = 6x + 2 \Rightarrow y = 3x^2 + 2x + c$ [1] $15 = 3(2)^2 + 2(2) + c \Rightarrow c = -1$ [1]

Therefore we have $y = 3x^2 + 2x - 1$ 3. $s = \frac{1}{3}t^3 + 5t + \frac{2}{t} + c$ [1] $3 = \frac{1}{3} + 5 + 2 + c$ [1]

so that $s = \frac{1}{3}t^3 + 5t + \frac{2}{t} - \frac{13}{3}$.[1] Therefore, t = 3, $s = \frac{61}{3}$ [1].

4. (a) $R(x) = 250x - \frac{1}{20}x^2 + c$ [1] $R(0) = 0, c = 0$, so $R(x) = 250x - \frac{1}{20}x^2$ [1]

   (b) $R(100) = 250(100) - \frac{1}{20}(100)^2 = 24500$ [1]